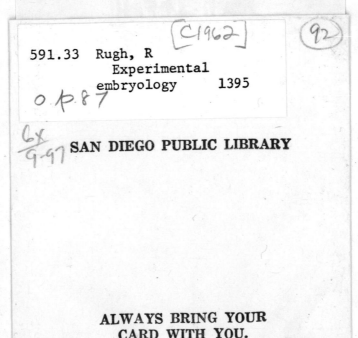

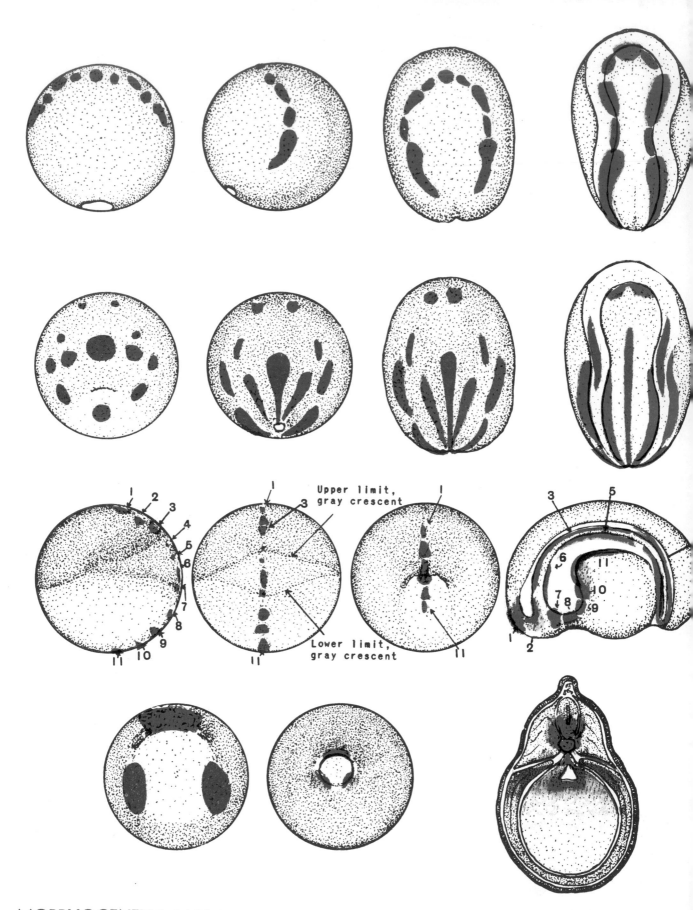

MORPHOGENETIC MOVEMENTS DURING GASTRULATION AND NEURULATION

(Redrawn from Vogt and Goerttler)

EXPERIMENTAL EMBRYOLOGY

Techniques and Procedures

591.33

by

ROBERTS RUGH

Associate Professor of Radiology

College of Physicians and Surgeons

Columbia University

Burgess Publishing Company

Minneapolis 15, Minnesota

Other books by the author:

LAB. MANUAL OF VERTEBRATE EMBRYOLOGY, 1961, Burgess Publishing Co.
THE MOUSE, ITS REPRODUCTION AND DEVELOPMENT, 1968, Burgess Publishing Co.

CONTENTS

I. TECHNIQUES IN EXPERIMENTAL EMBRYOLOGY

II. THE AMPHIBIA

III. EXPERIMENTAL FISH EMBRYOLOGY

IV. EXPERIMENTAL CHICK EMBRYOLOGY

V. EXPERIMENTAL MAMMALIAN EMBRYOLOGY

INTRODUCTION

The material of this "Experimental Embryology" represents many years of the most intense research on the part of innumerable embryologists, from all parts of the world. The author disclaims any originality except in those sections relating specifically to his particular investigations. The book is a compendium of data, directions, and references not generally found in textbooks, but information which is necessary in training the prospective experimental embryologist in the fundamentals of this relatively new and dynamic field of research.

There are contained herein some 50 separate experimental procedures, from Androgenesis to Xenoplastic Grafts, all of which have been tested in the course "Mechanics of Development" developed by the author while at New York University. The present, completely rewritten book incorporates all the improvements in the various techniques that have come to the author's attention. Each procedure is presented as foundational to some basic concept so that the qualified graduate student may be stimulated to pursue further research in the field. The approach is entirely <u>experimental</u>; the subject matter is exclusively the <u>embryo</u>.

The organization of each exercise is based upon the general plan of a publishable scientific manuscript. The usual historical background is omitted, and the discussion (if any) is limited because this is the function of related textbooks. The reference list contains only the most recent and pertinent papers, and certain review articles. Only occasionally there are included papers more than 15 years old, and these because they have been established as classics within the field. It is felt that interested investigators can acquire a complete bibliography through the references given.

It is Recommended that the Student's Report Include the Following:

1. EXPERIMENTAL PROCEDURE: Any modifications of the procedure as outlined.
2. EXPERIMENTAL DATA: This section must be complete in every detail.
3. DISCUSSION: This should be based upon "2" above.
4. CONCLUSIONS: These should be based entirely upon the findings of the student.
5. REFERENCES: Only new references which are not included in this exercise.

It would be impossible for any student, under any conditions, to complete the work outlined in this book during a single academic year. There are three solutions to this matter, all of which have been tried in our laboratory and any of which is satisfactory:

1. Assign a new procedure for each of the regular weekly laboratory sessions. This is a very heavy assignment and the student would necessarily spend more than the usual four hours per week in the laboratory. The plan has the advantage of making it simpler for the instructor to anticipate the needs of the entire class, from week to week. He can often schedule the procedures in such a way that they follow in a natural sequence and often conveniently overlap. The major disadvantage is that the student acquires only a passing acquaintance with the various techniques and is apt to assume that he is master of all of them.

2. Select a logical series of experimental procedures designed to be completed during the first semester, and progressing from the gross to the microscopic, the crude to the refined, the simple to the complex. There is no attempt to cover the entire gamut of techniques. The responsibility of representative selection falls on the instructor, but the student will be quite thoroughly grounded in the basic procedures, and will thereby be qualified later to pursue independent investigation. This has been

the most frequently followed program at New York Univeristy during the first semester. During the second semester the students have been assigned individual and original problems for investigation.

3. Assign some of the introductory procedures to the entire class, such procedures as "Induction of Ovulation", "Breeding and Care of Embryos", and "Temperature and Rate of Development". Then delegate each student to carry out two or three integrated procedures, with the responsibility of completed and thorough work later to be reported in full to the class. This plan deprives the student of experience in many of the techniques in experimental embryology, but it places upon him a responsibility to the entire class which often kindles the research attitude. By such a plan most of the exercises can be attempted by an average class of about 15 students.

A suggested sequence of exercises, which has been used at New York University, is given below. The assignment is based upon a weekly class session of about 4 hours, and supplemental time as may be required by the individual student.

1. INDUCTION OF OVULATION AND ARTIFICIAL FERTILIZATION

2. NORMAL DEVELOPMENT
    a. Relation of temperature to early development.
    b. Relation of osmotic pressure to early development.
    c. The appearance of behavior patterns.

3. EXPERIMENTS WITH THE EGG
    a. Germinal vesicle studies.
    b. Artificial parthenogenesis.
    c. Androgenesis.

4. EXPERIMENTS WITH THE CLEAVAGE STAGES
    a. The effect of unequal pressure on cleavage.
    b. The production of double embryos.
    c. The behavior of isolated embryonic cells.

5. EXPERIMENTS ON THE BLASTULA AND GASTRULA
    a. Vital staining and morphogenetic movements.
    b. The organizer.

6. EXPERIMENTS WITH THE NEURULA
    a. Parabiosis.
    b. Regeneration.
    c. Embryonic inductions in the blastema tissue.

7. EXPERIMENTS WITH LATER STAGES
    a. Wound healing.
    b. Hypophysectomy.
    c. Limb or eye transplantations.

This program would carry the student through about $1\frac{1}{2}$ semesters. There would remain about 2 months during which the instructor could direct the students in some of the more difficult techniques with either the fish or the chick embryos.

Through the very generous help of Dr. Jane Oppenheimer and Dr. Nelson T. Spratt, Jr. the sections on fish and on chick embryos have been expanded very considerably. It is believed that the traditional reluctance to use these forms is being broken down by the brilliant work of investigators such as these, and the laboratory of experimental embryology can no longer be limited to amphibian forms but will take in all embryos from the lowest to the highest phyla.

It would be impossible for the author to properly acknowledge all of the help that he has received in organizing this book. He has enjoyed universal and wholehearted cooperation, often entailing considerable time and effort on the part of contemporary investigators. Where figures, graphs, or photographs have been reproduced, and where specific investigators have constructively helped to organize certain sections, specific acknowledgements are made. It is with pleasure that the author acknowledges here the permission granted by The Wistar Institute of Anatomy to reproduce items from papers appearing in their various journals. It must be emphasized again that this book is made possible by the efforts of many experimental embryologists, many deceased, many active, and an increasing number "presumptive". If biology students who attempt these various procedures are thereby stimulated to make further contributions to the field of experimental embryology, all the effort expended in its compilation will have been justified.

Roberts Rugh

New York
September 1948

INTRODUCTION TO THIRD EDITION

This third edition of the Experimental Embryology appears simply as a direct response to the persistent demands on the part of a small but select group of advanced experimentalists who found the previous edition so useful that they began to make photostatic copies when the supply was exhausted.

Many of the old references have been deleted, and new ones added. New sections include the disassociation and reaggregation of cells; basic tissue culture techniques; and use of the mouse embryo. For the last decade the author has been studying the effects of ionizing radiations on the rodent (mouse and rat) embryos and he is convinced that the mammalian embryo can now be made available to all advanced biology students for important, rewarding, and exciting research. This chapter on the mouse embryo is merely an introduction to the possibilities ahead.

Most publishing houses are conducted on a cold and closely calculating business basis. For Burgess of Minneapolis to republish a book such as this, which can never have wide adoption because of its very specialized subject, is a generous gesture which, the author hopes, will stimulate many biologists to research in embryology.

Roberts Rugh

New York
February 1962

REFERENCE BOOKS FOR EXPERIMENTAL EMBRYOLOGY

ADAMS, A. E., 1941 - "Studies in Experimental Zoology." Edwards Bros., Ann Arbor, Mich.

AREY, LESLIE B., 1954 - "Developmental Anatomy." W. B. Saunders, Philadelphia.

ATKINS, H. J. B., 1960 - "The Tools of Biological Research." C. C. Thomas, Springfield, Ill. pub.

BACCI, G., et al, 1954 - "Problemi di sviluppo." Casa Editrice Ambrosiana, Milan.

BAKER, J. R., 1958 - "Principles of Biological Microtechnique: A study of fixation and dyeing." Wiley & Sons, N.Y.

BALINSKY, B. I., 1960 - "An Introduction to Embryology". W. B. Saunders, Philadelphia.

BARTH, L. G., J. J. Barth, 1954 - "The Energetics of Development." Columbia Univ. Press, N.Y.

BARTH, L. G., 1953 - "Embryology." The Dryden Press, New York.

BERTALANFFY, L. von, J. H. Woodger, 1933 - "Modern Theories of Development." Oxford Univ. Press.

BISHOP, S. C., 1943 - "Handbook of Salamanders." Comstock Pub. Co., Ithaca.

BONNER, JOHN T., 1958 - "The Evolution of Development." Cambridge U. Press.

BOULENGER, G. A., 1920 - "A Monograph of the American Frogs of the Genus Rana" Proc. Am. Acad. Arts & Sci. 55:413.

BRACHET, A., 1931 - "L'Oeuf et les Facteurs de l'Ontogenese." G. Doin & Co., Ed.

BRACHET, J., 1960 - "Embryologie Chimique." Masson et Cie, Paris.

BRACHET, J., 1960 - "The Biochemistry of Development." Pergamon Press, N.Y.

CHILD, C. M., 1915 - "Individuality of Organisms." Univ. Chicago Press.

CHILD, C. M., 1921 - "Origin and Development of the Nervous System." Univ. Chicago Press.

CHILD, J. M., 1924 - "Physiological Foundations of Behaviour." Henry Holt Co., N.Y.

CHILD, 1941 - "Patterns and Problems of Development." Univ. Chicago Press.

COPE, E. D., 1889 - "The Batrachia of North America." Bull. U. S. Nat'l. Museum #34:1.

COSTELLO, D. P., M. E. DAVIDSON, A. EGGERS, M. H. FOX, C. HENLEY, 1957 - "Methods for obtaining and handling marine eggs and embryos." Marine Biol. Lab., Woods Hole, Mass.

COWDRY, E. V., 1943 - "Microscopic Technique in Biology and Medicine." Williams & Wilkins, Baltimore.

DALCQ, A. M., 1928 - "Les Bases Physiologuc de la Fécondation et de la Parthenogénése." Les Presses Universitaire de France.

DALCQ, A. M., 1938 - "Form and Causality in Early Development." Cambridge Univ. Press.

DALCQ, A. M., 1957 - "Introduction to General Embryology." Oxford Univ. Press.

deBEER, G. R., 1926 - "Introduction to Experimental Embryology." Clarendon Press.

deBEER, G. R., 1930 - "Embryology and Evolution." Clarendon Press.

DETWILER, S. R., 1936 - "Neuroembryology." Macmillan.

DICKERSON, M. C., 1906 - "The Frog Book." Doubleday Page & Co., N.Y.

DRIESCH, H., 1928 - "Science and Philosophy of the Organism." Macmillan

DURKEN, B., 1928 - "Lehrbuch der Experimentalzoologie." Verlag von Gebruder, Borntrager.

DURKEN, B., 1929 - "Grundriss der Entwicklungsmechanik." Gebruder, Borntrager, Berlin.

DURKEN, B., 1932 - "Experimental Analysis of Development." Geo. Allen, London.

FARRIS, E. J., 1950 - "Care and Breeding of Laboratory Animals." 515 pp. John Wiley & Sons, N.Y.

FAURE-FREMIET, E., 1925 - "Cinetique du Developpement." Paris.

GALIGHER, A. E., 1934 - "The Essentials of Practical Microtechnique." A. E. Galigher, Berkeley, Calif.

GOLDSCHMIDT, R., 1923 - "Mechanisms of Physiology of Sex Determination." Metheum & Co., London.

GOMORI, G., 1952 - "Microscopic Histochemistry: Principles and Practice." Univ. Chicago Press.

GRAY, J., 1931 - "Experimental Cytology." Cambridge Univ. Press.

GRAY, P., 1958 - "Handbook of Basic Microtechnique." McGraw-Hill, 252 pp.

HAMBURGER, V. E., 1960 - "A Manual of Experimental Embryology." Univ. Chicago Press.

HARRIS, D. B., ed. 1957 - "The Concept of Development." Univ. Minnesota Press.

HARRISON, R. G. - "Cellular Differentiation and Internal Environment." Pub. #14 Am. Ass'n. Adv. Sci. 77:97.

HENDERSON, L. J., 1913 - "The Fitness of the Environment". Macmillan.

HERRICK, C. J., 1948 - "The Brain of the Tiger Salamander." Univ. Chicago Press.

HORSTADIUS, SVEN, 1950 - "The Neural Crest." Oxford Univ. Press.

HUXLEY, J. S., G. R. deBEER, 1934 - "The Elements of Experimental Embryology." Cambridge Univ. Press.

JENKINSON, J. W., 1909 - "Experimental Embryology." Clarendon Press.

JENNINGS, H. S., 1925 - "Prometheus." E. P. Dutton, N.Y.

JORDAN, H. E., J E. KINDRED, 1948 - "Textbook of Embryology." D. Appleton, N.Y.

JUST, E. E., 1939 - "Basic Methods for Experiments on Eggs of Marine Animals." Blakiston, N.Y.

JUST, E. E., 1930 - "The Biology of the Cell Surface." Blakiston, N.Y.

KALISS, N., 1960 - "Symposium on the Normal and Abnormal Differentiation and Development." Jour. Nat. Cancer Inst. Monogr. #2, pgs. 187.

KELLICOTT, W. E., 1913 - "General Embryology." Henry Holt, N.Y.

KELLICOTT, W. E., 1913 - "Chordate Development." Henry Holt, N.Y.

KELLOG, R., 1932 - "Mexican Tailless Amphibians in the United States National Museum." Bull. U.S. Nat. Mus. #160.

KORSCHELT, E., 1927 - "Regeneration und Transplantation." Borntrager Berlin.

KORSCHELT, E., 1936 - "Vergleichende Entwicklunsgeschichte der Tiere." Fisher, Jena

KORSCHELT, E., F. HEIDER, 1900 - "Textbook of Embryology of the Invertebrates." Macmillan.

KUHN, ALFRED, 1955 - "Vorlesungen über Entwicklungsphysiologie." Springer-Verlag, Berlin.

LEHMANN, F. E., 1945 - "Einführung in die Physiologische Embryologie." Borkhauser, Basel.

LILLIE, F. R., 1919 - "The Problem of Fertilization." Univ. Chicago Press.

LILLIE, R. D., 1954 - "Histopathologic Technique and Practical Histochemistry." Blakiston, N.Y.

LISON, L., 1936 - "Histochimie Animale, Methodes et Problemes." Gauthier-Villars, Paris.

LOEB, J., 1913 - "Artificial Parthenogenesis." Univ. Chicago Press.

LOEB, J., 1916 - "The Organism as a Whole." E. B. Putnam.

MANGOLD, O., 1928-'31 - "Das Determinationsproblem." Ergebn. d. Biol., Vols. 3, 5, 7.

MANGOLD, O., 1930 - "Methodel fur Wissenschaftliche Biologie." Vol. 11.

MAY, R., 1945 - "La Formation du Systeme Nerveu." Gauthier-Villars, Paris.

McBRIDE, E. W., 1914 - "Textbook of Embryology." Macmillan (2 vols.)

McCLUNG, C. E., 1937 - "Handbook of Microscopic Technique." Hoeber, N.Y.

McELROY, W. D., B. GLASS, 1958 - "A Symposium on the Chemical Basis of Development." Johns Hopkins Press, Baltimore.

MERTENS, R., L. MILLER, 1928 - "Liste der Amphibien und Reptilien Europas." Abhandl. d. Senckenbergischen Naturf. Gesellsch. 41:3.

MEYER, A. W., 1939 - "The Rise of Embryology." Stanford Univ. Press.

MORGAN, T. H., 1927 - "Experimental Embryology." Columbia Univ. Press.

MORGAN, T. H., 1934 - "Genetics and Embryology." Columbia Univ. Press.

NAT'L. ACAD. SCI.-NAT. RES. COUNCIL, 1959 - "The Developmental Biology Conference Ser. 1956." Univ. Chicago Press.

NEEDHAM, A. E., 1952 - "Regeneration and Wound Healing." Methuen, London.

NEEDHAM, J., 1930 - "Chemical Embryology." Macmillan (3 vols.)

NEEDHAMN, J., 1942 - "Biochemistry and Morphogenesis." Cambridge Univ. Press.

OSTER, G., A. W. POLLISTER, 1956 - "Physical Techniques in Biological Research." Academic Press, N.Y.

PANTIN, C. F. A., 1946 - "Notes on Microscopical Techniques for Zoologists." Cambridge Univ. Press.

PATTEN, B. M., 1958 - "Foundations of Embryology." McGraw-Hill, N.Y.

PEARSE, A. G. E., 1960 - "Histochemistry: Theoretical and Applied." Little-Brown & Co., Boston. 998 pgs.

POPE, C. H., 1944 - "Amphibians and Reptiles of the Chicago Area." Chicago Museum Nat'l. History.

PRZIBRAM, H., 1929 - "Zoonomie, Experimentalzoologie." Leipzig u. Wien.

RAVEN, CHR. P., 1958 - "Morphogenesis: The Analysis of Molluscan Development." Pergamon Press, N.Y.

RAVEN, CHR. P., 1954 - "An Outline of Developmental Physiology." McGraw-Hill, N.Y.

RICHARDS, A. N., 1931 - "Outline of Comparative Embryology." J. Wiley, N.Y.

RITTER, W. E., E. W. BAILEY, 1928 - "The Organismal Conception." Univ. Calif. Pub. #31.

ROBERTSON, T. B., 1924 - "Chemical Basis for Growth and Senescence." J. B. Lippincott, Philadelphia.

RUGH, R., 1948 - "Experimental Embryology: A Manual of Techniques and Procedures." Burgess Pub. Co., Minneapolis. Out of print.

RUGH, R., 1961 - "The Frog: Its Reproduction and Development." McGraw-Hill, N.Y. (Rev. ed.)

RUGH, R., 1961 - "A Laboratory Manual of Vertebrate Embryology."

RUNNER, M. N., C. P. DAGG, 1960 - "Metabolic mechanisms of teratogenic agents during metamorphosis." Jour. Nat. Cancer Inst. Monogr. #2, 41-56.

RUSSELL, E. S., 1930 - "Interpretation of Development and Heredity." Oxford Univ. Press.

SCHLIEP, W., 1929 - "Die Determination der Primitiventwicklung." Akademische Verlag-Gesellschaft.

SPEMANN, H., 1938 - "Embryonic Development and Induction." Yale Univ. Press.

STEJNEGER, L., T. BARBOUR, 1939 - "A Check List of North American Amphibians and Reptiles." Harvard Univ. Press.

THOMPSON, D'Arcy, 1917 - "On Growth and Form." Putnam.

TOKIN, B. P., 1959 - "Regeneration and Somatic Embryogenesis." Izdatel'stvo Leningradskoga Universiteta.

TYLER, A., 1942 - "Developmental Processes and Energetics." Quart. Rev. Biol. 17:197-353.

TYLER, A., R. C. BORSTEL, C. B. METZ, eds. 1957 - "The Beginnings of Embryonic Development." Am. Ass'n. Adv. Sci. #48.

WADDINGTON, C. H., 1936 - "How Animals Develop." W. W. Norton, N.Y.

WADDINGTON, C. H., 1940 - "Organizers and Genes." Cambridge Univ. Press.

WADDINGTON, C. H., 1956 - "Principles of Embryology." Macmillan.

WEED, A. C., 1922 - "New Frogs from Minnesota." Proc. Biol. Soc., Washington
 35:107.
WEISMANN, A., 1893 - "Germplasm." C. Scribner, N.Y.
WEISS, P., 1930 - "Entwicklungsphysiologie der Tiere." Dresden u. Leipzig.
WEISS, P., 1939 - "Principles of Development." Henry Holt, N.Y.
WHITMAN, C. O., 1898 - "Evolution and Epigenesis." Woods Hole Lectures.
WILLIER, B. J., P. WEISS, V. HAMBURGER (eds.) 1955 - "Analysis of Development."
 W. B. Saunders, Philadelphia.
WILSON, E. B., 1925 - "The Cell in Development and Inheritance." Macmillan.
WORDEMANN, M. W., C. P. RAVEN, 1946 - "Experimental Embryology in the Nether-
 lands." Elsevier, N.Y.
WRIGHT, A. H., 1933 - "Handbook of Frogs and Toads." Comstock Pub. Co., Ithaca.
WURMBACH, H., 1957 - "Lehrbuch der Zoologie." Gustav Fischer Verlag, Stuttgart.
ZUBEK, J. P., P. A. SOLBERG, 1954 - "Human Development." McGraw-Hill, N.Y.
ZWARENSTEIN, H., N. SAPEIKAM, H. A. SHAPIRO, 1946 - "Xenopus laevis, a Bibli-
 ography." Univ. Capetown Pub., The African Bookman.

"When it is recalled that the 9,200,000,000 cells in the human cerebral cortex are the nervous elements of this organ and that they collectively constitute rather less than a cubic inch of protoplasm, it seems almost incredible that they should serve us as they do. They are the materials whose activities represent all human states, sensations, memories, volitions, emotions, affections, the highest flights of poetry, the most profound thoughts of philosophy, the most far-reaching theories of science, and, when their action goes astray, the ravings of insanity. It is this small amount of protoplasm in each of us that our whole educational system is concerned with training and that serves us through a lifetime in the growth of personality."

- G. H. Parker

I. TECHNIQUES IN EXPERIMENTAL EMBRYOLOGY

Equipment and Procedures in Experimental Embryology

GENERAL INTRODUCTION

"Biologically Clean": These two words should be the most frequently emphasized in any laboratory of experimental embryology, even as they are in any tissue culture laboratory. Glassware, instruments, solutions and hands must be "biologically clean" before any experimental results may be considered valid. The term means that, barring any experimental conditions imposed which might alter the situation, there is no possible contamination of the living material either by chemical substances, by living parasites or by harmful organisms such as bacteria or viruses. The experimental conditions should be such that any embryo, introduced into that environment, would be expected to survive. The following precautions, in the interest of biological cleanliness, are suggested:

1. Glassware: Regardless of the source of the glassware used, it should be thoroughly scrubbed with hot soap and water, rinsed in running tap water for at least 2 hours, rinsed in distilled water and air-dried either by or under the direct supervision of the person planning to use it. If the glassware is cleaned with the usual cleaning fluid (potassium dichromate saturated in 10% sulfuric acid) it must be thoroughly washed and rinsed for a longer period in order to remove the tenacious chemicals (Richards '36). Properly cleaned glassware may be wrapped in clean paper towelling and heat sterilized for 1/2 hour at 100° C. As long thereafter as the glassware remains wrapped it may be considered as sterile.

2. Hands: A surgeon usually spends as much time scrubbing his hands as in operating, and such cleanliness in experimental embryology will result in more dependable and reproducible results. Formaldehyde, osmic or hydrochloric acid fumes, adherent to the hands, will contaminate instruments and ultimately the embryos. Thin white surgeons rubber gloves are advised in tissue culture experiments.

3. Instruments: If the instruments have never before been used, they may be thoroughly washed, rinsed, and sterilized in the autoclave at 15 pounds pressure for 30 minutes; cooled; immersed in 95% alcohol until used. Dissecting instruments from other laboratories should never be "trusted". Each student should provide himself with a new set of stainless steel instruments (never chromium plated) and should keep them in a plastic tube, or in a cotton-filled box, to be reserved exclusively for his operational procedures with living embryos.

It is often necessary to preserve eggs or embryos but the operating instruments should never come into contact with any fixatives. The student may use an unsterile or even contaminated set of instruments for the handling of such material to be preserved. Often eggs, embryos or even tissues may be introduced into a fixative with the flat end of a toothpick, thus avoiding the contamination of instruments. Once an instrument has come into contact with a fixative, it should thereafter be regarded as "contaminated" and not "biologically clean."

4. Embryos: Dead or dying embryos are probably the most common source of contamination of cultures, because they are infested with bacteria and necro-toxins. Ailing embryos should be isolated, and crowding should be avoided. The culture medium should, at all times, appear to be clear. Healthy embryos may be passed through several changes of sterile medium in order to free them of adherent bacteria. Some stages of development, particularly of aquatic forms, may tolerate brief immersion

in hypertonic salt solutions or dilute potassium permanganate, either of which appears to be bacteriocidal. Generally such treatment is unnecessary, and should be avoided, if other precautions are taken. Also, if the embryos are kept at the lowest but tolerable temperatures, and the dishes are covered, there is less likelihood of infections killing them. (See special directions for chick and mouse embryos)

The sooner the student insures personal and operative "biological cleanliness." the sooner will he obtain reproducible experimental data, and enjoy the experiences of experimental embryology. It is a complete waste of time and talent to allow contamination to invalidate experimental data.

THE EXPERIMENTAL PROGRAM

Every experimental program is built upon a foundation of facts, or theories, well supported by demonstrated facts, and must follow a very definite course if the results are to be reproducible and acceptable. It should help the beginning investigator to outline such a research protocol in order to instill in him the habit of rigid and complete planning. This does not imply that anyone can forsee the results of an experiment. Indeed, the research worker must at all times avoid the pitfall of prejudicial planning, of a program designed to prove rather than investigate some pre-conceived concept. A research worker, true to his opportunities, will be entirely open-minded to the consequences of his research. His planning should be designed to investigate an unexplored area, and his reward will be discovery, often in unpredictable directions.

The unplanned, or the unintelligently-planned research program, usually results in wasted materials, effort, and talent. The uninitiated investigator too often finds, at the conclusion of his program, that he has omitted some vital procedure or has tragically by-passed some fruitful corollary. Thus, as experience is accumulated, the initial research program will become much more specific, but as the research is in progress the ramifications become more varied. With experience, the results of genuine experimentation are more subject to prediction and more apt to open up new and wider vistas of challenge. The research worker does not, therefore, put his program into a machine and await the end results but rather designs his program on the basis of facts and theories, and is ever alert during the investigation for new challenges for an inquiring mind. The program should never be final, unalterable, but pragmatic and subject to change as new facts are revealed.

In light of the above, an outline is suggested which might be useful not only in planning an experiment but in reporting it for publication in a scientific journal. Again, this is only suggestive, but is offered as a protocol for complete research thinking and planning.

THE RESEARCH PROTOCOL

PURPOSE: Here the major purpose of the investigation should be succinctly stated. For example, it could be: "To determine the effect of temperature on the growth rate of the tadpole of the frog, Rana pipiens."

Such a statement gives immediately the one major variable, temperature and the test object or situation, growth rate, and, most important, the form used, Rana pipiens tadpoles. There can be no doubt by anyone that if the purpose is achieved, there will be established some correlation between temperature and growth rate.

But, one cannot always anticipate that results will be positive so that the purpose might be stated: "To investigate the possible relation between temperature and growth rate of <u>Rana pipiens tadpoles</u>". Thus, if the investigation proves that no relation exists, even the negative data will be significant.

Further, one cannot anticipate that the results will be encompassed by the original statement of purpose. But the more specific and succinct is the original statement of purpose, the more clear-cut will be the entire research program.

MATERIALS: There are two major classes of material that may be used in experimental embryology, or any experimental procedure in biology, namely (a) Biological and (b) Physical and/or Chemical.

One should list species or strain of animal used, as well as age, sex, and numbers. If it is an embryonic stage, that should be properly defined.

One should list all of the chemicals and apparatus that are to be used so that anyone attempting to repeat this experiment can do so under identical conditions.

EXPERIMENTAL PROCEDURE: In this section one must outline exactly what he intends to do.

a. The controls.
b. The number, age, sex stage of development, or other conditions of the animals or embryos.
c. The single experimental variable imposed.
d. The method of collecting data.

<u>THE CONTROLS</u>: Every experiment, every research project, must include a "control" or "controls. It is difficult to conceive of a situation in which a control is not possible, and most experiments are not valid without adequate controls.

The control is the standard, the normal, the untreated organism or situation with which experimentally induced results are to be compared. One simply cannot evaluate experimental data without controls, without organisms or embryos exactly identical but without the imposed experimental variable. Only by direct comparison of an experimental situation with a control situation can we evaluate any deviations caused by the experimental variable.

The ideal control, in any animal experiment, is a genetically identical individual, if such is obtainable. Identical twins, derived from the same zygote by cell separation at the two-cell stage, would therefore be ideal in the sense that one could be regarded as the exact (genetic) biological duplicate of the other. One could be kept protected from the single variable of interest while the other could be subjected to it, to determine the effect. Isolation cultures among the protozoa or bacteria, resulting in clones which may be separated and followed, all derived from a single parent, would constitute ideal experimental material. This is because these unicellular forms have asexual reproduction, the progeny resulting from binary fission and therefore being identical with each other as well as with the single parent.

Among multicellular forms, and all embryos, this ideal situation is generally impractical so that we usually satisfy the condition of a control with litter mates, derived from the same parents and at the same time. Certainly these are not genetically identical, but nonetheless, they are more closely identical than any other possible combination of paired individuals.

Thus, while one's interest may be directed toward the effect of some experimental variable, he cannot even recognize his results if he does not have proper and adequate controls with which to compare. The <u>CONTROL</u> is absolutely essential to every experiment.

The novice might ask about controls for extirpation or transplantation experiments. Obviously, if an extirpation results in a specific organ loss, the control would be an extirpation from another region to determine whether there results a similar organ loss. Likewise, in transplantations there is the donor tissue and the location in the host field, either condition which must have a control to specifically circumscribe potentialities. In these qualitative experiments large numbers of controls are not necessary, but similarly placed transplants of other donor material, or varied locations within the host area of the same anlagé, would constitute adequate controls. The function of the control is to prove positively that the results obtained could not have been obtained with any other set of circumstances.

THE NUMBER, AGE, SEX, ETC. OF ANIMALS USED: The results of many experiments are the more convincing the greater the numbers of experimentals and controls used, within certain limits. If every experimental animal shows a particular response never seen among the controls, then 10-20 controls and experimentals should suffice. However, if the differences between experimentals and controls are (calculated to be) small, then, on a purely statistical basis, larger numbers are necessary. In the latter instance the results are primarily quantitative, even though they may be concerned with qualitative differences. Thus, it is important to plan on a sufficient number of animals all used at one time. There are, for instance, seasonal differences even within a species, and also diurnal differences (cycles) in certain rhythmic functions, so that in order to obtain large numbers it is not safe simply to accumulate data from small numbers over an extended period.

The purpose of any experiment is generally to study the effect of a single variable, e.g., temperature. It is important therefore that all other physical and biological variables be eliminated between the experimental and controls, or at least be reduced and recognized. One variable among animals that is not always recognized is sex, though the differences are usually obvious! There are few biological experiments in which sex does not play a part, though sometimes a negative one. In general the female is the more hardy, the more resistant to trauma, etc. Another variable that must be recognized is age. Certainly the embryos of different ages are very different, so that one cannot put together data from temperature observations on the blastula, gastrula, and neurula stages of the frog tadpole, for instance. Another area of variation is in physiological activity, the more difficult to recognize. Thus, one must try to obtain a large number of identical animals or embryos; half of which may then be subject to the one experimental variable in order to determine the valid biological response.

THE SINGLE EXPERIMENTAL VARIABLE IMPOSED: The above statements emphasize the necessity of preparing the animals or embryos so that the results obtained are clearly due to the single variable imposed. If one is experimenting on temperature effects he must be absolutely certain that no other variable is involved. Aside from the few biological variables above mentioned, among the physical variables would be light, agitation, salinity, number of organisms per unit of space (concentration), etc. any one of which could easily becloud the results of the intended variable of temperature. Both the biological and the physical and chemical variables must be eliminated or so controlled that there remains but a single variable between the control and the experimental animals.

METHOD OF COLLECTING DATA: This will depend entirely upon the material, and the nature of the experiment. In any case it should be systematic and complete, so that anyone else could step in and complete the experiment at any point of progress. Dates should appear by every set of data collected, and every measurable or detectable bit of information should be recorded in a book which never leaves the laboratory. The practice of collecting data on scraps of paper, later to be transposed to the record book, is to be discouraged.

Sketches, accompanied by photographs, are very useful in qualitative experiments. But in every case the illustration must be fully labelled. No one can remember accurately such minute data for any length of time. When the data are all available it is well to reduce it to a table and then, if possible, to a graph.

Brief mention must be made here of the necessity in all scientific research for absolute honesty, to the minutest detail. One false entry or record, one faked operation or even incomplete data will ruin forever the reliability of all data collected by that individual. Science must be a body of knowledge based upon fact, as truly as the human mind can perceive it. One quickly discovers that facts in science are more exciting than any concoction of the human imagination.

DISCUSSION: In this section will appear all references to related or pertinent experiments and objective discussion of their meaning with respect to the findings of the data presented. The discussion should never be exhaustive, should never be a means to "padding" the paper, and only those papers of recent date should be included. It is presumed that intelligent readers will be familiar with the earlier works in the field, and through references included, other and earlier references become available. The author should freely admit disparities, and point toward further work that would be instructive.

SUMMARY AND CONCLUSIONS: The summary may be a part of the discussion, although some authors offer a single paragraph summary as the first of the items in the conclusion. In a proper discussion the points of a summary would naturally appear. The conclusions, if no summary is offered, should start with a very succinct statement of the project, animals used, and the general findings. Succeeding conclusion statements would then relate the newly proven facts. It should be remembered that often a reader will read the introduction and the conclusions, possibly look at the illustrations, in order to decide whether the material is of particular interest to him. This lends importance to these sections. However, it is a cardinal error to include in any summary or conclusions any statements not born out by the data of the paper.

REFERENCES: There are many ways of presenting this information and one should consult the Journal to which he intends to send the manuscript. In any case, a complete reference should include the names and initials of all authors, the date of publication, the complete title, and the detailed reference including the volume of the Journal and the inclusive pages. This is a very important section of any scientific report.

The general outline, therefore, for a manuscript would be as follows:

Statement of purpose
Materials and methods
Experimental data
Discussion
Summary and conclusions
References

EQUIPMENT AND INSTRUMENTS NEEDED
BY EACH STUDENT IN EXPERIMENTAL EMBRYOLOGY

OPTICAL EQUIPMENT

Standard microscope with usual lenses; oil immersion optional.
Dissecting microscope (binocular):
    Objectives 1.7 x and 3.5 x most useful, with 10 x oculars.
    The U-shaped base should be removable for indirect lighting.
Microscope lamp: Spencer diaphragm most useful.
Heat absorbing flask: A 250 cc. round bottom Pyrex flask filled with distilled water and supported on vertical stand by screw clamp. This device will absorb the infra-red heat rays and also provide a means of concentrating the cold light.

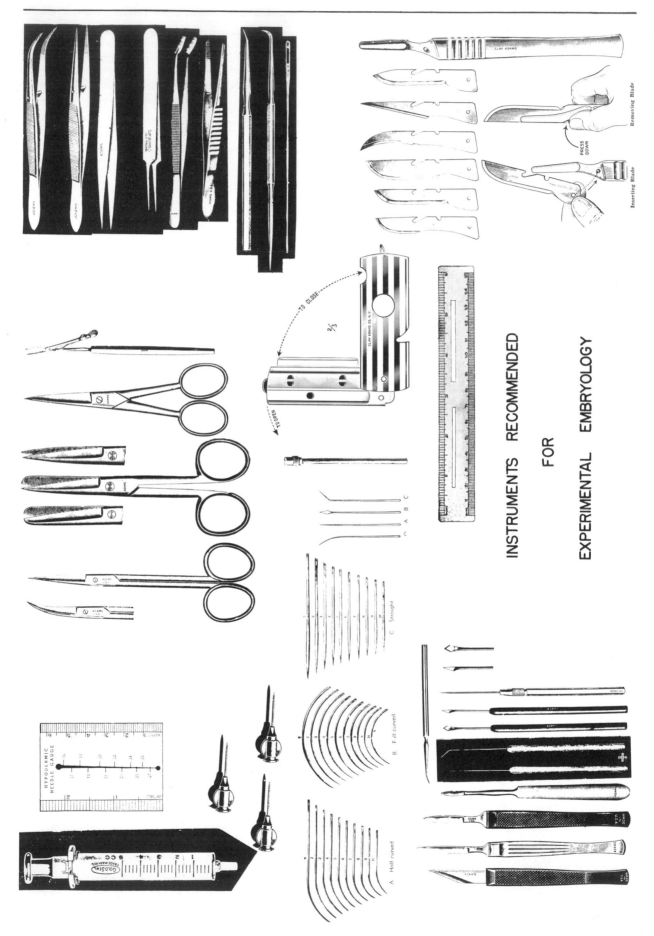

INSTRUMENTS RECOMMENDED

FOR

EXPERIMENTAL EMBRYOLOGY

GLASSWARE AND CULTURE DISHES

2 enamel pans 3.5 x 12 x 24 inches for culturing tadpoles.
2 battery jars with weighted covers, for living frogs.
2 crystallizing dishes with covers, 12 inch size, for early stages of amphibian develop-
      ment.
12 Syracuse dishes
12 #1 Stenders with covers
12 #2 Stenders with covers
24 regulation finger bowls
 6 Petri dishes with covers
 6 shell depression slides
1/2 gross microscopic slides
1 oz. #1 cover slips, square or round.
2 ft. soft glass tubing, 3 mm. diameter.
2 ft. soft glass rod, 4 mm. diameter
4 ft. soft glass rod, 2 mm. diameter.
2 hypodermic syringes, 2 cc. cap., with #18 needles.
2 glass plates, convenient size 5 x 7 inches.

METAL INSTRUMENTS AND EQUIPMENT

2 watchmaker's forceps, stainless steel #5
2 adjustable needle holders
3 scissors: fine pointed to heavy and blunt
2 fine, sharp scalpels, one a lancet type
2 rigid section lifters, two sizes
2 pairs of forceps, regulation but fine and heavy
1 triangle file
1 Bunsen burner with wire gauze and rubber tubing

MISCELLANEOUS EQUIPMENT

1/2 lb. Permoplast, cream colored, to be used for operating depressions.
1/4 lb. beeswax, white, clear
1/4 lb. soft (low melting point) paraffin
2 China marking pencils, one blue and the other red.
1 diamond point or carborundum pencil
2 needle holders, to hold operating needles of various sizes
1 plastic cover for needle holder
2 ft. rubber tubing, 11-12 mm. outside diameter
2 ft. rubber tubing 8-9 mm. outside diameter

THE PREPARATION OF INSTRUMENTS

1. The Micro-burner: This may be set up for class use. However, its preparation may
be described since individuals may prefer to have accessible their own burner. Its
function is to give a small but intense flame.

Secure a 5-inch piece of 7 mm. soft glass tubing and in a hot flame reduce the diameter of one end to about 1 mm. Then place a right angle in the tube, at its center
(with a flame tip) and when cool, pass the flamed end through a hole in a large cork.
Mount the cork in a burette clamp attached to a ring stand so that the micro-burner
is turned upward. To the other end of the tube attach a rubber tubing joined to the
gas outlet. Apply a screw clamp to the rubber tubing. By regulating the screw clamp

a micro-flame of intense heat may be secured. The usual type of micro-burner, where the tube is drawn out to a thin tip of small bore, is not so likely to remain uniform when in use. Hypodermic needles may be used as micro-flame tips. (See illustrations following).

2. Glass needles: There are two types of handles used for glass needles. The standard type consists of a 7 mm. diameter glass rod cut into 10 cm. lengths by flaming longer pieces in the center and drawing them out. In this manner one end of the rod is tapered. The tapering end should be brought into the flame so that it retracts to knob for attachment of the needle, made separately. See that the knob and rod are perfectly straight. Prepare 10 such needle handles. The second type of needle holder consists of the regulation steel needle holder with adjustable screw into which various needles may be inserted and fastened. This type is convenient and entirely satisfactory.

The needles may be made on the electric needle-puller but this is not necessary. Secure some 4-5 mm. diameter soft glass rod and in a flame tip draw it out perfectly straight until a thickness of about 1 mm. is secured. Break this into about 7-8 cm. lengths and in the micro-flame, put a hook or a bend toward the end of each piece. Hang this "hook" over any support (Metal rod) attached to the ring stand in such a manner that it is directly above a 20 x 60 mm. (or larger) glass vial. In the bottom of the vial place a small amount of cotton. At about 2 cm. from the base of the hanging glass rod apply the micro-flame from the side. It will take practice to apply the correct amount of heat. When the glass at the point of heat application is melted, the weight of the hanging rod will drop it into the cotton in the glass vial, providing a needle point of microscopic dimensions. With practice it may be possible to do this in two steps, the first heating will lengthen and thin out the rod and the second will draw an even finer point. In any case the tapering micro-point should not be long and flexible and will probably have to be trimmed with sharp scissors. Draw out many such needles at one time and mount them temporarily in plasticene, i. e., until ready to attach them to holders or to mount them in a needle board. These needle points may be attached to the glass handles (described above) by bringing them together in a small flame. The needles may be attached at a slight angle which will facilitate operations. (See illustrations following).

3. Steel needles: The ordinary steel needles are much too coarse for work with small embryos. However, the finest Insect needles may be secured, cut short, and mounted in wooden handles and will be extremely useful.

4. Hair loops: This device is for handling embryos or isolated tissues. Draw out the end of some 5-6 mm. soft glass tubing so that the total length is about 10 cm. and the smaller end has a diameter of about 1 mm. Close the larger end in a flame. The smaller end should be cut off with a diamond pencil or flamed to make it smooth. Secure some blonde hair from a newborn infant and cut it into 1 inch lengths. With forceps insert one end of the hair into the capillary opening and then the other end into the same opening. Regulate the insertion of the hair so that a relatively small loop protrudes. Melt a small amount of soft paraffin on a glass slide and dip the hair-loop into the paraffin, whereupon some of the paraffin will run up into the tube, and harden upon cooling. This will hold the hair loop in place. To remove any paraffin adherent to the hair loop itself, warm a slide in a flame, place on it a small piece of filter paper, and gently touch the hair-loop to the filter paper. Avoid melting the paraffin within the capillary tube.

5. Glass ball tip: This instrument is also used for moving embryos about without injury to them. Using 6-7 mm. soft rod of about 18 cm. lengths, draw out the center (with a flame tip) and break off the excess thread down to within 2-3 cm. of the widening

part of the rod. Hold the pointed end of the rod in a flame and a glass ball will form
on the end. It can be kept symmetrical by constant spinning of the rod while heating.
If it is planned to put a gentle curve in such a rod, this should be done when the rod
is drawn out rather than later. Such ball-tips are used also for making depressions
in Permoplast, suitable for embryos. It is well, therefore, to have a small assort-
ment of sizes of such ball-tips.

6. Glass pipettes: Three types of pipettes will be used: wide-mouthed, micro-pipette,
and micro-pipette with lateral control (see diagrams).

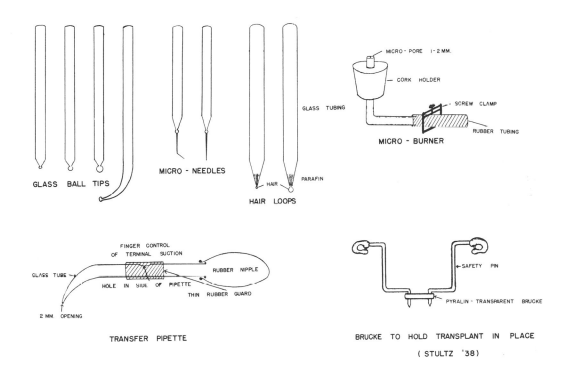

The wide-mouthed pipette is used for the transferring of embryos. It is simply a
wide bore pipette (6-7 mm. diameter) with a curved and smooth-edged tip. This can
be made by cutting off the tip of a medicine dropper and should be available at all
times.

The micro-pipette is made of soft glass with 7-8 mm. outer diameter, pulled out to
microscopic dimensions in a manner similar to the making of micro-needles (above).
The tip end of such pipettes are often closed but may be trimmed off. These pipettes
may be used with ordinary rubber nipple or may be used with rubber tubing and
mouth suction.

The micro-pipette with lateral control has special use in the transfer of isolated
pieces of embryos to regions where transplants are desired. It is made in the following manner: Pull out some 7-8 mm. soft glass tubing so that the handle portion has
a length of about 10 cm. It is better if the capillary end has a slight curve and tapers
rapidly. Close the capillary end by melting it in the Bunsen flame and attach a piece
of rubber tubing to the larger open end of the pipette. Bring the side of the pipette,
at about 3-4 cm. above the capillary end, into a small hot flame. If the capillary end
is curved, the point of heating should be on the opposite side of the curve. When this
point is soft, blow gently into the rubber tubing and the melted glass will bulge outward. The size of the heated area will determine the size of the bulge. Break off

the glass bubble down to the wall of the pipette and smooth off the edges in a micro-burner. With diamond point cut off the closed tip of the capillary end so that the aperture will be about 1 mm. in diameter. Cut a short piece of thin-walled rubber tubing and slip it (from larger end) over the pipette to the point where it covers the

RUBBER TUBING OVER
SIDE HOLE

SPEMANN MICROPIPETTE FOR TRANSPLANTATIONS

lateral hole. Heat the broad end of the pipette until very soft, press down on metal surface to give a ridge to hold the rubber nipple. Add rubber nipple to this end, and the pipette is ready for use. (See illustrations above).

This latter pipette is of special value in the transfer of small pieces of tissue under solution. With nipple, suck in solution until the capillary end is filled almost to the lateral hole. Remove fingers from nipple and place a forefinger over the rubber-covered lateral hole. With the capillary point under the solution, force out a small amount of the contents of the pipette by gently pressing on the lateral rubber cover with the forefinger. Then, by releasing the gentle pressure a small amount of fluid, or tissue, may be drawn up into the pipette and held there. This tissue may be oriented at any place by slight pressure on this lateral membrane. The capillary end must hold solution (not drip) even when held vertically with the point suspended. Practice the use of this pipette with small objects.

7. Glass bridges: These are small pieces of cover glass, thinnest grade, used to hold transplanted tissues in place for 15+ minutes while they "take" or heal onto the host. Using a diamond point pencil and ruler, cut thin cover glasses into strips of about 2-3 mm. wide and 5-10 mm. long. With forceps run the edges of these glass strips through a micro-flame to make them smooth. To put a slight curve in some of the pieces of cover glass, grasp the edge of a piece with forceps and bring the center of it over a micro-burner with a 1 mm. flame. The weight of the cold end will bend the cover slip slightly when the center is heated. The height of the bridge should be determined by the size of the embryo to be used as host. Frequently flat cover slips will prove to be adequate, especially when the host is held in a depression. The bridges should be sterilized in 70% alcohol over cotton and kept thus in a covered stender dish.

There is a refinement of this type of bridge (or Brücke) described by Schultze, (1938). The cover itself consists of transparent Pyralin of less than 2 mm. thickness cut into rectangular blocks of 1/8 inch by 3/8 inches each. Holes are drilled through each end of the block with #70 or #71 wire gauge drill. The edges of the block are smoothed off with fine file and then dipped in very weak balsam to increase transparency. Take care that balsam does not fill the holes. Small safety pins, (preferably gold plated to prevent rusting) are straightened out and then given three right angle bends as shown in the diagram. The pins are then forced through the holes, to the extent of 5-6 mm. Such a graft cover may be pressed down onto the graft exactly as desired, the pins anchored in the Permoplast and the Pyralin allowing constant observation of the graft. In most transplantations such an elaborate Brücke is not necessary.

OPERATING PROCEDURES

Most operations will be carried out in Syracuse dishes or salt cellars. Since embryonic tissues often adhere to glass, the base of the Syracuse dish is lined with one or another plastic substance. The following are satisfactory:

  a. Permoplast - American Art Clay Co., Indianapolis, Indiana.
  b. Beeswax to which has been added lampblack, to take glare off background.
  c. Rainbow Wax - American Art Clay Co., Indianapolis, Indiana.
  d. White refined beeswax.
  e. Pieces of cellophane or Pyralin.
  f. Agar, 2% or more concentrated.

The Permoplast is probably best for delicate operative procedures, as it is easily molded without heating. However, under solution it tends to fragment. It may be necessary to compensate for this by melting it with about 20% low melting point paraffin.

For frog work, melted beeswax to which enough lampblack has been added to give it a dark gray appearance, will prove to be satisfactory. Occasionally, after the dishes are prepared, the wax base will, under water, float off the bottom. To prevent this, place a few pieces of 2 mm. glass rod in the bottom of each dish before adding the melted beeswax. These will add sufficient weight to hold the wax in place. Have at least 10 operating dishes available at all times. Grooves to hold embryos may be made with ball tips before the beeswax hardens.

OPERATING SOLUTIONS

The operating medium will vary with the age, the condition of the embryo (or tissue) and the species used. Operations are generally performed in more concentrated solutions, and, after healing, are returned to weaker salt solutions (see exercise on "Wound Healing").

For operations on Urodeles the Urodele Operating Medium is used and the embryos will heal normally if left in these solutions. After the operation wound has healed the Urodele embryo is transferred to Urodele Growing Solution. For the Anura, double strength and then Normal Standard Solutions are used. Brief boiling of the solutions to sterilize them may be necessary. If convenient, large volumes could be autoclaved, filtered and stored as stock solutions. Controlled salt solutions are more satisfactory than Spring Water or conditioned tap water because there is greater uniformity.

In all cases remember that surface rather than volume is important. The embryos need be just covered in the solution and no more, providing evaporation is reduced to a minimum.

GLASSWARE

Ovulating animals should be kept in fish bowls or small battery jars, properly covered. If eggs are to be layed in these containers, it will be necessary to provide them with appropriate solutions. The Urodeles generally attach their eggs to vegetation.

For fertilization of frog's eggs, finger bowls or Petri dishes are used and all eggs from a single female may be inseminated in a single container providing they are flooded in 15 minutes and separated to lots of about 25 per finger bowl before the first cleavage. Development will continue to hatching in finger bowls but beyond hatching a different procedure will be necessary (see section on "Culturing of Embryos").

Operations are performed in dishes described above. Following the operation, when the transplant has "taken", the embryo may be transferred to a covered stender, the bottom of which has a thin layer of 4-5% agar. This provides a softer base than glass so that there is less danger of injury. Such operated animals should be kept at constant temperature toward the lower levels of tolerance for the particular species under investigation.

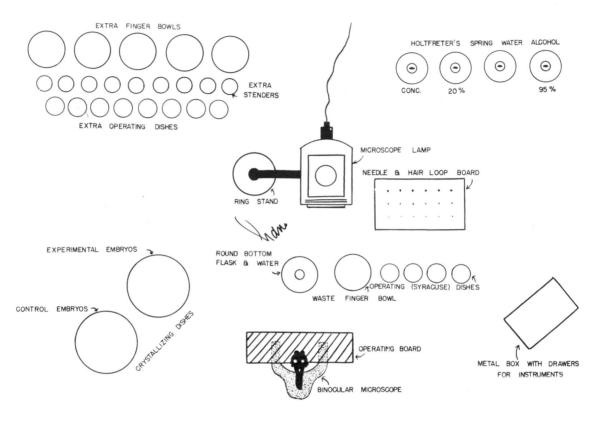

PLAN FOR OPERATING TABLE

ASEPSIS

The amphibian embryo is relatively immune to infection, or bacterial contamination. Operated embryos are, of course, exposed to such conditions but the wounds heal so rapidly that simple aseptic precautions are generally sufficient to protect the embryo.

In recent years Detwiler, Copenhaver, and Robinson (1947) have demonstrated that sodium sulfadiazine (0.5%) in any of the various operating or culture media is perfectly harmless to the embryo, and will reduce the operative casualties on the central nervous system from 95% to 5%. The sulfadiazine may partially crystallize out, but these crystals are harmless except as they may mechanically pierce the ectoderm of the embryo.

At later larval stages, or just after metamorphosis, amphibia may become susceptible to fungus or other skin infections. These can be treated locally with dilute mercurochrome, neo-silvol, or very concentrated salt solutions painted onto the affected area. Generally a copper penny in the same tank will keep down all fungus.

MEMBRANES

The eggs of all amphibians are surrounded by secondary (jelly) membranes secreted by the oviduct in addition to the vitelline membrane. These membranes presumably protect the embryo from bacteria and injury during development. Any operations on such embryos require that such membranes be removed. It must be remembered, therefore, that the unprotected embryo is rather easily injured and that it is more susceptible to physical and chemical changes in the environment, as well as to bacterial infection.

A. URODELA

The Urodele jelly is rather tough and may be peeled off of the eggs with sharp pointed watchmaker's forceps. The vitelline membrane will be resistant to puncturing so that it may be necessary to use glass micro-needles to make the initial break. Urodele egg capsules should be opened in Urodele Growing Solution.

B. ANURA

The Anuran egg is surrounded by loose jelly which is adherent to the vitelline membrane. Attempts have been made to remove this jelly by Ultra-violet light or by dilute KCN, but there is no reliable chemical method of jelly removal which allows the embryo to survive. Should someone discover a method of fertilizing body cavity eggs (devoid of jelly) this would be a boon to experimental embryology. The Anuran egg jelly can be removed to some extent by rolling the egg on filter paper or paper toweling, pushing it along with the flat side of a scalpel. The danger in this method is, of course, excessive mechanical injury to the egg so that the correct rate and amount of absorption (by filter paper) and the exact amount of rolling will have to be determined empirically. With practice it is possible to pierce the jelly with one prong of the forceps, slide a prong of a second pair of forceps along the first, and cut through the jelly with an outward movement. Then the split jelly capsule can be shelled off of the egg. The enzyme hyaluronidase, so effective in denuding the mammalian egg, may prove of similar value with the amphibian egg. (Personal communication from D. C. Metcalfe and reference to Kurzrok 1948: Am. Jour. Clin. Pathology, p. 491.)

STANDARD LABORATORY EQUIPMENT IN EXPERIMENTAL EMBRYOLOGY*

MAJOR EQUIPMENT

1. <u>Water table</u> - wood or stone table provided with current of tap water to depth of 1 inch to be used for holding finger bowls, etc., at fairly constant temperatures.

2. <u>Refrigeration</u> - electric refrigerators (or constant temperature rooms) with heating units installed so that the temperatures may be regulated. Best temperatures are 4° C., 10° C., and 20° C.

3. <u>Incubators</u> - thermostatically controlled boxes which can be regulated at temperatures above the laboratory temperatures. Best temperatures are 25° C., 29° C., 32° C., and 35° C. Chick incubators regulated at 103° F. for few eggs (Oaks, Chicago) or for several hundred eggs (Buffalo Incubator Company, Buffalo) should be on hand.

---

* Note: The following list is rather exhaustive because it includes equipment needed to carry on all of the complicated procedures outlined. The list is intended as a guide for the Instructor. Many of the experiments can be conducted with a pair of watchmaker's forceps, a scalpel, a binocular microscope, and heat absorbed lighting. It is not necessary, therefore, to provide all the items in this list in order to encourage research in experimental embryology.

4. Centrifuge - heavy electric centrifuge with large capacity as well has smaller electric and hand centrifuges.

5. Animal cage - a wooden frame with slatted or no floor, screened sides and top, should be made to fit into the water table if the table is large enough. The cage may be divided into compartments with the doors opening on top. If the cage is to sit in water, the wood should be treated with some waterproofing. Frogs and salamanders may be kept in such a cage on the water table in healthy condition if they are provided with cool running water.

6. Aquaria - the sizes and shapes of aquaria depend upon the particular animals concerned. For Urodele and Anuran tadpoles (larvae) the low, flat tanks with considerable surface are best. Ideal dimensions are the 12 x 12 x 4 enamel (restaurant) pans.
    For fish, four sizes are desirable:
    — for fry - 1/2 gallon battery jars or 10¢ store aquaria.
    — for tropicals and breeding pairs - $16\frac{1}{4}$ x 8 1/5 x $8\frac{1}{2}$ inches wide is best (5 gallons).
    — for larger fish, or large groups of non belligerent fish - $20\frac{1}{4}$ x $10\frac{1}{2}$ x $12\frac{1}{4}$ inches high (about 10 gallon capacity).
    — for Zebra fish which are very active - $24\frac{1}{2}$ x $6\frac{1}{2}$ x 6 inches wide.
    All fish tanks should have slate bottoms and glass covers. One corner of the glass cover may be cut off to facilitate removal, and for feedings.

    The larger tanks may be sub-divided by cutting a piece of glass to fit and then covering the edges of the glass with split rubber tubing and inserting the glass into the tank. The rubber tubing will hold the plate in position and at the same time block the passage of small fry from one compartment to the other.

7. Microtome - Spencer rotary probably the best.

8. Embedding ovens - Columbia probably the best.

9. Slide warmer - Chicago Apparatus Company, thermostatically controlled electric warmer.

10. Balances - Coarse (200 + gram capacity) and sensitive types.

GLASSWARE

1. Battery jars or aquaria for individual use of students; each with weighted wire screen cover.
2. Crystallizing dishes or 10 inch finger bowls, with covers.
3. Finger bowls - regulation size, made to fit into each other.
4. Petri dishes (10 cm.) with covers.
5. Stender dishes with covers, both #1 and #2.
6. Syracuse dishes - regulation size.
7. Coplin staining jars, Homeopathic and Shell Vials.
8. Salt cellars for embedding oven.
9. Erlenmeyer flasks - 500 cc. capacity for storing sterile media.
10. Lantern slide covers - used as glass base for operating and for protecting binocular and compound microscope stages when using wet mounts.
11. Graduates - 10 cc. and 100 cc.
12. Beakers - 100 cc. and 600 cc.
13. Slides: Regulation microscope slides.
            Depression slides, cell type.
14. Cover slips - glass. Best size, 7/8 inch square and #1.
15. Glass rods - Diameters from 4 to 7 mm. Soft glass.
16. Glass tubing - Diameters from 4 to 7 mm. Soft glass.

SOLUTIONS AND REAGENTS

1. Distilled water - glass distilled preferred. Supply in large carboys with siphon and pinch clamp.

2. Spring water - if possible supply in carboys with siphon and pinch clamp. Great Bear Spring Water (N. Y. City) is excellent.

3. Conditioned tap water - to be stored in carboys after conditioning. This will be necessary where the City water supply is treated so that embryos cannot survive in it. This may be tested with sperm or early embryos. Conditioning is achieved by running tap water into large tank in which there will be maximum of surface exposed and in which plant material is abundant. Artificial aeration will help to eliminate chlorine. Passing tap water through fine gravel and charcoal is rarely necessary but would aid in conditioning highly toxic water. Three or four days of such conditioning should be sufficient.

4. Standard (Holtfreter's) Solution - this should be available to the students in several concentrations and large volumes. For the convenience of the instructor, the dry salts may be made up in appropriate concentrations and stored in vials to be added to carboys of glass distilled water when needed. The concentrations needed are 200%, 100% and 20%. The formula for Holtfreter's solution (J. Holtfreter, 1931 - Arch. f. Ent. mech. 124:404) is:

$$NaCl \dots\dots\dots\dots\ 0.35\ \ gr.$$
$$KCl \dots\dots\dots\dots\ 0.005\ gr.$$
$$CaCl_2 \dots\dots\dots\ 0.01\ \ gr.$$
$$NaHCO_3 \dots\dots\ 0.02\ \ gr.$$
$$Water \dots\dots\dots 100.00\ \ cc.\ (glass\ distilled\ preferred)$$

5. Amphibian Ringer's - should be available in concentrated form:

$$NaCl \dots\dots\dots\dots\ 0.66\ \ gr.$$
$$KCl \dots\dots\dots\dots\ 0.015\ gr.$$
$$CaCl_2 \dots\dots\dots\ 0.015\ gr.$$
$$NaHCO_3 \dots\dots\ to\ pH\ 7.8$$
$$Water \dots\dots\dots 100.0\ \ \ cc.$$

6. Urodele stock solution:

    Great Bear Spring Water ... 10 liters
    NaCl .... 70 grams
    KCl .... 1 gram
    $CaCl_2$ .... 2 grams

    Urodele Operating Medium: (hypertonic)
    Stock solution .... 2 parts
    Great Bear Spring Water ... 1 part

    Urodele Growing Medium: (isotonic)
    Stock solution .... 2 parts
    Great Bear Spring Water ... 4 parts

    Steinberg medium: - solution made up complete and autoclaved. Essential to use glass distilled water and can be used for raising whole embryos. (pH 7.4)
    20 cc. of 17% NaCl
    10 cc. of 0.5% HCl
    10 cc. of 0.8% $Ca(NO_3) \cdot 4H_2O$
    10 cc. of 2.05% $MgSO_4 \cdot 7H_2O$
    4 cc. of 1% N·HCl
    560 mg. of Tris*
    946 cc. glass distilled water

---

* Buffer available from Sigma Chem. Co., St. Louis.

The Niu-Twitty Solution - Three solutions made separately in hot water, cooled, and then mixed.   Good for urodele embryos and isolates.

Solution A	Solution B	Solution C
3,400 mg. NaCl	110 mg. Na_2HPO_4	200 mg. $NaHCO_3$
50 mg. KCl	20 mg. KH_2PO_4	250 cc. dist. water
80 mg. $Ca(NO_3) \cdot H_2O$	250 cc. dist. water	
100 mg. $MgSO_4$		
500 cc. dist. water		

7. Locke's solution - for chick embryos:

   NaCl .... 0.9   gr.
   KCl .... 0.04   gr.
   $CaCl_2$ .... 0.024 gr. (anhydrous)
   $NaHCO_3$ .... 0.02   gr.
   Water ....100.0   cc.

8. Special variations of the above solutions:
   a. Calcium-free Standard (Holtfreter's) Solution.
   b. Sodium-free Standard (Holtfreter's) Solution.
   c. Potassium-free Standard (Holtfreter's) Solution.
   d. Buffer-free Standard (Holtfreter's) Solution.
   e. Nuclear medium for germinal vesicle studies (Calcium-free Ringer's).

      NaCl .... 0.6 gr.
      KCl .... 0.01 gr.
   Glass Distilled Water ....100.00 cc.

9. Anesthetics: (See also page 20)
   a. MS-222 (Sandoz Chem. Co., 63 Van Dam St., N.Y.C.) Excellent for embryos. Make up 1/3000 concentration in Spring Water and in Standard Solution of the above concentrations and keep refrigerated. (Tricain Methanesulfonate) Must be used freshly diluted.
   b. Chloretone - 1/3000 in Spring Water or in Holtfreter's.
   c. Ether - anesthetic form.
   d. Chloroform.
   e. Magnesium sulphate (Epsom salts), crystal form.

10. Killing and fixing solutions:
   a. Smith's fixative - best for yolk-laden amphibian eggs.   Two solutions to be mixed just before use.   Not to be used if discolored.

      Solution A: K Bichromate .. 0.5 gr.
                   Water .... 87.5 cc.
      Solution B: Formalin 10   cc.
                   Acetic (glacial). 2.5 cc.

   b. Bouin's fixative - safest of all fixatives, particularly for late stages.
      Saturated (aqueous) picric acid.. 75 cc.
      Formalin (commercial)......... 25 cc.
      Glacial acetic acid............. 5 cc.
   (Can use 95% alcohol instead of water for more rapid fixation)

   c. Bouin-Dioxan - excellent for yolk embryos and rapid technique. (See Puckett, 1937 - Stain Tech. 12:97).   Use Bouin's and Dioxan in equal parts (Caution: Dioxan is volatile and toxic).

   d. Michaelis' fluid - for yolk embryos.
      Conc. H_gCl_2 - aqueous..... 20 pts.
      Conc. picric   aqueous..... 20 pts.
      Glacial acetic acid........ 1 pt.
      Water distilled .... 40 pts.

e. Kleinberg's picro-sulphuric - for polar bodies and spindles (McClung).

Water .... 200 vols.
Conc. H_2SO_4 .... 2 vols.
Picric acid   -   to saturation

f. Chrom-acetic fixative - excellent for cytological studies of amphibian egg and embryos:

Chromic acid 10%.......... 25 pts.
Glacial acetic acid......... 10 pts.
Sat. aq. picric acid........ 100 pts.

g. Gilson's fixative - Carnoy & Lebrun, 1897: La Cellule 12:

Nitric acid - 80% .... 15 cc.
Glacial acetic acid......... 4 cc.
Corrosive sublimate .... 20 grams
Alcohol 80%............... 100 cc.

h. Gatenby's fluid:

K. Bichromate - 2% aqueous 100 cc.
Chromic acid 1% .... 100 cc.
Nitric acid................ 6 cc.

i. Stockard's solution - for fish embryos:

Formalin .... 5 pts.
Glacial acetic .... 4 pts.
Glycerine .... 6 pts.
Water .... 85 pts.

j. Acetic alcohol:

Absolute alcohol........... 90 cc.
Glacial acetic .... 10 cc.

k. Corrosive acetic:

$HgCl_2$ .... 5 gr.
Glacial acetic .... 10 cc.
Water .... 90 cc.

l. Formalin - two concentrations should be available, 10% and 4%.

11. Bleaching Agents:
  a. Javelle water - potassium hypochlorite.
  b. Mayer's chlorine - to be made up just before use
     (1) Place few crystals potassium chlorate in vial.
     (2) Add 2-3 drops HCl.
     (3) When green chlorine fumes evolve, add 2-10 cc. of 70% alcohol.
     (4) Transfer specimens from pure 70% alcohol to this mixture until bleached.
  c. Ammoniated alcohol - 2% NH_4OH in 70% alcohol to decolorize picric acid stain.

CYTOPLASMIC STAINS

  a. Eosin - 0.5% in 95% alcohol.
  b. Light green (Grübler's) - 0.5% in 95% alcohol.
  c. Fast green (Nat. Aniline Co., N.G. f.3) 0.5% in 95% alcohol.
  d. Safranin O (Nat. Aniline Co., N.S.-10) 1% in aniline water.
  e. Orange G - sat. in clove oil.
  f. Masson stains (A, B, C.) Excellent for cell types (pituitary).
  g. Alizarine S - (used in Spaltoholz technique).

VITAL DYES*

a. Nile blue sulphate - 1/200,000
b. Methylene blue - 0.5%
c. Neutral red - 1%
d. Bismarck brown - 1%
e. Janus green - 1% (see section on "Vital Staining")

NUCLEAR STAINS

a. Iron haematoxylin
b. Feulgen, nucleal reaction
c. Harris' acid haemalum

12. Miscellaneous reagents:
    a. Iodine - s urated iodine in 70% (to follow Zenker's fixation).
    b. Ammoniated alcohol - 5% NH_4OH in 70% alcohol for removal of picric.
    c. Glacial acetic acid - and Normal acetic (60 cc. Glacial/liter).
    d. Hydrochloric acid - concentrated, 1% and Normal.
    e. Sodium hydroxide - concentrated, 1%, Normal and 0.003N.
    f. Ammonium hydroxide - concentrated.
    g. Potassium hydroxide - 1%.
    h. Hydrogen peroxide - concentrated (can be used as bleaching agent).
    i. Acetone
    j. Glycerine
    k. Cleaning fluid (K. Bichromate saturated in sulphuric acid).
    l. Clearing agents:
       (1) Xylol (toluene, toluol, benzene (benzol)
       (2) Cedar oil
       (3) Aniline oil
       (4) Oil of wintergreen (methyl salicylate)
       (5) Oil of cloves
       (6) Dioxan (volatile and the fumes are toxic)
       (7) Chloroform
    m. Mounting media:
       (1) Canada balsam - dissolved in xylol
       (2) Gum damar
       (3) Clarite
       (4) Egg albumen - best as albumen water (3%)
    n. Embedding media:
       (1) Paraffin: M.P. range from $45^{\circ}C.$ to $58^{\circ}C.$
       (2) Beeswax: pure white
       (3) Bayberry wax (Candle Factory, Falmouth, Mass.)
       (4) Rubber - white rubber to be added to paraffin
    o. Vaseline
    p. pH indicators (LaMotte sets for entire range)

MISCELLANEOUS EQUIPMENT

a. Operating base
   (1) Permoplast - American Art Clay Company, Indianapolis, Indiana.
   (2) Rainbow wax -   "   "   "   "   "   "
   (3) Beeswax with lampblack to give proper background shade.
b. Lampblack
c. Agar
d. Cellophane, pliofilm or pyralin.

---

* These are concentrated stock solutions.

e. <u>Lucite</u> - used to conduct light for considerable distances, without heat transmission. Can be used to curve light and point it into operating dish.

f. <u>DeKhotinsky's cement</u> - for mounting razor blade fragments onto glass handles.

g. <u>Paper</u>
   (1) Toweling
   (2) Lens
   (3) Filter

h. <u>Marking devices</u>
   (1) China marking pencils: red, blue or black
   (2) Diamond point
   (3) Carborundum mounted on glass rod

i. <u>Cloth</u>
   (1) Cheese
   (2) Black velvet (to reduce movement of ciliated larvae)

j. <u>Antiseptics</u>
   (1) Streptomycin sulfate
   (2) Penicillin
   (3) Sulfadiozine

k. <u>Measuring devices</u>
   (1) Millimeter ruler
   (2) Glass plate with mm. graded graph paper mounted beneath

l. <u>Thermometers</u> - range 0°C. to 110°C.

m. <u>Glass blowing equipment</u> - and flame board
   (1) Bunsen burner with tubing
   (2) Wing tip
   (3) Micro-burner (metal or glass made with screw clamp regulation of flame).

n. Tripod with wire gauze

o. <u>Vial board</u> - made to hold shell, or homeopathic vials of various sizes.

p. <u>Brushes</u> for cleaning vials, etc.

q. <u>Slide boxes</u> - cap 25 and 100 slides.

r. <u>File</u>, triangular.

s. <u>Pyralin cover for needles and needle board</u>.

SOME OF THE EQUIPMENT SUPPLY COMPANIES

Baker & Adamson Chemical Company - 40 Rector Street, N.Y.
Bauch & Lomb Optical Company - Rochester, N.Y.
Central Scientific Company - 220 East 42nd Street, N.Y.
Ciba Pharmaceutical, Summit, N.J.
Clay Adams - 44 East 23rd Street, N.Y.
Eastman Kodak Company - Rochester, N.Y.
Eimer & Amend - 633 Greenwich, N.Y. City
Fischer Scientific - Pittsburgh, Penn.
General Biological Supply House (Turtox) - Chicago, Ill.
Harvard Apparatus Company - Dover, Mass.
International Equipment Company - 352 Western Avenue, Boston, Mass.
Merck & Company - Rahway, N.J.
Spencer Lens Company - Buffalo, N.Y.
Standard Scientific Supply Company - 34 West 4th, N.Y. City

SOURCES OF ANIMAL MATERIAL

FISH; AQUARIUM EQUIPMENT, INCLUDING PLANTS

Aquarium Stock Company - 31 Warren St., New York City
Columbia Tropical Aquarium Company - 643 Broadway, New York City
Crescent Fish Farm - 1624 Mandeville Street, New Orleans, La.

Eastern Gardens - Kissena Blvd. & Rose Avenue, Flushing, L.I., N.Y.
Everglades Aquatic Nurseries - 706 Plaza Place, Tampa, Florida.
Grassy Forks Goldfish Hatchery - Martinsville, Indiana.
Japanese Goldfish Hatchery - North Branch, New Jersey.
Metal Frame Aquarium Company - Bloomfield Ave., Pine Brook, New Jersey.
Nassau Pet Shop - 129 Nassau Street, New York City.
Tricker, William - Brookside Avenue, Saddle River, New Jersey or Rainbow Terrace - Independence, Ohio.
U. S. Bureau of Fisheries - Washington, D.C.
Wurst, C. - 3843 Frankford Avenue, Philadelphia, Pa.
    (dried salmon and ant eggs, and flies for food)

AMPHIBIA

(Adults as well as eggs may be secured from most of the following)

Carribean Biological Laboratories - Biloxi, Miss.
Everglades Aquatic Nurseries - 706 Plaza Place, Tampa, Florida. (Hyla only)
Fletcher, O. K., Jr., - Biol. Dept., Univ. Georgia, Athens, Georgia.
Hazen, J. M., - Alburgh, Vermont.
LeRoy, A. - Alberg, Vermont.
Louisiana Frog Company - Rayne, La. (Rana catesbiana, clamitans, pipiens, sphenocephala)
Marine Biological Laboratory - Woods Hole, Mass.

HISTOLOGICAL HINTS FOR EGGS AND EMBRYOS

INTRODUCTION

Satisfactory slides of embryonic material are difficult to obtain. This is true of chorionated and yolk-laden fish eggs as well as the early stages of amphibian development. The essential steps are the removal of membranes, proper fixation, incomplete dehydration, and short embedding in wax-paraffin mixtures, to avoid brittleness and cracking.

ANESTHETICS

In general, anesthetics are not necessary when eggs or embryos are to be fixed immediately. Occasionally it is desirable to fix an embryo in a certain position, or to reduce body movements during fixation, when anesthesia is in order.

a. MS-222: This imported poison is the most satisfactory anesthetic available, used in 1/3000 concentration either in Standard (Holtfreter's) Solution, Spring Water, or Locke's solution (for chick embryos). The embryos are immobilized in about 1 minute and, after return to normal medium, recover in about 10 minutes without ill effects. Must be used fresh.

b. Chloretone: Generally 0.5% concentration in whatever medium the embryo is accustomed, will give slow but quite satisfactory anesthesia.

c. Magnesium sulphate: (Epsom salts) Simply drop a few crystals into small volume of water containing the embryo and await immobilization.

d. Cyanide: KCN 1/1000 in salt solutions acts as an anesthetic. Must avoid anoxia.

e. Ether and chloroform: These volatile anesthetics are for air breathing forms; hence will find little use with embryonic material.

f. Chilling: Embryos are rapidly retarded in all of their activities by adding to their media some cracked ice. Such embryos may be operated upon and will recover, upon return to normal temperatures, without ill effects. It may take 10-15 minutes to adequately stupefy the organisms.

REMOVAL OF JELLY CAPSULES

It is easier and allows better fixation if the jelly membranes are removed from eggs and embryos prior to the killing process.

The Urodele egg is provided with a distinct jelly capsule which may be punctured with needles or sharp watchmaker's forceps, and pulled off of the egg. If a tear is made by means of a pair of forceps, the embryo will usually "shell out". If the capsule is placed on a piece of paper towelling, filter or blotting paper, to which it will adhere, this operation may be facilitated.

The Anuran egg generally has looser but more adherent jelly capsules. This jelly may be removed by cutting single eggs away from the mass and placing them on coarse paper and rolling them along with the flat side of a scalpel until the bulk of the jelly rolls off onto the paper. A better method is to pierce the jelly with one prong of the #5 watchmaker's forceps, slide a prong of a second pair of forceps along the first, and, with an outward motion cut through the jelly. It may then be peeled off.

Remove frog egg jelly with 10% Chlorox (see Shumway: 1942 Anat. Rec. 83:309) or by brief Trypsinization.

It has been reported that ultra-violet light will dissolve off the jelly capsules of eggs but it is very likely that the same irradiation will damage the egg or embryo. Chemical removal of the jelly, after fixation, may be achieved by placing the embryo and capsule into 10% sodium hypochlorite or chlorox diluted with 5-6 volumes of water. The jelly can be shaken off within a few minutes. Javelle water (potassium hypochlorite) diluted 3-4 times may also be used. Following fixation in Gilson's fluid, the jelly hardens sufficiently so that it may be picked off the embryo which is subsequently hardened in alcohol.

KILLING AND FIXING PROCESSES

The fixation method of choice depends upon the end results desired. It has recently been discovered that decapsulated amphibian eggs can be briefly boiled to coagulate them, prior to normal chemical fixation. For cytological preparations the corrosive-acetic or chrom-acetic fixations are best; for early embryos with much yolk, Smith's fluid is recommended; and for later embryos and tissues in general, alcoholic Bouin or Bouin-dioxan mixtures are suggested. Fixation may be speeded up by the addition of 1% Turgitol (Carbide & Carbon Company, N.Y.C.) which reduces the surface tension of the fixative.

    a.   Smith's fluid: This fixative is made up of two solutions which, when brought together, rapidly deteriorate. It is therefore necessary to mix them just before use and to never use it when it has become discolored (dark). The fixative should be used for 12-24 hours, followed by thorough washing (12-24 hours) in running tap water. If the material is discolored, follow bleaching directions below (bichromate bleach). Tissues or embryos fixed in Smith's may be permanently preserved in 4% formalin directly after washing. This fixative is good for yolk-laden eggs and will give a minimum of distortion.

    b.   Bouin's fluid: The most universally satisfactory fixative known, made up in aqueous or alcoholic solutions. Fixation may be as short as 1 hour (tail tips); 24 hours for whole embryos; or much longer if it is inconvenient to change because Bouin's is a preservative as well as a fixative. The yellow of the picric acid is best removed by adding about 2% NH_4OH to the 70% alcohol when dehydrating, changing the solution every hour until the color is entirely gone. Lithium carbonate acts more slowly and may leave crystals, while the ammonia will eventually all evaporate. If chromophils are to be studied, such tissues must subsequently be properly neutralized by long exposure to pure 70% alcohol.

c. Bouin-Dioxan: This is a rapid and entirely satisfactory method of fixation and dehydration, the proportions being half-in-half, and the fixation time 12-24 hours. The mixture prevents shrinkage and hardening that often attends the use of other reagents. Other ratios used are Bouin-2 parts, Dioxan-1 part. If it is necessary to decolorize, transfer directly to ammoniated 70% alcohol, later to pure dioxan for dehydration.

d. Michaelis' fluid: Fixation for 8 hours, after which jelly must be removed before transferring to alcohols or dioxan for dehydration.

e. Gatenby's fluid: Used in ratio of about 2 cc. per egg for 12-24 hours during which time the jelly capsules will fall off the eggs.

f. Gilson's fluid: Short fixation (15-45 minutes) for cytological studies, recommended particularly for oogenesis.

g. Chrom-acetic fixative: Excellent for cytological studies of amphibian egg and early embryos.

h. Acetic-alcohol: Fix tissues for 8 hours, transfer directly to absolute alcohol.

i. Formalin fixatives: Gross fixation of embryos or tadpoles which are not to be sectioned may be accomplished in 4% formalin, preferably made up in the same medium used for the living organisms. Prokofieva, 1935 - Cytologia 6:148 recommends 50% formalin 8 pts.; 5% chromic acid 2 pts. as fixative for chromosome structure of Anuran eggs. For Urodele larvae he recommends 10% formalin 7 pts., and 1% chromic acid 3 pts.

j. The following procedure has proven to be very good for amphibian eggs. (See Goldsmith, 1929. Trans. Am. Micr. Soc. 48:216.)
(1) Fix in Goldsmith's fluid:

        Chromic acid 1%.......... 15 parts
        K Dichromate 2% .... 4 parts
        Glacial acetic .... 1 part
        (Fix small pieces 2 hours, large pieces 24 hours)

(2) If eggs are left in fixative 24-48 hours, the jelly will be removed.
(3) Wash 24 hours in running water.
(4) Carry to 70% alcohol through gradual changes.
(5) Change to 1 part aniline oil, and 2 parts 70% alcohol for 2 to 6 hours.
(6) Change to 2 parts aniline oil, and 1 part 95% alcohol for 2 to 6 hours.
(7) Change to pure aniline oil until clear - 1 or more hours.
(8) Change to 50% aniline oil plus 50% toluene for 1 to 6 hours.
(9) Change to 100% toluene, for 1 to 3 hours.
(10) Place in 100% toluene for 1 to 3 hours.
(11) Place in saturated 53° paraffin in toluene for 1 to 4 hours.
(12) Place in 53° paraffin for 3 to 4 hours, at 55°C.
(13) Embed in 53° paraffin.

k. The following procedure has been used with considerable success by Dr. C. L. Parmenter in studying the cytology of the amphibian egg.
(1) Fix for 24 hours in Smith's fluid.
(2) Preserve eggs in jelly in 5% formalin.
(3) To remove jelly: Use 20% solution chlorox in distilled water for 3 to 4 minutes. Watch and stop before the cortex is injured.
(4) Rinse thoroughly in distilled water, several changes.
(5) Dehydrate to 70% alcohol with 5 minute changes in ascending.
(6) Dehydrate further: (Leave in this overnight)

        80% alcohol .... 96 cc.
        Phenol .... 4 cc.
        (See King & Slifer, 1933; Science 78.)

(7) Dehydrate further in 95% alcohol - 2 thirty minute changes.

(8) Carboxylol - 1 hour. (This may be too drastic for some eggs.)

(9) Infiltrate with tissue mat; 56-58° M.P. paraffin for 1 hour..

(10) Imbed, section and mount.

(11) Preliminary to staining, remove paraffin with xylol; rinse in absolute alcohol and dip (or flood with pipette) quickly into a solution of equal parts of absolute alcohol, ether, and 10% celloid in solution. Place in 70% alcohol to harden the very thin coating of celloidin on the sections. This coating is a precaution against loss of an occasional section during staining, etc. It does not inter- fere with staining and need not be removed.

(12) Use any stain desired. Neither Feulgen nor acid haematoxylin will stain yolk.

WASHING

Most tissues in aqueous fixatives should be washed in running tap water for 6-24 hours, the time depending upon the size of the tissue. The function of washing is to remove salts, crystalline substances that may have been added with the fixative, and any extra- neous materials within the tissues. The completion of washing cannot be determined by loss of color in the tissues. In Bouin-dioxan fixation, the washing process is generally omitted until the sectioned material is passed down through the alcohols. Alcoholic iodine is used to remove excess corrosive sublimate.

BLEACHING

Two processes are included under this title. First, the removal of color added in the fixation process. This may be accomplished by 12 hour changes in saturated aqueous solutions of lithium carbonate when picric acid has been used. A more satisfactory bleaching agent, because it is more rapid and leaves no residue, is a 2% solution of am- monium hydroxide (NH_4OH) in 70% alcohol used in half-hour changes until no more of the yellow picric color is visible.

The second process has to do with the actual bleaching of tissue pigments, and this may be accomplished with any of the following:

a. Mayer's chlorine method: Transfer specimens from 70% alcohol to freshly made Mayer's solution, cover, and leave for period of from several minutes to several days, depending upon the degree of bleaching desired.

b. Javelle water: Slow but satisfactory bleaching agent.

c. Bichromate bleach: Following bichromate fixation such as Smith's tissues may be bleached in 10 cc. of 2% sodium bisulphite to which is added (just before using) 2-4 drops of concentrated HCl. Acts over 6-12 hours.

d. Hydrogen peroxide: Used as 2% solution but will macerate tissues if used for long period.

DEHYDRATION

The standard method of dehydration is to run the tissues up through a graded series of alcohols (35% to absolute alcohol) with 15-30 minute stops for tissues and 2-5 minute stops for sections or small eggs, longer stops for sizeable tissues. To conserve alcohol, dehydration may be accomplished in small vials by decanting off and changing the alcohols. If 5% glycerine or triethanalamine is added to the dehydrants, the tissues will not become so brittle and will be easier to section.

It has been found that dioxan is an excellent substitute for alcoholic dehydration. Following the washing (or even without washing) the tissues are put directly into dioxan for 2 two-hour changes. Larger tissues may be left in dioxan for a month without any deleterious effects. If the dioxan is kept in covered jars and over copper sulphate, it should last a long time. The dioxan fumes are known to be poisonous to humans.

Amphibian eggs and yolk-laden embryos should not be completely dehydrated. It is thought that the dioxan method does not give complete dehydration and that this is one of the reasons that dioxan gives better results with amphibian eggs.

CLEARING

Clearing follows dehydration and must be accomplished before embedding. In any case, the absolute alcohol should be mixed with the clearing agent so that the transition is gradual. Several steps of 15-30 minutes each are best. The dehydrant dioxan acts as its own clearing agent.

Xylol - this agent tends to make yolk-laden eggs and embryos rather brittle and sections are apt to crack. This tendency can be somewhat compensated by the addition of 5% lanolin (Sheep fat) to the xylol. Xylol will become cloudy if the embryos were not sufficiently dehydrated.

Benzole - same as xylol.

Dioxan - this is both a dehydrating and clearing agent, and can be mixed with fixatives. The transfer to paraffin is generally made by way of a paraffin-xylol mash. Used for both cytological and histological preparations.

Chloroform - tissues are transferred from absolute alcohol to a mixture of equal parts of alcohol and chloroform until they sink to the bottom of the container, thence to pure chloroform for final clearing. Keep the vial covered.

Wintergreen oil - excellent for yolk masses and glandular tissue, used as chloroform. Tissues become translucent and may thus be photographed.

Clove oil - used same as wintergreen oil.

Aniline oil - same as wintergreen oil except that it will mix with lower alcohols down to 80%. Stained sections are dehydrated to 95%, then to equal parts of 95% and aniline oil for 10 minutes; finally to 2 ten-minute changes in pure aniline oil. Mount in aniline-balsam. Good for mitotic figures.

EMBEDDING

This is accomplished by infiltration with paraffin, wax, rubber, or mixtures of these. Whatever clearing agent is used, the process of embedding should be gradual and at a temperature slightly above the melting point of the mixtures. To the vial containing the clearing fluid and cleared tissue, add shavings of the embedding mixture and bring to about 40°C. for several hours. The paraffin will become gradually more concentrated with the evaporation of the clearing agent. Then transfer to embedding substance for 2 half-hour changes.

If dioxan is used for dehydration and clearing, warm a mixture of 25 cc. dioxan, 5 cc. xylol and 20 cc. of 50°C. paraffin and transfer the tissues to this mixture for 30 minutes.

Then transfer to pure 50°C. paraffin for 15 minutes and finally to 2 changes of 53-55°C. paraffin. For eggs, a lower melting point paraffin is better. Prolonged embedding tends to make the eggs brittle.

Various embedding substances may be used, starting with paraffin of different melting points, the softer paraffin being best for the yolk eggs and glandular tissue and the hard paraffin for tissues in general.

a. Paraffin alone often crystallizes when cooled, or it may even flake, particularly if the xylol has not been entirely removed. In order to prevent crystallization and to facilitate ribbon formation, a mixture has been devised which allows sections down to 2 microns even during the summer, without the use of ice.

Paraffin M. P. 48°-50°C. - 90 gms.
Beeswax, white - 5 gms. (for ribboning)
Bayberry wax, pale green - 5 grms. (for hardening)

The same mixture can be used for tissues rather than eggs but the higher melting point paraffins would be advised.

b. Tissue mat - a commercial mixture probably very similar to the above, excellent.

c. Rubber - small amount of white, rubber may be melted into the paraffin to give better ribbons. Particularly good for large sections or semi-hard (i. e., cartilage) tissue.

The conventional method of embedding involves paper boxes made in appropriate sizes. Syracuse dishes lined with glycerine or white vaseline may be used for large tissues or large numbers of tissues. Paraffin buttons made by pipetting a small amount of melted paraffin onto a clear slide will prove satisfactory for small tissues.

The most satisfactory method is to use Plaster of Paris (see Solberg '39) embedding boxes. These are made by cutting out several blocks of soft paraffin, cut into the shapes and sizes desired, and making certain that the sides of the blocks all slant outward from the bases. Place these blocks with larger surface down on glazed paper and cover carefully with wet Plaster of Paris. When dry, tear off the paper and dig out the soft paraffin with a scalpel. Finally shave off the excess Plaster of Paris until a thin-walled embedding box is made. To use, first submerge the box in cool water, pour out all of the water; add melted paraffin; add tissue and orient it with hot needle; bring box into ice water but do not submerge it until there is a surface film. When the film entirely covers the paraffin, plunge the whole box beneath the surface of the water and the paraffin block will pop out and come to the surface.

SECTIONING

Amphibian cells are among the largest known so that sections should rarely be less than 10 microns. When organ systems are to be studied, sections may be as much as 25 microns.

The standard rules to be followed are: to use a clean, sharp knife at a fair angle; to clean the knife-blade frequently with xylol; and to section yolk-laden material very slowly. Examine the knife under binocular magnification for knicks. If yolk-eggs are embedded so that the knife cuts from vegetal toward the animal pole, cracks will be avoided.

Some investigators expose the amphibian egg by cutting off one or two sections and then soaking the entire block in water, overnight. Such an egg will expand beyond the cut surface and several sections will be lost, but frequently very nice serial sections of the remaining portion of the egg can be acquired. A second soaking, half-way through the egg, may be necessary. Apparently a small amount of water invades the paraffin and egg and reduces brittleness.

Another modification is to paint each section with a very thin coating of celloidin and mastix. Rubber-paraffin mixtures have been used. The early stages of amphibian development are difficult to section satisfactorily.

MOUNTING SECTIONS

The conventional method is to coat the slide with a thin layer of egg-albumen prior to mounting the sections. Some stains will show up the unevenness of the albumen and it is difficult to control the amount applied. A more satisfactory method is to float the sections on the slide and over albumen water made up of 10 cc. of (boiled) distilled water which has been cooled and to which has been added 1 drop of egg albumen. Enough of this albumen-water should be used to allow complete expansion of the sections over the warming oven, held at 40°-45°C. Adherence should be complete in 12 hours. Sections may be floated on a 40°C. water bath and mounted on slides submerged and brought up under them.

Thick sections and large yolk masses may require additional treatment before they will adhere permanently to the slides. In the hydration process leading to the staining, the mounted sections should be taken through xylol and absolute alcohol and then immersed briefly in a very thin solution of cellodin before going into the lower alcohols. The alcohols and stains will penetrate the celloidin satisfactorily.

During the hydration process (descent through the alcohols) the yolk-laden sections of amphibian eggs often come loose from the slide, no matter what precautions in albumen-fixation are taken. To avoid this, just before going into the 95% alcohol from the 100% (absolute) alcohol, dip the slides into the following mixture:

             Celloidin 8% . . . . 50 cc.
             Absolute alcohol . . . . 450 cc.
             Ether . . . . 450 cc.

This will provide the sections with a very thin coating of celloidin which will hold them in place but will in no way interfere with staining, and subsequent dehydration.

HYDRATION OF MOUNTED SECTIONS

This may be accomplished with 1-2 minute shifts in the various alcohols after the embedding substance (paraffin) has been completely dissolved off. Dioxan may be used in hydration as well as dehydration.

STAINING

The choice of stain depends entirely upon the end results desired.

Nuclear stains: (Where destaining is necessary, used acidified 70% alcohol.)

    a. Delafield's haematoxylin - should be deep wine colored, aged for months, and used in concentrated form for 3-10 minutes. Follow with wash in tap water to blue the stain. Cytoplasmic stains not necessary since Delafield's gives the cytoplasm a slight pink color.

    b. Harris' haematoxylin - excellent for chromosome studies in tail tips. Use like Delafield's although better to dilute (4x) and stain longer. Destain with 35% acid alcohol and blue in tap water.

c. Harris' acid haemalum - dilute to 25% with distilled water, stain as with haematoxylin and rinse in tap water.

d. Heidenhain's Iron haematoxylin - still the most reliable and satisfactory nuclear stain. The alum must be in form of violet crystals when the mordant is made up. Mordant in 4% for 12 hours, stain in 0.5% haematoxylin for 3-12 hours (shorter time if 0.1% Turgitol is used) and destain in 2% alum under binocular magnification. The slide should be rinsed in water when the tissue has become grey and the nuclear constituents first become visible. Rinse thoroughly and dehydrate quickly.

There is a modification of the Heidenhain's Iron Haematoxylin method which shortens the staining time and makes the nuclei and chromosomes blue-black instead of intense black, and the cytoplasm retains a slight stain which increases the visibility of the spindle fibres. Two solutions are needed:

1. Haematoxylin: 1% in absolute alcohol
   Ferric chloride, C. P. 1.2%
2. HCl...................... 0.2%

Prepare solutions separately. Before using, mix equal volumes of 1 and 2; stain about 20 minutes; destain in a weak ferric chloride (0.1%) under binocular magnification. Intensity of stain relative to concentration of HCl.

e. Feulgen stain - this is a chemical test for thymo-nucleic acid and if properly used will give excellent chromosome stain without any trace of the cytoplasm. Polar bodies of the frog's egg will stand out as red or violet in color. The modifications recommended are:
(1) Hydrolysis 10-12 minutes at 60°C. in N-HCl
    (use 82.5 cc. conc. HCl to 1000 cc. water)
(2) Rinse in cold N-HCl.
(3) Rinse in distilled water.
(4) Stain in acid-fuchsin about 80 minutes.
            Basic fuchsin .... 1 gm.
            Distilled water .... 200 cc.
    This is made up as follows: Bring water to boil, add basic fuchsin and stir thoroughly. Cool to 50°C.; filter through coarse filter; add 20 cc. of dilute HCl; cool to 25°C.; add 1 gm. of anhydrous sodium bisulphite. When the solution becomes colorless it is ready for use. Keep in the dark, and do not use if it becomes discolored.
(5) Pass sections through 3 baths of dilute fulfurous acid
            Distilled water .... 200 cc.
            10% aq. solution of anhydrous
                sodium bisulphite........ 10 cc.
            Dilute (N) HCl............ 10 cc.
(6) Rinse in distilled water.
(7) Counterstain (if desired) with 0.5% Grubler's light green in 95% for 5 to 7 seconds only.
(8) Mount in gum damar.

f. Mayer's haemalum - very good for sections containing chromosome figures.

Cytoplasmic stains:

a. Light green - 0.25% in 95% alcohol. Good for spindle fibres. Stain 1-2 minutes.

b. Eosin - 0.5% in 95% alcohol. Merely dip the slides into this quickly. Should not be used when chromosomes are to be studied or photographed.

c. Safranin O - 1% in aniline water, wash in tap water.

d. Orange G - sat. solution in clove oil, use only 30-60 seconds.

e. Masson stain - differential stain; excellent for pituitary cell types.

Solution A	Solution B	Solution C
Acid fuchsin .... 0. 3 gm.	This is a 1%	Glacial acetic .. 2. 0 cc.
Ponceau de xylidine . 0. 7 gm.	aqueous	Distilled water. . 100. 0 cc.
Distilled water .....100. cc.	phosphomolyb-	Aniline blue to
Glacial acetic ...... 1. 0 cc.	dic acid	saturation ....(3. gm.)

Staining procedure: Masson A for 30-60 seconds: Rinse in distilled water;
Masson B for 2-3 minutes; drain, do not rinse; Masson C for 10 minutes to 2
hours, depending on tissue; rinse in distilled water; 1% acetic acid for 5 minutes
to remove excess phosphomolybdic acid; equal parts of 1% acetic and absolute
alcohol for 1 minute or dropped directly onto the slide; absolute alcohol; xylol,
etc.

PERMANENT MOUNTING

While balsam dissolved in xylol is the standard mounting medium, dried balsam will chip
and often takes on a yellow tinge with age.   Clarite is preferred.

Special staining procedure for skeletons, particularly good for post-metamorphis stages
of amphibia and chick embryos beyond the 10th day.

a. Fix in 95% alcohol two weeks to harden.
b. Put in 1% KOH for 24 hours.
c. Put in tap water and pick off as much of fleshy material as possible.
d. Put in 95% alcohol; change once during 6 hour period.
e. Put in ether for 1-2 hours to dissolve away any fat; use acetone if there is little
    or no fat.
f. Put in 95% alcohol for 6 hours; change once.
g. Put in 1% KOH for 6 days.
h. Put in Alizarin red "S" for 12 hours.
i. Put in 1% KOH for 24 hours.
j. Put in Moll's solution for 24 hours.
k. Store in 100% glycerine.

RECOMMENDED REFERENCES:

Lee: "Vade Mecum"
McClung: "Handbook of Micrascopical Technique"

CLEANING AND BLEACHING OF VERTEBRATE SKELETONS

1. Solution of Ammonia - 2%.

2. Mixture of 50% Benzene and 50% Naptha.

3. Hydrogen peroxide - 2%.

Clean off all soft tissues, picking them away to the bone with scalpel. Place the skeleton
successively in each of the above solutions for about 12 hours each. Skeleton will come
out clean and bleached.

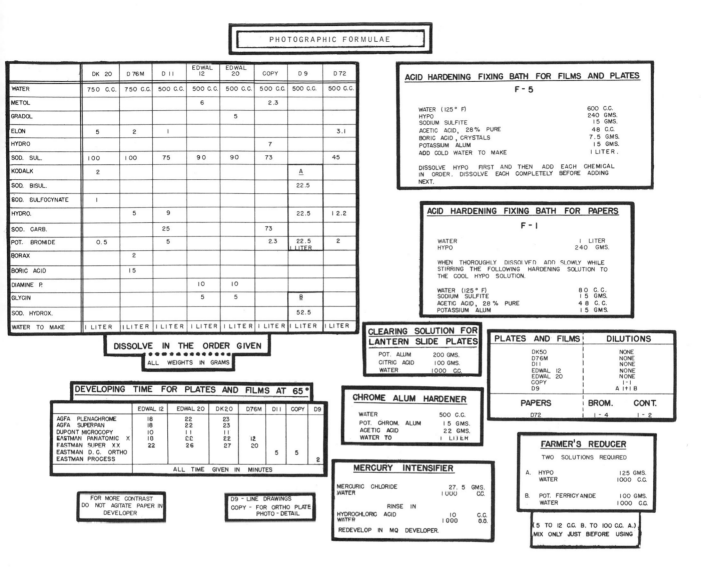

PHOTOGRAPHIC FORMULAE

	DK 20	D 76M	D 11	EDWAL 12	EDWAL 20	COPY	D 9	D 72
WATER	750 C.C.	750 C.C.	500 C.C.	500 C.C.	500 C.C.	500 C.C.	500 C.C.	500 C.C.
METOL				6		2.3		
GRADOL					5			
ELON	5	2	1					3.1
HYDRO						7		
SOD. SUL.	100	100	75	90	90	73		45
KODALK	2						A	
SOD. BISUL.							22.5	
SOD. SULFOCYNATE	1							
HYDRO.		5	9				22.5	12.2
SOD. CARB.			25			73		
POT. BROMIDE	0.5		5			2.3	22.5 / I LITER	2
BORAX		2						
BORIC ACID		15						
DIAMINE P.				10	10			
GLYCIN				5	5		B	
SOD. HYDROX.							52.5	
WATER TO MAKE	I LITER	I LITER	I LITER	I LITER	I LITER	I LITER	I LITER	I LITER

DISSOLVE IN THE ORDER GIVEN

ALL WEIGHTS IN GRAMS

DEVELOPING TIME FOR PLATES AND FILMS AT 65°

	EDWAL 12	EDWAL 20	DK 20	D 76M	D 11	COPY	D 9
AGFA PLENACHROME	18	22	23				
AGFA SUPERPAN	18	22	23				
DUPONT MICROCOPY	10	11	11				
EASTMAN PANATOMIC X	18	22	22				
EASTMAN SUPER XX	22	26	27	20	12		
EASTMAN D. C. ORTHO					5	5	
EASTMAN PROCESS							2

ALL TIME GIVEN IN MINUTES

FOR MORE CONTRAST DO NOT AGITATE PAPER IN DEVELOPER

D9 - LINE DRAWINGS
COPY - FOR ORTHO PLATE
PHOTO - DETAIL

ACID HARDENING FIXING BATH FOR FILMS AND PLATES

F - 5

WATER (125° F)	600 C.C.
HYPO	240 GMS.
SODIUM SULFITE	15 GMS.
ACETIC ACID, 28% PURE	48 C.C.
BORIC ACID, CRYSTALS	7.5 GMS.
POTASSIUM ALUM	15 GMS.
ADD COLD WATER TO MAKE	I LITER.

DISSOLVE HYPO FIRST AND THEN ADD EACH CHEMICAL IN ORDER. DISSOLVE EACH COMPLETELY BEFORE ADDING NEXT.

ACID HARDENING FIXING BATH FOR PAPERS

F - 1

WATER	I LITER
HYPO	240 GMS.

WHEN THOROUGHLY DISSOLVED ADD SLOWLY WHILE STIRRING THE FOLLOWING HARDENING SOLUTION TO THE COOL HYPO SOLUTION.

WATER (125° F)	80 C.C.
SODIUM SULFITE	15 GMS.
ACETIC ACID, 28 % PURE	48 C.C.
POTASSIUM ALUM	15 GMS.

CLEARING SOLUTION FOR LANTERN SLIDE PLATES

POT. ALUM	200 GMS.
CITRIC ACID	100 GMS.
WATER	1000 C.C.

CHROME ALUM HARDENER

WATER	500 C.C.
POT. CHROM. ALUM	15 GMS.
ACETIC ACID	22 GMS.
WATER TO	I LITER

MERCURY INTENSIFIER

MERCURIC CHLORIDE	27.5	GMS.
WATER	1000	C.C.

RINSE IN

HYDROCHLORIC ACID	10	C.C.
WATER	1000	C.C.

REDEVELOP IN MQ DEVELOPER.

PLATES AND FILMS	DILUTIONS
DK50	NONE
D76M	NONE
D11	NONE
EDWAL 12	NONE
EDWAL 20	NONE
COPY	I - I
D9	A I + I B

PAPERS	BROM.	CONT.
D72	I - 4	I - 2

FARMER'S REDUCER

TWO SOLUTIONS REQUIRED

A.	HYPO	125 GMS.
	WATER	1000 C.C.
B.	POT. FERRICY ANIDE	100 GMS.
	WATER	1000 C.C.

5 TO 12 C.C. B. TO 100 C.C. A.
MIX ONLY JUST BEFORE USING

REFERENCES

ADAMS, A. E., 1928 - "Paraffin sections of tissue supra-vitally stained." Sc. 68:303.

BACON, R. L., 1947 - "The adaptation of block surface staining of fetuses embedded in ethyl methacrylate." Anat. Rec. 99.

BASSETT, D. L., 1947 - "Ethyl methacrylate as a preserving medium for gross anatomical serial sections." Anat. Rec. 99.

BECKER, R. F., 1940 - "Experimental analysis of Kuo-Vaseline technique for studying behavior development in chick embryos." Proc. Soc. Exp. Biol. & Med. 45:689.

BELAR, K., 1928 - "Methodik der wissenschaftlichen Biologie." ed. by T. Peterfi, Vol. 1:779.

BRACHET, J., 1947 - "Embryologic Chimique". Masson et Cie., Paris.

BRADBURY, F. R. & D. O. Jordon, 1942 - "The surface behavior of anti-bacterial substances. I. Sulfanilamide and related substances." Bioch. Jour. 36:287.

BRAGG, A. N, 1938 - "The organization of the early embryo fo Bufo cognatus as revealed especially by the mitotic index." Zeit. f. Zellforsch. u. mikr. Anat. 28:154.

COLE, E C., 1946 - "Improved fixation in vitally stained methylene blue preparations." Stain Tech. 21:163.

COPENHAVER, W. M., 1939 - "Initiation of beat and intrinsic contraction rates in the different parts of the Amboystoma heart." Jour. Exp. Zool. 80:192.

DAVIDSON, M. H., 1945 - "The preparation of frog embryology slides." Turtox News. 23:33.

DAWSON, A B., 1939 - "Visualization of the vertebrate skeleton in the entire specimen by clearing and selective staining." Am. Biol. Teacher. 1:91.

DAWSON, A B., 1939 - "Differential staining of the anterior pituitary of the cat." Stain Tech. 14:133.

DETWILER, S. R. & G. E. McKENNON, 1929 - "Mercurochrome (di-brom oxymercuri-fluorescin) as a fungicidal agent in the growth of amphibian larvae." Anat. Rec. 41:205.

DETWILER, S. R., W. M. COPENHAVER & C. O. ROBINSON, 1947 - "The survival of Amblystoma embryos when treated with sodium sulfadiazine and quinine sulphate." Jour. Exp. Zool. 106:109.

DICKIE, M M., 1944 - "A new differential stain for mouse pituitary." Sc. 100:297.

DRURY, H. F., 1941 - "Amyl acetate as a clearing agent for embryonic material." Stain Tech. 16:21.

FANKHAUSER, G., 1932 - "Cytological studies on egg fragments of the Salamander Triton." Jour. Exp. Zool. 62:185.

FEULGEN, R. 1923 - "Die Nuclealfarbung." Abderh. Handb. Biol. Arbeit. 5:1055.

FORBES, J., 1943 - "Glycerin jelly mounting medium for frog eggs and early embryos." Trans. Am. Micr. Soc. 62:325.

GRAY, P., 1932 - "Notes on the practice of fixation for animal tissues." Jour. Roy. Micr. Soc. 53:13.

GREGG, H. R. & W. O. PUCKETT, 1943 - "A corrosive sublimate fixing solution for yolk-laden amphibian eggs." Stain Tech. 18:179.

HENRY, R. J. & E. C. SMITH, 1946 - "Use of Sulfuric-Acid-Dichromate mixture in cleaning glassware." Sc. 104:426.

KORNHAUSER, S. I., 1943 - "A quadruple tissue stain for strong color contrasts." Anat. Rec. 85:35.

LONG, M. E., H. C. TAYLOR, 1956 - "Nuclear variability in human neoplastic disease." Annals Mg. Acad. Sci. 63:1095-1105.

MASSON, P., 1928 - "Carcinoids and nerve hyperplasia of the appendicular mucosa." Am. Jour. Path. 4:181 (description of Masson stain).

MATHEWS, S. A., S. R. DETWILER, 1926 - "The reactions of Amblystoma embryos following prolonged treatment with chloretone." Jour. Exp. Zool. 45:279.

McGOVERN, B. H. & R. RUGH, 1944 - "Efficacy of M-amino ethyl benzoate as an anesthetic for amphibian embryos." Proc. Soc. Exp. Biol. & Med. 57:127.

MOORE, BETTY, 1940 - "Chromosomes of frog eggs and embryos stained by the Feulgen method to avoid excessive staining of yolk granules." Anat. Rec. 78:suppl. 122.

NEBEL, B. R., 1940 - "Chlorazol Black E as an aceto-carmine auxiliary stain." Stain Tech. 15:69.

NICHOLS, C. W., 1940 - "A simple method for mounting embryological material." Stain Tech. 15:3.

PATTON, P. L., 1943 - "A cool light for dissecting microscopes." Sc. 98:392.

PETRUNKEVITCH, A., 1937 - "On differential staining." Anat. Rec. 68:267.

PICKELS E. G., 1942 - "Apparatus for rapid, sterile, removal of chick embryos from eggs." Proc. Soc. Exp. Biol. & Med. 50:224.

POLLISTER, A. W., 1939 - "The structure of the Golgi apparatus in the tissues of the Amphibia." Quart. Jour. Micr. Sc. 81:235.

PRICE, J. W., 1943 - "A device for observing living fish embryos at controlled temperatures." Ohio Jour. Sc. 43:83.

PRICE, J. W. & S. V. FOWLER, 1940 - "Eggshell cap method of incubating chick embryos." Sc. 91:271.

PUCKETT, W. C., 1937 - "The dioxan-paraffin technic for sectioning frog eggs." Stain Tech. 12:97.

PUCKETT, W. O., 1941 - "The Methacrylate plastics as mounting media for biological materials." Anat. Rec. 80:453 (See ibid, 78:105).

PROKOFIEVA, A., 1935 - "On the chromosome morphology of certain Amphibia." Cytologia. 6:148.

RICHARDS, A. W., 1936 - "Killing organisms with chromium as from incompletely washed bichromate sulfuric-acid cleaned glassware." Physiol. Zool. 9:246.

ROTHLIN, W., 1932 - "MS 222 (Lösliches Anaesthesin), ein Narkotikum für Kaltblüter." Schweiz. med. Wchnschr. 45:1042.

SCHWIND, J. L., D. O. REMP, & S. STURGESS, 1937 - "A method of measuring the volume of Amphibian embryos." Sc. 86:355.

SEAMAN, G. R., 1947 - "Penecilin as an agent for sterilization of Protozon cultures." Sc. 101:327.

SLATER, D. W. & E. J. DORNFELD, 1939 - "A Triple stain for amphibian embryos." Stain Tech. 14:103.

SOLBERG, A. N., 1939 - "The preparation of plaster of Paris embedding boxes." Stain Tech. 14:27.

SPEMANN, H., 1920 - "Mikrochirurgische Operationstechnik." Abderhalden, Handb. Biol. Arb. v. 3.

STULTZ, W. A., 1935 - "Devices for experiments on amphibian embryos." Anat. Rec. 64: suppl. 43.

STULTZ, W. A., 1938 - "The use of plastic materials for operation on amphibian embryos." Sc. 88:553.

TYLER, A., 1946 - "Rapid slide-making method for preparations of eggs, Protozoa, etc." The Collecting Net. 19.

WEISS, P., 1936 - "A convenient retractor for use in operations and dissections of small-sized animals." Sc. 84:164.

WILLIAMS, T. W., 1941 - "Alizarin Red S and Toluidine Blue for differentiating adult or embryonic bone and cartilage." Stain Tech. 16:23.

II. THE AMPHIBIA

A. The Normal Development of the Amphibia

1. NOTES ON THE BREEDING HABITS OF SOME COMMON AMPHIBIA

Natural breeding on the part of different species of the Amphibia covers all the seasons of the year, in the various latitudes. The one characteristic feature of all but a very few specialized forms is that breeding occurs in or near water regardless of the habitat during the balance of the year. In general, the Amphibia lay their eggs and then desert them. This means that there is a very high mortality and in order to survive, the race must produce a great excess of eggs. It has been estimated (Smith: Science 1947, v. 105, p. 619) that the maximum number of eggs layed by any amphibian species is probably in the neighborhood of 35,000. It is interesting that the high numbers are layed by the pre-dominantly aquatic Anura while among the Urodela the number of eggs layed may be less than 100, in certain species. The aquatic environment is apparently the more hazardous when compared with the mildly damp environment where one occasionally finds Urodele eggs.

Regarding the insemination of the eggs, the frogs shed their products into the water si-multaneously during amplexus; many of the toads similarly shed their gametic products but the eggs are layed in strings and the male inseminates each egg as it emerges from the cloaca. Finally, among the Urodela it is necessary for the female to pick up sperma-tophores and to take them into her cloaca and genital tract where the eggs are fertilized before being layed. Thus there is considerable variation in the breeding procedure among the various species of Amphibia.

There are a number of forms which, because they are relatively common, are likely to be available for use in our laboratories. For this reason there is presented below a table showing the common name, location, breeding periods, and egg production of these forms.

BREEDING HABITS OF SOME COMMON AMPHIBIA

Animal	Popular Name	Locality	Breeding	# Eggs
FROGS				
ACRIS GRYLLUS	Cricket frog	Central U.S.	May to July	Few
HYLA CRUCIFER	Spring peeper	Eastern seaboard	April	1,000
HYLA VERSICOLOR	Tree frog	Eastern U.S., Canada	May and June	50
PSEUDACRIS NIGRITA	Swamp tree frog	All U.S. except N. Eng.	March and April	500 to 1,500
RANA CATESBIANA	Bullfrog	East of Rockies	May to August	6,000 to 20,000
RANA CLAMITANS	Green frog	Eastern N. America	June to August	5,000
RANA PALUSTRIS	Pickerel frog	Eastern N. America	April and May	2,000
RANA PIPIENS	Leopard frog	Entire U.S.	March to May	5,000
RANA SYLVATICA	Wood frog	Entire U.S.	March to May	3,000
TOADS				
BUFO AMERICANUS	American toad	Northeastern U.S.	April and May	6,000
BUFO FOWLERI	Fowler's toad	Central & East U.S.	April to June	8,000
XENOPUS LAEVIS	African clawed-toad	South Africa	April to Sept.	15,000

Animal	Popular Name	Locality	Breeding	# Eggs
SALAMANDERS				
AMBLYSTOMA JEFFERSONIANUM	Jefferson salamander	East U.S., South Canada	Early Spring	300
A. OPACUM	Marble salamander	East & Middle West	Sept. to Oct.	100-250
A. PUNCTATUM (MACULATUM)	Spotted salamander	Eastern U.S.	January to May	100-200
A. TIGRINUM	Tiger salamander	U.S., Canada, Mexico	Dec. to April	100
EURYCEA BISLINEATA	Two-lined salamander	Central & East U.S.	April to June	20 to 30
HEMIDACTYLIUM SCUTATUM	Four-toed salamander	Eastern U.S.	Spring	30
PHETHODON CINEREUS	Red-backed salamander	Entire U.S.	June and July	14
TRITURUS PYRRHOGASTER	Japanese fire salamander	Japan	?	80
TRITURUS VIRIDESCENS (DIEMYCTYLUS)	Common newt	U.S., South Canada	April to June	20 to 30

FROGS

ACRIS GRYLLUS, the cricket frog: This frog is found largely in the Central States, from Michigan to Dakota and south to Texas. It is very small, the head and body never measuring more than 1¼ inches. The toes of the hind limbs are webbed. While the color varies there is always a triangular mark between the eyes and a dark oblique stripe on the side of the body. The male's throat skin is grayish-yellow, and its fingers are shorter and body smaller than that of the female.

Breeding takes place in shallow, plant-filled water during May to July. The eggs are laid singly and are attached to stems and twigs. Metamorphosis occurs about the middle of September.

HYLA CRUCIFER, the Spring Peeper. This small frog is found all along the eastern coast and abundantly in Florida. The adults rarely exceed 1 3/8 inches in length but may be recognized by their high, shrill, clear call so frequently heard in the spring during breeding. There is an oblique cross on the back, the general color being brown of various shades. The digits are not webbed as they are in the genus Rana, but the tips of the toes have discs for climbing on smooth surfaces. The thumb of the male bears a pad on its inner surface, the chin and throat are loose and dark and the males are always smaller than the females.

Acris gryllus,
the cricket frog.
(Courtesy C. H. Pope
1944: Chicago Mus.
Nat. Hist.)

Hyla crucifer
the spring peeper.

The spring peeper's eggs
attached to the submerged
stem of a plant. After Wright.

(Courtesy C. H. Pope 1944: Chicago Mus. Nat. Hist.)

FROGS

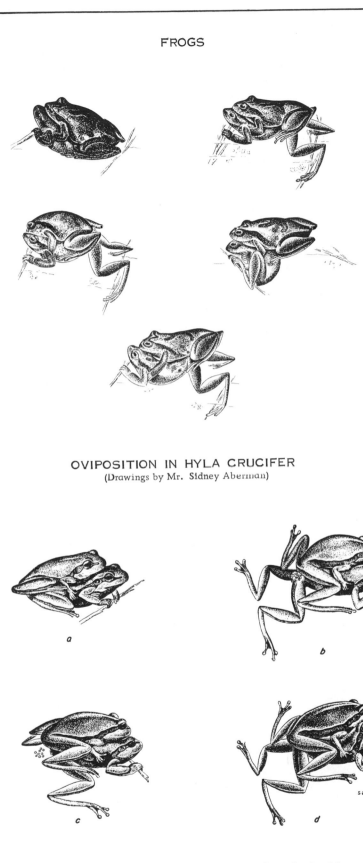

OVIPOSITION IN HYLA CRUCIFER
(Drawings by Mr. Sidney Aberman)

a. Normal amplexus of Hyla andersonii; b. First phase of oviposition;
c. Second phase of oviposition; d. The back depression release mechanism.

(From Aronson 1943: Copeia 4:236 - Drawings by Mr. Sidney Aberman)

Breeding normally occurs in April when the temperature is about 52°F. The eggs (about 1,000) are layed singly at night while the pair is floating at the surface of the pond. The male inseminates each egg as it emerges from the cloaca of the female. The eggs are small, about 1.0 in diameter, and are generally dark in color. Each egg is surrounded by firm jelly. Hatching occurs in 4 to 16 days depending upon the water temperature, and temperature tolerance is from about 42°F. to 83°F. Metamorphosis is reached in 90 to 100 days, occurring in July. The eggs are excellent for operative procedures. The tadpoles live on diatoms and algae while the adults feed on insects and spiders. Can be fed Drosophila in the laboratory (preferably the vestigial mutant).

HYLA VERSICOLOR, the tree frog. This small (2 to 2½ inches) arboreal species is partial to woodlands and bushy areas but may be found far removed from moist areas, around buildings, walls, fences. It is found in eastern United States and Canada. The skin is moist and slightly rough; the toes are webbed and their tips expanded into disks for adhering to tree bark; the back may be uniformly colored or blotched, but is never stripped. There is a white spot under the eye and yellow and brown markings on the groin. These frogs can change their body color considerably. The male has the usual thumb pad and throat characteristics.

Breeding occurs in quiet ponds surrounded by high vegetation between the middle of May and the middle of June when the air temperature is at least 72°F. Egg-laying takes about an hour, the paired animals depositing about 50 eggs at a time until one or two thousand are layed. The jelly, which holds the entire egg mass together, is of loose consistency. The eggs are brown at the animal pole and yellow or cream at the vegetal pole. The eggs hatch in 4 to 5 days into larvae ¼ inch in length. The tadpole reaches a length of 2 inches and metamorphoses in 45 to 60 days, never measuring more than 1 inch. The newly metamorphosed frogs are green and without characteristic markings. The length of life is probably about 9 years.

These forms are herbivorous, living on minute algae and diatoms in early life and later living on non-aquatic insects.

PSEUDACRIS NIGRITA, the swamp tree frog. This frog is found widely distributed over the United States (except in New England) and the males rarely exceed 1¼ inches and the females 1½ inches in length. It has three broad, dark stripes that extend down the back, and the tips of the toes bear small disks. The skin of the chin and the throat of the male is loose and dark.

Pseudacris nigrita, the swamp tree frog.

(Courtesy C. H. Pope 1944: Chicago Mus. Nat. Hist.)

Breeding is in any small body of water, permanent or temporary, from the middle of March to the middle of April. About 500 to 1,500 eggs are layed in clusters. Hatching occurs in about 2 weeks, and larval life lasts from 40 to 90 days while the tadpole attains a length of 1¼ inches.

RANA CATESBIANA, the bullfrog. This large frog is found East of the Rockies from Mexico to Canada, and is known to have a life span of 15 years. Its typical haunts are small lakes and permanent ponds with much vegetation, generally shadowed by willows and other low trees.

The species can be recognized by the fully webbed hind feet, pointed toes, uniformly dull green back (no warts or plicae) and the size of adults ranges from 4 to 8 inches, from snout to anus. The males have a slightly larger tympanic membrane than do the females, a pigmented thumb pad, and yellow throat.

Its natural food in the larval stage is diatoms and algae; as young frogs it is insects and other small invertebrates; and as adults, any moving object, invertebrate or vertebrate, that can be ingested. This includes fish, frogs, salamanders, young turtles, moles, mice, and even birds. In the laboratory the bullfrog may be fed smaller frogs.

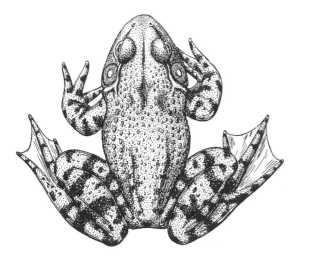

The male bullfrog,
Rana catesbiana.

(Courtesy C. H. Pope 1944:
Chicago Mus. Nat. Hist.)

Oviposition of Rana cates-
beiana; lateral view.

(From Aronson 1943: Am. Mus. Nov. #1224)
(Artist Mr. Richmond E. Lawler)

The breeding season depends upon the latitude, but ranges from June to August. The air temperature must be at least 72°F. and the bottom water temperature at least 66°C. before the eggs are layed. The eggs are small, but as many as 20,000 may be layed by a single female, and the egg jelly is loosely applied. The eggs will develop between 59°F. and 90°F., and the hatching span at 68°F. is about 134 hours. There is a long larval (tadpole) life, the mature tadpole of 4 to 6 inches total length being ready to metamorphose 2 or 3 years after the egg is layed. Metamorphosis generally occurs in late July and in August.

RANA CLAMITANS, the green frog is found where bullfrogs are found but they prefer permanent, plant-grown aquatic ponds, swamps, meadows, and slow streams. It is a common form in Eastern North America, even at considerable altitudes.

The green frog can be recognized by its predominantly green back, with small and widely separated spots, paired ridges of skin from the eyes backward along the back, and webbed and pointed toes as in the bullfrog. It is rarely more than 4 inches in body length. The tympanum is usually very large, and this is the most readily determined difference between the green frog and immature bullfrogs.

The male Rana clamitans, the
green frog, with inflated vocal
sacs as seen from above.

(Courtesy C. H. Pope 1944:
Chicago Mus. Nat. Hist.)

The tadpoles, which grow slowly, feed on diatoms, and algae; the young frogs and adults eat insects, crustacea, spiders, snails, earthworms. The food consists largely of non-aquatic forms.

The male has a yellowish throat but also a yellow spot or ring in the center of its tympanum, and its head is wider than that of the female. Breeding occurs in quiet, shallow plant-grown ponds from May to August, generally in late June and early July, even in the same latitude and environment. The eggs may number as many as 5,000 and they are approximately the size of those of Rana pipiens, 1.5 mm. in diameter. The eggs and tadpoles can tolerate a low oxygen environment, the tadpoles generally hibernating in mud for one winter and then quickly passing through metamorphosis in early Spring at 370 to 400 days. Low temperatures are disastrous, the embryos being unable to survive 10°C. The time lapse from stage #12 to gill circulation at 15°C. is about 220 hours.

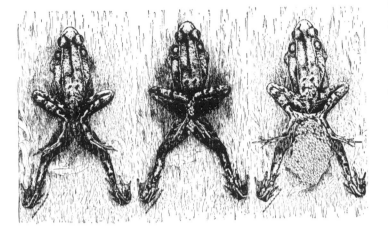

Typical amplexus of
Rana clamitans; lateral
view.

Egg-laying posture of
Rana clamitans just
prior to the onset of
the oviposition;
dorsal view.

Upstroke of the male
Rana clamitans and
the appearance of the
first batch of eggs;
dorsal view.

Downstroke of the male
Rana clamitans and
the formation of the
surface film; dorsal
view.

(From Aronson 1943: Am. Mus. Nov. #1224. Artist Mr. M. Sorensen)

RANA PALUSTRIS, the pickerel frog. This is also known as the Spring Leopard Frog, and is found largely in the East, in sphagnum bogs or in cool clear water surrounded by high grass and other vegetation. The adults rarely exceed 3 inches in body length.

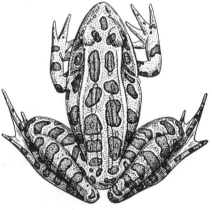

The color is light brown with numerous squarish dark spots with dark borders, arranged largely in two rows between the lateral plicae which run posteriorly from the eyes. The underside of the legs is bright yellow or orange. The thumb pad of the male is unusually large.

These frogs breed in late April and in May, the 2,000 bright yellow eggs measuring about 1.6 mm. in diameter. The water temperature is generally between 50° and 65°F., and development is normal between 46°F. and 86°F. The eggs hatch in about 2 weeks, the tadpole reaches a length of about 3 inches and metamorphosis occurs in about 80 days. Under laboratory conditions of 15°C. temperature, it takes 200 hours to go from stage #12 to gill circulation. Development is slightly faster than that of Rana pipiens.

Rana palustris, the
pickerel frog, as
seen from above.

(Courtesy C. H. Pope
1944: Chicago Mus.
Nat. Hist.)

RANA PIPIENS, the leopard frog. This is the common leopard frog most frequently used in our laboratories. It is found in almost all parts of the United States and parts of Canada and Mexico. The adults rarely exceed 4 inches in body length (96 mm.) but females must be 72 mm. or longer before they can be considered sexually mature. The general color is green with light dorsal plicae. The rounded dark spots on the skin have light colored borders. The underside is white. The male is darker and smaller than the female, with firm abdominal muscles, lateral cheek pouches when croaking, and prominent thumb pad. These frogs are omnivorous feeders and difficult to maintain as adults in the laboratory except under conditions simulating hibernation when they can go for long periods without food. The newly metamorphosed frogs may be fed earthworms cut into 1 inch lengths. These segments of worm will continue to move and thus attract the frogs.

Male Rana pipiens, the leopard frog, with vocal sacs inflated, as seen from above.

(Courtesy C. H. Pope 1944: Chicago Mus. Nat. Hist.)

These frogs breed from March to May depending upon the latitude in which they are found. They lay about 5,000 eggs (diameter about 1.75 mm.) which generally reach metamorphosis during the summer. The span from fertilization to hatching is about 8 days and to metamorphosis (in the laboratory at 23°C.) is about 75 days. The eggs are normally layed in water at about 15°C. and the upper limit of temperature tolerance is about 31°C. Leopard frogs have been known to live for 5 years.

End of oviposition. The male, about to release, is showing the pre-release movements. Note the female (beneath) shaping the eggs into a clump.

(From Aronson 1942: Bull. Am. Mus. Nat. Hist. 80:127)

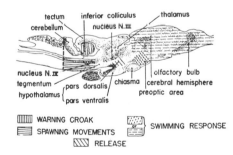

Diagrammatic sagittal section through the brain of Rana pipiens indicating the regions of the brain that were found to be of primary importance for the medication of each of four phases of sexual behavior.

(From Aronson 1945: Bull. Am. Museum Nat. Hist. 86:89)

RANA SYLVATICA, the wood frog. This frog is found only in the Northern States and Canada. It rarely exceeds 2-3/4 inches in body length, and is light brown in color with a dark streak on either side of the head and a dark line from the tip of the snout to the eye. There is also a black patch over the tympanum. The dorsal plicae are prominent but not of a different color. The head is pointed. Its feeding habits are like those of Rana pipiens.

These frogs breed in ponds, in wooded regions where there are dead leaves and mud. They begin breeding in early March in water at about 12°C. The eggs are larger than those of Rana pipiens (about 2.0 mm.) and number about 3,000. Depending upon the temperature, metamorphosis is reached in from 40 to 50 days. Development is normal even at 4°C., indicating wide temperature tolerance but at a lower level than for Rana pipiens. Stage #12 to gill circulation stage requires only about 95 hours at 15°C. and at 20°C. metamorphosis is achieved in 45 days.

Exceptional cases of cross-oviposition

Noble and Aronson (1942) report that when Rana clamitans or Rana sylvatica males assume the amplectic position with ovulating Rana pipiens females, the grip is lateral and below the axillae rather than ventral, as with pairs of Rana pipiens. This grasp seemed to make it difficult for the female to oviposit and the caudal half of the male's body tended to float away from the female. Even though the cloacae are not approximated (see figure below) the eggs are not generally fertilized or, if fertilized, rarely develop beyond the gastrula stage in hybrid crosses.

Rana sylvatica, the wood frog.

(Courtesy C. H. Pope 1944: Chicago Mus. Nat. Hist.)

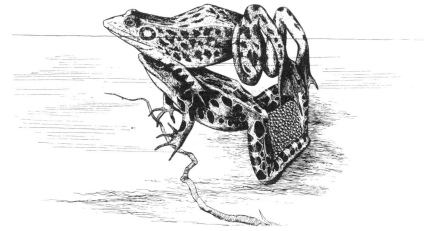

Female Rana pipiens ovipositing with male Rana clamitans

(Drawing made by the Illustrators Corps of The American Museum of Natural History. Loaned through courtesy of L. R. Aronson.)

TOADS

BUFO AMERICANUS, the American toad. This toad, common in gardens as a night prowler, is found in the northeastern United States. The adults vary in size from 2 to 4 inches in body length, the males being smaller and possessing black chins. The ventral surface of these toads is sand colored and granular while the dorsal surface is warty. The eyes are protruding and two large parotid glands extend backward from the eyes. The color is olive green. Food consists primarily of large insects found around gardens.

Breeding occurs in April and May, the eggs being layed in long spiral tubes of jelly and totalling up to 20,000 in exceptional cases. The average is about 6,000. The time necessary for hatching is 2 to 17 days, depending upon the temperature, and for metamorphosis in nature is about 60 days and occurs in August. The temperature tolerance is from about 50°F. to 86°F.

BUFO FOWLERI, Fowler's toad. This smaller toad is found along beaches, roadsides, and in sandy areas where there may be shallow water in the central, east and northeastern States. The adults measure not more than 3 inches in length. The general color is green with middorsal light stripe. The male throat is black. The warts are generally small, rounded and uniform, and generally at least 3 warts are enclosed in each dark patch. Conspicuous shoulder glands, the parotids, are oval and long and in contact with long ridges behind the eyes. Food the same as Bufo americanus.

Breeding occurs from April to June, a little later than for Bufo americanus. About 8,000 eggs are layed in strings, each egg measuring about 1.0 to 1.2 mm. in diameter. The metamorphic span takes about 40 to 60 days and is generally complete by August.

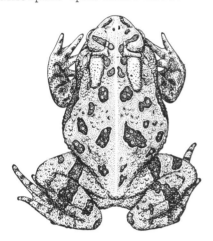

Bufo fowleri, Fowler's toad.

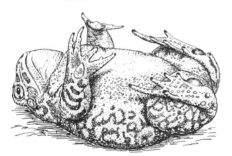

Fowler's toad feigning death. After Dickerson.

Bufo americanus, the American toad.

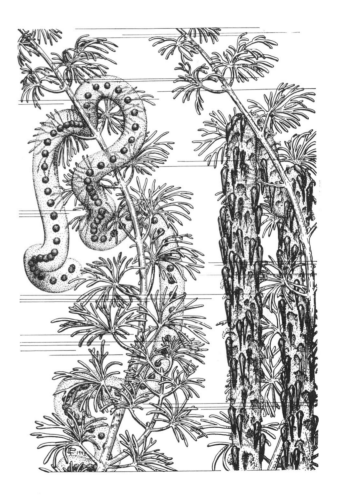

Left: Egg cables of American toad twenty-four hours after they were laid. Right: Same cables three days later, showing newly hatched larvae. After Dickerson.

(Courtesy C. H. Pope 1944: Chicago Museum of Nat. Hist.)

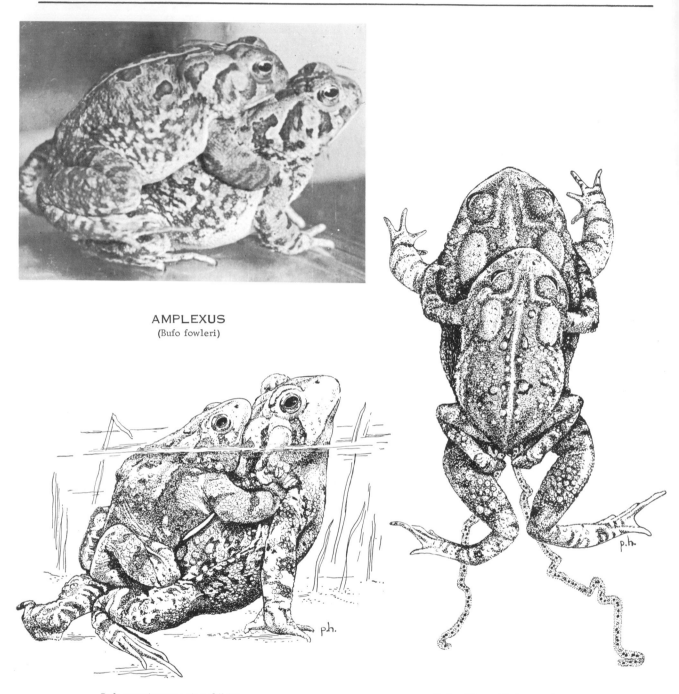

AMPLEXUS
(Bufo fowleri)

Bufo americanus pair exhibiting
the back-arch release mechanism.

Oviposition of Bufo americanus.

(From Aronson 1944: Am. Mus. Nov. #1250. Artist Miss P. Hutchinson)

XENOPUS LAEVIS, the South African clawed toad. This form has been classified as a
toad and as a frog, its skin texture being more that of the frogs and its breeding habits
more like the toad. It is found in Africa, from the Cape to Abyssinia, and measures
about 4 inches maximum in the adult stage.

It is purely an aquatic form, with clawed toes, no distinct tympanic membrane, tongue-
less, single posterior median opening for the Eustachian tubes, dilated sacral vertebrae,
carnivorous, and has Siluroid appearing larvae. It is sluggish, never leaving the water

and remaining submerged most of the time. Its greatest activity is seizing food, which it does rapidly. It is negative to light. It should be fed on alternate days strips of beef, beef heart, liver, earthworms, Tubifex, small newts, tadpoles, Daphnia.

It reaches sexual maturity in 2 years. Inguino-amplexus usually in July, thousands of eggs being extruded but often not all fertilized. Egg measure 1.5 mm., with jelly it is 3.0 mm. Embryos hatch out in 37 hours and Siluroid type transparent tadpoles appear on third day. The tadpoles feed on Chlamydomonas. Developmental temperature must be at least 22°C.

The adult female: South African clawed toad Xenopus laevis.

(Photo by courtesy of Drs. Weisman and Coates, from "The South African Frog in Pregnancy and Diagnosis." N.Y. Biologic Research Foundation, 1944.)

Dorsal view   Ventral view

Amplexus (coupling) in Xenopus laevis.

(From Dr. H. A. Shapiro 1936: Brit. Jour. Exp. Biol. 13:48)

AMBLYSTOMA JEFFERSONIANUM, Jefferson's salamander. This salamander is found in southeastern Canada and northeastern United States westward to Minnesota and southward to Virginia. It prefers cold climate and the adults measure about 7 inches from tip to tip. It is primarily nocturnal, burrowing in loose soil and leaf mold, under logs. It is bluish black or dark brown in color with numerous bluish white flecks concentrated on its sides. The swollen vent of the male protrudes noticeably and its tail is longer and flatter than that of the female.

Breeding occurs in early spring and the exact time is dictated by the temperature. The site is any pond, permanent or temporary, and the eggs are layed singly at the rate of about 4 per minute and are attached to each other and to a twig. Never more than 300 eggs are layed, and the four jelly capsules often take on a greenish color due to the growth of a unicellular plant. Mating occurs just before laying, and incubation takes about 6 weeks in nature and about 2 weeks at laboratory temperatures. The larval period lasts from 56 to 125 days, depending upon whether the pond dries up, and at metamorphosis the larva is about 1-7/8 inches long. Sexual maturity is achieved in about 21 months.

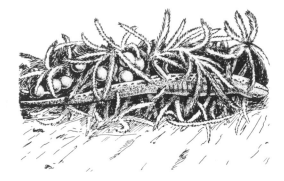

Amblystoma jeffersonianum, Jefferson's
salamander. (After Bishop)

Hemidactylium scutatum, the four-toed salamander
found on May 11th. (After Bishop)

EGG—LAYING OF SALAMANDERS

(Courtesy C. H. Pope. Chicago Mus. Nat. Hist.)

AMBLYSTOMA OPACUM, the marbled salamander. This 4 inch salamander is found in
the East and Middle West, but not north of a line from Boston to Chicago. It is quite
abundant on Long Island and at Bear Mountain, but is difficult to find except during the
breeding season during the latter part of September and October. This is a black salamander with conspicuous light colored bands across the back. These bands are wider on
the sides of the body than on the back. The light colored markings of the male are white
and of the female tend to be gray. The male has the characteristically protruding vent.

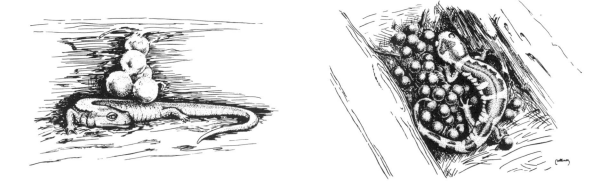

Plethodon cinereus, the red-backed
salamander, found on July 16th.

Amblystoma opacum, the marbled salamander found
on October 26th in North Carolina. (After Bishop)

BROODING OF EGGS BY FEMALE SALAMANDERS

(Courtesy C. H. Pope 1944: Chicago Mus. Nat. Hist.)

Breeding occurs in the Fall following an elaborate courtship at the breeding grounds which are on the edge of dry pond beds. Spermatophores are picked up by the female and she proceeds to deposit singly from 100 to 250 eggs in a nest which is nothing more than a depression under moss or a log. The duration of the pre-hatching stage depends entirely upon the rainfall and may not occur until Spring. The adults can drown but the larvae require the Fall rains to hatch. The eggs withstand desiccation but shrink as they dry. They hatch at about 70°F. and mature about 15 months later.

AMBLYSTOMA PUNCTATUM, the spotted salamander formerly known as A. maculatum. This is the most common of the large American salamanders and is found in the Eastern United States. There are two irregular rows of bright orange spots along the back. The background color is bluish black. The males have dark bellies and protruding vents.

Breeding occurs immediately after the Spring thaws, and there is a brief courtship on the part of the male before it drops up to 40 spermatophores, in shallow water. The water temperature may be as low as 13°C. The females pick up the spermatophores with their cloacal lips and proceed to lay from 100 to 200 eggs in semi-solid clumps of jelly about 6 inches below the surface, often attached to a stick or stem. The jelly is sometimes opaque, but the embryos are normal. The jelly masses lie freely in the water.

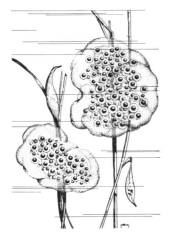

Typical egg clusters of spotted salamander as they appeared on April 9. A spermatophore can be seen on leaf below large cluster. (After Bishop)

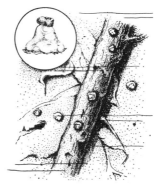

Spermatophores of spotted salamander in situ on April 14. Inset: A single one, greatly enlarged. (After Bishop)

(Courtesy C. H. Pope 1944: Chicago Mus. Nat. History)

These eggs will tolerate refrigerator temperatures as low as 4°C. and if kept at such low temperatures the time to gastrulation may be extended to about 10 days. The optimum temperature for development is between 12°C. and 15°C., but the embryos will tolerate 20°C. at the upper limit. At 10°C. the embryos pass from stage #7 to stage #25 in about 300 hours (13 days). These are excellent eggs and embryos for operative procedures.

AMBLYSTOMA TIGRINUM, the tiger salamander. This salamander is found throughout the United States and in Canada and Mexico. There are numerous yellow spots which cover the body but are largely concentrated along the sides of the belly, in contrast with

A. punctatum. The background color is deep brown to black and this is the largest of the salamanders except the mudpuppy and siren. It measures about 10 inches in length. The males are the larger sex and their vents protrude.

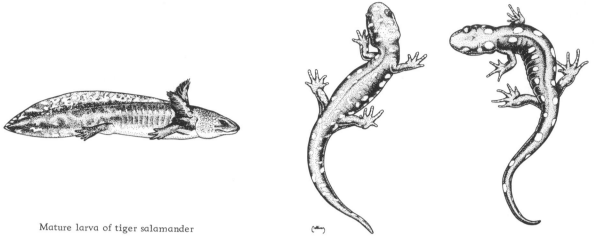

Mature larva of tiger salamander

(Courtesy C. H. Pope 1944:
Chicago Mus. Nat. History)

Amblystoma tigrinum,
the tiger salamander.

Amblystoma punctatum,
the spotted salamander.

Breeding begins in early spring, generally a bit earlier than for A. punctatum, in February, (January in the Carolinas).   The egg clusters (about 100) are attached to twigs about a foot below the surface of the water, and are enclosed in a very loose fitting jelly. The egg is a bit darker than that of A. punctatum but the egg species can be readily distinguished by the consistency of the jelly. Development is rapid, with hatching in less than 28 days and metamorphosis in about 75 days. Laboratory larvae at 20°C. may not metamorphose for 4 months, 156 days at 15°C., or 80 days at 25°C. Temperature tolerance is great, and development from stage #7 to stage #25 takes about 200 hours at 10°C.

EURYCEA BISLINEATA, the two-lined salamander. This form is found in central and eastern States, having a maximum size of 4 inches, and is characterized by having five toes on the hind limb and a distinct labio-nasal groove. It is a slender salamander, round like a lead pencil, and is found is streams, springs, and bogs. Sex differences are not clear cut, except that the males upper front teeth are bicuspid.

Breeding extends from April to June. After an elaborate courtship, the female picks up the spermatophores and then lays the 20 to 30 eggs, one at a time, on the under side of stones or other objects. Incubation takes about a month, metamorphosis in about a year and sexual maturity the following Spring.

HEMIDACTYLIUM SCUTATUM, the four-toed salamander. This salamander has a wide distribution in the eastern United States, measuring no more than 4 inches in length. Except for the mudpuppy this is the only common salamander with four-toes. The color of the back is orange-brown with a pseudo-reptilian appearance of overlapping plates.

The belly surface is spotted white.   The male body is smaller but its tail is longer than that of the female.

Mating occurs in late summer and autumn, and breeding is in the spring in open bogs, shaded woodland pools, or along quiet streams.   The nests are mere cavities in decayed wood, grass or moss.   About 30 eggs are layed and incubation takes from 6 to 8 weeks, depending upon the environmental temperature.   The aquatic larval period is about 6 weeks, and sexual maturity is $2\frac{1}{2}$ years.

PLETHODON CINEREUS, the red-backed salamander.   Rather widely distributed throughout the United States, particularly in the middle west, but not overly abundant.   There are five toes on the hind limbs.   It is never more than 4 inches in length, is wholly terrestrial, and has two phases; one with black and the other with red back.   The male snouts are swollen and they are smaller than the females.

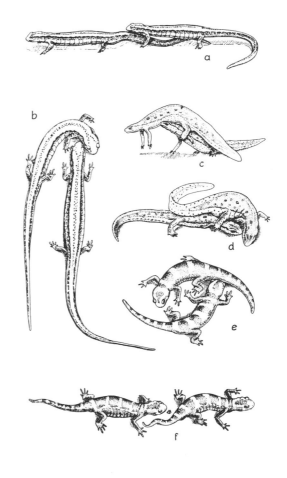

Mating occurs in October and again in the spring, with egg-laying in June and July. The eggs are layed in cavities in well-decayed logs or stumps and a single cluster may contain only about 14 eggs.   Development is very different from that of other Amphibia.

TRITURUS PYRRHOGASTER, the Japanese fire-salamander.   This form is very common in Japan and is characterized by a black warty skin and a bright red belly, with scattered black spots.   The size is generally about 6 inches, the males being a bit smaller and having large vents and pointed tails.   May be fed strips of fresh liver which they will ingest from the water without prompting.

Courtship of salamanders. a and b: Two-lined salamander. c and d: Newt.   e and f: Marbled salamander (spermatophore between pair in f). a, b, e, and f after Noble and Brady; c and d after Bishop.

(Courtesy C. H. Pope 1944: Chicago Mus. Nat. Hist.)

Since these forms are imported, they are used in the laboratory and may be caused to ovulate by the injection of frog pituitary glands or extracts of mammalian pituitaries. Generally the best procedure is to inject two female frog pituitaries on alternate days for three injections, then place the female in water with Elodea on which she can lay the eggs. Females in colonies may have spermatophores, but if this is not the case the males can be induced to drop spermatophores by pituitary treatment.   The eggs are generally layed after the third injection and a good female will give as many as 80 eggs.   The females seem to retain their spermatophores for a long period and the eggs are inseminated as they are layed.

TRITURUS VIRIDESCENS, the common newt, formerly known as Diemcytulus viridescens. These small vermillion spotted newts are found throughout the United States and southern

MALE

FEMALE

TRITURUS PYRRHOGASTER

(From A. Ichikawa 1937: Jour. Fac. Sci., Hokkaido
Imp. Univ., Ser. VI, Vol. VI, No. 1)

TRITURUS TOROSUS

Above: adult T. torosus female. Middle: adult T. torosus
male in breeding condition. The extreme glandular development during the mating season leaves the skin of Triturus
males in a smooth, transparent condition, almost jelly-like
in consistency. The color of the skin during this period is
characteristically quite pale in T. torosus, although it may
be sometimes considerably darker than in the specimen shown
here. Below: male of T. sierrae in breeding condition.

(From Twitty 1942: Copeia, #2)

TRITURUS GRANULOSUS

Above: adult male of T. granulosus from Mendocino County
in breeding condition. Extreme development of the tail fin
is characteristic of the breeding males in this species. Adult
pigmentation is more variable in this than in other species of
Californian Triturus, and may be either somewhat darker or
considerably lighter than in the specimen shown here. The
sides of breeding males generally exhibit a characteristic
steely-blue coloration (which is, however, sometimes approximated also in torosus males). Particularly during terrestrial
periods the back and sides of both sexes are often quite dark,
almost black, and the belly a yellowish or pinkish orange. In
general the granulosus of Santa Clara County are less darkly
pigmented than those farther north (see Bishop, 1941). Middle
and below: lateral and ventral views of an adult T. rivularis
female. The band across the cloaca is very characteristic,
but not invariable, and may appear also in lesser degree of
development in other Californian species of Triturus.

(From Twitty 1942: Copeia, #2)

Canada, particularly in the East. It lacks the series of vertical grooves on the side of the body, characteristic of salamanders. The back and sides are olive and the belly is light yellow with most of the bright vermillion spots on the sides and belly. The male possesses a row of pits, the hedonic glands, on the side of the head and can also be distinguished by its protruding cloaca. These forms may be fed strips of liver, or small earthworms, but the food must be moving to be attractive.

Breeding occurs in April and May, following an elaborate courtship which is terminated when the female picks up the spermatophores dropped by the male. The eggs are layed in sluggish water and are attached singly to stems, leaves, and other submerged objects. Spermatogenesis can be encouraged in the laboratory with temperatures of 53°F. or higher and sperm discharge is achieved by temperatures above 73°F., even in the winter time. From egg-laying to hatching is about 20-35 days, the larval period lasting about 80 days when the larva transforms into a bright orange, and terrestrial "red-eft". This stage cannot live in the water and possesses a skin which is highly repellent to water. Transformation into an aquatic form occurs after several (2 to 4) seasons and breeding then begins, in water. This form responds readily to anterior pituitary induced ovulation in the laboratory at almost any time of the (academic) year.

REFERENCES

ADAMS, A. E., 1940 - "Sexual conditions in Triturus viridescens. II. The reproductive cycle of adult aquatic forms of both sexes." Am. Jour. Anat. 66:235.

APPLINGTON, H. W., 1942 - "Correlative cyclical changes in the hypophysis and gonads of Necturus maculosus." Am. Jour. Anat. 70.

ARONSON, L. R., 1944 - "The mating pattern of Bufo americanus, Bufo fowleri, and Bufo terrestris." Am. Mus. Nov. #1250.

ARONSON, L. R., & G. K. NOBLE, 1945 - "The sexual behavior of Anura. 2. Neural mechanisms controlling mating in the male leopard frog, Rana pipiens." Bull. Am. Mus. Nat. Hist. 86:89.

BELLERBY, C. W. & L. HOGBEN, 1938 - "Experimental studies on sexual cycle of the South African clawed toad (Xenopus laevis)." Jour. Exp. Biol. 15:91.

BERK, L., 1938 - "Studies in the reproduction of Xenopus laevis. 1. The relation of external environmental factors to the sexual cycle." S. Afr. Jour. Med. Sci. 3:72.

BISHOP, S. C., 1925 - "The life history of the red salamander, Pseudotriton." Nat. Hist. 25:385.

BISHOP, S. C. & C. CRISP, 1933 - "The nests and young of the Allegheny salamander Desmognathus fuscus." Copeia. 1933, p. 194.

BISHOP, S. C., 1941 - "The salamanders of New York." N.Y. State Mus. Bull. 324, Univ. State N.Y., Albany.

BISHOP, S. C., 1943 - "Handbook of salamanders." Comstock Pub. Co., Ithaca.

BLANCHARD, F. N., 1923 - "The life history of the four-toed salamander." Am. Nat. 57:262.

BLES, E. J., 1905 - "The life history of Xenopus laevis." Tr. Roy. Soc. Edin. 41:789.

BRAGG, A. N., 1937 - "Observations on Bufo cognatus with special reference to breeding habits and eggs." Am. Midland Nat. 18:273.

BRAGG, A. N., 1944 - "Egg laying in leopard frogs." Proc. Oklahoma Acad. Sci. 24.

BRANIN, M. L., 1935 - "Courtship activities and extra seasonal ovulation in the four-toed salamander." Copeia. 1935, p. 172.

BROWN, M. G., 1942 - "An adaptation in Amblystoma opacum embryos to development on land." Am. Nat. 76:222.

CONANT, R., 1958 - "A field guide to reptiles and amphibians of eastern North America." Houghton Mifflin, Boston.

DeALLENDE, I. L. C., 1938 - "Aparato sexual femenino del Bufo arenarum." Inst. de Fisiologia Fac. de Ciencias Medicos Cardoba (Argentina).

DUNN, E. R., 1926 - "The salamanders of the family Plethodontidae."

GALGANO, M., 1943 - "Tratti fondamentali del ciclo sessuale annuale negli Anfibi dei nostri climi." Boll. di Zool. 14:57.

GLASS, F. M. & R. RUGH, 1944 - "Seasonal study of the normal and pituitary-stimulated frog (Rana pipiens). I. Testes and thumb pad." Jour. Morph. 74:409.

GREEN, H. T., 1925 - "The egg laying of the purple salamander (Gryinophilus)." Copeia. 141:32.

GREEN, N. B., 1938 - "The breeding habits of Pseudacris brachyphona with a description of the eggs and tadpole." Copeia. #2, p. 79.

HINSCHE, G., 1926 - "Uber Brunst- und Kopulationsreaktionen des Bufo vulgaris." Zeitschr. vergl. Physiol. 4:564.

HITCHCOCK, H. B., 1939 - "Notes on the newt Triturus viridescens." Herpetologica. 1:149.

KOPSCH, FR. 1952 - "Die Entiwicklung des braunen Grasfrsoches, Rana fusca R." Georg Thieme, Verlag, Stuttgart.

KUMPF, K. F., 1934 - "The courtship of Amblystoma tigrinum." Copeia. 1934, p. 7.

LANTZ, L. A., 1930 - "Notes on the breeding habits and larval development of A. opacum." Ann. Am. Mus. Nat. Hist. 5:322.

LANDGREBE, F. W. & G. L. Purser, 1941 - "Breeding of Xenopus in the laboratory." Nature. 148:115.

LIU, C. C., 1931 - "Sexual behavior in the Siberian toad, Bufo raddei and the pond frog, Rana nigromaculata." Peking Nat. Hist. Bull. 6:43.

NOBLE. G. K., 1931 - "The Biology of the Amphibia." McGraw-Hill, N.Y.

NOBLE, G. K. & L. R. ARONSON, 1942 - "The sexual behavior of Anura. I. The normal mating pattern of Rana pipiens." Bull. Am. Mus. Nat. Hist. 80:127.

NOBLE. G. K. & M. K. BRODY, 1933 - "Observations on the life history of the marbled salamander, A. opacum." Zoologica. 11:#8.

O'DONNELL, D. J., 1937 - "Natural history of the amblystomid salamanders of Illinois." Am. Midland Nat. 18:1063.

OLIVER, J. A., 1955 - "Natural history of North American amphibians and reptiles." Van Nostrand, New York.

ORTON, G., 1952 - "Key to the genera of tadpoles in the United States and Canada." Midland Naturalist. 47:382-395.

POPE, C. H., 1944 - "Amphibians and Reptiles of the Chicago area." Chicago Museum Nat. Hist.

RIEMER, W. J., 1958 - "Variation and systematic relationships within the salamander genus Taricha." Univ. Calif. Pub. Zool. 56:301-390.

ROSTAND, J., 1934 - "Toads and toad life." Methuen & Company, London.

SAVAGE, R. W., 1934 - "The breeding behavior of the common frog Rana temporaria and of the common toad Bufo bufo." Proc. Roy. Soc. London. 1:55.

SCHMIDT, K. P., 1953 - "A check list of North American amphibians and reptiles." Am. Soc. Icthyol. & Herpet., Univ. Chicago Press.

SHAPIRO, H. A., 1936 - "The role of distance receptors in the establishment of the mating reflex in Xenopus laevis, The Nares." Jour. Exp. Biol. 14:38.

SMITH, B. G., 1911 - "Notes on the natural history of Amblystoma jeffersonianum, A. punctatum and A. tigrinum." Bull. Wisc. Nat. Hist. Soc. 9:14.

SMITH, C. L., 1938 - "The clasping reflex in frogs and toads and the seasonal development of the brachial musculature." Jour. Exp. Biol. 15:1.

SMITH, R. E., 1944 - "Mating behavior in Triturus torosus and related newts." Copeia. 4:255.

STEBBINS, R. C., 1951 - "Amphibians of western North America." Univ. Calif. Press.

STEBBINS, R. C., 1954 - "Amphibians of western North America." McGraw-Hill.

TWITTY, V. C., 1936 - "Correlated genetic and embryological experiments on Triturus." I. Hybridization. II. Transplantation." Jour. Exp. Zool. 74:239-302.

TWITTY, V. C., 1942 - "The species of California Triturus". Copeia #2, 65.

WARING, H., F. W. LANDGREBE, & R. M. NEIL, 1941 - "Ovulation and oviposition in Anura." Jour. Exp. Biol. 18:1.

WRIGHT, A. H. & A. N. WRIGHT, 1933 - "Handbook of Frogs and Toads." Comstock Publishing Company.

"The foundation of all embryonic development consists of the processes by which cells become differentiated from each other and from their common progenitors. These processes of cellular differentiation, though basic to an understanding of embryogeny, remain largely unknown, although two major factors are generally recognized as important in governing the course of cell development. First, the genetic makeup of cells defines the limits and the potentialities of their development, and, second, the diverse cellular environments of the embryo elicit the specific developmental responses in cells which lead to their maturation into the wide variety of cell types that characterize the adult. The local and highly specific cell environments are produced by cellular activity and are constantly changing as the responsible cells change. Thus, a continuously evolving, dynamic interchange between embryonic cells directs their differentiation into specialized adult cells and finally into senescent cells incapable of sustaining the life of the organism". From Markert and Silvers, 1956 Genetics 41:429-450, modified by Ebert 1960 in "Ageing", ed., N.W. Shock, A.A.A.S. Pub.

2. THE CULTURE OF AMPHIBIAN EMBRYOS AND LARVAE TO METAMORPHOSIS

Early amphibian embryos possess an abundance of yolk which provides them with all the nutriment necessary for a considerable period of development. Tadpoles of both the Anura and the Urodela can survive for many days after hatching, by utilizing the yolk found between the embryonic gut and the belly ectoderm. The most important single factor for survival during the earliest stages of development is the temperature, and second to this is the culture medium. In order that the research worker can reduce to a minimum the environmental variables, some suggestions regarding the culturing of common amphibian forms are given here.

CULTURE MEDIUM

All amphibia lay their eggs in water. The pond water in which the form to be studied is known to breed is the ideal water to use. Since this is not always practical, laboratory substitutes have been devised, based partly upon a chemical analysis of such pond waters. In general it has been found that slightly hypotonic media are preferred, and development can proceed even in distilled water to some extent (see section on Osmo-Regulation). Tap water, in large cities particularly, may be so highly chlorinated that it is toxic to embryos or, in some instances, enough metallic ions escape from the lead, copper, or iron piping that the embryos cannot survive. Tap water which has been run through sand and charcoal, filtered, and allowed to stand for several days with abundant plant material in it, will generally prove quite satisfactory. The sand and charcoal take out the debris and dissolved gases, and the living plant material (Elodea, Valecineria, Sagittaria, Nitella, etc.) helps to increase the oxygen content.

It is now quite clear that sodium, calcium, and potassium ions must be present in an approximate ratio of 50:1:1 in order that development of aquatic embryos be normal. Each of these ions has specific value in cleavage and the developmental process, and if the ratio is maintained the forms can tolerate quite a range in concentration. Solely by the empirical method a number of formulae have been devised, each presumably suitable to particular forms. Some of these formulae follow:

STANDARD (HOLTFRETER'S) SOLUTION:

This solution has proven to be the most satisfactory of the synthetic media. The total salt content is 0.385%, which is hypotonic to adult tissues but seems to be isotonic to the early embryonic stages of the Anura. It is recommended that this solution be made up in double or quadruple strength as a stock solution. The normal concentration follows:

$$NaCl \dots\dots\dots\dots\dots\dots \quad 0.35 \quad grams$$
$$KCl \dots\dots\dots\dots\dots\dots \quad 0.005 \quad "$$
$$CaCl_2 \dots\dots\dots\dots\dots \quad 0.01 \quad "$$
$$NaHCO_3 \text{ (Buffer)} \dots\dots \quad 0.02 \quad "$$
$$\text{Distilled water} \dots\dots\dots 100.00 \ cc.$$

(Note: This solution is satisfactory for T. pyrrhagaster if the NaCl is reduced to half and the buffer is omitted.)

AMPHIBIAN RINGER'S SOLUTION:

This solution is hypertonic to Standard Solution and to embryos and embryonic tissues, but is satisfactory for adult tissues of the Amphibia.

NaCl .... 0.66 grams
KCl .... 0.015 "
$CaCl_2$ .... 0.015 "
$NaHCO_3$ (Buffer)......... 0.030 " (amount necessary to
Distilled water .... 100.0 cc. regulate pH at 7.8)

ORIGINAL FROG RINGER'S: (S. Ringer 1880: Jour. Physiol. 13:380)

NaCl .... 0.65 grams
KCl .... 0.014 "
$CaCl_2$ .... 0.012 "
$NaHCO_3$ .... 0.02 "
NaH_2PO_4 .... 0.001 "
Glucose .... 0.20 "
Water .... to 100.

SPRING WATER:

Great Bear Spring Water. This has proven to be entirely satisfactory for the early development of Anuran embryos particularly. Its chemical analysis is available from the dispensing company in New York City.

URODELE STOCK SOLUTION:

The same constituent salts are found in the Urodele media but in slightly different proportions. This stock solution could be made up in 20 liter carboys and could be diluted for either operating or growing media, using the Great Bear Spring Water for dilutions.

NaCl .... 70.0 grams
KCl .... 1.0 "
$CaCl_2$ .... 2.0 "
Spring Water .... 10.0 liters

URODELE OPERATING MEDIUM:

This medium is slightly hypertonic to the growing medium. Embryos may be left in this medium for several hours after transplantations, etc., and then should be transferred to the Growing Solution.

Urodele Stock Solution ..... 2 parts
Great Bear Spring Water ... 1 part

URODELE GROWING SOLUTION: Urodele larvae grow very satisfactorily in this medium.

Urodele Stock Solution ..... 1 part
Great Bear Spring Water ... 4 parts

In making up synthetic media it is recommended that glass distilled water be used where it is practicable. It has been found that with copper stills, enough copper goes into solution, in some stills, to make the water slightly toxic to embryos. In any crucial experiment the investigator should pre-test the medium against the embryos to be studied to that he can eliminate this as a possible factor in his experimental results. The data from the Osmo-Regulation experiments will be of value in this regard.

FOOD

FOR THE LARVAE:

Feeding is not necessary for some days after the mouth of the tadpole (larva) is open. This is because all amphibian larvae are provided with an abundance of reserve food in the form of yolk which is digested and absorbed directly by the tissues.

A.   Anura:

Feeding is not necessary until stage #25. Most Anuran larvae are vegetarians, and the most satisfactory food consists of slightly boiled lettuce or spinach. These greens should be thoroughly washed to rid them of any adherent arsenic or lead which may have been sprayed on them as insecticides by the gardener. Boiling the greens simply softens the plant tissues. The danger, at least in the beginning, comes from over-feeding. The tanks must be cleaned daily to keep faecal and bacterial accumulation at a minimum. For Xenopus larvae cooked, dehydrated, and finely powdered beef liver is an excellent supplement to greens, and algae. Liverworst has been used successfully with many Anura. Other foods used are powdered egg-yolk; bacto-beef extract mixed with whole wheat flour, dried and pulverized; raw liver, minced; algae and Protozoa. The lettuce feeding seems to produce fewer abnormalities but development is slower than with spinach (Hyman, 1941). Briggs (1942) has shown that a pure spinach diet produces certain minor abnormalities and kidney stones, so that a mixed diet is recommended. On pure lettuce or spinach, or a mixture of the two, tadpoles can be reared through metamorphosis with considerable ease. Anura are essentially vegetarian until after metamorphosis, then they are omnivorous with a leaning toward the carnivorous.

B.   Urodela:

The Urodele larvae require living, moving food. At first, rich cultures of Protozoa and young Daphnia are fed to the larvae after stage #40. The carapace of the older Daphnias will tear the gut of the larvae. The eyesight of these forms is very poor and their neuro-muscular responses are slow, so that the living food must be active. After a week or two of this diet, when the larvae are more hardy, they can tolerate such foods as the red worm (Tubifex), the white worm (Enchytrea), Daphnia (all sizes, but the young ones are better), mealflies, mealworms, wax moths (Galleria), Drosophila (vestigial mutant), plant lice, small ants, and, best of all, amphibian larvae (frog tadpoles of early stages). If not adequately fed the Urodele larvae will tend to nip off each others tails and occasionally larger specimens will devour the smaller ones. Beef liver favors A. tigrinum over A. punctatum while Daphnia and Enchytrea favor A. punctatum over A. tigrinum. Cannibalism is common, and Amblystoma larvae seem to grow best on a diet of Amblystoma.

If over-feeding is avoided, and any uningested food is removed daily from the tanks, it may not be necessary to change the culture medium more than once or twice each week. As the larvae grow, however, there will appear more faecal material in the tanks, and this should be sucked out with a suction bulb and glass tube or the water should be changed more frequently. The water must not be allowed to become turbid with bacteria.

FOOD FOR THE POST-METAMORPHIC STAGES:

After metamorphosis, with correlated changes in the histology of the digestive tract, the food requirements become radically different for all amphibia. Not only must there be more food, but it must represent a greater variety and should contain vitamins.

A. Anura:

After metamorphosis the situation becomes reversed in that the Anura require living, moving food. Living earthworms cut into 1-inch pieces, which will continue to move and attract the small frogs, are excellent as food. Blow flies, meal worms, ants, spiders, roaches, caterpillars, grasshoppers, will all be eaten as long as they move. Fish muscle, mammalian liver or muscle, dipped in a thin paste of Brewer's yeast and cod liver oil is an excellent food for recently metamorphosed frogs.

Xenopus is a slight exception in that it will eat anything bloody, particularly strips of raw liver. This form shows little activity except in taking of food, after which it settles down in the water again for as long as several days, coming to the surface only occasionally to get air.

Some of the potentially larger Anura (e. g. , R. catesbiana, the bullfrog) may grow rapidly and will require more food. These forms may be fed small crayfish, minnows, earthworms, and even small frogs of the same or other species. It is possible but difficult to train Anura to take non-living food.

The tree frogs (Hyla) require a continually humid environment such as an ordinary terrarium and their food consists of small insects. If the terrarium is glass covered, Drosophila (vestigial mutant) may be given to them, but it takes a good many flies to make an adequate meal. Hyla will take other living food such as earthworms.

Toads require a rather warm and dry environment, live on insects at first and then they will accept worms and even strips of beef, if the food is shaken before thier nostrils.

B. Urodela:

Salamanders are aquatic or semi-aquatic, and a few are actually terrestrial, hence the food requirements will vary somewhat with the species.

In general, the salamanders should be removed to a large crystallizing dish during feeding. The food at first may consist of clumps of white worms (Enchytrea), small earthworms or larger earthworms cut into 1-inch lengths suitable for ingestion. As the salamanders grow they can be trained to accept strips of beef or calves liver, if the liver is held in forceps and dangled before their nostrils. These forms act as though they are blind, but their olfactory senses are acute. After the feeding, remove all excess food, rinse off the specimens in fresh water, and return them to their tanks. Uningested or regurgitated food in the tank necessitates frequent complete change of medium, and occasional sterilization of the entire tank.

Triturus pyrrhogaster, the Japanese fire salamander, should be fed about three times each week, and each adult specimen should receive the equivalent of about 1 inch of liver, the diameter of a small pencil. With this routine they may be kept in healthy condition for many years, producing eggs (under pituitary stimulation) when desired by the Investigator.

SPACE AND OXYGEN

The space factor in development has not been adequately recognized but it plays a very important role in the rate of development. In general, the larvae will grow the faster in less crowded conditions, all other factors being equal. It is suggested that a ratio of 1 egg to 2 cc. of medium be used in finger bowls with a maximum of 25 eggs to 50 cc. of medium. As the embryos develop into larvae (tadpoles) this ratio will have to be changed so that at the beginning of feeding there are no more than 10 tadpoles per finger bowl of 50 cc. of medium. At this time it is better to transfer the tadpoles to a larger tank to allow for greater activity (see Rugh, 1934).

The amount of water per specimen is not the vital consideration, however. It is the surface area that is important, so that in a tank measuring 6 x 12 x 24 inches one can place
200 tadpoles in water not more than 1 inch in depth. Evaporation from this tank should
be compensated for by adding distilled water once each week, but under no conditions
should tadpoles be placed in deep water.

Amphibian embryos can tolerate a wide range of oxygen tension but they are very sensitive to anerobic conditions. Artificial aeration is not necessary but it is well to place in
the tanks some aquatic plants such as Elodea, Nitella, etc. which will continually add
some oxygen to the medium. Anuran larvae seem to require more oxygen than do the
Urodele larvae.

LIGHT

There is no evidence that light is necessary for normal amphibian development (Rugh,
1935). However, since larvae can derive nourishment from algae and they do require
oxygen, it is well to provide normal light so that plant food can grow and can provide
some of the necessary oxygen. Direct sunlight is not advised because of the heat factor.

TEMPERATURE

The temperature tolerance of various forms is given in the section on Temperature. The
range of tolerance for the various forms is about 24°C., but the scale is high for some
and low for others. The Urodela, for instance, develop better at the lower temperatures
while the Anura seem to develop better at the higher temperature levels.

Within the normal tolerance range it is possible to retard or accelerate the normal rate
of development of any of the forms without latering the developmental processes in any
way. For instance, one can keep Rana pipiens eggs at 15°C., 20°C., and 25°C. and have
three different stages of development simultaneously, all from the same original batch of
fertilized eggs.

The maximum range for all amphibian larvae is 0°C. to 40°C., with the optimum range
between 12°C. and 25°C. Most laboratories are kept at between 23°C. and 25°C. which
is satisfactory for the Anura but somewhat high for the Urodela.

BACTERIA AND PARASITES

The most common infection for adult frogs is Red-Leg. Numerous attempts have been
made to control this disease. The best method is to eliminate any infected animals upon
receipt; to keep the tanks cool and the animals in running water, and occasionally to treat
possibly infected animals with weak $KMNO_4$ solution. Copper lined tanks will reduce the
incidence of Red-Leg. Saprolegnia is another infection of high mortality and unknown
cure. The symptoms include body swelling or bloating. Infected animals should be destroyed immediately and the tank sterilized with permanganate. It is a practice in many
laboratories to place several copper pennies in the tanks with the frogs, enough copper
ions passing into the water to keep down these infections and yet not enough to be toxic
for the adults. (In even minute concentrations, copper, lead, zinc, mercury, and bronze
are toxic to embryos.)

Salamanders are sometimes seriously affected by a fungus, Monilia batrachus, which
attacks the lips and causes open sores. Frogs and toads seem to be immune. This
growth is contagious but if treated early by painting the lips with 2% mercurochrome, the
disease may be checked.

Parasites are often brought in with living food. These include worms, flies, and mites. However, these infected animals normally comprise the food of most amphibia so that there is little or no danger for them. If Tubifex (red worm) is used as food, it is well to keep them in running cold water for several days because they grow in sewage and are apt to bring in an excess of bacteria.

Oedema, or swelling of tissues with water, may be due to a malfunctioning of the embryonic kidneys although it is known to occur even before such organs are developed. Early tadpoles often develop an apparent oedema, but the swelling is due to an accumulation of dissolved gases in the digestive tract with some consequent bloating of the body. Generalized oedema can sometimes be relieved by placing the embryos in slightly hypertonic medium. If the oedema is localized, it can be relieved by puncturing with a needle to allow the escape of the excess fluid.

REFERENCES

ADOLPH, E. F., 1931 - "Body size as a factor in the metamorphosis of tadpoles." Biol. Bull. 61:376 (see ibid. 61:350).

ANDERSON, P. L., 1943 - "The normal development of Triturus pyrrhogaster." Anat. Rec. 86:59.

ARONSON, L. R , 1944 - "Breeding Xenopus laevis." Am. Nat. 78:131.

ATLAS, M , 1935 - "The effect of temperature on the development of Rana pipiens." Phys. Zool. 8.

BLES, E. J., 1905 - "The life history of Xenopus laevis." Tr. Roy. Soc. Edin. 41:789.

BRACHET, J., 1940 - "Etude histochimique des Proteines au cours du développement embryonnaire des poissons, des Amphibiens, et des Oiseaux." Arch. d. Biol. 51:167.

BRAGG, A. N., 1939 - "Observations upon amphibian deutoplasm and its relation to embryonic and early larval development." Biol. Bull. 77:268.

BRIGGS, R. & M. DAVIDSON, 1942 - "Some effects of spinach feeding on Rana pipiens tadpoles." Jour. Exp. Zool. 90:401.

BROWN, M. G., 1942 - "An adaptation in Amblystoma opacum embryos to development on land." Am. Nat. 76:222.

CAMERON, J. A., 1940 - "Effect of flourine on hatching time and hatching stage in Rana pipiens." Ecology. 21:288.

CAMERON, S. B., 1947 - "Successful breeding of Xenopus laevis, the South African clawed Toad-frog." Am. Jour. Med. Technology. May 1947.

DANIEL, J F. & E. A. YARWOOD, 1939 - "The early embryology of Triturus torosus." Univ. Calif. Pub. Zool. 43:321.

DEMPSTER, W. T., 1933 - "Growth in Amblystoma punctatum during the embryonic and early larval period." Jour. Exp. Zool. 64:495.

DETWILER, S. R., W. M. COPENHAUER, C. O. ROBINSON, 1947 - "The survival of Amblystoma embryos when treated with sodium sulfadiazine and guinine sulfate." Jour. Exp. Zool. 106:109.

DICKERSON, M. C., 1906 - "The Frog Book." Doubleday Page, pgs. 253.

DuSHANE, G. P. & C. HUTCHINSON, 1944 - "Differences in size and developmental rate between Eastern and Midwestern embryos of Amblystoma maculatum." Ecology. 25:414.

EAKIN, R. M., 1939 - "Further studies in regulatory development of Triturus torosus." Univ. Calif. Pub. Zool. 43:185.

EMERSON, H. & C. NORRIS, 1905 - "Red-leg an infectious disease in frogs." Jour. Exp. Med. 7.

FRANCIS, E. T., 1934 - "The anatomy of the salamander." Clarendon Press, Oxford.

GITLIN, D., 1944 - "The development of Eleutherodactylus partoricensis." Copeia. 1944, p. 81.

GOODALE, H. A., 1911 - "The early development of Spelerpes bislineata." Am. Jour. Anat. 12:174.

GRANT, M. P., 1931 - "Diagnostic stages of metamorphosis in Amblystoma jeffersonianum and Amblystoma opacum." Anat. Rec. 51:1.

HAMILTON, W. J., 1934 - "The rate of growth of the toad (B. americanus) under natural conditions." Copeia. 1934, p. 88.

HUMPHREY, R. R., 1928 - "Ovulation in the four-toed salamander Hemidactylium scutatum and the external features of cleavage and gastrulation." Biol. Bull. 54:307.

HUTCHINSON, C., 1939 - "Some experimental conditions modifying the growth of amphibian larvae." Jour. Exp. Zool. 83:257.

HYMAN, L., 1941 - "Lettuce as a medium for the continuous culture of a variety of small laboratory animals." Trans. Amer. Micr. Soc. 60:365.

KROGH A., 1931 - "Dissolved substances as food of aquatic organisms." Biol. Rev. 6:412.

LANDGREBE, F. W. & G. L. PURCER, 1941 - "Breeding of Xenopus in the laboratory." Nature, 148:115.

LYNN, W. G., 1942 - "The embryology of Eleutherodactylus nubicola, an anuran which has no tadpole stage." Carnegie Inst. Contrib. Emb. #190, p. 27. (Pub. #541).

LYNN, W. G. & B. LUTZ, 1946 - "The development of Eleutherodactylus Guentheri Stdur." Boletim do Museu. Nacional Zool., Brazil, 71:1.

McCLURE, C. F. W., 1925 - "An experimental analysis of oedema in the frog, with special reference to the oedema in red-leg disease." Am. Anat. Memoires. 12:1.

MERWIN, R. N. & W. C. ALLEE, 1941 - "The effect of carbon dioxide on the rate of cleavage in frog's eggs." Anat. Rec. 81: suppl. 126. (See ibid 1943, Ecology. 24:61.)

MOORE, A. R., 1915 - "An analysis of experimental edema in the frog." Am. Jour. Anat. 37.

MOORE, A. R., 1933 - "Is cleavage rate a function of the cytoplasm or of the nucleus?" Jour. Exp. Biol. 10:230.

MOORE, J. A., 1940 - "Adaptive differences in the egg membranes of frogs." Am. Nat. 74:89.

MORGAN, A. H. & M. GRIERSON, 1932 - "Winter habits and yearly food consumption of adult spotted newts, Triturus virides- cens." Ecology. 13:54.

MORGAN, T. H., 1905 - "The relation between normal and abnormal development of the embryo fo the frog. X. A re-exam- ination of the early stages of normal development from the point of view of results of abnormal development." Arch. f. Ent. mech. 19:588.

MORRILL, C. V., 1923 - "The peculiar reaction of the common newt to a liver diet." Anat. Rec. 26:83.

PATCH, E. M., 1927 - "Biometric studies upon development and growth in Amblystoma punctatum and tigrinum." Proc. Soc. Exp. Biol. & Med. 25:218.

PATCH, E. M., 1941 - "Cataracts in Amblystoma tigrinum larvae fed experimental diets." Proc. Soc. Exp. Biol. & Med. 46:205.

PETER, K., 1934 - "Die Gastrulation von Xenopus laevis." Zetsch. mikr. Anat. Forsch. 35:181.

PIKE, F. H., 1923 - "The effect of the environment in the production of malformations." Ecology. 4:420.

POLLISTER, A. W. & J. A. MOORE, 1937 - "Tables for the normal development of Rana sylvatica." Anat. Rec. 68:489.

PRATT E. M., 1940 - "Effects of vitamin E deficiency on the tadpole of Rana pipiens." Univ. Mich. MS. Thesis.

RANEY, E. C. & W. M. Ingram, 1941 - "Growth of tagged frogs (Rana catesbiana and Rana clamitans) under natural conditions." Am. Midland Nat. 26:201.

ROBB, R. C., 1929 - "On the nature of hereditary size limitation. II. The growth of parts in relation to the whole." Jour. Exp. Biol. 6:311.

ROSE, S. M., 1946 - "Disease control in frogs." Science. 104:330.

RUGH, R., 1934 - "The space factor in the growth rate of tadpoles." Ecology. 15.

RUGH, R., 1935 - "The spectral effect on the growth rate of tadpoles." Physiol. Zool. 8.

SAVAGE, R. M., 1937 - "The ecology of young tadpoles, with special reference to the nutrition of the early larvae of Rana temporaria, Bufo bufo, and Bombinator variegata." Proc. Zool. Soc. London Ser. A 107:249 (see ibid. 108:465).

SCOTT, H. H., 1926 - "The mycotic disease of Batrachiens." Proc. Zool. Soc. London, 683.

SHAW, G., 1932 - "The effect of biologically conditioned water upon the rate of growth in fishes and amphibia." Ecology. 13:263.

SHUMWAY, W., 1940 - "Stages in the normal development of Rana pipiens. I. External form." Anat. Rec. 78:139 (see ibid 1942, Vol. 83:309).

SMITH, B. G., 1926 - "The embryology of Cryptobranchus alleghenicnsis." Jour. Morph. 42:197.

STOCKARD, C. R., 1921 - "Developmental rate and structural expression." Am. Jour. Anat. 28:115.

TAYLOR, A. C. & J. J. KOLLROS, 1946 - "Stages in the normal development of Rana pipiens larvae." Anat. Rec. 94:7.

TWITTY, V. C., 1936 - "Correlated genetic and embryological experiments on Triturus." Jour. Exp. Zool. 174:239.

TWITTY, V. C. & L. E. DeLanney, 1939 "Size regulation and regeneration in salamander larvae under complete starvation." Jour. Exp. Zool. 81:399.

TWITTY, V. C. & W. J. van Wagtendonk, 1940 - "A suggested mechanism for the regulation of proportionate growth, supported by quantitative data on the blood nutrients." Growth 4:349.

TWITTY, V. C., 1961 - "Second-generation hybrids of the species of Taricha". Proc. Nat. Acad. Sci. 47:1416-1486.

TYLER, A., 1942 - "Developmental processes and energetics." Quart. Rev. Biol. 17:197.

WEISS, P., 1947 - "The problem of specificity in growth and development." Yale Jour. Biol. & Med. 19:235.

WEISZ, P. B., 1945 - "The development and morphology of the larva of the South African clawed toad, Xenopus laevis. II. The hatching and the first and second form tadpoles." Jour. Morph. 77:193.

WILDER, I. W., 1924 - "The relation of growth to metamorphosis in Eurycea bislineata." Jour. Exp. Zool. 40:1.

WRIGHT, A. H., 1929 - "Synopsis and description of North American tadpoles." Proc. U.S. Nat. Mus. 74:Art. 11:1.

WURMBACH, H., 1957 - "Le metabolisme de l'eau et la metamorphose des animaux." 76 Congr. Assoc. France (Perigueux).

"Embryology is an ancient manuscript with many of the sheets lost, others displaced, and with spurious passages interpolated by a later hand."
Cambridge Natural History, V. 79

"The very egg itself must have specific characters although they may be invisible, and the eggs of different animals are really distinct from one another as are their adults, the distinction becoming more and more vis- ible as development proceeds."
O. Hertwig

3. THE DEVELOPMENTAL STAGES OF AMPHIBIAN EMBRYOS

Starting with the (unpublished) Harrison series of stages for Amblystoma punctatum, there have appeared more and more descriptions of the early developmental stages of various forms. Through the generous cooperation of those who have worked out the normal morphology of a number of different amphibian forms, there follows all the series and stages that are now available. It is hoped that this list will be extended, not only for the sake of research usefulness, but in order to determine the extent of any deviations from a standard pattern of development. The author desires to express, here again, his appreciation for the cooperation of those who have made this collection possible. Reference is made to Shumway, Pollister, and Moore, Taylor and Kollros for Rana; to Weisz for Xenopus: to Eakin for Hyla regilla; to Priscilla Anderson for Triturus pyrrhogaster; to Twitty and Bodenstein for Triturus torosus; and to Mrs. Naomi Leavitt who painstakingly drew the Amblystoma series from living and preserved material, identifying the various stages as in the (unpublished) Harrison series.

On the following pages will be found the normal series for:

> Rana pipiens (Shumway)
> Rana pipiens (Mueller)
> Rana pipiens, photographs (Rugh)
> Rana pipiens metamorphosis (Taylor & Kollros)
> Rana pipiens, photographs of developmental abnormalities (Rugh)
> Rana sylvatica (Pollister & Moore)
> Xenopus laevis (Weisz)
> Hyla regilla (Eakin)
> Amblystoma punctatum (Leavitt)
> Triturus pyrrhogaster (Anderson)
> Triturus torosus (Twitty & Bodenstein)

a. Rana Pipiens

NORMAL STAGES IN THE DEVELOPMENT OF RANA PIPIENS
WALDO SHUMWAY

Reprinted from *The Anatomical Record*
Vol. 78, No. 2, October, 1940

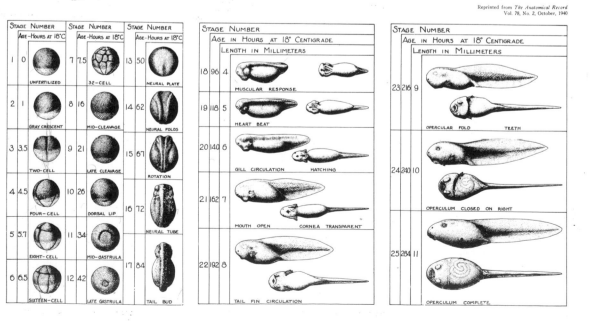

(See also Shumway 1942 - Anat. Rec. 83:309)

**METAMORPHOSIS
RANA CATESBIANA**

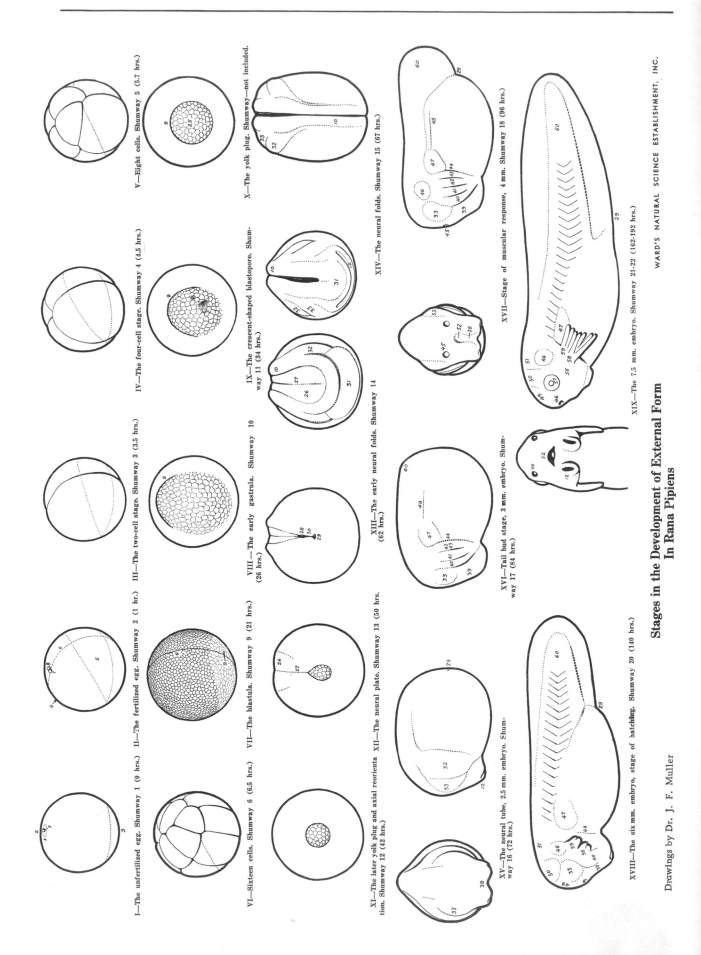

V—Eight cells. Shumway 5 (5.7 hrs.)

X—The yolk plug. Shumway—not included.

XIV—The neural folds. Shumway 15 (67 hrs.)

XVII—Stage of muscular response, 4 mm. Shumway 18 (96 hrs.)

IV—The four-cell stage. Shumway 4 (4.5 hrs.)

IX—The crescent-shaped blastopore. Shumway 11 (34 hrs.)

XIX—The 7.5 mm. embryo. Shumway 21-22 (162-192 hrs.)

WARD'S NATURAL SCIENCE ESTABLISHMENT, INC.

III—The two-cell stage. Shumway 3 (3.5 hrs.)

VIII — The early gastrula. Shumway 10 (26 hrs.)

XIII—The early neural folds. Shumway 14 (62 hrs.)

XVI—Tail bud stage, 3 mm. embryo. Shumway 17 (84 hrs.)

Stages in the Development of External Form
In Rana Pipiens

II—The fertilized egg. Shumway 2 (1 hr.)

VII—The blastula. Shumway 9 (21 hrs.)

XII—The neural plate. Shumway 13 (50 hrs.)

XV—The neural tube, 2.5 mm. embryo. Shumway 16 (72 hrs.)

I—The unfertilized egg. Shumway 1 (0 hrs.)

VI—Sixteen cells. Shumway 6 (6.5 hrs.)

XI—The later yolk plug and axial reorientation. Shumway 12 (42 hrs.)

XVIII—The six mm. embryo, stage of hatching. Shumway 20 (140 hrs.)

Drawings by Dr. J. F. Muller

KEY TO COLORS AND NUMBERS

Light blue - epidermis
Dark blue - neural plate
Red
Green
Yellow

ECTODERM

MESODERM
NOTOCHORD
ENDODERM

1. The fovea, indicating the position of the female pronucleus.
2. The animal pole.
3. The vegetal pole.
4. The sperm entrance point.
5. The gray crescent.
6. The gray crescent plane. Theoretically coincides with sperm entrance point plane, first cleavage plane, and median sagittal plane of future embryo.
7. The first polar body (first polocyte).
8. The second polar body (second polocyte). The relative size of these has been exaggerated.
9. Dorsal lip of the blastopore.
10. Neural fold.
11. Retina.
12. Sucker.
13. Lens placode.
14. Auditory placode.
15. Foregut.
16. Hindgut.
17. Limit of head region.
18. Limit of inturned material at end of gastrulation.
19. Notochord.
20. Limit of neural plate.
21. Somites.
22. Visceral pouches.
23. Blastocoel (segmentation cavity) - white
24. Gastrocoel (archenteron) - yellow (+ red and green).
25. Yolk plug.
26. Neural (medullary) plate.
27. Neural (medullary) groove.
28. Dorsal part of blastopore (neurenteric canal).

29. Ventral part of blastopore (proctodaeum, anus).
30. Primitive streak (fused lateral lips of blastopore).
31. Sense plate.
32. Gill plate.
33. Optic bulge.
34. Oral evagination of endoderm.
35. Rectum.
36. Hypophysis.
37. Infundibulum.
38. Stomodeal groove.
39. First visceral (mandibular) arch.
40. Second visceral (hyoid) arch.
41. Third visceral (first branchial) arch.
42. Fourth visceral (second branchial) arch.
43. Fifth visceral (third branchial) arch.
44. Sixth visceral (fourth branchial) arch.
45. Olfactory pits.
46. Auditory vesicle (otocyst, inner ear).
47. Pronephros.
48. Pronephric duct.
49. Forebrain (Prosencephalon).
50. Midbrain (Mesencephalon).
51. Hindbrain (Rhombencephalor).
52. Stomodeal pit (mouth).
53. Heart.
54. Liver.
55. Epiphysis (pineal body).
56. Origin of opercular fold.
57. Cornea.
58. First external gill.
59. Second external gill.
60. Tail bud, tail.

SECTIONS OF VARIOUS STAGES

Ward's Natural Science Establishment, Inc.

Drawings by Dr. J. F. Mueller

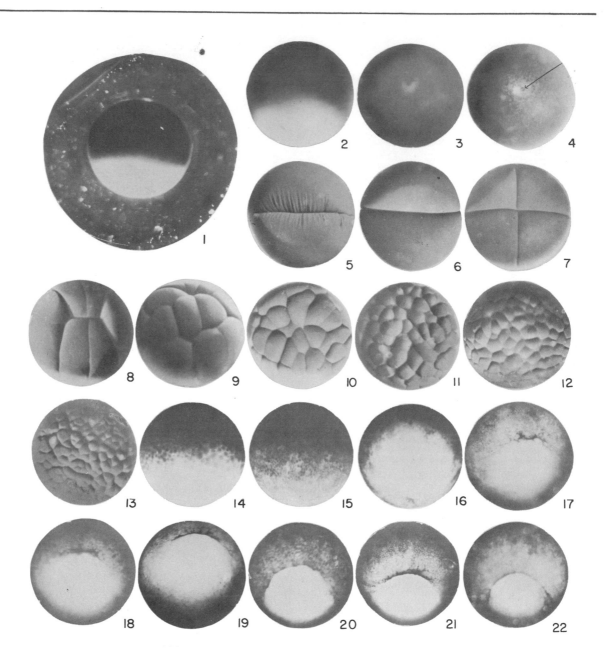

PHOTO NUMBER	SHUMWAY STAGE	DEVELOPMENTAL STAGE
1	1	Unfertilized egg
2	2	Fertilized, grey crescent
3, 4		Polar body formation
5, 6	3	First cleavage
7	4	Second cleavage, four-cells
8	5	Third cleavage, eight-cells
9	6	Fourth cleavage, sixteen cells
10	7	Fifth cleavage, 32-cell stage
11		Temporary morula, 64+ cells
12, 13	8	Early blastula
14-16	9	Late blastula, epiboly
17	10	Early dorsal lip
18-22	11	Active gastrulation

EARLY DEVELOPMENT OF THE FROG EMBRYO
RANA PIPIENS

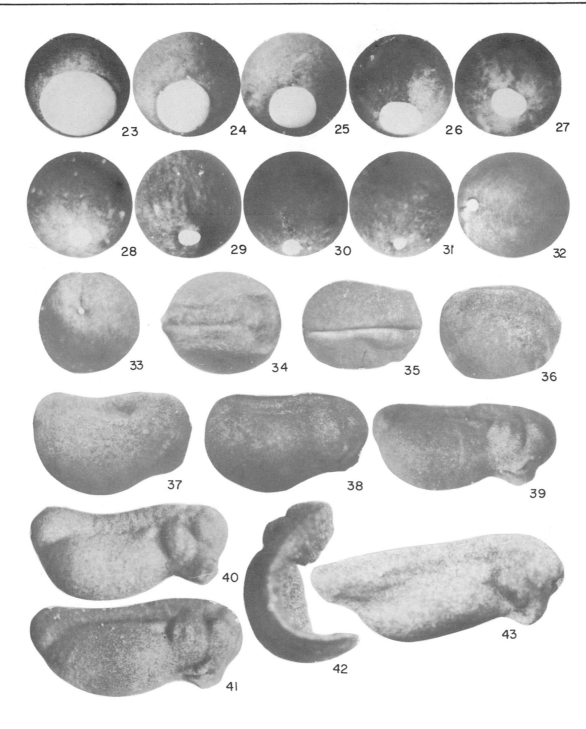

PHOTO NUMBER	SHUMWAY STAGE	DEVELOPMENTAL STAGE
23-27		Yolk plug formation
28-32	12	Disappearing yolk plug
33	13	Neural plate and groove
34	14	Neural folds
35	15	Neural groove, rotation
36	16	Neurula - neural tube closed
37-38	17	Early tail bud
39	18	Muscular response
40-41	19	Initial heart beat, myotomes
42-43	20	Hatching, gill development

LATE DEVELOPMENT OF THE FROG EMBRYO

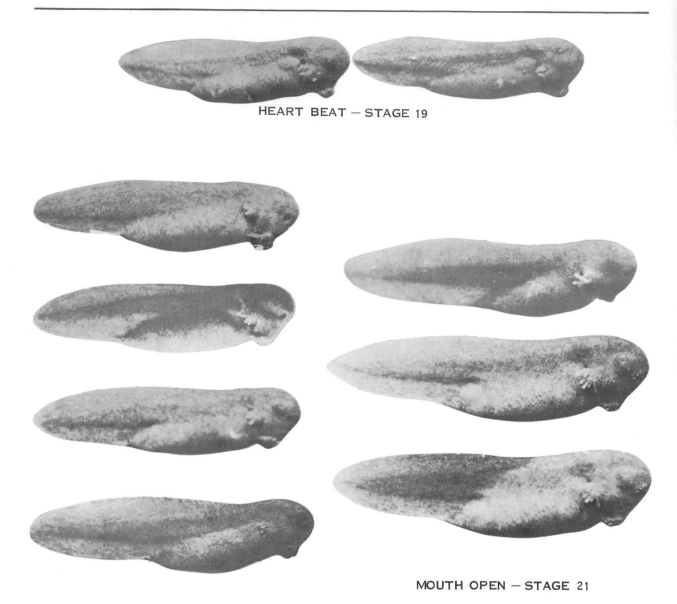

HEART BEAT — STAGE 19

GILL CIRCULATION — STAGE 20

MOUTH OPEN — STAGE 21

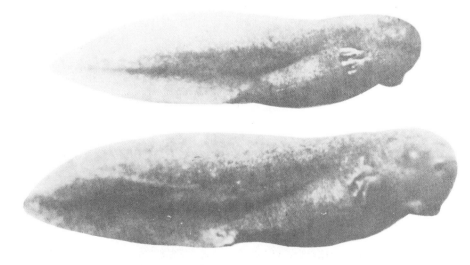

TAIL FIN CIRCULATION — STAGE 22   (RANA PIPIENS)

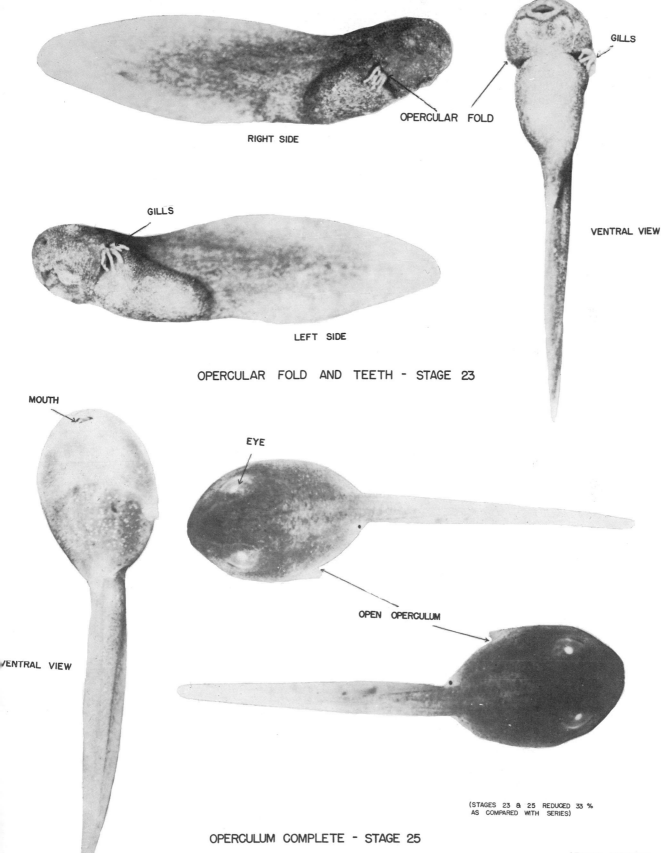

RIGHT SIDE

OPERCULAR FOLD

GILLS

VENTRAL VIEW

GILLS

LEFT SIDE

OPERCULAR FOLD AND TEETH - STAGE 23

MOUTH

EYE

VENTRAL VIEW

OPEN OPERCULUM

(STAGES 23 & 25 REDUCED 33 %
AS COMPARED WITH SERIES)

OPERCULUM COMPLETE - STAGE 25

(RANA PIPIENS)

NORMAL STAGES OF RANA SYLVATICA

TABLE 1

ST. NO.	AGE HRS. 18°	EXTERNAL FORM	ST. NO.	AGE HRS. 18°	EXTERNAL FORM	ST. NO.	AGE HRS. 18°	EXTERNAL FORM
1	0		7	6		13	36	
2	1		8	12		14	40	
3	2.5		9	16		15	45	
4	3+		10	19		16	50	
5	4.5		11	24		17	58	
6	5+		12	28				

DESCRIPTION OF STAGES*
STAGES 1 TO 17 (TABLE 1)

1. Egg at fertilization.
2. Establishment of gray crescent area as first external evidence of development, sharply defined at 1 hour.

3 to 6. Age given is time of appearance of cleavage furrow that establishes the number of cells drawn for the stage.

7 to 9. Later stages in cell multiplication, best determined by comparison of size of cells at vegetal pole.

10. Appearance of dorsal lip.
11. Blastopore approximately a semicircle.
12. Complete blastopore (yolk-plug) stage.
13. Slit blastopore or neural plate stage.
14. Neural fold stage.
15. Beginning of closure of neural folds, beginning of elongation. Cilia begin to rotate the embryo at about this stage.
16. Closure of neural folds completed.
17. Beginning of development of tail bud, marked off from body by ventral notch when embryo is viewed laterally.

* The stages illustrated and defined by age are of course essentially an arbitrary series of readily identifiable points in the continuous process of development. Defined in terms of these points, the total development is comprised in a series of periods, each extending from one stage until the next. In practice the points and the periods are not sharply distinguished and it is convenient to describe each period in terms of the stage that initiates it. Thus the development from onset of the heart beat to the beginning of gill circulation would be the period of stage 19.

TABLE 2

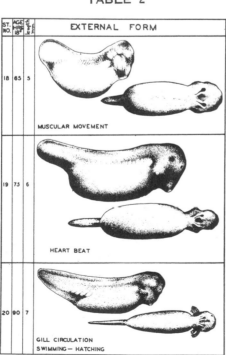

ST. NO.	AGE HRS. 18°		EXTERNAL FORM
18	65	5	MUSCULAR MOVEMENT
19	75	6	HEART BEAT
20	90	7	GILL CIRCULATION SWIMMING — HATCHING

TABLE 3

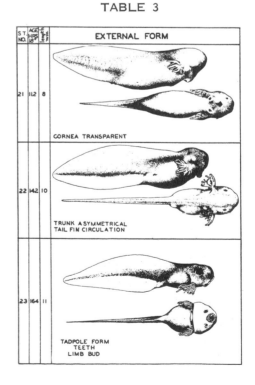

ST. NO.	AGE HRS. 18°		EXTERNAL FORM
21	112	8	CORNEA TRANSPARENT
22	142	10	TRUNK ASYMMETRICAL TAIL FIN CIRCULATION
23	164	11	TADPOLE FORM TEETH LIMB BUD

(From A. W. Pollister & J. A. Moore)

NORMAL STAGES OF RANA SYLVATICA
STAGES 18 TO 23 (TABLES 2 AND 3)

The figures are ventral and lateral views of all but stage 22, which shows dorsal instead of ventral aspect.

18. Stage begins with development of capacity for muscular movement, i.e., simple unilateral flexure in response to mechanical stimulation. This is very suddenly acquired and is closely correlated with attainment of the external form figured.
19. Time given indicates onset of heart beat which appears very suddenly and is accordingly a most useful marker for this stage. (Use of strong reflected light is necessary for identification of this early pulse.) Tail equals one-third the length of the body.
20. Beginning of circulation of blood corpuscles through a capillary loop of anterior gill is closely correlated with gill morphology, and is the best indication of the beginning of this stage. Shaking will hatch embryos early in this stage; they hatch spontaneously late in 20. Swimming ability is acquired in the latter part of this stage. Tail equals one-half the body length.
21. Cornea becoming transparent so lens is visible as light spot. Body and tail nearly equal in length.
22. Development of posterior bend in gut makes trunk appear asymmetrical from dorsal aspect. A few capillary loops are functional in the tail fin. Epidermis rapidly becoming transparent.
23. Trunk and head have rounded out and embryo assumes true larval or "tadpole" shape. Horny larval teeth developed. Posterior limb bud identifiable. Opercular fold beginning to develop. Active spontaneous swimming begins.

TABLE 4

Hours from first cleavage required to reach various stages at different temperatures

STAGE	10.4°C.	15.4°C.	18.5°C.
3	0	0	0
4	2+	1.3	1.0
5	5	2.2	2.0
6		3.0+	3.0
7	11	4.7	3.5
8	24	14.0	9.5
9	36	19.5	13.5
10	45	24.0	16.5
11	60	32.0	21.0
12	72	37.0	25.0
13	96	52.0	33.0
14	112	56.0	37.0
15	124	63.0	42.0
16	141	72.0	47.0
17	168	83.0	55.0
18	180	90.0	62.0
19	216	108.0	72.0
20	275	130.0	87.0

TABLE 5

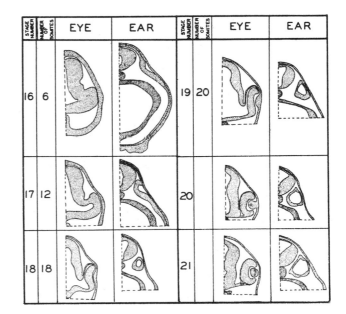

(From A. W. Pollister & J. A. Moore)
(Anat. Rec. 1937, 68:489)

INTERNAL ANATOMY (TABLE 5)

It has been found useful to have some means of readily identifying sectioned material in terms of the series of stages described above. There are, of course, no difficulties in doing this with embryos up to the time of closure of the neural folds (stage 15). For recognition of stages 16 to 21 table 5 was constructed. The number of somites was counted from frontal or sagittal sections. The development of the eye and ear, as seen in cross sections, are shown by the series of drawings made at a common magnification by a projection method.

b. Xenopus Laevis

THE NORMAL STAGES IN THE DEVELOPMENT OF THE
SOUTH AFRICAN CLAWED TOAD, XENOPUS LAEVIS

1. Unfertilized egg. Oblique view. Size 0.9-1.0 mm. diameter.
2. Grey crescent stage. Oblique lateral view.
3. First cleavage completed.
4. Second cleavage completed.
5. Third cleavage completed.
6. Early cleavage stage; approximately 32 cells.
7. Mid-cleavage stage. Determined by easily recognizable, unpigmented rows of macromeres.
8. Late cleavage; blastula stage. Determined by position of lower pigment border.
9. Early gastrula. Oblique ventral view to show semicircular blastoporal rim.
10. Mid-gastrula; yolk plug stage. Oblique ventral view.
11. Late gastrula stage. Heavy pigmentation in place of yolk plug, and loss of pigment in presumptive neural area. Oblique ventral view.
12. Neural plate stage. Very slight lateral compression. Dorsal view.
13. Neural fold stage. Slight elongation. Length 1.2 mm.
14. Neural folds in contact; ciliary rotation within egg covers. Top, dorsal view. Bottom, frontal view, showing presumptive frontal gland and oral sucker. Length 1.5 mm.
15. Neural tube stage. Top, dorsal view; eye vesicle distinct; tailbud indicated. Bottom, frontal view; ultimate size of frontal gland area as indicated. Length 1.8 mm.
16. Tail bud stage. Optic, otic and pronephric protuberances distinct. Total length 2 mm. Tailbud 0.2 mm.
17. Beginning of muscular response to mechanical stimulation. Gill plate distinct. Total length 2.8-3.1 mm. Tailbud 0.4 mm.
18. Gill buds (two pairs) distinct; will hatch if shaken. Total length 3.7-4.1 mm. Tail 0.7 mm.
19. Beginning of heart beat; can be observed under the microscope with strong illumination. Total length 4.9-5.2 mm. Tail 1.3 mm.
20. Spontaneous hatching; first indications of melanin pigmentation. Total length 5.4-5.7 mm. Head 0.9 mm. Body 2.4 mm. Tail 2.2 mm.
21. Beginning of first-form tadpole stage. Nasal pits distinct; active spontaneous swimming begins during the phase; epidermis begins to become transparent; mouth open at this time; oral sucker degenerated; cornea transparent. Total length 6.0-6.2 mm. Head 1.3 mm. Body 1.3 mm. Tail 3.5 mm.
22. Beginning of second-form tadpole stage. External gills disappeared; respiratory gulping, and feeding begin; thymus gland externally visible; lateral contour of mouth is round. Total length 9 mm. av. Head 2 mm. Body 1 mm. Tail 6 mm.
23. Beginning of third-form tadpole stage. Hind limb buds indicated; oral tentacle buds indicated; lateral contour of mouth is wedge-shaped. Total length 30 mm. av. Head 7 mm. Body 3 mm. Tail 20 mm.

"Not only do the body fluids of the lower forms of marine life correspond exactly with sea water in their composition, but there are at least strong indications that the fluids of the highest animals are really descended from sea water . . . . . the same substances are present in both cases, and in both cases sodium chloride predominates."
L. J. Henderson 1913: "Fitness of the Environment"

"Of course, I am not forgetting that development and evolution are in the main epigenetic processes by which the more complicated end stages are built upon the less complicated earlier ones, but I also refuse to forget that these earlier stages are also complex, that the egg or the Paramecium are complex organisms and that development is endogenetic as well as epigenetic. Both epigenesis and endogenesis are involved in all development and evolution."
E. G. Conklin, 1944

THE NORMAL STAGES IN THE DEVELOPMENT OF THE
SOUTH AFRICAN CLAWED TOAD, XENOPUS LAEVIS

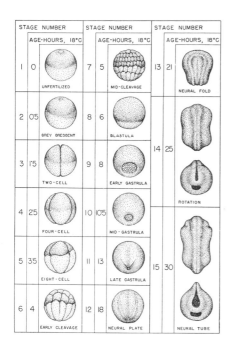

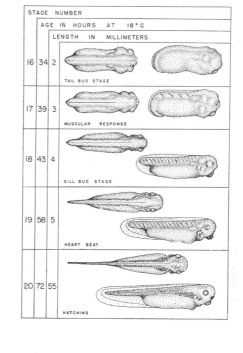

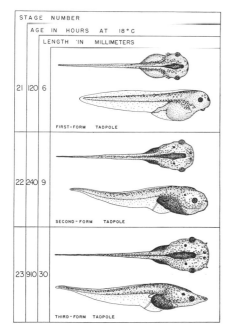

Drawings: Courtesy
Dr. Paul Weisz 1945:
Anat. Rec. 93

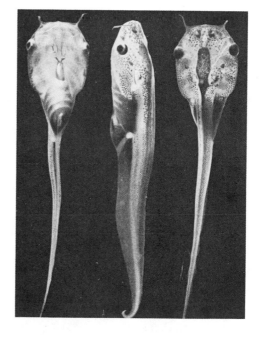

Dorsal, lateral and ventral views of a
35 mm. larva of Xenopus laevis.

Photo: Courtesy
Dr. Paul Weisz 1945:
Jour. Morph. 77

c. Hyla Regilla

STAGES IN THE NORMAL DEVELOPMENT OF HYLA REGILLA*

Stage #15:   Length 13/4 mm.; neural folds high and unfused in cranial part of neurula but in contact with each other in and posterior to region of hindbrain; presumptive optic vesicle indicated by intensely pigmented depression in ventro-lateral wall of future forebrain.

Stage #16:   Length 2 mm.; neural tube completely closed; sense and gill plates visible; optic vesicle forming as shallow, thick-walled diverticulum of forebrain.

Stage #17:   Length 2-1/2 mm.; tailbud separated from body proper by ventral notch; stomodeal depression slight; nonmotile; optic vesicle finger-like outpocketing.

Stage #18:   Length 3 mm.; tail about 1/3 length of body; caudal fin appearing; suckers indicated by two heavily pigmented areas joined medially by narrow pigmented band below stomodeum; beginning of muscular response to touch (simple flexure); optic vesicle fully formed and consisting of thick distal wall, relatively thin sides, and narrowing stalk.

Stage #19:   Length 4-1/3 mm.; tail rounded, more than 1/3 length of body, nasal placodes indicated by pigmented shallow depressions; suckers no longer joined by pigmented band; coil response to touch; beginning of heart beat; optic vesicle invaginating to form optic cup; lens placode invaginating into optic cup.

Stage #20:   Length 5-1/3 mm.; tail less rounded, almost 1/2 length of body; appearance of external gills, with circulation; melanophores appearing on dorsal part of body; brief and weak swimming movements; optic cup fully formed and consisting of thick, inner sensory layer and thin, outer tapetal layer, faintly pigmented at back of eye; lens vesicle formed but undifferentiated; optic stalk disappearing.

Stage #21:   Length 6 mm.; tail pointed, 1/2 length of body; external gills branching; nasal pits deep; sustained and strong swimming movements; lens vesicle faintly visible through cornea; optic nerve beginning to form.

Stage #22:   Length 6-1/2 mm.; tail longer than body; pigmentation on dorsal aspect of eye visible externally; retina differentiated into relatively narrow inner layer of nuclei (ganglion cells) and wide outer layer of nuclei separated by narrow band of white matter (inner molecular layer); rods and cones beginning to differentiate outer parts; lens fibers forming; optic nerve well developed.

Stage #23:   Length 7 mm.; proportion of tail to body about 4 to 3; operculum beginning to form; colon differentiated and bent dorsally; eye completely pigmented; retina further differentiated by formation of outer molecular layer separating nuclei of rods and cones (outer nuclear layer) from nuclei of bipolar neurones (inner nuclear layer); outer parts of rods and cones better differentiated, especially ellipsoid.

Stage #24:   Length 7-1/4 mm.; operculum covering gills; gut S-shaped; spacious pleuroperitoneal cavity ventral to colon; dorsal fin bowed; cavity of lens vesicle obliterated; outer segment, ellipsoid, and perhaps myoid of rods and cones well formed.

* These stages, from #15 to #24, differ slightly from those of Shumway for Rana pipiens and are here reprinted with the kind permission of Dr. R. M. Eakin (From 1947, Univ. Calif. Pub. Zool. 51:245).

> *"The hen does not produce the egg, but the egg produces the hen and also other hens . . . We know that the child comes from the germ cells and not from the highly differentiated bodies of the parents, and furthermore, that these cells are not made by the parents' bodies but these cells have arisen by the division of antecedent cells . . . Parents do not transmit their characters to their offspring, but these germ cells, in the course of long development, give rise to adult characters similar to those of the parent."*
> *E. G. Conklin in "Heredity and Environment"*

HYLA REGILLA

15   16   17   18   19   20   21   22   23   24

STAGES IN METAMORPHOSIS OF RANA PIPIENS   PLATE I

LIMB BUD STAGES

STAGE I.   The oral sucker elevation have completely disappeared. Four
rows of labial teeth are present, one preoral and three postoral.

   The pigmentation of stage 25 larvae is exclusively embrionic, being
located in dark granules scattered through the epithelial cells.
During the interval between this stage and stage I, chromatophores
appear and become numerous on the dorsal and lateral surfaces,
and extend progressively-ventrad. The limb bud at stage I is visible as a faintly circumscribed elevation in the groove between the
base of the tail and the belly wall. The height of the elevation
is less than one-half the diameter of the disc.

STAGE II.   The height of the limb bud elevation length of the limb bud)
is equal to one-half of its diameter.

   The first row of postoral labial teeth is usually divided at the
middle to form a pair of crescents. On the dorsal surface of the
head the lateral line system is becoming conspicuous as pigment-
free lines, especially in darkly pigmented individuals. The
melanophore patches covering the gill region on either side
usually meet in a narrow band ventral to the heart.

STAGE III.   The length of the limb bud is equal to its diameter.

   Stage III is followed by a period in which the limb bud grows
almost equally in diameter and length. The interval between
this and the following stage is comparatively long, but no
obvious character appears upon which to base a division of the
interval.

STAGE IV.   The length of the limb is equal to one and one-half times
its diameter.

STAGE V.   The length of the limb bud is twice its diameter. The distal
half of the bud is bent ventrad. There is no flattening of the tip.

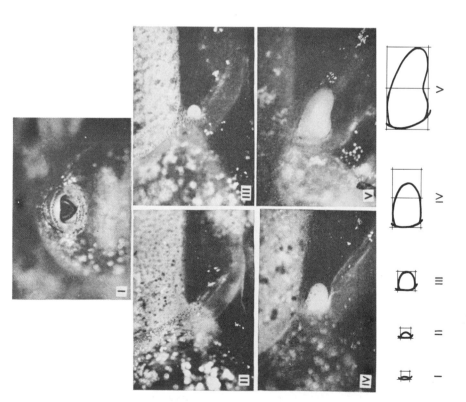

Courtesy Taylor and Kollros 1946:
Anat. Rec. 94:7

STAGES IN METAMORPHOSIS OF RANA PIPIENS   PLATE II

PADDLE STAGES

STAGE VI. The distal end of the limb bud is flattened mediolaterally to form the foot paddle. There are no interdigital indentations of the paddle margin.

STAGE VII. The fourth and fifth toe prominences are separated by a slight indentation of the margin of the foot paddle.

In this and the three following stages the margin of the paddle is considered indented when the region between two future toe prominences becomes slightly concave. Melanophores usually appear scattered over the bud at a much earlier stage. Soon after stage VII is reached they tend to form a distinct compact patch on the lateral surface. Guanophores appear sporadically on the limb bud.

STAGE VIII. The margin of the foot paddle is indented between toes 5-4 and 4-3.

The patch of melanophores on the limb lengthens into a streak extending from above the knee bend to the foot. This character may appear as early as stage VII, or be delayed until stage X.

STAGE IX. The margin of the foot paddle is indented between toes 5-4, 4-3, and 3-2.

In most cases slight spontaneous movements of the limb proper (flexion of knee and ankle) can be seen under the binocular microscope. These movements may not appear until the following stage. As a rule, shortly after spontaneous movements are observed similar movements may be elicited by stroking the limb or tail base with a hair. The melanophore streak often extends onto toes 4 and 5.

STAGE X. The margin of the foot paddle is indented between all five toes. The margin of the fifth toe web (see below) is directed toward the tip of the third toe.

As toes 4 and 5 lengthen, the angle of the interdigital notch formed by the margin of the web becomes more acute. This change is used in identifying the stages from X to XIII. The half of this web adjacent to the fifth toe is, for convenience, referred to as the fifth toe web. If a line coinciding with its margin be extended, it will be seen to pass successively through the tips of toes 3, 2 and 1 and the prehallux (line AB in the drawing of stage X, and arrows in the photographs of succeeding stages).

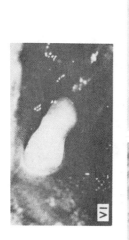

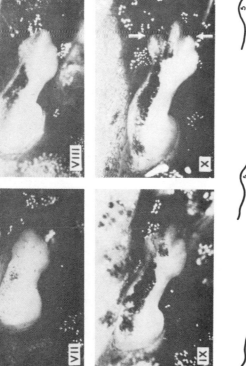

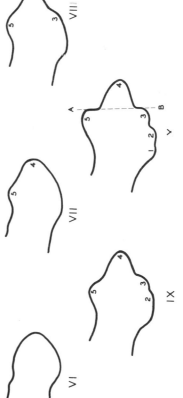

Courtesy Taylor and Kollros 1946: Anat. Rec. 94:7

STAGES IN METAMORPHOSIS OF RANA PIPIENS   PLATE III

FOOT STAGES OR PREMETAMORPHIC STAGES

STAGE XI.   The margin of the fifth toe web is directed toward the tip of the second toe.

The third toe usually has a melanophore streak.

STAGE XII.   The margin of the fifth toe web is directed toward the tip of the first toe.

Melanophores often appear upon the second toe.

STAGE XIII.   The margin of the fifth toe web is directed toward the prehallux.

STAGE XIV.   Pigment-free patches appear at the metatarsophalangeal joints, where the proximal toe pads will later develop.

At about this same time the "brow spot" appears as a light spot in the midline slightly anterior to the level of the eyes.   The naso-lacrimal duct, developing as a cord of cells between the nostril and eye, is visible through the skin as a light line.

STAGE XV.   The proximal toe pads appear.

Proximal toe pads (subarticular pads) are the wart-like elevations which develop on the ventral surface of the toes at the metatarso-phalangeal joint (arrow).

STAGE XVI.   The middle toe pads appear.

This is the second row of toe pads.   They form at the first inter-phalangeal joint on toes 3, 4, and 5.

STAGE XVII.   The distal toe pad appears at the second inter-phalangeal joint on toe four.

The cloacal tail-piece is unreduced (see photograph, and note on following stage).   Reflex withdrawal of the eyeball can frequently be elicited at this stage.

Courtesy Taylor and Kollros 1946: Anat. Rec. 94:7.

STAGES IN METAMORPHOSIS OF RANA PIPIENS   PLATE IV

METAMORPHIC STAGES

STAGE XVIII.   The cloacal tail-piece has disappeared.

In the previous stages the cloaca opens externally by an extension through the ventral tail fin called the cloacal tail-piece. It becomes progressively more prominent until stage XVII, after which it begins to regress. The complete disappearance of the tail-piece marks stage XVIII.

STAGE XIX.   The skin window becomes cleared.

The wall of the gill chamber at the point where the fore-legs will later protrude becomes thin and transparent. The disc-shaped clearing is referred to as the skin window (arrow).

STAGE XX.   One or both fore-legs have protruded.

When the fore-legs first protrude the mouth furnishings are still characteristically larval, the labial fringes being complete and the horny beak still present. During the following stage interval the horny beak is shed and resorption of the labial fringe begins at the median part of the labium.

STAGE XXI.   The angle of the mouth has reached a point midway between the nostril and the anterior margin of the eye.

At this point in the metamorphic period rapid changes in the mouth, pharynx and tail begin to occur. The gape of the mouth commences to widen soon after stage XX. The angle of the mouth extends progressively caudad and, when viewed from the side, passes certain land-marks which serve to indicate the attainment of stages XXI, XXII, and XXIII. The approximate extent of the gape is indicated in dorsal view by the relative position of a slight indentation of the margin of the jaw (arrow). A remnant of the labial fringe persists as a tuft at each corner of the mouth. The beginning of the resorption of the gills and the operculum is evidenced by the darkening of the opercular tissue (X). The tail assumes a darker and less transparent appearance than in the previous stage. The dorsal and ventral fins are shrunken and the length of the tail is considerably reduced, although it is still longer than the extended hind limb.

STAGE XXII.   The angle of the mouth has reached the level of the middle of the eye.

The extent of the gape is indicated in dorsal view by the relative position of an indentation in the margin of the jaw (arrow). The remains of the operculum are still darker in color and more restricted in extent (X). The tissue of the tail is also darker. Dorsal and ventral fins have almost disappeared, and the tail is now shorter than the extended hind limb.

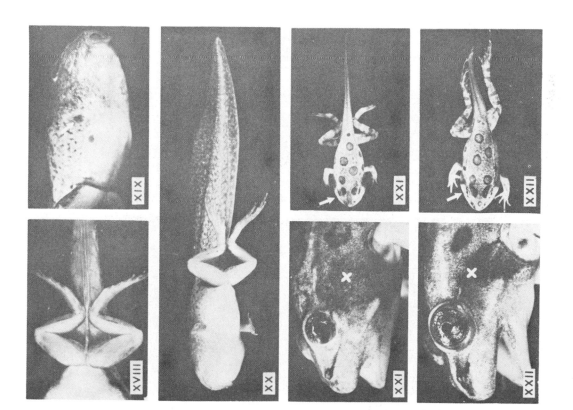

Courtesy Taylor and Kollros 1946: Anat. Rec. 94:7.

STAGES IN METAMORPHOSIS OF RANA PIPIENS   PLATE V

METAMORPHIC STAGES

STAGE XXIII.   The angle of the mouth has reached the level of the posterior margin of the eyeball.

No labial fringe remains.   The opercular patch (X) is still further reduced.

STAGE XXIV.   The annular ring of the tympanic cartilage is barely perceptible under the skin.

The opercular patch has been reduced to a dark line running from the tympanic membrane to the base of the fore-leg.   A stub of the tail still remains.

STAGE XXV.   The tail is completely gone.

The completion of resorption of the operculum and tail is indicated by the disappearance of dark tissue from the respective regions.

METAMORPHIC STAGES

Graph showing the average length in millimeters and average age in days of larvae at each stage.

Courtesy Taylor and Kollros 1946: Anat. Rec. 94.7.

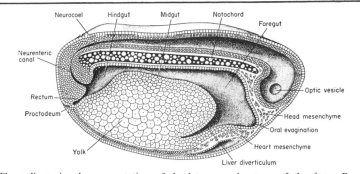

Three-dimensional representation of the late neurula stage of the frog, *Rana pipiens*. (Redrawn and modified after Huettner.)

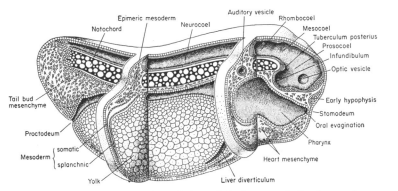

Three-dimensional representation of the tail bud stage of the frog embryo, *Rana pipiens*. (Redrawn and modified after Huettner.)

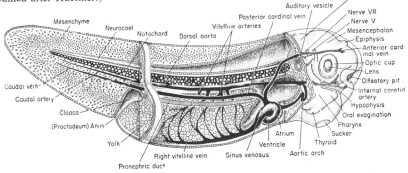

Reconstruction of the 7 mm. frog larva showing the major organ systems from the right side. (Redrawn and modified after Huettner.)

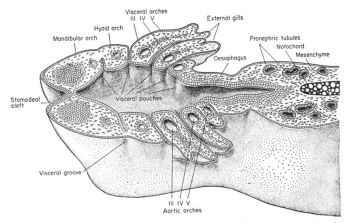

Frontal (horizontal) reconstruction of the external gill stage of the frog larva. (Redrawn and modified after Huettner.)

Reproduced from Rugh's - THE FROG, McGraw-Hill and Co., 1960.

The following plates illustrate the various types of abnormalities encountered in the development of Rana pipiens. These abnormalities may be caused by environmental factors such as extremes of temperature, lack of oxygen, toxic substances in the environmental medium, pressure, or variations in osmotic pressure. There are also internal factors which may cause such abnormalities, such as the age of the egg at the time of insemination, incompatability of the sperm and egg nuclei, etc. The student is advised to become acquainted with all of these types so that he will recognize them in his experimental work. A brief description of each of the types follows:

1. Depigmentation of the animal pole in vicinity of germinal vesicle common in eggs aged in the uterus.
2. Depigmentation in one blastomere, does not affect lines of tension in cleavage.
3. Eccentric cleavage, leaving depigmented area in larger blastomere.
4. Cytolysis plus depigmentation in one of two blastomeres, preceded cleavage.
5. Apparently normal cleavage but development will not progress far with the pigment scattered.
6. Severe cytolysis during earliest cleavages.
7. Third cleavage achieved even with depigmentation areas.
8. Pigment migration into cleavage furrows in aged egg.
9. Blastula cells with uneven distribution of pigment - aged egg.
10. Reversal of animal-vegetal pole pigmentation in aged egg blastula.
11. Typical cytolysis during the earliest cleavages - no furrows.
12. Late blastula going to pieces in attempting to gastrulate (typical of incompatible hybrids such as Bullfrog sperm and Leopard frog egg).
13. Same as #12, view of region where blastoporal lips would occur in normal egg.
14. - 16. Impeded invagination results in exogastrula and often the anterior region of the future embryo is pulled inward, leaving the curious ring formation.
17. Gastrulation achieved, but lips abnormal.
18. Pigment in large yolk plug cells, abnormal gastrulation.
19. Yolk plug stage but viability very low in eggs where the pigment is so scattered.
20. Curious reversal of pigment with the yolk plug containing practically all pigment and the presumptive epidermis being grey to yellow.

"About the fourth day the egg beginneth to step from the life of a plant to that of an animal. From that to the tenth it enjoys a sensitive and moving soul as Animals do, and after that it is completed by degrees and adorned with Plume, Bill, Clawes, and other furniture it hastens to get out. --- For all animals resemble one or other of those above mentioned (fowl, goose, duck, pigeon, frog, serpent, fish, crustacean, silkworms, sheep, goats, dogs, cats, deer, oxen, man) and agree with them either generally or specifically, and are procreated in the same manner, or the mode of their generation at least is referrable by analogy to that of one or other of them. ---- Before man attains maturity, he was a body, an infant, an embryo. And then it is indispensable to inquire further as to what he was in his mother's womb before he was an embryo or fetus. --- Nature, by steps which are the same in the formation of any animal whatsoever, goes through the forms of all animals, as I might say egg, worm, embryo, and acquires perfection with each step. "

William Harvey, 1578-1657

ABNORMALITIES

RANA PIPIENS

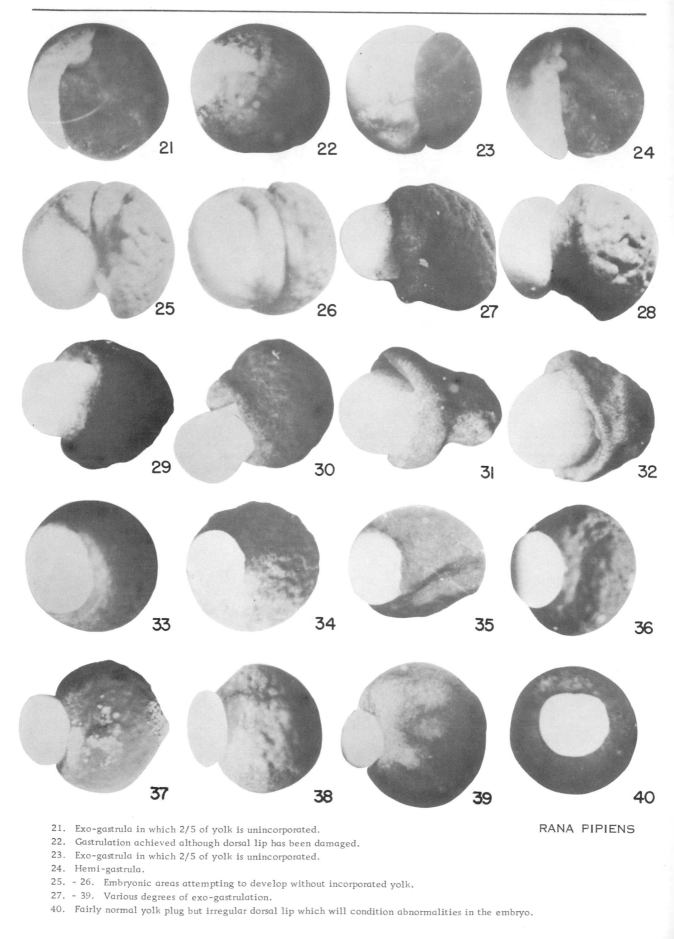

21. Exo-gastrula in which 2/5 of yolk is unincorporated.
22. Gastrulation achieved although dorsal lip has been damaged.
23. Exo-gastrula in which 2/5 of yolk is unincorporated.
24. Hemi-gastrula.
25. - 26. Embryonic areas attempting to develop without incorporated yolk.
27. - 39. Various degrees of exo-gastrulation.
40. Fairly normal yolk plug but irregular dorsal lip which will condition abnormalities in the embryo.

RANA PIPIENS

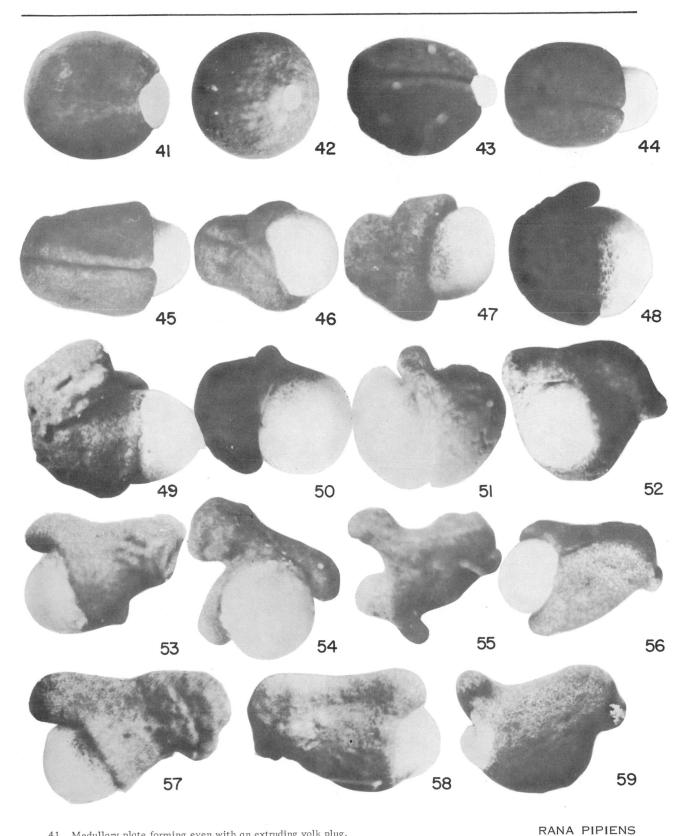

41. Medullary plate forming even with an extruding yolk plug.
42. Normal yolk plug but gastrular surface rough, indicating early disintegration.
43. - 46. Neurulae with extruding yolk plugs. If these develop the embryos have severe caudal abnormalities.
47. - 53. Hemi-embryos, due to incomplete invagination.
54. - 55. Rudimentary abnormal embryos due to failure to incorporate yolk.
56. Hemi-embryo in which there is slight development of the head region.
57. - 59. Anterior end fairly normal in hemi-embryos, internal structures very abnormal.

RANA PIPIENS

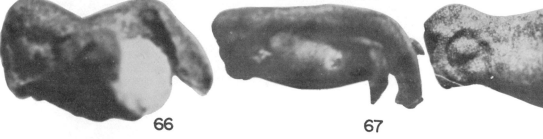

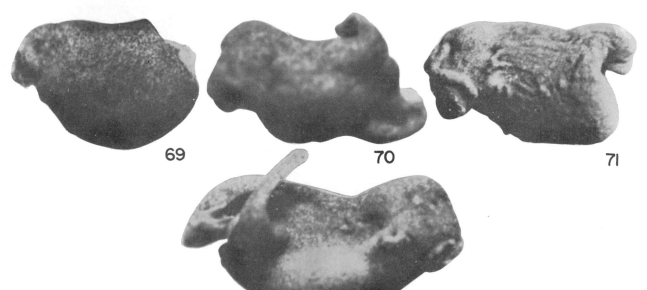

RANA PIPIENS

60. - 61. Yolk exposed laterally on tail bud embryo.
62. Persistent yolk plug prevents tail formation in tail bud stage.
63. - 66. Relation of persistent yolk to spina bifida.
67. - 72. Spina bifida in various degrees. Note fair degree of head formation in some cases.

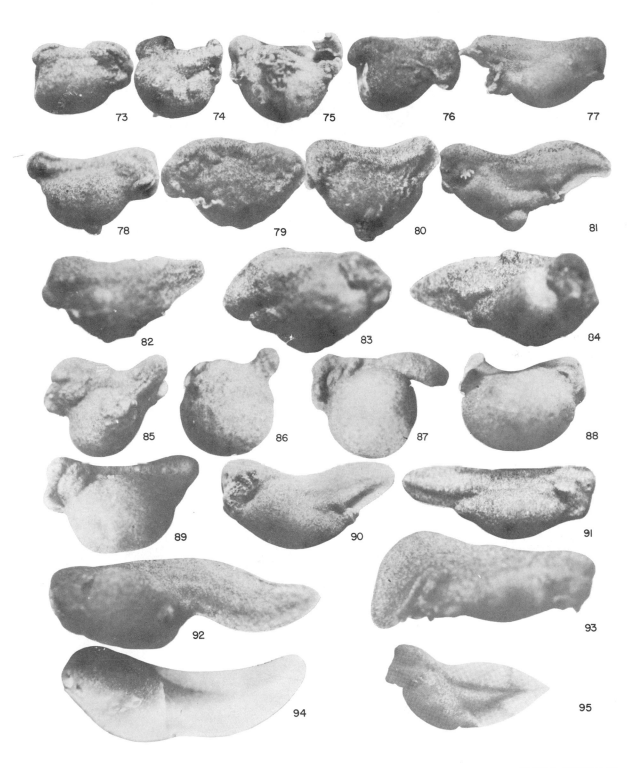

RANA PIPIENS

73. - 84. Types of abnormalities found most frequently among parthenogenetic or androgenetic tadpoles.
85. - 89. Oedema - associated with haploidy as well as osmotic unbalance.
90. - 94. Haploid tadpoles with reduction of head structures.
95. The typical haploid tadpole with microcephaly, dorsal-flexion of the tail, telescoping of the entire body, reduction of gills, etc.

d. Amblystoma Punctatum

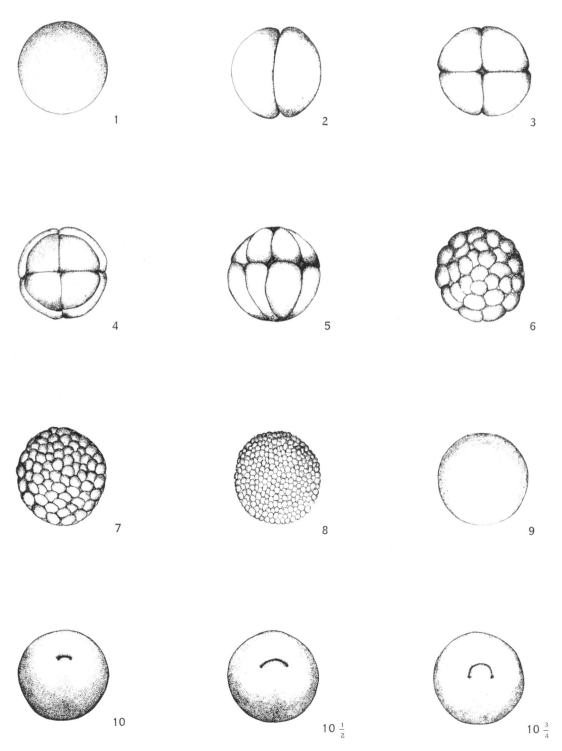

AMBLYSTOMA PUNCTATUM

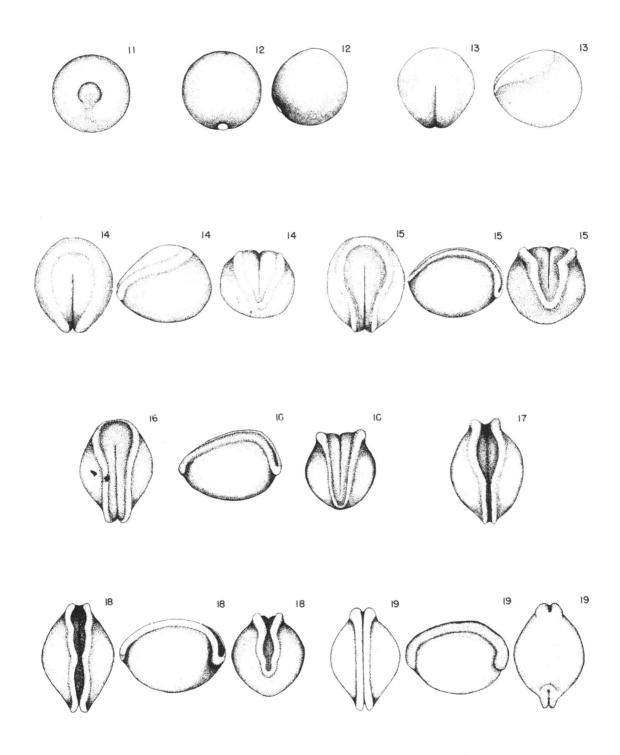

AMBLYSTOMA PUNCTATUM

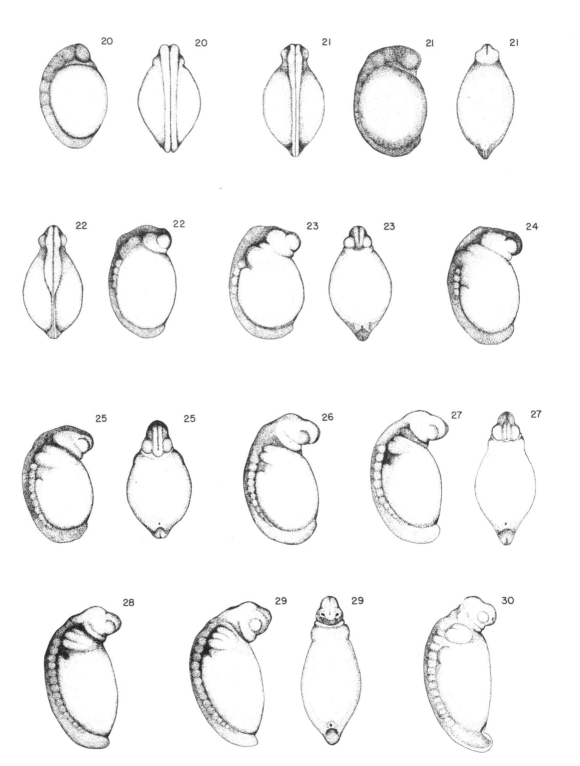

NAOMI LEAVITT

AMBLYSTOMA PUNCTATUM

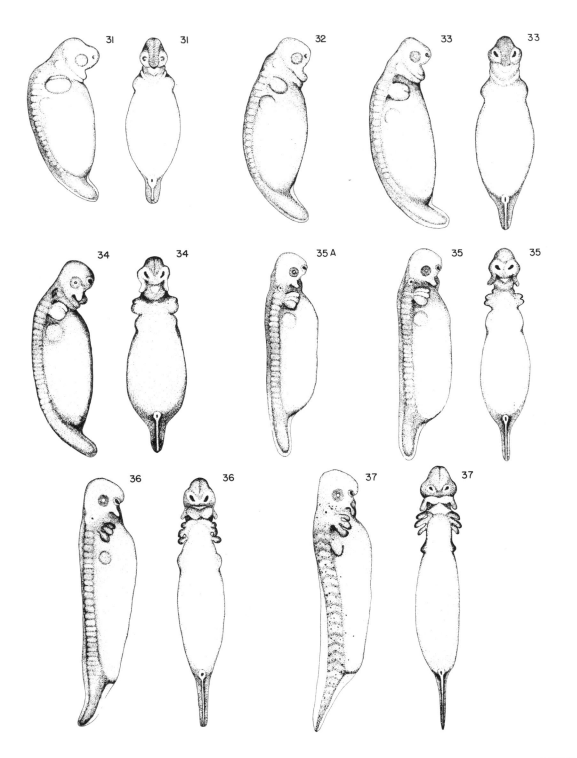

NAOMI LEAVITT

AMBLYSTOMA PUNCTATUM

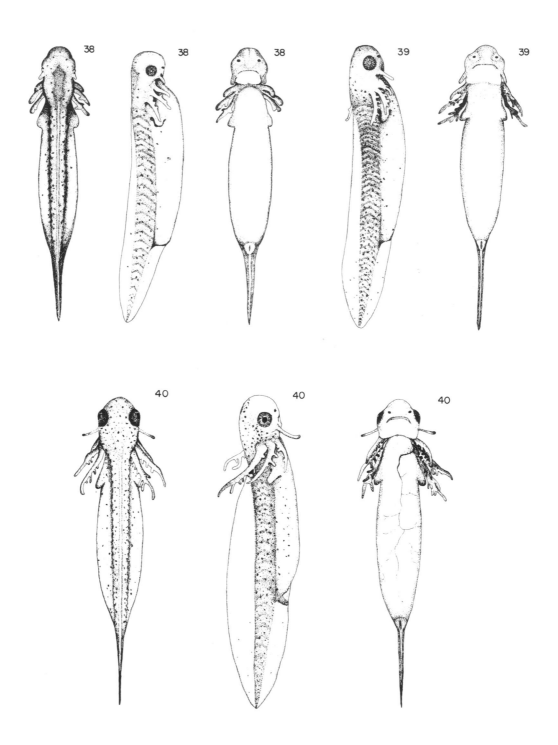

AMBLYSTOMA PUNCTATUM

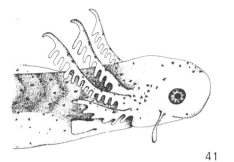

41

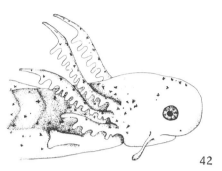

42

43

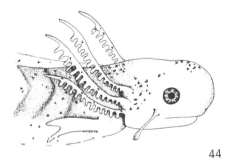

44

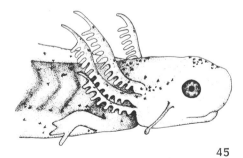

45

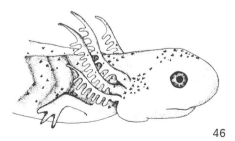

46

NAOMI LEAVITT

e. Triturus Pyrrhogaster

STAGES OF TRITURUS PYRRHOGASTER*
(at 18°C.)

T. PYR-RHOGASTER STAGES	HARRISON STAGES AMBLYSTOMA	AGE	LENGTH	REMARKS
1	1			Newly laid
2	2	$15\frac{1}{2}$ hrs.	2 mm.	First cleavage incomplete
3		20 hrs.		Second cleavage incomplete
4	3	21-3/4 hrs.		Four cell stage
5		$23\frac{1}{2}$ hrs.		Third cleavage incomplete
6	4	25 hrs.		Eight cell stage
7		26 hrs.	2 mm.	Fourth cleavage beginning
8	5	27 hrs.		Sixteen cell stage
9	6	31 hrs.		Thirty-two cells
10	9	2 days		Middle blastula
11	10	4 days		Early gastrula, dorsal lip blastopore
12	11[+]	$4\frac{1}{2}$ days	2 mm.	Middle gastrula, blastopore large
13	12	5 days	2 mm.	Late gastrula, yolk plug
14	13	6 days	2 mm.	Blastopore a slit, neural groove
15	15	7 days	2. 1 mm.	Early neural plate with folds
16	16[-]	7-$7\frac{1}{2}$ days	2. 1 mm.	Neural folds closing, gill plate
17	17	$7\frac{1}{2}$ days		Late neural folds
18	19	8 days		Neural folds fusing
19	20	$8\frac{1}{2}$ days	2. 8 mm.	Neural folds fused, 5-6 somites
20	27	10 days	2. 9 mm.	Optic vesicle, otocyst, gill plate
21	31	13 days	3. 9 mm.	Olfactory pit, optic cups, gill plate
22	35	15 days	5. 5 mm.	Balancer, gill plate, rhombo-coel
23	37	17 days	7. 5 mm.	Forelimb bud, external gills, balancer
24	40[+]	3 weeks	10. 5 mm.	Balancer, 2 digits on forelimb
25	46[-]	6 weeks	14. 3 mm.	Stomodeum, hindlimb bud, coiled gut

* From Priscilla L. Anderson 1943: Anat. Rec. 86:58. The Author presents this series without argument for or against the deviation from the Harrison staging used with the Amblystoma series.

"The development of an egg into a finished embryo is essentially due to factors residing in the egg itself".
Wilhelm Roux

"The elements of our own behaviour are found in all organisms".
E. G. Conklin, 1944

TRITURUS PYRRHOGASTER

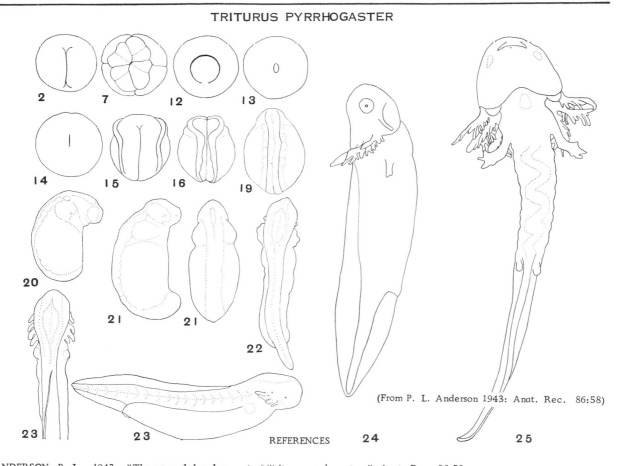

2 7 12 13

14 15 16 19

20

21 21

22

(From P. L. Anderson 1943: Anat. Rec. 86:58)

23 23 REFERENCES 24 25

ANDERSON, P. L., 1943 - "The normal development of Triturus pyrrhogaster." Anat. Rec. 86:58.

ATLAS, M., 1935 - "The effect of temperature on the development of Rana pipiens." Physiol. Zool. 8:290.

DEMPSTER, W. T., 1933 - "Growth in Amblystoma punctatum during the embryonic and early larval period." Jour. Exp. Zool. 64:495.

DuSHARE, G. P., C. HUTCHINSON, 1941 - "The effect of temperature on the development of form and behaviour in amphibian embryos." Jour. Exp. Zool. 87:245.

GALLIEN, L., O. BIDAUD, 1959 - "Table chronologique du developpement chez Pleurodeles waltii." Bull. Biol. 91:97.

GLUCKSOHN, S., 1931 - "Aussere Entwicklung der Extremitaten und Stadieneinteilung der Tarvenperiode von Triton taeniatus. und Triton cristatus." Arch. f. Ent. mech. 125:341.

HARRISON, R. G., 1929 - "Correlations in the development and growth of the eye studied by means of heteroplastic transplantation." Arch. f. Ent. mech. 120:1.

KNIGHT, F.C.E., 1938 - "Die Entwicklung von Triton alpestris bei verscheidenen Temperaturen, mit Normentafel." Arch.f. Ent. mech. 137:461.

MOORE, J. A., 1939 - "Temperature tolerance and rates of development in eggs of Amphibia." Ecology 20:459.

MOORE, J. A., 1940 - "Adaptive differences in the egg membranes of frogs." Am. Nat. 74:89.

MOORE, J. A., 1942 - "The role of temperature in speciation of frogs." Biol. Symposia 6:189.

MOORE, J. A., 1942 - "Embryonic temperature tolerance and rate of development in Rana catesbiana." Biol. Bull. 83:375.

MOORE, J. A., 1949 - "Geographic variation of adaptive characters in Rana pipiens." Evolution 3:1.

NIEUWKOOP, P. D., J. FABER, 1956 - "Normal table of Xenopus laevis." North-Holland Pub. Co., Amsterdam.

OKADA, Y. K., M. ICHIKAWA, 1947 - "A new normal table for the development of Triturus pyrrhogaster." Exp. Morph. 3:1. (Jap.)

POLLISTER, A. W., J. A. MOORE, 1937 - "Tables for the normal development of Rana sylvatica." Anat. Rec. 68:489.

ROTMANN, E., 1940 - "Die Bedeutung der Zellgrosse fur die Entwicklung der Amphibienlinse." Arch.f.Ent.mech. 140:124.

SATO, T., 1933 - "Uber die Determination des fetalen Augenspaltes bei Triton taeniatus." Arch.f.Ent.mech. 128:342.

SHUMWAY, W., 1940 - "Stages in the normal development of Rana pipiens." Anat. Rec. 78:139.

STAUFFER, E., 1945 - "Versuche zur experimentellen Herstellung haploider Axolotl-Merogone." Rev. Suisse de Zool. 52:232.

STONE, L. S., 1930 - "Heteroplastic transplantation of eyes between the larvae of two species of Amblystoma." Jour. Exp. Zool. 55:193.

TWITTY, V. C., H. A. ELLIOTT, 1934 - "The relative growth of the amphibian eye, studied by means of transplantation." Jour. Exp. Zool. 68:247.

TWITTY, V. C., J. L. SCHWIND, 1931 - "The growth of eyes and limbs transplanted heteroplastically between two species of Amblystoma." Jour. Exp. Zool. 59:61.

WRIGHT, A. H., 1914 - "Life-histories of the Anura of Ithaca." Pub. Carnegie Inst. Wash. #197.

f. Triturus Torosus

TRITURUS TOROSUS *

THE CALIFORNIA SALAMANDER

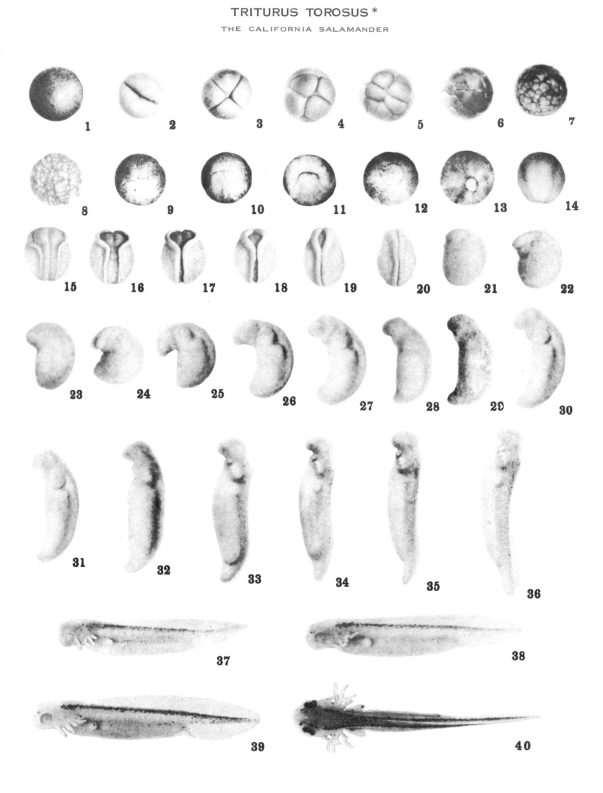

(Courtesy Twitty & Bodenstein)

* Now known as Taricha Torosa.

4. INDUCED BREEDING

DEFINITION: The induction of breeding activity by experimental means and under laboratory conditions, outside of the normal breeding season.

PURPOSE: To produce eggs and embryos suitable for laboratory experimentation at specified times.

MATERIALS:
    Biological: Rana, Bufo, or Xenopus adults (or other Anura).
                  Triturus, Amblystoma, Triton, or Eurycea adults (or other Urodela).

    Technical: Hypodermic syringe (2 cc. capacity) and #18 needle
                  Dissecting instruments
                  Battery or aquarium jars with weighted covers
                  Spring or pond water

METHOD: (General description for Rana pipiens; modifications for other forms appended.)
    Precautions:
1. Animals must be sexually mature. The females should have a body length of at least 74 mm. and the males should measure at least 70 mm., from snout to anus.
2. Animals should be well fed and in pre-breeding condition. Those animals taken directly from hibernation are the best.
3. Frogs should be kept in running cold water (below 18°C.) in which case they will be satisfactory for several weeks. Feeding is unnecessary during this laboratory confinement, if they were well fed before capture.
4. Avoid red-leg contamination. Examine frogs upon receipt. Red-leg is not to be confused with temporary rash brought on by sudden changes in temperature. The fungus condition known as red-leg is very contagious and tanks with infected animals should be sterilized with permanganate. A copper penny in the frog tank will give off enough metallic ions to keep the red-leg under control.
5. The fresh pituitary glands are injected into the abdominal cavity. Avoid injury to the median ventral abdominal vein, the sub-cutaneous veins, and to the internal organs. Glands should be used fresh but may be preserved in alcohol, or by freezing in water. They are always larger and heavier.
6. Female glands are twice as potent per gland as are the male glands. The number of glands necessary to induce complete ovulation varies with the season.
7. Eggs should be allowed to accumulate in the uteri before stripping any of them. Vigorous stripping is apt to damage the eggs.
8. Pre-check the medium in which the sperm suspension is made to be certain that the spermatozoa will survive. Spring or pond water are best.

    Control: It will not be necessary to run controls for this experiment in as much as the major purpose is to secure eggs and developing embryos. However, adequate controls for such an experiment would consist of the injection of another equivalent endocrine gland, such as an equivalent number of adrenals or thyroids. Such controls have invariably given negative results.

    Procedure: (Description for Rana pipiens; modifications for other forms appended.)
1. Removal of the anterior pituitary gland: Insert large, sharp-pointed scissors into the mouth of the donor, at the angle of the jaw. Cut posteriorly to a

point just behind the tympanic membrane, then across the skull to the other side of the head, and sever the skull from the body. Invert the jawless head and push aside the oral skin, thereby exposing the cross formed by the parasphenoidal and transverse bones. Insert the sharp point of smaller scissors into the cranial cavity, ventral to the exposed medulla, and cut through the floor of the cranium on either side of the brain in an anterior direction. Avoid injury to the brain tissue because in doing so the pituitary may be lost. The two parallel cuts should extend well anterior to the transverse bone. With forceps, deflect this flap of bone in a forward direction, thereby exposing the brain. The anterior pituitary gland should be seen lying just posterior to the optic chiasma and will appear as a pinkish, kidney-shaped body surrounded to some extent by white endolymphatic tissue. Occasionally the

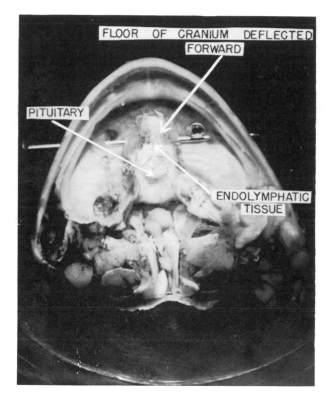

ANTERIOR PITUITARY GLAND OF FROG

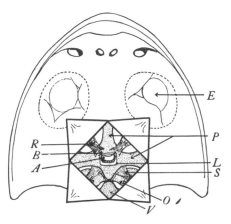

Diagram showing position of the pituitary gland of the frog as it might be seen through the parasphenoidal bone, lying just beneath the brain.

A - Anterior lobe of the pituitary gland.
    Note its more posterior position.
B - Pars intermedia and pars nervosa.
E - Eye ball as seen through oral skin.
L - Endolymphatic tissue adherent to the pituitary.
O - Exoccipital bone.
P - Parasphenoidal bone.
R - Retractor bulbi muscle. The attachment of this muscle to the parasphenoidal bone must be partially removed.
S - Levator anguli scapuli muscle.
V - First vertebra.

gland will remain adherent to the floor of the brain case and will have been deflected forward with the bone. Remove the gland by grasping the white endolymphatic tissue surrounding it, using sharp forceps. This endolymphatic tissue has no known endocrine function. Place the gland in 1 to 2 cc. of water in a small stender. In a similar way proceed with the removal of as many glands as are necessary. Pituitary donors need not be freshly caught animals but they must be sexually mature and in a pre-breeding condition.

In general, the female glands are about twice as potent as those from the male, but there is no qualitative difference. The suggested doses for Rana pipiens are as follows:

	Male Pituitaries	Female Pituitaries
September to January	10	5
January to February	8	4
March	5	3
April	4	2

2. Injection of the hormone: For recipients, carefully select large and obviously healthy females which have been recently received from hibernation. Such females may be kept in the refrigerator at 4°C. in a small amount of water for a number of weeks but should not be kept at laboratory temperatures for more than a week if they are to be used for ovulation induction. Healthy females received from hibernation in January may thus be kept until June (i. e., at 4°C.). At the laboratory temperatures the ovarian eggs deteriorate rapidly.

Before attaching the needle to the hypodermic syringe, draw up into its barrel the requisite number of anterior pituitary glands. It will be best if the glands are freed from their attached endolymphatic tissue and remain whole as they pass into the syringe. There will be some loss if the glands are damaged. Apply a large-bore hypodermic needle (#18) to the syringe, and then insert the point of the needle through the skin and abdominal muscles of the female frog, in the lower quadrant of the abdomen. Do not insert the needle far enough to damage any of the vital organs and specifically avoid the ventral abdominal and the subcutaneous veins. Inject downward, as the glands are heavier than water. As the glands pass through the needle into the abdominal cavity they will be broken up into a fine suspension, ready for quick absorption. Absorption is probably accomplished largely through the numerous ciliated peritoneal funnels on the ventral faces of the kidneys, which funnels open directly into the venous sinuses. The female frog should now be placed in a small amount of water in a wire-covered battery jar or aquarium. If eggs are required within 24-48 hours, the female should be kept at about 25°C.; while if the eggs are not needed for 4 to 5 days the frog may be kept at 10°C. and the eggs will be just as good.

3. Test of ovulation: The presence of eggs in the uteri can be determined only by "stripping", or squeezing of eggs from the uteri. It is not necessary to sacrifice the frogs to get the eggs. Stripping is accomplished in the following manner, without damage either to the frog or its eggs.

The legs of the frog are grasped in the left hand so as to prevent body movements on the part of the frog. The palm of the right hand is placed over the back of the frog, and the fingers encircle the body just posterior to the forelimbs. By gentle closure of the right hand in the direction of the cloaca, eggs will be forced from the uteri. The body may be bent at the pelvic region to facilitate removal of the eggs. If jelly alone or fluid issues from the cloaca the female should be replaced and tested again within 24 hours. It is general practice to remove and discard the first few eggs that emerge because occasionally cloacal fluid allows the swelling of the nearby jelly on uterine eggs and this renders such eggs rather difficult of insemination. It is well also to dry off the cloacal region of the frog prior to stripping. The fertilization percentage will be higher if the eggs are allowed 24 hours for physiological maturation in the uterus.

Each sexually mature female of Rana pipiens should give about 2,000 eggs all in metaphase of the second maturation division, ready to be fertilized.

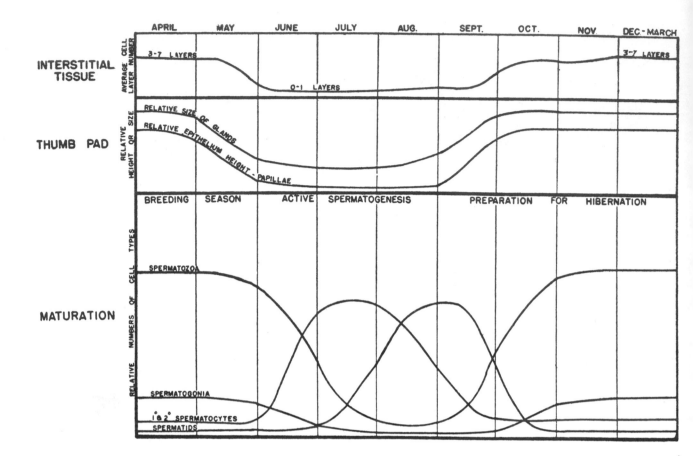

**NORMAL CYCLIC CHANGES IN PRIMARY & SECONDARY
SEXUAL CHARACTERS IN THE FROG, RANA PIPIENS**

Glass & Rugh 1944: Jour. Morph. 74:409

4. Artificial fertilization: Male frogs need not be injected with the pituitary
hormone unless it is desired to show amplexus. In this case, inject the male
at the same time the female is injected, with the same dose of pituitary
glands, and place them together in the same container. Amplexus, at laboratory temperatures, will be achieved in about 24 hours and fertilized eggs
will be layed in the aquarium, generally early in the morning. Use water in
which embryos are known to develop.

From September until April mature, functional spermatozoa can be secured
from Rana pipiens males of body length of more than 70 mm. simply be dissecting the testes in Spring or Pond Water, or any medium in which they are
known to be viable. Generally two pairs of testes are dissected in about 10
cc. of water and are allowed to stand for 5-10 minutes at laboratory temperatures in order to allow the spermatozoa to become active.

THE LEOPARD FROG: RANA PIPIENS

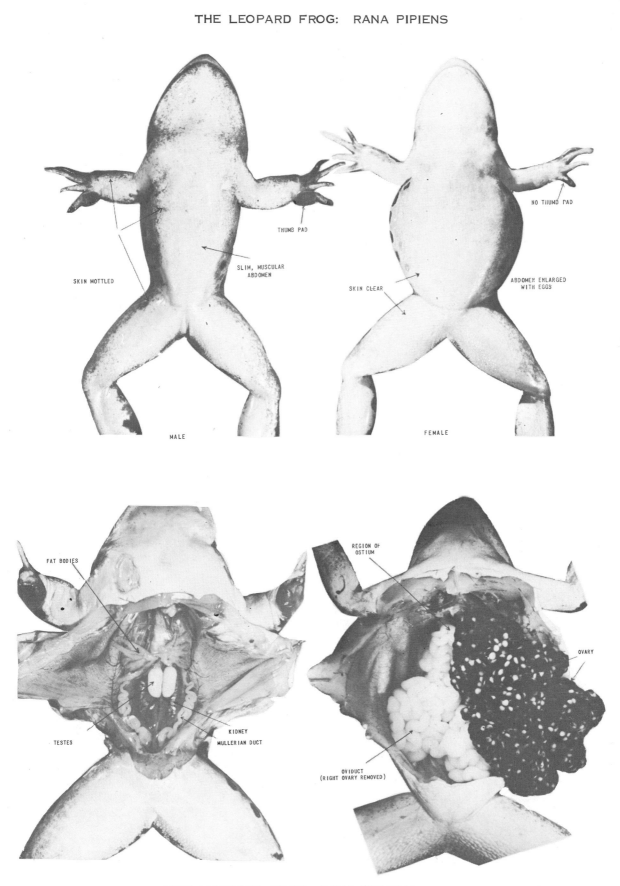

THE LEOPARD FROG: RANA PIPIENS

The sperm suspension may be divided between several finger bowls, Petri dishes or large stenders so that in each there will be a thin film of suspension on the bottom of the container. Eggs are stripped directly into this sperm suspension in such a manner that all eggs are exposed. If this is not accomplished it will be necessary to pipette some of the suspension onto the eggs. The inseminated eggs should stand for about 5 minutes and then should be flooded with the same water used to make up the sperm suspension. The eggs should be barely covered with this water. In about 20 minutes pour off this first water and add enough fresh water to again cover the eggs. It is the exposed surface rather than the volume of water that is important for respiration of the eggs. If the eggs are successfully inseminated they should all rotate so that the animal hemisphere is uppermost within about an hour and by $2\frac{1}{2}$ hours the eggs should be in the 2-cell stage at laboratory temperature of 23° - 25°C.

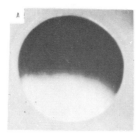

(a) Egg of Rana pipiens at the moment of insemination.

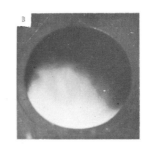

(b) Egg of Rana pipiens 29 minutes after insemination, showing grey crescent.

5. Care of the material: As the jelly membranes swell (by imbibition) the egg mass will expand and it may become necessary to add some water to cover. The jelly mass generally sticks to the bottom of the container but may be separated by means of a stiff, clean section lifter. This may be done as soon as 1 hour after insemination. The jelly should be allowed to swell to its maximum and then the egg mass should be cut up into small groups of eggs. This should be done before the first cleavage. The optimum ratio is about 25 eggs per finger bowl of 500 cc. water.

The optimum temperature for the normal development of the eggs of Rana pipiens is 18° - 25°C. Development can be slowed down without the production of abnormalities if the eggs are kept at the lower temperatures, but never lower than 10°C. By retarding the developmental rate of some eggs it is possible to have various stages of development available at all times. Remember, however, that when eggs are removed from a cold to a warm environment, sufficient time must be allowed for the adjustment before the eggs are to be used for experimental procedures. Eggs and embryos should never be transferred suddenly from one temperature level to another.

INDUCED BREEDING IN OTHER AMPHIBIA

There is reason to believe that any amphibian which is sexually mature and which has not recently undergone its normal breeding reaction, will respond to the pituitary hormone by ovulation (female) or by the release of spermatozoa (male). In general, the Anura will respond to pituitaries from other Amphibia but not from mammalian extracts of the pituitary hormone. Exceptions to this statement are Bufo and Xenopus. The Urodela, in contrast, will respond readily to the pituitary hormone from almost any source.

There follows an alphabetical list of the more common Amphibia which have responded to pituitary treatment in the manner described for Rana pipiens. The references given are not complete but represent one of the major sources of other references for the particular form.

Amblystoma tigrinum	- Burns & Buyse, 1931
Bombinator pachypus	- Moskowska, 1933
Bufo americanus	- Wills, Riley & Stubbs, 1933
Bufo arenarum	- Novelli, 1932
Bufo calamita	- Cunningham & Smart, 1934
Bufo D'Orbignyi	- Houssay, 1930
Bufo fowleri	- Rugh, 1935
Bufo vulgaris	- Rostand, 1934
Desmognathus fuscus	- Noble & Evans, 1923
Discoglossus pictus	- Kehl, 1930
Eurycea bislineata	- Noble & Richards, 1930
Gryinophilus porph.	- Noble & Richards, 1932
Hyla aurea	- Creaser & Gorbman, 1935
Hyla crucifer	- Rugh (unpublished)
Leptodactylus ocellatus	- Novelli, 1932
Pseudobranchus striatus	- Noble & Richards, 1932
Rana aurora	- Creaser & Gorbman, 1935
Rana catesbiana	- Rugh, 1935
Rana clamitans	- Rugh, 1935
Rana esculenta	- Rostand, 1934
Rana japonica	- Osima, 1937
Rana nigricauda	- Osima, 1937
Rana palustris	- Rugh, 1935
Rana pipiens	- Rugh, 1935
Rana temporaria	- Ponse, 1936
Rana vulgaris	- Adams, 1931
Rhyacotriton olympicus	- Noble & Richards, 1932
Stereochilus marginatum	- Noble & Richards, 1932
Triton cristatus	- Adams, 1931
Triturus pyrrhogaster	- Barth, 1933
Triturus torosus	- Witschi, 1937
Triturus viridescens	- Stein, 1934
Xenopus laevis	- Aronson, 1944

Name	Size Range: mm.		Number Eggs	Egg size (mm)	Breeding Period	Induced Breeding
	males	females				
Acris gryllus	15-30	16-33	250	0.9-1.0	Feb.-Oct.	Almost anytime
Bufo americanus	52-86	54-110	4000-8000	1.0-1.4	Apr.-Aug. 1	Oct. to Apr.
Bufo fowleri	51-75	55-84	4000-8000	1.0-1.4	Apr.-Aug. 15	Nov. to Apr.
Hyla andersonii	30-41	38-48	Laid singly	1.2-1.4	May 1-Aug. 1	Oct. to Apr.
Hyla cinereus	36-48	32-48	Small groups	0.8-1.6	Apr. 15-Aug. 15	Nov. to Mar.
Hyla crucifer	18-30	20-34	800-1000	0.9-1.1	Apr. 1-June 15	Oct. to Mar.
Hyla versicolor	32-52	33-60	30-40 in groups	1.1-1.2	Apr.-Aug. 15	Nov. to Mar.
Pseudacris brachyphona	25-30	27-35	?	?	Mar.-June	Sept. to Apr.
Pseudacris nigrita f.	20-30	22-34	?	0.9-1.1	Feb.-May 15	Sept. to Apr.
Pseudacris nigrita f.	21-32	20-38	500-800	0.9-1.2	Mar. 15-May 20	Aug. 20-Feb.
Rana catesbiana	85-180	90-200	6000-8000	1.2-1.7	June-Aug.	May-Aug.
Rana clamitans	52-95	60-100	2000-4000	1.5	June 1-Aug. 15	Nov. to July
Rana palustris	46-64	50-80	2000-3000	1.6	Apr. 15-May 15	Oct. to Mar.
Rana pipiens	52-80	54-102	2000-3000	1.6	Apr. 1-May 15	Sept. 1-May 1
Rana septentrionalis	48-72	50-76	?	?	June 15-Aug. 15	Nov. to May
Rana sphenocephala	50-78	53-82	?	1.6	Feb.-Dec.	All year
Rana sylvatica	34-60	34-70	2000-3000	1.8-2.4	Mar. 15-May 1	Sept. to Mar.
Rana virgatipes	40-63	41-66	200-600	1.5-1.8	Apr.-Aug. 15	Nov. to Mar.

DATA ON EGG SIZE, EGG PRODUCTION, AND PERIOD
FOR OVULATION INDUCTION

MODIFICATIONS OF THE PROCEDURE

A. ANURA

Rana:

The procedure as outlined is satisfactory for Rana pipiens from about September 1 until the normal breeding season of the species in April. The procedure for other species of Anura is essentially the same except for the season, the dose of the hormone, and the source of the hormone.

The above table indicates that it is possible to secure Anuran eggs at any season of the year, providing the appropriate species is chosen. Since there is also considerable overlapping of susceptible seasons, material is available for hybridization experiments. Properly planned, amphibian eggs can be available for experimentation at all times. The genus Rana is available over wide areas, and their normal breeding season varies considerably.

The dose of the hormone varies somewhat, depending both on the donor and the recipient. In general the larger species seem to require more of the glands from the smaller species. In none of the genus Rana has there been uniform success with any source but other amphibian glands, the mammalian extracts being generally negative.

Bufo:

The toad will react not only to the pituitaries from other Anura but also to the pituitaries from other Phyla, to the extracts of mammalian pituitaries and even to the extract of pregnancy urine (antuirtin-S) and Preloban (Xenopus). The response is most reliable, however, when either frog or toad pituitaries are used.

The eggs are deposited in a manner quite different from the frog in that they are layed singly in long strings of jelly, each egg being inseminated by the male (during amplexus) as it emerges from the cloaca of the female. It is therefore necessary to induce amplexus in toads and allow the paired animals to lay their eggs naturally. Amplexus may be induced by injecting the male with doses of pituitary glands equivalent to those used for the female, and placing the pair together in a small amount of water. Several changes of the water may be necessary before the eggs are layed, to eliminate the faecal and other matter in the water. The water should be appropriate to survival of sperm and eggs.

Hyla:

The tree toads and other closely related species are difficult to secure out of breeding season but if caught during or just before hibernation they may also be induced to lay their eggs in the laboratory. The method is similar to that for Bufo and during amplexus the male may be seen to bring his cloaca down close to the cloaca of the female as each egg emerges, indicating separate insemination of each egg. The Hyla egg is small but excellent for operative procedures.

Xenopus:

This is the African clawed-toad which has attained fame through its use in pregnancy tests. It is extremely sensitive to the pituitary hormone, and ovulation can be induced by the pituitary (or gonad stimulating hormones) from any source. The method of inducing the breeding reactions and caring for the early embryos has recently been described in detail by Aronson (1944) Weisman and Coates (1944) and by Cameron (1947) whose papers should be consulted. It is likely that the Xenopus egg and embryo will become increasingly valuable as a laboratory form for experimentation purposes.

B.   URODELA

Among the salamanders the eggs are generally inseminated as they pass through the genital tract of the female, after she has picked up the sperm bundles (spermatophores) dropped in the water by the males. Artificial insemination of the Urodele egg is possible but rather difficult, since the sperm found in the spermatophores are not properly activated. The process of artificial insemination consists of the removal of activated sperm from the genital tract of the female and applying them to oviduccal eggs of a pituitary-stimulated female, not impregnated. The sacrifice of the several animals is necessary and only a few eggs are secured. The more satisfactory procedure, therefore, is to inject the pituitary hormone into females known to carry spermatophores, whereupon they will deposit fertilized eggs.

There are two methods which may prove of practical value in the production of fertile eggs of the Urodela: First, pituitary stimulation of the male two days prior to the stimulation of the female thereby causing it to deposit the spermatophores. If this is accomplished in a proper environment the females may be induced to pick up the spermatophores with their cloacal lips after which they may be stimulated to ovulate. Second, some success has been reported from Europe (Triton) where the paired animals are well fed, then placed in the dark at hibernation temperatures (4° - 8°C.) for a month or more, and then are brought out into the light at Spring temperatures (18° - 25°C.), whereupon they will spontaneously produce fertile eggs.

Triturus: (pyrrhogaster, torosus* or viridescens**)

These newts can be kept in the laboratory for long periods, are fed on liver and earthworms, and can be induced to ovulate either with amphibian (R. pipiens) pituitaries or

---

* Now known as Taricha Torosa.

** Now known as Diemyctylus viridescens.

with mammalian extracts of the anterior pituitary hormone. Spermatophores are retained
for many months and (particularly with T. pyrrhogaster, the Japanese newt) the majority
of females will give fertile eggs almost any time (October to May). The breeding tanks
for Urodeles should be shallow, with facilities for their climbing out onto floating pieces
of wood or onto sand. Aquatic plants (Elodea) should be provided not only for aeration
but for the attachment of eggs. Eggs will be layed singly, in large jelly capsules, and
will always be attached to plants. Instead of injecting large doses of pituitary it is well to
inject about two female (frog) glands per day for several days since Urodele eggs are
constantly maturing. If the animals are well fed they may be induced to lay a few eggs
per day over long periods.

Ambystoma: (mexicanum, opacum, punctatum, tigrinum)

These species apparently do not retain their spermatophores for very long before ovulation, hence it is generally more practical to collect the eggs in nature. Ambystoma
opacum eggs are available late in September; A. punctatum and tigrinum eggs from January through May; and A. mexicanum eggs in the Spring, time variable.

A. punctatum males will drop their spermatophores in slowly running streams or in
ponds during the late March rains even when the temperature may be as low as 13°C.,
several days prior to the migration of the females from the woods. Females captured
after they pick up spermatophores, but before oviposition, will lay their eggs in the laboratory spontaneously or under pituitary stimulation.

The eggs of A. opacum and A. punctatum are excellent for operative procedures because
they develop rather slowly and are very hardy. The eggs of A. tigrinum are hardy but
develop very rapidly, while the axolotl (A. mexicanum) eggs do not stand operative procedures very well.

OBSERVATIONS AND TABULATION OF DATA:

With each attempted induction of ovulation the following data should be recorded:
1. Number and source of anterior pituitary glands.
2. Physiological condition of recipient, i.e., size, evidence of sexual maturity,
   and extent and conditions of laboratory confinement.
3. Temperature at which the injected female was kept.
4. Date of injection and date or time of appearance of the first eggs within the uteri.
5. Percentage ovulation, determined by estimate of the volume of eggs remaining
   in the ovary after the reaction has been completed.

DATE	SPECIES FEMALE	# PITUITARIES	PIT. SOURCE	TEMP. MEDIUM	HRS. TO OVUL.	% CLEAVING EGGS

DISCUSSION:

While the relationship of the anterior pituitary hormone to sexual activity has been sus-
pected and then demonstrated for many years, it was in 1929 that Wolf in Wisconsin and
Houssay in Brazil almost simultaneously published results of their observations that the
Amphibia could be induced to ovulate by means of anterior pituitary implantations. Thereafter many investigators, inspired by the urgent need for more embryological material,
have described successfully induced ovulations in a wide variety of forms.

Since the mammalian pituitary hormone can induce sexual activity and ovulation in some
amphibia, and the amphibian pituitary hormone can induce heightened sex activity and hypertrophy of the reproductive organs in mammals, it is no longer tenable that there is any
species specificity in the gonadotropic activity of the anterior pituitary gland hormones.
It is true that frogs have thus far proven to be negative to the mammalian extracts, but
toads are most responsive to these same hormones. It is true that ovulation in mammals
has not been induced, even with large doses of Anuran pituitaries, although the genital
system has responded, indicating that there may be a great difference in threshold and in
the quantitative value of the glands. Nevertheless, there is evidence that there is present
a gonadotropic hormone which will stimulate sexual activity in the amphibia in the pituitaries from fish, reptiles, birds, and mammals. That the reverse has not been equally
demonstrated may be only an indication that the gland attains greater gonadotropic potency
with the ascendency in the evolutionary scale. The negative reactions of frogs to mammalian extracts may be due to toxic reactions to the extractants, or to some very specific
protein sensitivity. No doubt this exception will eventually be explained.

It has not yet been determined just how the anterior pituitary hormone acts to induce
ovulation in the Amphibia. Attempts have been made to eliminate the circulatory and/or
the nervous connections. Once the pathway of action is determined it may be possible to
explain certain individual or species variations that have thus far eluded investigation.

CONCLUSIONS:

It is now possible to induce ovulation among the amphibia so that eggs and embryos of
the various species are available at all seasons of the year.

REFERENCES

ADAMS, A. E., 1930 - "Egg-laying in Triturus viridescens following pituitary transplants." Proc. Soc. Exp. Biol. & Med.
27:433.

ADAMS, A. E., 1931 - "Induction of ovulation in frogs and toads." Proc. Soc. Exp. Biol. & Med. 28:677.

ADAMS, A. E. & B. GRANGER, 1938 - "Induction of ovulation in Rana pipiens by pituitaries of Triturus viridescens." Proc.
Soc. Exp. Biol. & Med. 38:552.

ALEXANDER, S. S. & C. W. BELLERBY, 1938 - "Experimental studies on the sexual cycle of the South African clawed toad
(Xenopus laevis)." Jour. Exp. Biol. 15:74 (see ibid, 15:74).

APLINGTON, H. W., 1957 - "The insemination of body cavity eggs and oviduccal eggs of amphibia." Ohio Jour. Sci. 57:91-99.

ARONSON, L. R., 1944 - "Breeding Xenopus laevis." Am. Nat. 78:131.

BARDEEN, H. W., 1932 - "Sexual reactions of certain Anurans after anterior lobe implants." Proc. Soc. Exp. Biol. & Med.
29:846.

BARDEN, R. B. & L. J. Kezer, 1944 - "The eggs of certain Plethodontid salamanders obtained by pituitary gland implantation."
Copeia, 2:115.

BELLERBY, C. W., 1934 - "A rapid test for diagnosis of pregnancy by ovulation of the South African clawed toad after pregnant
urine administration." Nature, 133:494.

BENAZZI, M., 1939 - "Esperienze intorno alla ovulazione provocata negli Anfibi." Monitore Zool. Italiano. 50:101.

BERK, L. & H. A. SHAPIRO, 1939 - "Histological changes in the accessory sex organs of female Xenopus induced by the administration of endocrine preparations." S. Afr. J. Med. Sci. 4.

BLAIR, A. P., 1946 - "The effects of various hormones on primary and secondary sex characters of juvenile Bufo fowleri." Jour.
Exp. Zool. 103:365.

BRANIN, M. L., 1935 - "Courtship activities and extra seasonal ovulation in the four-toed salamander Hemidactylium scutatum." Copeia. 1935, p. 172.

BUXTON, C. L., E. T ENGLE, 1950 - "Time of ovulation." Am. Jour. Obst. & Gynec. 60:539.

BUYSE, A. & R. K. BURNS Jr., 1931 - "Ovulation in the neotonic Amblystoma tigrinum following administration of extract of mammalian anterior hypophysis." Proc. Soc. Exp. Biol. & Med. 29:80.

CAMERON, S. B., 1947 - "Successful breeding of Xenopus laevis, the South African clawed toad." Am. Jour. Med. Techn. May 1947.

CARTER, G. S., 1932 - "The endocrine control of seasonal variations of activity in the frog." Jour. Exp. Biol. 10:256.

CREASER, G. W., 1942 - "Ovulation induced in Rana pipiens by bird pituitary preparations." Anat. Rec. 84: suppl. 70.

CREASER, C W. & A. GORBMAN, 1939 - "Species specificity of the gonadotropic factors in vertebrates." Quart. Rev. Biol. 14:311.

DAVIS, M. E. & A. K. KOFF, 1938 - "The experimental production of ovulation in the human subject." Am. Jour. Obstetrics & Gynec. 36:183.

DAWSON, A. B. & H. B. FRIEDGOOD, 1940 - "The time and sequence of pre-ovulatory changes in the cat ovary after mating or mechanical stimulation of the Cervix uteri." Anat. Rec. 76:411.

De ALLENDE, I. T. C., 1939 - "Accion de la prolactina sobre el oviducto de los batracios." Rev. Soc. argent. de Biol. 15:190.

DEL CASTILLO, E B. & A. NOVELLI, 1938 - "Actions gonadotropiques synergique ou antagoniste de l'hypophyse des poissons, des batraciens, et des oiseaux." Comp. rendu. Soc. Biol. 12:1043.

EMERY, F. E., 1937 - "Augmentation of gonad stimulating hormone of the hypophysis by copper." Proc. Soc. Exp. Biol. & Med. 37:731.

GITLIN, G., 1942 - "The effect of repeated injections of sheep anterior pituitary extract on the weight of the ovaries of Xenopus laevis." S. Afr. Jour. Med. Sci. 7:16.

GRANT, R., 1940 - "Seasonal changes in the weight and ovulation-inducing potency of the glandular lobe of the pituitary in mature female Rana pipiens." Anat. Rec. 78: suppl. 86.

GRIFFITHS, R. B., 1941 - "Triploidy (and haploidy) in the newt, Triturus viridescens, induced by refrigeration of fertilized eggs." Genetics 26:69.

HANAOKA, K., 1938 - "Sex modificati in semi-differentiated salamander, Hynobius retardatus, from implantation of testis and hypophysis." Proc. Imp. Acad. Tokyo, 1938.

HILSMAN, H. M., 1933 - "The ovarian cycle in Triturus viridescens." Anat. Rec. 57:82.

HOGBEN, L. T., E. CHARLES & S. SLOMER, 1932 - "Studies on the pituitary. VIII. The relation of the pituitary gland to calcium metabolism and ovarian function in Xenopus." Jour. Exp. Biol. 8:343.

HOUSSAY, B. A., 1937 - "Ovulacion y postura del Sapo Bufo arenarum Hensel. V. Transporte de los ovules por el oviducto y el utero." Rev. d. l. Soc. Argentina de Biol. 23:275.

HOUSSAY, B. A., L. GIUSTI, & J. M. LASCANO-GONZALES, 1929 - "Implantation d'hypophyse et stimulation des Glandes et des fonctions sexuelles du Crapaud." Comp. rend. Soc. de Biol. 102:864.

HUMPHREY, R. R., 1928 - "Ovulation in the four-toed salamander, Hemidactylium scutatum, and the external features of the cleavage and gastrulation." Biol. Bull. 54:307.

ICHIKAWA, A., 1940 - "Masculinization and feminization of adult Triturus pyrrhogaster. Pituitary-induced sexual reaction in the experimental animals." Jour. Fac. Sci. Hokkaido Imp. Univ. 7:39.

KAMMERAD, A., 1942 - "Induced ovulation in Amphiuma." Proc. Soc. Exp. Biol. & Med. 49:195.

KAYLOR, C T., 1937 - "Experiments on androgenesis in the newt, Triturus viridescens." Jour. Exp. Zool. 76:375.

KEHL, B., 1930 - "Action d'un extrait d'hypophyse anterieure de mammifere sur la ponte des Batraciens." Comp. rendu. Soc. Biol. 103:744.

KEMP, N E., 1953 - "Synthesis of yolk in oocytes of Rana pipiens after induced ovulation." Jour. Morph. 92:487-511.

KEMP, N. E., 1956 - "Electron microscopy of growing oocytes of Rana pipiens." Jour. Bioph. & Biochem. Cytology. 2:281-292.

KRAUS, S. D., 1947 - "Observations on the mechanism of ovulation in the frog, hen, and rabbit." Western Jour. Surgery, Obstetrics, & Gynec. 55:424.

MARTINS, T., 1929 - "Sur les effets de l'implantation du lobe anterieur de l'hypophyse de grenouilles ches les souris infantiles." Compt. rend. Soc. Biol. 101:957.

MAYO, V., 1937 - "Some effects of mammalian follicle-stimulating and luteinizing hormones in adult female urodeles." Biol. Bull. 73:373.

McPHAIL, M. K. & K M. WILBUR, 1943 - "The stimulating action of colchicine on pituitary-induced ovulation of the frog." Jour. Pharmac. & Exp. Therap. 78:304.

MOORE, J. A., 1937 - "The effect of pituitary in nuclear changes in the egg of the frog." Niol. Bull. 73:388.

MOSKOWSKA, A., 1933 - "Etudes endocrinologiques (testicule et hypophyse) chez le Bombinator." Bull. Biol. France et Belgique. 66:502.

NADAMITSU, S., 1957 - "Fertilization of coelomic and oviduccal eggs of Triturus pyrrhogaster." Jour. Sci. Hiroshima Univ. Nov. p. 51-53.

NOBLE, G. K., & L. R. ARONSON, 1942 - "The normal mating pattern of Rana pipiens." Bull. Am. Mus. Nat. Hist. 80:127.

NOBLE. G. K. & L. B. RICHARDS, 1932 - "Experiments on the egg-laying of salamanders." Am. Mus. Nov. #513.

NOVELLI, A., 1932 - "Action sexuelle du lobe anterieure de l'hypophyse chez le Crapaud femelle." Comp. rendu. Soc. Biol. 111:474.

OSIMA, M., 1937 - "Experimental studies on the function of the anterior pituitary. I. Induced sexual activity in frogs." Sc. Rep. Tohoku Imp. Univ. 12:195.

PATCH, E. M., 1933 - "Fertility and development of newt eggs obtained after anterior lobe implants." Proc. Soc. Exp. Biol. & Med. 31:370.

PONSE, K., 1936 - "La ponte artificielle chez Rana temporaria." Compt. rendu. Soc. Biol. 121:1397.

ROBINSON, T. W. & H. C. HILL, Jr., 1942 - "Studies on induced ovulation in Rana pipiens." Proc. Fed. Am. Soc. Exp. Biol. 1:73 (Also 1940 Trans. Ill. State Acad. Sci. 33:223).

ROSTAND, J., 1936 - "Hypophyse et ovulation chez les Batraciens." Compt. rendu. Soc. Biol. 117:1079.

RUGH, R., 1935 - "Ovulation in the frog. I. Pituitary relations in induced ovulation." Jour. Exp. Zool. 71:149.

RUGH, R., 1935 - "Ovulation in the frog. II. Follicular rupture to fertilization." Jour. Exp. Zool. 71:163.

RUGH, R., 1935 - "Pituitary-induced sexual reactions in the Anura." Biol. Bull 68:74.

RUGH, R., 1937 - "A quantitative analysis of the pituitary-ovulation relation in the frog." Physiol. Zool. 10:84.

RUGH, R., 1939 - "Relation of the intact pituitary gland to artificially induced ovulation." Proc. Soc. Exp. Biol. & Med. 40:132.

RUGH, R., 1946 - "The effect of adult anterior pituitary hormone on the tadpoles and immature male frogs of the bullfrog, Rana catesbiana." Biol. Bull. 90"29.

RUGH, R. & G. T. SAMARTINO, 1945 - "Frog ovulation in vitro." Jour. Exp. Zool. 98:153.

RYAN, F. J. & R. GRANT, 1940 - "The stimulus for maturation and for ovulation of the frog's egg." Physiol. Zool. 13:383.

SHAPIRO, H., 1939 - "Seasonal changes in the ovulation response of Xenopus laevis to methyl testosterone." Jour. Endocrin. 1:1.

SHAPIRO, H A., 1943 - "Accion de la hipofisis de Bufo arenarum sobre Xenopus laevis." Rev. de la Soc. Argentian de Biol. 19:187 (See also 1939 S. Afr. J. M. Sc. 4:21).

SHAPIRO, H A. & Z. ZWARENSTEIN, 1937 - "Effects of progesterone and testosterone on Xenopus and its excised ovary." Jour. Physiol. 89:3.

SIMS, W. L. & D. W. BISHOP, 1947 - "Seasonal variation in the gonadotropic potency of dried anterior pituitaries of Rana pipiens." Science. 106:588.

SPAUL, E. A., 1924 - "Experiments on the injection of pituitary body (anterior lobe) extracts into Axolotls." Jour. Exp. Biol. 2:33.

STEIN K. F., 1934 - "Effects of avian pituitary glands in salamanders." Proc. Soc. Exp. Biol. & Med. 32:157.

STREET, J. C., 1940 - "Experiments on the organization of the unsegmented egg of Triturus pyrrhogaster." Jour. Exp. Zool. 85:383.

VANDERPLANCK, F. L., 1935 - "The effects of pH on breeding (Xenopus)." Aquarist and Pondkeeper. 6:135.

VOLNO-YASENETSKII, A. V., 1955 - "Effect of Co^{60} gamma radiation on the process of ovulation, fertilization, and embryonic development of the frog." Doklady Akad. Nauk. SSSR 100:389-391.

VOSS, H., 1934 - "Kunstliche Eiablange beim Axolotl hervorgerufen durch das thyreotrope Hypophysenvorderlappenhormon." Arch. f. Ent. mech. 132:805.

WARING, H., F. W. LANDGREBE, & R. M. NEILL, 1941 - "Ovulation and oviposition in Anura." Jour. Exp. Biol. 18:11.

WEISMAN, A. I. & C W. COATES, 1944 - "The South African Frog in pregnancy diagnosis." N.Y. Biol. Res. Foundation.

WILLS, I. A., G. M. RILEY, & E. M. STUBBS, 1933 - "Further experiments on induction of ovulation in toads." Proc. Soc. Exp. Biol. & Med. 30:784.

WOLF, O. M., 1929 - "Effect of daily transplants of anterior lobe of pituitary on reproduction of frog (Rana pipiens)." Proc. Soc. Exp. Biol. & Med. 26:692.

WOLF, O. M., 1937 - "Induced breeding reactions in isolated male frogs. Rana pipiens." Biol. Bull. 73:399.

WRIGHT, P. A. & F. L. HISAW, 1946 - "Effect of mammalian pituitary gonadotropins on ovulation in the frog Rana pipiens." Endocrin. 39:247.

YOUNG, J. Z. & C. W. BELLERBY, 1935 - "The response of the Lamprey to injection of anterior lobe pituitary extracts." Jour. Exp. Biol. 12:246.

ZAHL, P. A., 1935 - "Cytological changes in frog pituitary considered in reference to sexual periodicity." Proc. Soc. Exp. Biol. & Med. 33:56.

ZIMMERMAN, L., R. RUGH, 1941 - "Effect of age on the development of the egg of the leopard frog, Rana pipiens." Jour. Morph. 68:329.

ZWARENSTEIN, H., 1937 - "Experimental induction of ovulation with progesterone." Nature. 139:112 (See ibid, 140:588).

ZWARENSTEIN, H., 1942 - "Seasonal variations in sensitivity to progesterone-induced ovulation." Tr. Roy. Soc. S. Africa. 29:28.

"... criticism, an open and honest look at the world and at ourselves, must be desired actively and courted assiduously. It must become the mistress of the scientist. The scientific critic must be a creative artist, wise, knowing, fair, with taste and talent, who also remembers with Petrarch that love, hate, and envy are the three poisons which kill sound criticism."

W. B. Bean, Perspectives in Biology and Medicine 7:224, 1958.

5. OVULATION AND EGG TRANSPORT

DEFINITION: A study of the process by which the egg is released from the ovary and is carried to the uterus.

PURPOSE: To become acquainted with the changes in the egg that occur between its hibernation environment in the ovary and its delivery into the chamber (the uterus) for oviposition, and to study the functions of the various parts of the reproductive tract of the female in relation to the preparation of the egg for insemination.

MATERIALS:

Biological: Mature frogs, male and female (Rana pipiens).

Technical: Dissecting instruments; hypodermic syringe and #18 needle; wide-mouthed pipettes; finger bowls, Syracuse dishes, Petri dishes, stenders, Standard (Holtfreter's) Solution.

METHOD:

Precautions: The ovulating female must be studied at the height of sexual activity, before all of the eggs have reached the uteri. The opened body cavity should be kept moist with Standard Solution.

Control: No control is possible for this type of experiment for it is a matter of observation of a normal process.

Procedure: Induce ovulation in a female Rana pipiens in the usual manner (see "Induced Breeding") and keep the frog at a laboratory temperature of about 23° to 25° in a small amount of water. Test in 16 to 24 hours for the presence of eggs in the uteri and examine every 6 hours, or less, thereafter until eggs begin to appear. Within 2 to 3 hours after the appearance of the first eggs in the uteri, the following observations are to be made.

Cut off the head of the frog and remove its appendages, leaving the torso. Avoid unnecessary squeezing of the body. Lay the torso on a biologically clean cork dissecting board or on paper towelling and open the abdomen from the pelvic girdle to the xiphisternum, avoiding all parts of the genital tract. Cut away a large piece of the ventral abdominal wall, including the peritoneum, and pin it down (inverted, with peritoneum uppermost) to Permoplast in concentrated Standard Solution in a Petri dish. Pin back the abdominal wall and remove the viscera so as to expose the entire reproductive tract. With a pipette add about 5 to 10 cc. of Standard Solution to the body cavity and suck out any blood clots.

THE OVARY

Remove one ovary completely and place it in Standard Solution in a finger bowl shielded from all heat. Examine with the naked eye and then under low power magnification. Identify the following:

a. Lobes of the ovary - how many are there?

b. Movement of the ovarian lobes - how frequent; can movement be stimulated; is it the smooth or striated muscle type of movement? Do the lobes move simultaneously or separately?

c. Egg follicles: Locate an egg emerging from its follicle. Is the emergence slow or rapid; is it accompanied by a flow of fluid or blood; do all eggs emerge simultaneously; do any eggs rupture into the cavity of the ovary; are the eggs in any way distorted as they emerge from their follicles? (See papers by Rugh 1935: Jour. Exp. Zool. 71:163.)

THE BODY CAVITY EGGS

In the body cavity of the ovulating female, or in the finger bowl with the excised ovary, there will be seen some recently ovulated eggs. Since these eggs have not passed through the oviduct they will not be surrounded by jelly but will possess only their vitelline membranes which were developed while the egg was in its ovarian follicle. With a wide-mouthed pipette remove some of these eggs to Syracuse dishes containing Standard Solution.

1. Onto a strip of abdominal muscle, previously excised and mounted on Permoplast with the coelomic surface uppermost, place some body cavity eggs and observe under low power magnification. The peritoneal epithelium is highly ciliated in the female and the eggs will be seen to move across the muscle. Movement is in the direction in which the ostium was located in respect to the excised muscle and peritoneum. Eggs remaining within the body cavity may be observed for movement. *

2. In a Syracuse dish place a small piece of black silk and some Standard Solution. Onto this silk place several eggs from the body cavity. There should be no movement except that due to convection currents in the solution. With the black silk as a background, attempt to remove the vitelline membrane with a very sharp (fine) glass needle and then peeling the membrane off with watchmaker's forceps. This is a rather difficult operation but less so with these eggs which possess no jelly covering. Proficiency comes with practice.

3. Pipette at least 100 body cavity eggs directly into a normal sperm suspension; leave for 10 minutes; pour off the suspension; and then add Standard Solution or Spring Water.

   Body cavity eggs have not proven fertilizable although insemination does produce surface figures on some of the eggs which strongly resemble amphi-asters, and possibly abortive attempts to cleave. Should any of the jelly-free body cavity eggs show cleavage, they should be isolated and observed. If it becomes possible to fertilize the body cavity eggs and have them develop normally, without jelly, it will be a boon to experimental embryology since the artificial removal of jelly often means damage to the egg.

OVULATING FEMALE FROG
(16 Hours after pituitary injection)

---

* Through the author there is available a 16 mm. silent moving picture showing these processes.

The body cavity eggs of an ovulating female could be transplanted to the body cavity of a non-ovulating female and there would be picked up by body cavity cilia and transferred to and through the oviducts to reach the uteri where they are fertilizable. This can be done simply by making a small abdominal incision in a non-stimulated female, under anesthesia, and transferring the eggs by pipette. The incision can be sewed with silk thread, without particular aseptic precautions.

4. That the female body cavity is extensively lined with ciliated epithelium can be further demonstrated by excising a portion of the liver and placing it on a microscopic slide in some Standard Solution. Using direct and reflected lighting and low power magnification it will be possible to observe the surface and the edge of this piece of liver for evidences of ciliary currents and cilia. As the surface becomes slightly dried it will be possible to observe fields of cilia, rather unevenly distributed. A thin strip of the edge of the liver placed under a coverslip and examined with transmitted light under high power magnification will show the continuous action of marginal cilia. Similarly examine the liver of the male frog. The presence of cilia may be considered as a secondary sexual character of female frogs.

THE OVIDUCTS

The oviducts of this ovulating female should be filled with eggs. Observe a single egg through the walls of the oviduct as it is being propelled toward the uterus. The egg will be seen to rotate (spirally) within the oviduct at the rate of about one complete turn in 14 seconds. Does the next egg in line rotate in the same direction? What is the cause of rotation?

Since the body cavity eggs cannot be fertilized and will not cleave, it is of interest to find where this change in fertilizability occurs. Arrange finger bowls with concentrated sperm suspension, made up of 2 testes per 10 cc. of Standard Solution, and label the bowls as follows:

    a. Upper third of oviduct
    b. Middle third of oviduct
    c. Lower third of oviduct
    d. Uterus

Tie a piece of cotton thread (or dental floss) around the uterus at its upper extremity, at the point of junction with the oviduct. Similarly tie a thread around the lower limit of the uterus after separating the two uteri. Then excise the entire oviduct and keep it moist with Standard Solution. Cut the oviduct into thirds and slit each section open and shell out the eggs (with the aid of forceps) into the appropriately marked finger bowl. To get a sufficient number of eggs both oviducts may be used. Treat the fertilized oviducal eggs in the normal manner and observe for:

    a. Percentage cleavage and normality of development.
    b. Amount and arrangement of the jelly on eggs from different levels of the oviduct.

The eggs in the uterine sac are presumably normal and can be expelled into a normal sperm suspension as control eggs for the above observations. These eggs are all in metaphase of the second maturation division and are excellent material for physiological experiments.

The above observations will consume several hours of time but can all be made on a single ovulating frog if the tissues are kept moist in appropriate Standard Solution and are not allowed to become overheated. Spring Water may be used instead of Standard Solution.

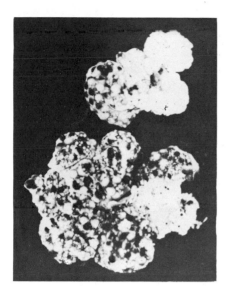

EGG EMERGING FROM FOLLICLE

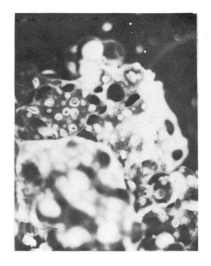

EGG EMERGENCE & EMPTY FOLLICLES

FEMALE   RECEIVED   4   FEMALE   PITUITARIES
FEMALE   RECEIVED   1   FEMALE   PITUITARY

OVULATION

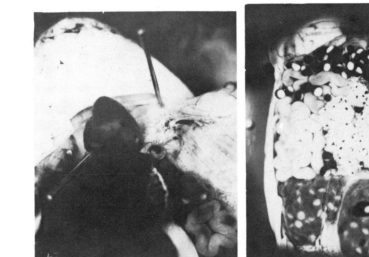

OOCYTE

EGG   ENTERING   OVIDUCT

BODY CAVITY OF OVULATING FROG

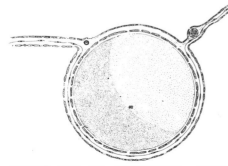

MATURE EGG OF HIBERNATING   FROG

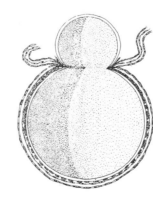

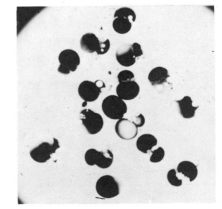

EGG   EMERGENCE   FROM   OVARIAN   FOLLICLES

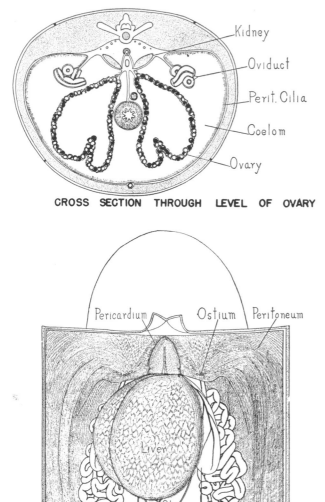

CROSS SECTION THROUGH LEVEL OF OVARY

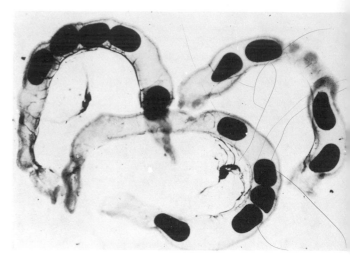

EGGS BEING TRANSPORTED THROUGH OVIDUCT

EGGS FROM BODY CAVITY AND OVIDUCT

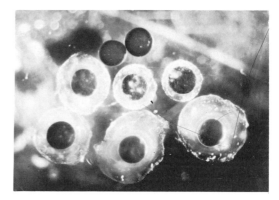

DISTRIBUTION OF CILIA IN BODY

CAVITY OF FEMALE FROGS

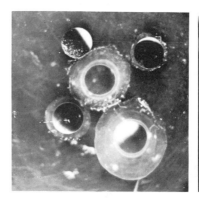

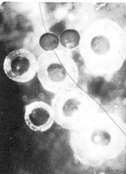

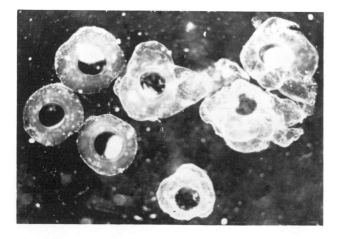

CONTROL EGGS - EGGS TRANSPLANTED
TO NON - OVULATING FEMALE

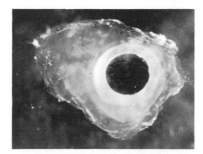

BLASTULA: EGG FROM FEMALE A.

JELLY FROM FEMALE B.

RANA PIPIENS

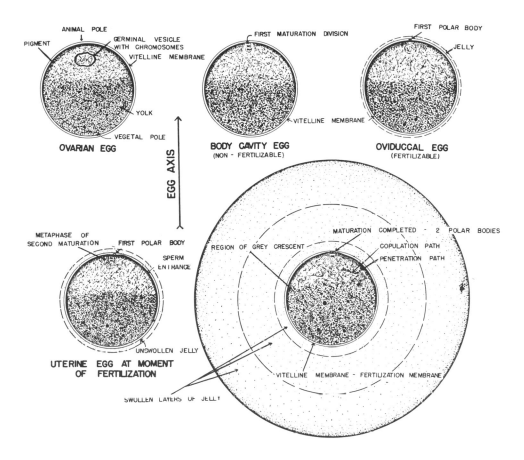

MATURATION AND FERTILIZATION OF THE FROG'S EGG

Growth period of egg and development of vitelline membrane -- May to September.

Hibernation period, no changes -- October to March.

Breakdown of germinal vesicle - at time of ovulation { Natural in March & April
                                                        Induced September to March

Elimination of first polar body - during transit through oviduct (jelly applied from oviduct).

Second maturation to metaphase stage - in uterus, and until fertilization or death.

Elimination of second polar body - 15 - 30 minutes after insemination.
   Jelly swells rapidly when egg is placed in water.

Fusion of pronuclei - 1-1/2 - 2 hours after insemination.

First cleavage - 2-1/2 hours after insemination.

OBSERVATION AND TABULATION OF DATA:

1. A complete description of the rupture and the emergence of the egg from its follicle
    should be made and compared with descriptions for the same process in mammals.

2. The relationship of ovarian movements should be determined by comparing such move-
    ments with those in a non-ovulating ovary.

3. Analysis of the effects of insemination of body cavity eggs should be made and should
    be supplemented with a cytological study using both Heidenhain's Iron-haematoxylin
    and Feulgen techniques.

4. A portion of the coelomic epithelium, liver, and oviduct containing eggs should be
    studied histologically to identify cilia. Such tissue should be compared with similar
    tissues of the non-ovulating female and of an adult male.

5. The distribution of jelly and the development of eggs from different parts of the ovi-
    duct should be studied.

DISCUSSION:

The rupture of the ovarian follicle of the Amphibia is quite different from that of Mammals. The function of the pituitary in the initiation of this process is not definitely
known, although it is invariable. The dose of the anterior pituitary hormone in amphibia
regulates the number of eggs released, so that ovulation is not an all-or-none phenomenon. It would be of interest to determine whether the pituitary hormone acts through
the circulatory or the sympathetic nervous system, of both, or whether it might act
directly.

The fact that the jelly-free body cavity eggs cannot be fertilized and will not develop has
been a slight deterrent to experimental procedures with amphibian eggs for in many experiments the jelly must be removed. Whether the answer to this dilemma rests within
the jelly, or with changes in the egg, or with both, has not yet been determined.

The nucleus of the ovarian egg is in the germinal vesicle stage, prior to any maturation
divisions. This germinal vesicle breaks down at the time of ovulation and as the egg
passes through the upper third of the oviduct the first polar body is given off. The second maturation division begins immediately and by the time the egg reaches the uterus
the metaphase of the second maturation division has been achieved. The egg remains in
suspended metaphase until it is either fertilized or disintegrates.

Coelomic cilia in the Amphibia represent a clear-cut secondary sexual character, developing only in the female after the attainment of sexual maturity and the elaboration from
the ovary of an ovarian hormone. There is some evidence that theelin will cause the development of cilia in mature males. The function of the coelomic cilia of the female is
no doubt for the transport of the eggs to the ostium and through the oviducts to the uteri,
but they are present and active at all times. The coelom and genital ducts may therefore
function also as accessory excretory organs.

During sexual activity, normal or induced by anterior pituitary hormone, the oviducts
are much enlarged due to imbition and to the secretory activity of their glands. Oviducts
of non-ovulating frogs will transport eggs and deposit jelly, but do it in an irregular manner. Such eggs are fertilizable.

CONCLUSION:

Through a simulation of the breeding activity of the frog by the injection of the mature female with the anterior pituitary hormone, it is now possible to study the entire reproductive process from the rupture of the ovarian follicle to the appearance of the fertilizable
egg in the uterus. (See references on pages 101-103)

6. EARLY BEHAVIOR PATTERNS IN THE AMPHIBIA

PURPOSE: To determine the time of onset of various types of response to external stimuli in amphibian embryos, and the succeeding appearance of integrated reactions.

MATERIALS:

Biological: Amblystoma, Hyla, Rana, and Bufo embryos from tailbud stages onward.

Technical: Detwiler racing ring (see diagram)

METHOD:

Precautions:
1. The staging of the embryos to be tested must be exact. Even within a single stage there may appear individual differences in behavior.
2. Repeated stimulation may lead to fatigue, particularly in the first phases of response. Ample time must be allowed for recovery. In later stages the stimulus (hair loop) must be applied to the same region of the body of all larvae, preferably the dorso-lateral body wall, near the myotomes.
3. The hair loop is the most satisfactory instrument for stimulation, being pliable and least likely to damage the surface cells. A ball tip or flexible glass needle may be used with caution.
4. Eliminate any extraneous stimuli such as excessive heat, light, or anisotonic media.

Controls: The response of earlier and later stages will constitute one type of control, but the embryos without any external (tactile) stimulation may be considered as controls.

Procedure:
1. To become acquainted with the various types of response, select a group of embryos such as Amblystoma stages #20 - #46 or Rana stages #16 - #33. Place individuals in Syracuse dishes with the appropriate medium and allow them to become adjusted to the new environment for several minutes. Under low power magnification (binocular microscope) gently stimulate the various embryos with the hair loop to elicite a response. Immediately classify the response as one of the following:

   The chronological onset of behavior patterns in the amphibian larvae has been studied by Coghill (1929) by DuShane and Hutchinson (1941). The latter authors describe eight steps as follows:
   a. Premotile stage: no response to tactile stimulation.
   b. Myotomic response: a non-nervous response of myotomes as a result of direct stimulation. Both response and recovery are slow.
   c. Early flexure: bending of the body away from the point of stimulation, with rapid recovery. The initial evidence of this response will be at the anterior end, but eventually the tail response will bring it close to the head.
   d. Coil: the early flexure response when extended so that the tail passes the head. The reaction is away from the point of stimulation. There may appear a compensatory coil in the opposite direction in later stages.
   e. S-reaction: undulatory contraction wave passing down the stimulated side, but not vigorous enough to result in swimming progression.
   f. Early swimming: forward progress as a result of the integration of the S-reactions. The progression is never more than 3 body lengths.

ANURA

(Species_____)

BEHAVIOR PATTERN

Stages:	16	17	18	19	20	21	22	23	24	25	26	27	28	29	30	31	32	33
Premotile stage																		
Myotomic response																		
Early flexure																		
Coil																		
S-reaction																		
Early swimming (3 lengths)																		
Strong swimming (3-10 lengths)																		
Late swimming (10 lengths plus)																		
Free swimming - no stimulus																		
Spontaneous eye movements																		
Body resists rotation																		
Hind leg buds appear																		
Hind leg buds motile																		
Withdrawal leg reflex																		

BEHAVIOR PATTERN

URODELA

(Species _____)

Stages:	20	22	24	26	28	30	32	34	36	38	40	42	44	46
Premotile stage														
Myotomic response														
Early flexure														
Coil														
S-reaction														
Early swimming (3 lengths)														
Strong swimming (3-10 lengths)														
Late swimming (10 lengths plus)														
Free swimming - no stimulus														
Spontaneous eye movements														
Body resists rotation														
Hind leg buds appear														
Hind leg buds motile														
Withdrawal leg reflex														

    g. Strong swimming: forward swimming progression from 3 to 10 body lengths.

    h. Late swimming: forward progression more than 10 body lengths.

The data for these observations may be cumulative. It would be physically impossible to complete the data in a matter of hours, for the stages are not simultaneously available. For each observation (i. e., each specimen observed) a single record should be indicated on the following chart, indicating the stage and the most advanced type of response. When the record is complete, there should be a minimum of 10 observations (10 specimens analyzed) for each stage.

Youngstrom (1938) has added a few, more advanced stages in response. These are:

    a. The larva becomes free swimming - tactile stimuli unnecessary.

    b. Beginning of spontaneous eye movements.

    c. Body resists rotation.

    d. Hind leg buds appear.

    e. Hind leg buds become motile.

    f. Beginning of withdrawal leg reflex.

2. It is suggested that the student determine the onset of response to light stimulation. The more highly pigmented Anura may respond earlier than the lighter colored Urodela; or neither may respond to variations in light until the retina develops.

A regulation Spencer diaphragm miscroscope lamp with heat-absorbing, water-filled, round bottom (500 cc.) flask will provide an adequate spot light. After proper focusing of the light onto the binocular microscope stage, turn off the light and in the dim (ceiling) light of the room orient the embryos of various stages within the field of the microscope. After a minute or two, turn on the spot light while observing the embryo through the microscope and note any reaction to the light. The embryos should be oriented toward and also away from the source of light.

3. Detwiler (1946) has devised a method of quantitating the distance travelled by the individual Amblystoma larvae (stages #39 and upwards) which are normal and those which have had parts of the embryonic central nervous system removed. He found that larvae lacking the midbrain began to show a failure in locomotor capacity at stage #41, and that the hemispheres were relatively unimportant in the general locomotor activity of the larvae.

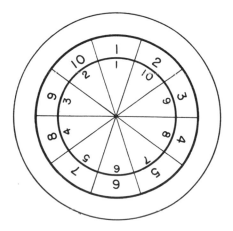

An improved device placed beneath a Syracuse dish for quantitating the distance traveled by individual Amblystoma larvae (stages 39 to 46). The outer heavy circle corresponds to the inner wall of the dish; the inner heavy circle indicates a glass ring the height of the dish. The space between the two represents a "moat" approximately 7 mm. in diameter. Each larva was placed in the moat and stimulated twenty-five successive times at approximately 5-second intervals, and the total distance was recorded in units (sectors of arc). The glass ring has been added to the original device (Detwiler, 1945, Fig. 1), to prevent larvae from occasionally short-cutting as they swim along the wall of the dish.

From Detwiler, 1946: Jour. Exp. Zool. 102:321.

It is recommended that the student remove parts of the brain anlage at stage #21 (Amblystoma), allow the larva to develop to stage #39 or later and determine the locomotor capacity as compared with the controls, using the figure on the following page. The operation should be performed in 0.5% sodium sulfadiazine (Detwiler and Robinson, 1945). The Syracuse dish in which is placed a glass ring, providing a "moat" for the swimming larva, can be placed directly over the figure below and readings of the distance moved can be recorded in sectors. Ablation experiments are qualitative in that no two operated larvae could possibly be identical. Sketches of the excision and later larva should be made.

SPECIES	STAGE	CONDITION OF LARVA	AVERAGE OF 25 STIMULATIONS
1.			
2.			
3.			
4.			
5.			
6.			
7.			
8.			
9.			
10.			

REFERENCES

COGHILL, G. E., 1929 - "Anatomy and the problem of behavior." Cambridge. Univ. Press.

COGHILL, G. E., 1936 - "Correlated anatomical and physiological studies of the growth of the nervous system in Amphibia. XII. Quantitative relations of the spinal cord and ganglia correlated with the development of reflexes of the leg in Amblystoma punctatum." Jour. Comp. Neur. 64:135.

DETWILER, S. R., 1936 - "Neuroembryology." Macmillan.

DETWILER, S. R., 1947 - "Quantitative studies on the locomotor capacity of larval Amblystoma lacking Mauthner's neuron or the ear." Jour. Exp. Zool. 104:343.

DuSHANE, G. P. & C. HUTCHINSON, 1941 - "The effect of temperature on the development of form and behavior in Amphibian embryos." Jour. Exp. Zool. 87:245.

FABER, J., 1936 - "The development and coordination of larval limb movements in Triturus taeniatus and Amblystoma Mexicanum" Arch. Ne'erl. de Zool. 11:498.

HARRISON, R. G., 1904 - "An experimental study of the relation of the nervous system to the developing musculature in the embryo of the frog." Am. Jour. Anat. 3:197.

HARRISON, R. G., 1908 - "Embryonic transplantation and the development of the nervous system." Anat. Rec. 2:385.

HERRICK, C. J., 1939 - "Internal structure of the thalamus and midbrain of early feeding larvae of Amblystoma." Jour. Comp. Neur. 70:89.

HOOKER, D., 1952 - "The prenatal origin of behaviour." Univ. Kansas Press.

KARCZMAR, A. G. & T. KOPPANYI, 1947 - "The effect of stimulant drugs on overt behavior." Anat. Rec. 99: Art. #139. (See also Art. #138.)

MATHEWS, S. A., S. R. DETWILER, 1926 - "The reactions of Amblystoma embryos following prolonged treatment with chloretone." Jour. Exp. Zool. 45:279.

WINDLE, W. F., 1936 - "The genesis of somatic behavior in mammalian embryos." Jour. Physiol. 87:31.

YOUNGSTROM, K. A., 1938 -"Studies on the developing behavior of Anura." Jour. Comp. Neur. 68:351. (See also Jour. Neurophysiology 1938, 1:357)

B. *Experiments on Early Development - Non-Operative*
7. FERTILIZATION OF THE FROG'S EGG

PURPOSE: To determine the ideal conditions of concentration, time, and temperature for maximum fertilization of normal eggs of the frog, Rana pipiens.

MATERIALS: (This experiment can be done best with groups of 4 students)
  Biological: Mature male frogs
                Ovulating female frogs

  Technical: Finger bowls, paired Petri dishes
                Controlled temperatures at $4^oC.$, $10^oC.$, $20^oC.$, and $28^oC.$
                  (If these exact temperatures are not available, the range should be covered and the temperatures should be stable.)

METHOD:
  Precautions:
    1. All glassware must be biologically clean.
    2. Glassware and solutions must be brought to the various temperatures prior to the introduction of spermatozoa, unless otherwise directed.
    3. Separate pipettes (medicine droppers) must be used for the transfer of sperm suspensions from each container. They should be biologically clean and marked for identification. Mark the pipettes at the 1 cc. level.
    4. Eggs from the ovulating female should be tested against normal sperm suspensions to determine whether they are fertilizable.

  Control: The control consists of "4" above, and those eggs which are exposed to the "normal" concentration. This is considered as one (1) pair of adult testes per 10 cc. of Spring Water.

  Procedure: Three distinct sets of observations are to be made, and the data is to be plotted on graphs.

A. DILUTION AND FERTILIZATION

In this first experiment, the temperature shall be that of the laboratory and eggs are to be stripped into the sperm suspensions within 30 minutes of the maceration of the testes. The only variable will therefore be the dilution, or the concentration of the spermatozoa.

1. Prepare 10 Petri dishes, (5 covers and 5 bases). Label the pairs N, 0.1 N., 0.01 N., 0.001 N., and 0.0001 N.

2. Quickly remove and cut into small pieces (with fine scissors) two (2) pairs of testes from adult frogs. These should be further mashed with a flattened end of a glass rod, all in 20 cc. of Spring Water. Note the time of testes excision.

3. If possible centrifuge by hand the sperm suspension to throw down the larger pieces of testes, or allow them to settle in a tapered test tube. See that the total volume is 20 cc. Decant off the homogeneous suspension (do not remove any pieces of tissue) into the two Petri dishes marked "N", 10 cc. in each.

4. With a clean and dry pipette (medicine dropper), previously marked at the 1 cc. level, remove 1 cc. of the sperm suspension from the bottom Petri dish marked "N" and mix thoroughly with 9 cc. of Spring Water in bottom Petri dish marked 0.1 N. In a similar manner transfer 1 cc. of "N" from the top Petri dish to the top Petri dish marked 0.1 N, adding 9 cc. of Spring Water. In a similar manner transfer 1 cc. of each thoroughly mixed sperm suspension to 9 cc. of Spring Water in the next dish,

so that there will be progressive dilution as indicated above. It is very important that clean and dry pipettes be used for each transfer, in order to insure proper concentrations. Each succeeding dish should contain a sperm suspension representing a 10% concentration of the previous dish. Using paired Petri dishes, the number of eggs per dilution can be doubled.

5. Exactly 30 minutes after the testes are first cut into pieces, begin stripping eggs from an ovulating female into bottom Petri dish marked "N". Estimate about 50 eggs per dish, and then strip into the bottom Petri dish containing the next concentration. A single ovulating female should provide enough eggs for the 5 bottom Petri dishes. A second female will be used for the remaining 5 top Petri dish series. Gently rotate the dishes so that each egg is exposed to the sperm suspension.

6. After 5 minutes, flood each dish with Spring Water so that the eggs are entirely covered. Do not disturb them further until three (3) hours after the time of insemination. Series "A" and series "B" below represents the top and bottom Petri dish series, or eggs from two different females.

CONCENTRATION

| | | SERIES "A" | | | SERIES "B" | |
OF SPERM	# eggs	# cleave	%	# eggs	# cleave	%
N (control)						
0.1 N						
0.01 N						
0.001 N						
0.0001 N						

COMPOSITE GRAPH OF SPERM CONCENTRATIONS AND FERTILIZATION

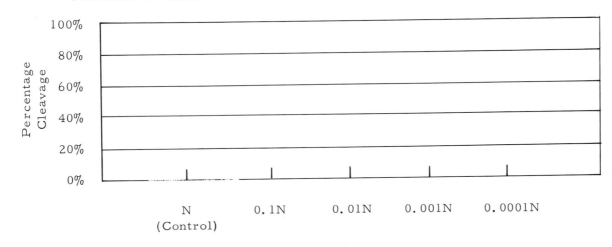

CONCENTRATIONS OF SPERMATOZOA

These observations need not be carried beyond the 4-cell stage, or about 4 hours after insemination.

B. TIME AND CONCENTRATION RELATIONS

The preceding experiment is concerned with the dilution factor alone, in which insemination was simultaneous for all concentrations of spermatozoa. In this section the factor of time is also involved, being superimposed upon the various sperm concentrations. In this way the student can determine which of the concentrations will last the longest in terms of giving highest percentage of fertilizations.

It will be necessary to use #2 covered Stenders for this exercise. These Stenders must be biologically clean and should be properly tested. The covers will tend to reduce the evaporation during the longer time intervals. Secure, wash, and label 28 such Stenders as indicated on the following table.

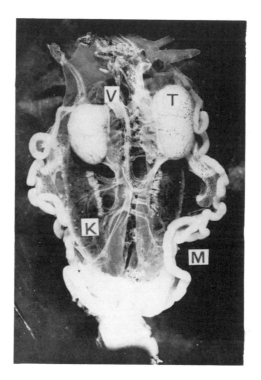

TIME/CONCENTRATION - CLEAVAGE %

Conc.	Time(min.)	Time (hours)						
	30	1	2	6	12	18	24
1.0 N	(control)						
0.1 N							
0.001 N							
0.0001 N							

Remove the testes from 7 adult male frogs, cut into very small pieces and mash with blunt end of glass rod. When thoroughly macerated, dilute to 70 cc. with Spring Water. Decant off the homogeneous suspension from the remaining small pieces of testes, and place 10 cc. of this suspension in each Stender marked "N". In a manner similar to that of the preceding section, remove 1 cc. of the suspension from each of these "N" Stenders and place it in the adjacent 0.1 N Stender, and add 9 cc. of Spring Water. This will be repeated from 0.1 Stender to 0.01 N Stender, and so on. This entire preparatory procedure should be completed within 10 minutes of the time when the sperm suspension is ready. The timing of the sperm suspensions should begin with the time of dilution from "N", and should not be more than 10 minutes after testes maceration.

Again, this set of observations need not be carried beyond the 4-cell stage, or about 4 hours after the eggs are inseminated. It is important that the Stenders be covered, and that they be kept at the same temperature throughout the experiment.

In recording the data, it is suggested that the total number of eggs stripped, the number of eggs cleaving, and the percentage cleavage all be indicated. For example, 98/49 - 50% would mean that 98 eggs were inseminated, of which 49 cleaved representing 50% of the total. It must be remembered that #2 Stenders are not the ideal receptacle for artificial insemination and such eggs as are stripped must be adequately exposed to the sperm suspension. Further, a single female should be adequate for the entire series, if only about 50 eggs are removed into each Stender. If more than a single female is available, it is better to use fresh females for the older sperm suspensions. Remember in all cases to flood the eggs 15 minutes after stripping them into the various sperm suspensions.

C. TIME-TEMPERATURE RELATIONS

In this experiment only "N" concentration is used, i.e., two testes per 10 cc. of Spring Water. The variables are time and temperature.

Prepare two (2) ovulating females in advance so that the uteri are filled with eggs at the time the sperm suspensions are made up. Prepare two (2) additional ovulating females to be ready 48 hours later.

Covered finger bowls should be placed at each of the following temperatures: 4°C. (refrigerator); 10°C.; 20°C.; and 30°C. Four temperatures covering a range of 26°C. will be adequate. While it is not essential that the four temperatures be exactly those listed, it is important that the temperatures chosen cover this range and be maintained accurately.

Remove the testes from 12 adult males, and make up a homogeneous sperm suspension in a total of 120 cc. of Spring Water. Place 30 cc. in each of the four finger bowls at the four temperatures.

At the time intervals of 30 and 60 minutes, 6, 24, 48, and 72 hours, remove exactly 5 cc. of sperm suspension from each of the four temperatures into Petri dishes and strip eggs from ovulating females into each suspension. The control for this experiment consists of a fresh sperm suspension into which eggs from the same female are stripped, simultaneously with the stripping into the experimental sperm suspensions.

Tabulate the data as follows:

TEMPERATURE	TIME (percentage cleavage)					
	30 min. (control)	1 hr.	6 hr.	24 hr.	48 hr.	72 hr.
4°C.						
10°C.						
20°C.						
30°C.						

Indicate total number of eggs/number cleaving = percentage

REFERENCES

APLINGTON, H. W., 1957 - "The insemination of amphibian body cavity and oviduccal eggs." J. Ohio Sci. 57-91-99.
BATAILLON, E. & TCHOU-SU, M., 1934 - "L'analyse experimentale de la fecondation et sa definition par les processes cin-
    etiques." Ann. des Sc. Nat. Zool. 17:
CLARK, J. M., 1936 - "An experimental study of polyspermy." Biol. Bull. 70:360.
COSTELLO, D. P., 1940 - "The fertilizability of nucleated and non-nucleated fragments of centrifuged Nereis eggs." Jour.
    Morph. 66:99.
DALCQ, A., 1928 - "Les Bases Physiologiques de la Fecondation." Paris.
FANKHAUSER, G. & C. MOORE, 1941 - "Cytological and experimental studies of polyspermy in the newt, Triturus viridescens."
    Jour. Morph. 68:347.
LILLIE, F. R., 1919 - "Problems of Fertilization." Univ. Chicago Press.
van OORDT, P.G.W.J., 1956 - "Regulation of the spermatogenetic cycle in the common frog, Rana temporaria." 116 pp.,
    G. W. van der Weil & Co., Arnheim.

> "The human mind is first confronted with the effect and not with the cause. It is only after the effect is defined that reasons for (or, more correctly, events preceding) the effect are sought. The relationship between the two is then clarified through an analysis of the intermediate steps, usually referred to as the 'mechanism of action', or, for disease, 'pathogenesis'. There are few, if any, simple or single causes in biology. There are, instead, complex situations and environments in which the probability of certain events is increased."
>
> M. B. Shimkin, Jour. Chron. Dis. 8:38, 1958.

> "Science does not explain anything. Science is less pretentious. All that falls within its mission is to observe phenomena and to describe them and the relations between them."
>
> A. J. Lotka, 1925

8. HYBRIDIZATION AND EARLY DEVELOPMENT

PURPOSE: To demonstrate the effects upon early development of the egg when activated by foreign spermatozoa, and to determine the relative influence of the maternal and paternal factors in hybrids which pass the critical period of gastrulation.

MATERIALS:

Biological: Ovulating females of any Amphibian species, and sexually mature males of a variety of species. (Pre-breeding, sexually mature females of any species of Amphibia can be induced to ovulate by pituitary injection.)

Technical: Standard equipment.

METHOD:

Precautions:

1. Avoid contamination with sperm suspensions other than that intended for use. All instruments and glassware should be sperm-sterile.
2. Examine sperm suspensions under the microscope for motile spermatozoa.
3. Cleaving eggs should be separated from others, and placed in finger bowls of Standard Solution (or Urodele Growing Medium) at cool temperatures, not more than 25 eggs per 50 cc. of medium per finger bowl.

Controls: Eggs inseminated with spermatozoa of the same species. This should be done after the hybridization experiments, to avoid contamination.

Procedure: A summary (Moore, 1941) of the hybrid crosses between American species of Rana follows:

	FEMALE		MALE
NO CLEAVAGE OCCURS	Rana clamitans	X	Rana sylvatica
	Rana clamitans	X	Rana pipiens
	Rana clamitans	X	Rana palustris
	Rana clamitans	X	Rana catesbiana
	Rana clamitans	X	Rana septentrionalis
	Rana clamitans	X	Rana hechscheri
	Rana septentrionalis	X	Rana clamitans
	Rana septentrionalis	X	Rana pipiens
DEVELOP TO BEGINNING OF GASTRULATION ONLY (Cleavage rate maternal)	Rana sylvatica	X	Rana pipiens
	Rana sylvatica	X	Rana palustris
	Rana sylvatica	X	Rana catesbiana
	Rana sylvatica	X	Rana sphenocephala
	Rana pipiens	X	Rana sylvatica
	Rana pipiens	X	Rana catesbiana
	Rana pipiens burnsi	X	Rana sylvatica
	Rana palustris	X	Rana sylvatica
	Rana catesbiana	X	Rana pipiens
WILL DEVELOP PAST THE STAGE OF GASTRULATION: MAY EVEN METAMORPHOSE	Rana pipiens	X	Rana palustris
	Rana pipiens	X	Rana sphenocephala
	Rana pipiens	X	Rana pipiens burnsi
	Rana pipiens burnsi	X	Rana pipiens
	Rana pipiens burnsi	X	Rana palustris
	Rana sphenocephala	X	Rana pipiens
	Rana sphenocephala	X	Rana palustris
	Rana palustris	X	Rana pipiens

If Hyla or Bufo eggs or sperm are available, hybridization with Rana should be attempted. In most, if not all, cases these hybrids would fall into the second group above.

RECORD OF THE EXPERIMENTAL DATA FROM HYBRID CROSSES

Egg source	Sperm source	Condition*	Cleavage %	Gastrulation %	Neurula %

Hamburger, 1936, has hybridized three European species of Triton, namely cristatus, taeniatus (formerly vulgaris) and palmatus (formerly helveticus). The crosses were made both ways but some were more viable than others. Recently (1947) Connon hybridized three species of California Tritons, namely torosus, rivularis, and granulosa (formerly similans, Twitty, 1942). If the oviduct of the ovulating Urodele is opened and the eggs are transferred into a concentrated sperm suspension in Standard Solution, hybridization can be achieved. In these forms where development can be carried quite far, the inheritance of pigment patterns may be studied as they are influenced by maternal and paternal genes.

By combining hybridization with androgenesis Porter (1941) has ingeniously discovered that there are two (morphological) varieties of Rana pipiens. One he collected in Vermont and the other near Philadelphia. These differences are not normally found, even though the crosses may be frequently made, because in normal hybrids the nuclear differences are compensated for by the cytoplasmic differences and the resulting larvae are normally viable. **

---

* Condition refers to any variables concerning either of the gametes such as prior irradiation with x-rays, or ageing of the eggs, etc.
** If x-ray facilities are available, it is instructive to irradiate the spermatozoa of any of the crosses in Group 2 on the following page with at least 10,000 r units prior to the insemination of the eggs of the other species. Generally some of these eggs will pass the critical stage of gastrulation. (See Rugh and Exner, 1940.)

OBSERVATIONAL AND EXPERIMENTAL DATA:

Materials for a hybrid cross from each of the groups on the preceding page should be made possible by the Instructor. The results should be analyzed with respect to (a) Rate of cleavage (b) Type of cleavage (c) Stage of breakdown.

Rana palustris

Rana palustris ♀
X
Rana pipiens ♂

Rana pipiens

HYBRIDIZATION OF RANA

(Courtesy Dr. J. A. Moore)

REFERENCES

BALTZER, F., 1933 - "Ueber die Entwicklung von Triton-Bastarden ohne Eikern." Ver h. d. Dtsch. Zool. Ges. 35:119.
BATAILLON, E. & TCHOU-SU, 1929 "Analyse de la fecondation chez les batraciens par l'hybridization et la polyspermie physiologie." Arch. f. Ent. mech. 115:779 (See also C. R. Acad. Sci. 191:690)
BRACHET, J., 1944 - "Acides nucleiques et morphogenese au cours de la parthenogenese, la polyspermie et l'hybridation chez les anoures." Soc. Roy. Zool. et Belg. 75:49.
CONNON, F. E., 1947 - "A comparative study of the respiration of normal and hybrid Triturus embryos and larvae." Jour. Exp. Zool. 105:1.
DURKEN, B., 1938 - "Uber die Keimdrusen und die Chromosomen der Artbastarde Rana arvalis ° x Rana fusca o ." Zeitschr. Indukt. Abstam. u Vererbungsl. 74:331.
HADORN, E., 1934 - "Uber die Entwicklungsleistungen bastardmerogonischen Gewebe von Triton palmatus (°) x Triton cristatus (o) imm Ganzkeim und als Explantat in vitro." Arch. f. Ent. mech. 131:238.
HAMBURGER, V., 1936 - "The larval development of reciprocal species hybrids of Triton taeniatus, x Triton cristatus." Jour. Exp. Zool. 73:319.
HERTWIG, P., 1936 - "Artbastarde bei Tieren." Handbk. d. Vererbungswiss, Lief 21.
HUMPHREY, R. R., 1944 - "The functional capacities of heteroplastic gonadal grafts in the Mexican axolotl and some hybrid offspring of grafted animals." Am. Jour. Anat. 75:263.
MONTALENTI, G., 1938 - "L'ibridazione interspecifica degli Anfibi Anuri." Arch. Zool. Italian 25, Suppl. Attualita Zool. 4:157.
MOORE, J. A., 1941 - "Developmental rate of hybrid frogs." Jour. Exp. Zool. 86:405.
MOORE, J. A., 1947 - "Studies in the development of frog hybrids. II. Competence of the gastrula ectoderm of Rana pipiens ° x Rana sylvatica o hybrids." Jour. Exp. Zool. 86:349.
MOORE, J. A., 1955 - "Abnormal combinations of nuclear and cytoplasmic systems in frogs and toads." Advances in Genetics 7:139-182.
NEWMAN, H. H., 1923 - "Hybrid vigor, hybrid weakness and the chromosome theory of heredity." Jour. Exp. Zool. 37:169.
PARISER, K., 1936 - "El Desarrollo Y La Relacion Numerica Entre Los Sexos En Los Hibridos Interspecificos Obtenidos Por Fecundacion Artificial En El Genero Triton." Revista Espanola di Biologia. 5:11.
PORTER, K. R., 1941 - "Diploid and androgenetic haploid hybridization between two forms of Rana pipiens." Biol. Bull. 80:238.
RUGH R. & F. EXNER, 1940 - "Developmental effects resulting from exposure to x-rays. II. Development of leopard frog eggs activated by bullfrog sperm." Proc. Amer. Philosophical Soc. 83:607.
SCHONMANN W. 1938 - "Der diploide Bastard Triton palmatus ° x Salamandra o ." Arch. f. Ent. mech. 138:345.
TCHOU-SU, M., 1931 - "Etude cytologique sur l'hybridation chez les Anoures." Arch. d'anat. micr. 27:1. (See also 1936 C. R. Ac. Sci. 202:242.)
TWITTY, V., 1939 - "Correlated genetic and embryological experiments on Triturus." Jour. Exp. Zool. 74:239.
WHITE, M. J. D., 1946 - "The spermatogenesis of hybrids between Triturus cristatus and T. marmoratus." Jour. Exp. Zool. 102:179.

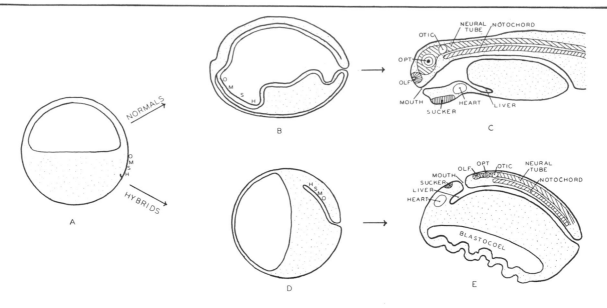

Embryo formation in normal development and in the pipiens ♀ X sylvatica ♂ hybrids. O, M, S, and H represent the cells of the invaginating material that will ultimately be found adjacent to the olfactory organ, mouth, sucker, and heart. OLF, olfactory organ; OPT, optic vesicle.

Moore (1946) has found that in hybrids between Rana pipiens females and Rana sylvatica males that development is normal to early gastrulation. The arrested gastrulae remain alive for a number of days, and show restricted invagination of the dorsal lip region. This is illustrated in the accompanying diagrams.

(From Moore 1946: Jour. Exp. Zool. 101:173)

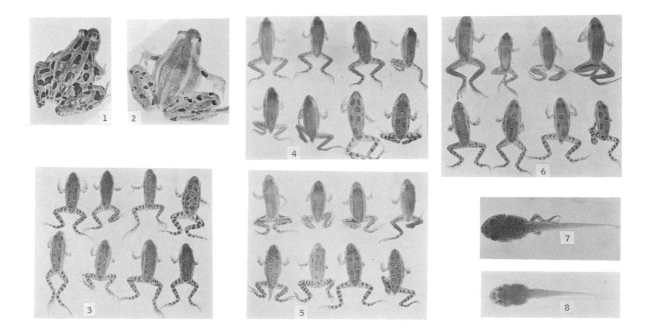

Fig. 1. A typical Rana pipiens female. Fig. 2. A typical Rana burnsi female. Figs. 3 to 6: Hybrids from various crosses. Fig. 3. pipiens female x pipiens male. Fig. 4. burnsi female x burnsi male. Fig. 5. pipiens female x burnsi male. Fig. 6. burnsi female x pipiens male.

In Figs. 5 and 6 note that the burnsi young have spots on the hind legs. This is probably indication of their heterozygous (Bb) nature. In Fig. 4 some of the burnsi have spots on the hind legs (upper row) while the two at the lower left are devoid of the black leg spots. The former are probably Bb and the non-spotted.

Figs. 7 and 8 - two types of tadpoles, spotted and non-spotted. The spotted tadpoles in most cases give rise to pipiens young, and the non-spotted tadpoles, in most cases, give rise to burnsi young.

(Courtesy J. A. Moore 1924: Genetics 27:408)

9. THE EFFECT OF AGE OF THE EGG ON EMBRYONIC DEVELOPMENT

PURPOSE: To determine the effect on early development of the ageing of the amphibian egg prior to insemination.

MATERIALS:

Biological: Ovulating females of Rana pipiens, sexually mature males.

Technical: Controlled temperatures at 10°C. and 20°C.

METHOD:

Precautions: The ovulating females must be kept moist and at the constant temperatures designated.

Control: Eggs fertilized within 24 hours of the time the first ones reach the uteri may be considered as the control eggs.

Procedure:

1. Inject two freshly captured, sexually mature females of Rana pipiens each with the pituitary glands from 5 or 6 adult female frogs (or from twice as many male frogs). Place one at laboratory temperatures, the other at 10°C.

2. Beginning 24 hours after the pituitary injection, test each female by gentle stripping to determine when the first eggs reach the uteri. (Expect the frog at the laboratory temperature to have uterine eggs within 24-48 hours, the other within 4 to 5 days.)

3. As soon as eggs appear in the uteri and are easily expressed from the cloaca, consider this the initial time in the ageing process of the eggs. Fertilize 200-300 eggs from each female immediately. These will be considered the control eggs. Determine the percentage cleavage and separate the dividing eggs into appropriate receptacles with adequate surface and 2 cc. of fluid per egg. Keep them at laboratory temperatures, not higher than 23°C.

4. At daily intervals with the 20°C. female, and every second day with the 10°C. female, strip and fertilize about 100 eggs from each frog into fresh standard sperm suspension. Determine the number of eggs fertilized, segregate, and care for these eggs as under "3" on preceding page. (It can be expected that the uterine eggs at 20°C. may be fertilizable for about 5 to 7 days, while those uterine eggs at 10°C. may be fertilized for 10 to 14 days.

OBSERVATIONS AND DATA:

There are three sets of data which are to be collected from these observations:
1. The percentage cleavage at the different ages and temperatures.
2. The percentage of cleaving eggs which gastrulate, neurulate, and hatch.
3. The variety of abnormalities that are produced, correlated with the age of the egg.

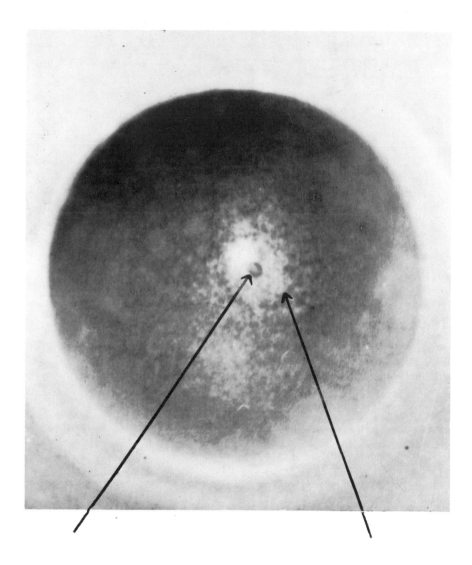

POLAR BODY PIT   MARGIN OF
                                             DEPIGMENTED CORTEX

DEPIGMENTATION OF ANIMAL HEMISPHERE OF AGED EGG
(SEE ALSO PAGE 77)

Second polar body elimination 20 minutes after insemination of frog's (R. pipiens) egg at 23° - 25° C.

"*Living things are analyzed into organs, tissues, cells, chromosomes, genes, and their functions into tropisms, reflexes, and forced
movements, while the synthesis of all of these elements into the broader
aspects of the organism and its relation to environment are too much
neglected.*"

E. G. Conklin 1944

The data should be complete and arranged in tabular form, but the final results should be indicated in the form of two graphs, one for the 20°C. eggs and another for the 10°C. eggs. Photographs, drawings, and cytological sections are very instructive.

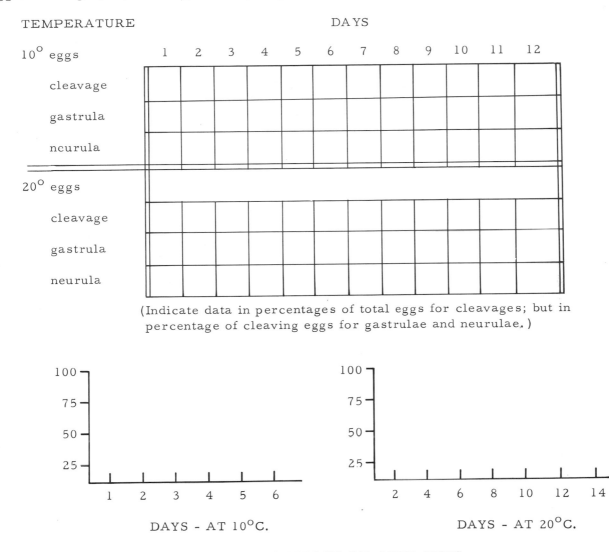

(Indicate data in percentages of total eggs for cleavages; but in percentage of cleaving eggs for gastrulae and neurulae.)

CLEAVAGE PERCENTAGE OF AGED EGGS

REFERENCES

BLANDAU, R. J. & W. C. YOUNG, 1939 - "The effects of delayed fertilization on the development of the Guinea Pig ovum." Am. Jour. Anat. 64:

BRIGGS, R. W., 1941 - "The development of abnormal growths in Rana pipiens embryos following delayed fertilization." Anat. Rec. 81:121.

DALCQ, A. M., 1938 - "Form and Causality in Early Development." Cambridge Univ. Press.

HERTWIG, R., 1925 - "Uber experimentelle Geschlechtsbestimmung bei Froschen." Sitzber. der math.-natur. Abt. der Bayer. Akad. der Wiss. Jahrgang, 1925.

HOLTFRETER, J., 1943 - "Properties and functions of the surface coat in Amphibian embryos." Jour. Exp. Zool. 93:251.

LEHMANN, F., 1937 - "Die Wirkung chemischer Factoren in die Embryonalentwicklung." Rev. Suisse de Zool. 44:1.

WITSCHI, E., 1921 - "Development of the gonads and transformation of sex in the frog." Am. Naturalist, 55.

WITSCHI, E., 1934 - "Appearance of accessory 'Organizers' in over ripe eggs of the frog." Proc. Soc. Exp. Biol. & Med. 31:419.

ZIMMERMAN, L. & R. RUGH, 1941 - "Effect of age on the development of the egg of the leopard frog, Rana pipiens." Jour. Morph. 68:329.

ZORZOLI, A. & R. RUGH, 1941 - "Parthenogenetic stimulation of aged Anuran eggs." Proc. Soc. Exp. Biol. & Med. 47:166.

10. a. TECHNIQUES FOR STAINING CHROMOSOMES IN THE TAIL-FIN

It is often desirable to determine the chromosome count in an androgenetic, gynogenetic, or parthenogenetic embryo or tadpole. This can be accomplished the better with the Urodela than with the Anura, due in part to the larger amount of pigment in the epidermis of most Anura. There are two methods of preparing the material. The one involves fixing the entire larva and subsequently peeling off the entire tail epidermis. This is better with Anuran material. With such a large sheet of cells one can generally find abundant chromosome figures. There is a technical difficulty of keeping the tail epidermis flattened through the staining procedure. The second method is suitable for Urodele larvae and allows them to survive, since only the distal 1/3 or the tail fin is cut off.

THE METHOD OF PARMENTER (for Anura)

There is a stage in larval development when the yolk in the tail fin has been reduced to a minimum and yet the cells themselves have not become so small that the chromosomes are difficult to identify. For the frog tadpole this stage is attained in from 15 to 20 days at laboratory temperatures, at the beginning of feeding. The tail fin should be well formed, thin, and transparent. The steps in the process are as follows:

1. Fix the entire tadpole in Bouin's or Michaelis' fluid for 2 hours.

2. Transfer to 70% alcohol to which 2% ammonia has been added. This will shortly remove the yellow coloring of the picric acid.

3. Transfer through appropriate (alcohol) steps to water; leave for 12-24 hours. This will tend to soften the tissues somewhat.

4. Place the head of the tadpole in a depression of a shell-depression slide, with the tail flattened on the slide in a few drops of water.

5. With a sharp scalpel trim off the entire margin of the tail fin. Remove as little of the tissue as possible, but cut to the junction with the body.

6. With sharp scissors make a circular cut around the body of the tadpole just behind the mouth. The cut should not be so deep that it injures internal organs.

7. Along the mid-dorsal line cut through the body flap to the junction with the tail. Cut through the mid-ventral line in a similar manner. These cuts will provide lateral flaps of relatively tough body epidermis which is continuous with the lateral tail-fin epidermis. With the tadpole on its side, the tail fin immersed in water, it will now be possible to grasp the tough body epidermis with forceps and gradually peel off the lateral tail-fin epidermis. This can be done with the aid of a hair loop which can be worked beneath the epidermis as it is raised with the forceps. It is not recommended that a needle be used. If the tail-fin has been properly trimmed, two continuous sheets of epidermis from a single tadpole may be secured.

8. If the sheets of epidermis tend to curl, put a few knicks in the edges with a sharp scalpel. Transfer with wide-mouthed pipette.

9. Stain, dehydrate, and clear tail-fins in shell vials or small Stenders.

   a. Stain:

      Heidenhain's Iron Haematoxylin: Mordant 12 hours, stain 2 hours, destain under binocular observation. This is still the best chromosome stain but it has the disadvantage that the destaining must be exact and any persistent yolk material stains black.

<u>Harris' Acid Haemalum</u>:*   The time and concentration of stain must be determined empirically. It is suggested that 50% stain be used for 8 to 10 minutes, without destaining. Wash in alkaline tap water.

b.   <u>Dehydration</u>: This may be accomplished rapidly through the alcohols, with 5-minute changes in each grade, or through three 15-minute changes in dioxan.

c.   Clear in xylol and mount in clarite.

Such large pieces of epidermis may be difficult to handle. If time permits, such pieces can be fastened to slides with thin celloidin and then stained. If permanent mounts are not required, chromosome counts can be made within 4 hours after fixation by reducing the hydration time.

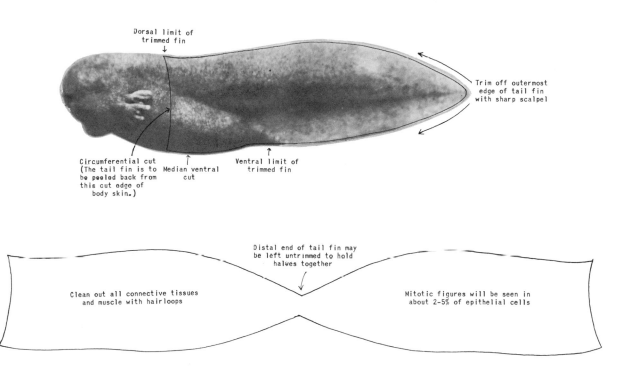

The following method of preparing chromosome figures in tail tips is excellent for Triturus, fair for Amblystoma, but poor for Rana and other Anura. In any case, the tail tip which has regenerated for 12-14 days after amputation is better than the original tail tip since it will be freer of pigment. One can generally count on from 3% to 5% of the cells showing mitotic figures, if the tail tip is taken from animals in which the yolk resorption is complete and feeding has begun. The (unpublished) procedure is as follows:

1.   Anesthetize several larvae in 1/3,000 MS 222 or chloretone, and transfer from the finger bowl to a Syracuse dish with lamp-black and paraffin bottom.

2.   With sharp scissors or scalpel clip off not more than the distal third of the tail.

---

* Mayers Haemalum or Conklins Haematoxylin are also satisfactory.

3. Transfer tail tip with minimum fluid to the fixative: (use wide-mouthed pipette)*
        Bouin's   - 100 cc.
        Urea   -   1 gr.
        Glacial acetic -   5 cc. (extra)
    Fix for a minimum of 3 hours, longer does no harm.

4. Transfer to 70% alcohol for the removal of the yellow picric stain. This may be
    facilitated by adding a few drops of NH_4OH, but the ammonia must be completely
    removed in pure alcohol before staining.

5. Transfer to Columbia watchglasses or to shell vials where the minimum amount
    of reagents will be used. Hydrate through 5 minute changes in progressively
    dilute alcohols to distilled water.

6. Stain for 15 minutes in 1/3 Harris' acid haematoxylin. The exact timing and con-
    centration of the stain will vary with the age of the stain and the freshness of the
    tail tip. Destaining is not practicable. (This procedure is from Henley-Costello
    modified after Fankhauser)

HARRIS' ACID HAEMATOXYLIN

Grubler's haematoxylin ....   0. 5 gms.
Warm 95% alcohol ....   5. 0 cc.
Potassium alum .... 10. 0 gms.
Warm distilled water .... 100. 0 cc.
Red mercuric oxide........................   0. 25 gms.

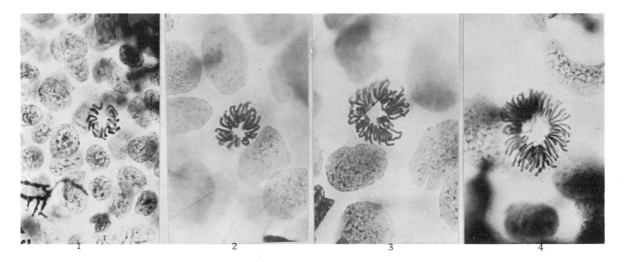

SALAMANDER TAIL-TIP PREPARATIONS FROM G. FANKHAUSER

        1 - Haploid chromosome complex   3 - Triploid
        2 - Diploid   4 - Pentaploid

(Courtesy of G. Fankhauser from Sharp's "Fundamentals of Cytology" 1943)

---

* Note: In transferring the tips from one medium to another (if the decanting method is not used) grasp the thick proximal margin
    of the tail tip to prevent injury to the thinner distal portions of the tail tip.
    See section on "Amphibian Germinal Vesicle" for a list of the diploid chromosome numbers of commonly used forms.

As soon as the stain turns a deep purple, remove from the flame and cool rapidly under running water. Just before using, add exactly 2.5 cc. of glacial acetic acid to 50 cc. of the above mixture. Dilute 1/2 to 1/3 for use. Mayer's acid haemalum may be equally good if freshly made up.

7. Transfer through two changes of tap water to which 5 or 6 drops of 1% sodium bicarbonate (or ammonia) has been added to each 10 cc. of volume. This alkalinization will make the stain an intense bright blue.

8. Rinse in distilled water; dehydrate with 5 minute changes in progressively more concentrated alcohols to 95% where two changes are made, followed by 3 or 4 changes in absolute alcohol. Transfer to carbol-xylol for 5 minutes, then into two changes of xylol. (If the atmosphere is not humid and the transfer can be made directly from the absolute alcohol to xylol, the stain is apt to be more permanent.)

9. Mount in clarite on cleaned slides under slightly compressed (cleaned) cover slips. Several tail tips may be mounted on a single slide which can be marked with diamond point for identification.

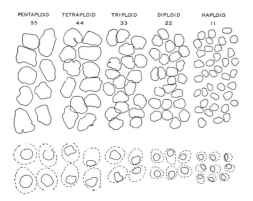

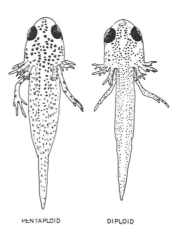

RELATIVE SIZES OF NUCLEI AND CELLS FROM THE TAILFINS OF LARVAE OF TRITURUS VIRIDESCENS WITH DIFFERENT NUMBERS OF CHROMOSOME SETS

Above: Surface view of nuclei of epidermis cells. Nuclear size increases approximately in proportion to chromosome number. Below: Nuclei and cell boundaries of single gland cells (Leydig cells). Cell size increases with nuclear size.

(From Fankhauser 1945: Quart. Rev. Biol. 20:20)

Body cavity of pentaploid distended with fluid (ascites). In both larvae the melanophores are "expanded". Tracings of photomicrographs.

"TRITURUS VIRIDESCENS"

(From Fankhauser 1940: Proc. Nat. Acad. Sci. 26:526)

REFERENCES

COSTELLO, D. P., C. HENLEY, D. E. KENT, 1957 - "The effects of p[32] on mitosis in tail-tips of larval salamanders." Jour. Exp. Zool. 136"143-170.

COSTELLO, D. P., D. G. HOLMQUIST, 1957 - "Spontaneous and cold-induced heteroploidy in Triturus Granulosus." Jour. Elisha Sc. Soc. 73:363-378.

FANKHAUSER, G., 1940 - "A Pentaploid Larva of the Newt, Triturus Virdidescens." Proc. Nat. Acad. Sci. 26:526

FANKHAUSER, G., R. R. HUMPHREY, 1959 - "The origin of spontaneous heteroploids in the progeny of diploid, triploid, and tetraploid axolotl females." Jour. Exp. Zool. 142:379-422.

GALLIEN, L., par 1959 - "Recherches sur quelques aspects de l'hetero ploidie experimentale chez le Triton Pleurodeles waltii." Jour. Emb. & Exp. Morph. 7:380-393.

10. b. SMEAR METHOD FOR CHROMOSOME PREPARATIONS*

Very recently it has become possible to prepare and examine chromosomal complexes of various animals, including man, by the smear method. Entire chromosomal configurations from somatic or germinal cells may be studied without the tedium of sectioning and reconstituting.

All the methods now used are based upon two rather simple innovations. These include the treatment of dividing cells with hypotonic media prior to fixation, and then flattening the cells prior to examination. In this manner the chromosomes are spread with minimum overlapping, all within a single optical plane, allowing photographic karyotype analysis and recording. The chromosomes are cut out of an enlarged print of a metaphase cell and paired, on the basis of relative lengths and the position of the centromere. This shows the karyotype of the individual, and genetic variations become evident. The photographs are generally taken under oil immersion or phase microscopy, at approximately 1100 x or even less.

1. MITOTIC CHROMOSOMES: The source of rapidly dividing cells may be the embryo, malignant tissue, testis, or other tissues that may be growing or regenerating. Tissue cultures afford an excellent source, and in these bone marrow, solid tissues, or blood cells may be used and studied.

   a. Blood Cell Cultures: A 10 ml heparinized blood sample is centrifuged at 300 rpm for 2 minutes and the plasma, which contains the white blood cells, is pipetted off and placed in a sterile culture bottle. Tissue culture medium 199 is added, making up about 60-80 percent of the final volume. The cell concentration should be 1,000-2,000 cells/mm^3. Penicillin and streptomycin are also added, plus a mitogenic agent, Phytohemagglutinin. After incubation for 3 days at 37°C., Colchicine (2 x 10^{-5} molar final concentration) is added for 1 hour. The cells are spun down in a centrifuge (300 rpm for 3 minutes) and the medium is replaced with 1% sodium citrate solution. After 2-4 minutes this is removed (after centrifugation) and the acetic alcohol added. Several changes of this fixative may be used, after which a drop of the cell suspension can be placed on a slide and allowed to air dry. This preparation can be stained with acetic orcein and is then ready for examination. Alternatively, the acetic alcohol can be replaced with 45% acetic acid and a small drop of this cell suspension squashed beneath a siliconized coverslip. This slide can be floated off at the time of staining with acetic orcein and made permanent, or the stain can be applied by capillary action and the chromosomes examined in the wet preparation. (see Hungerford et al, 1959).

   b. Bone Marrow: A bone marrow sample may be incubated for 6-24 hours in a medium made up of glucose-saline and human AB serum. The treatment of the cells at the end of the period of incubation is the same as described above for blood cell samples, (see Ford, Jacobs, Lajtha 1958). The quality of the preparation can usually be enhanced by separating the marrow cells from the large number of erythrocytes present in marrow samples, by using TC-199 instead of glucose-saline, and by using the patient's own plasma in place of human AB serum.

   Bone marrow can also be cultured by a plasma clot technique such as is described on the following page for solid tissues.

---

* This section is written with the generous aid of Dr. O. J. Miller, who also provided the excellent photographs of human chromosomes.

c. Solid Tissues: The specimen may be embedded and cultured in a plasma clot (see Harnden 1960) or digested with trypsin, the resulting suspension being cultured (see Puck et al, 1958).   In either case, subcultures are grown on coverslips or slides, to which the cells remain attached during all treatments.   The cells can be cultured for weeks or months.   Colchicine is usually added for the last 4-6 hours, to provide metaphase figures, and is followed by hypotonic citrate, fixation, air-drying and staining (as above).

2. MEIOTIC CHROMOSOMES: The testis is the only practical source of meiotic chromosomes.   Small fragments of the testis are placed, immediately upon removal, in hypotonic saline or citrate, and the tissue is teased apart.   Fixation is in acetic alcohol, followed by bulk Feulgen staining, and squashing of tiny fragments beneath a siliconized coverslip as in the manner described above.   For examination of chromosomes at phases other than metaphase, hypotonic pretreatment should be omitted. However, the spreading of the chromosomes is then much less satisfactory (see Ford & Hammerton, 1956)

CHROMOSOMAL COMPLEXES OF THE HUMAN MALE AND FEMALE

(Courtesy of Drs. O. J. Miller and W. R. Breg, pre-publication permission)

REFERENCES

BARR, Murray L., 1959 - "Sex Chromatin and Phenotype in Man." Science, 130:679-685.

BLOOM, W., R. B. URETZ and R. E. ZIRKLE, 1960 - "Changes in Chromosomes after Localized Ultraviolet Irradiation." The Anatomical Record, 136:166.

FORD, C. E. and J. L. HAMERTON, 1956 - "A colchicine, Hypotonic Citrate, Squash Sequence for Mammalian Chromosomes." Stain Techniques. 31:247-251.

FORD, C. E., P. A. JACOBS and L. G. LAJTHA, 1958 - "Human Somatic Chromosomes." Nature. 181:1565-1568.

GREENBLATT, R. B., J. M. MANTAUTOU, N. R. TIGERMAN, L. ROGERS, Jr., and F. H. SHEFFIELD, 1957 - "A Simplified Staining Technique for the Study of Chromosomal Sex in Oral Mucosal and Peripheral Blood Smears." Am. J. Obstet. Gynecol. 74, September, 629-34.

HARNDEN, D. G., 1960 - "A Human Skin Culture Technique used for Cytological Examinations." Brit. Jour. Exp. Path. 41:31.

HAY, J. C., 1960 - "Further Observations on the Sex Chromatin of Mammalian Cells." The Anatomical Record 136:315.

HUNGERFORD, D. A., A. J. DONNELLY, P. C. NOWELL, and S. BECK, 1959 - "The Chromosome Constitution of a Human Phenotypic Intersex." Am. J. Human Genetics 11:215.

KODANI, M., 1958 - "The Supernumerary Chromosome of Man." Am. Jour. Human Genetics. 10:125.

KURMICK, N. B., 1952 - "Histological Staining with Methyl-Green-Pyronin." Stain Technocology 27 #5.

MAKINO, Sajiro, 1953 - "Chromosome numbers of some American Rodents." Science 118:630.

MELANDER, Y., and K. G. WINGSBRAND, 1953 - "Gomori's Hematoxylin as a Chromosome Stain." Stain Technocology Vol. 28.

MILLER, O. J., U. MITTWOCH and L. S. PENROSE, 1960 - "Spermatogenesis in Man, with Special Reference to Aneuploidy." Nature 178:1020.

MOORE, B., 1957 - "Chromosomal Vesicles and double Nuclei in Amphibian Embryo." J. of Morph. 101:209-223.

PENROSE, L. S., 1961 - "Recent Advances in Human Genetics." pgs. 194, J. & A. Churchill, London Pub.

PUCK, T. T., S. J. CIECIURA and A. ROBINSON, 1958 - "Genetics of Somatic Mammalian Cells. III. Long-term Cultivation of Euploid Cells from Human and Animal Subjects." Jour. Exp. Med. 108:945.

REITABE, J., 1957 - "Observations on the So-Called Sex Chromatin in Man." Acta Geneticae Medicae et Cemellogiae, 6:393-361.

SACHS, L., 1953 - "Simple Methods for Mammalian Chromosomes." Stain Technology, Vol. 28.

SILVA-LUZUNZA, Edna, 1957 - "Cytological Demonstration of Sex in Fresh Unstained Preparations under the Phase Contrast Microscope." Exp. Cell Res. 13:405-409.

TABATA, T., 1959 - "A Chromosome Study in Some Malignant Human Tumors." Cytologia 24:367-77.

TJIO, J. H., 1959 - "The Somatic Chromosomal Constitution of Some Human Subjects with Genetic Defects." Prox. of the National Academy of Sciences. 45:1008-1016.

URETZ, R. B. and R. E. ZINKLE, 1958 - "Parallel Action Spectre for Chromosomal Stiakinese and Paling Produced by UV Microbeams." Rad. Res. 9:197.

VIALLI, M. and G. GERZELI, 1957 - "Sexual Differences in Nuclear Size and DeoxyriboNucleic Acid Content per Nucleus in Rana Esculenta." Nature. 179:1195.

WELSHONS, W. J. and L. B. RUSSELL, 1959 - "The Y-Chromosome as the Bearer of Male Determining Factors in the Mouse." Proc. Nat'l. Acad. Science. 45:560-566.

WITSCHI, E., 1957 - "Sex Chromatin and Sex Differentiation in Human Embryos." Science. 126:1288-1290.

"Scientists are the most important occupational group in the world today. At this moment, what they do is of passionate concern to the whole of human society."
Sir Chas. Snow, Science 133:256, 1961.

"Research is to see what everybody else has seen and think what nobody has thought."
Dr. Albert Szent-Györgyi

"The world is moving so fast these days that the man who says it can't be done is generally interrupted by someone doing it."
Elbert Hubbard

"The common facts of today are the products of yesterday's research."
Dean Duncan MacDonald

"We respond to fame's trumpeting of an individual scientist, but are often deaf to her orchestrations; yet of all human activities the occupation of science is more like a symphony than a solo."
W. Grey Walter

11. TEMPERATURE AND EMBRYONIC DEVELOPMENT

PURPOSE: To determine the range of temperature tolerance and the degree of acceleration or retardation of development conditioned by the single factor, temperature.

MATERIALS:

Biological: Recently fertilized eggs of any amphibian.

Technical: Incubators and refrigerators regulated to within 0.5°C. at the following
temperatures: 4.0°C., 10°C., 20°C. The laboratory temperature is
generally about 23°-25°C. and running tap water ranges from about
11°C. to 20°C.

METHOD:

Precautions:

1. The incubators and refrigerators should be checked daily, and the exact
temperature recorded.
2. A reserve supply of culture medium should be kept at the various temperatures,
so that changes can be made without altering the temperature.
3. The number of eggs and embryos per finger bowl of known volume of medium
should be the same for all observations. The usual ratio is 25 eggs per 50
cc. of medium.

Controls: The control series may consist of eggs kept at the (fluctuating) laboratory
temperatures. This represents the normal, or average condition for most of the
experiments in this course. However, there is a breeding temperature which
must be optimum for each of the various available amphibian eggs. The ideal
control temperature would therefore be this optimal breeding temperature.
Moore (1942) gives these data in the following tabular form, for five species of
Rana. For various Urodeles, consult other tables on the following pages:

(RANA) Species	Breeding Time	Water temp.	Northern limit	Embryonic temp. tol.	Hours to stage 20	Temp. coeff.	Egg diam.
sylvatica	mid Mar.	10°	67° 30'	25-24°	72	1.98	1.9mm.
pipiens	early Apr.	12°	60°	6-28°	96	2.13	1.7 "
palustris	mid Apr.	14-15°	51-55°	7-30°	105	2.30	1.8 "
clamitans	May	24°	50°	12-32°	114	2.61	1.4 "
catesbiana	June	21°	47°	15-32°	134	2.88	1.3 "

The relation between breeding habits, geographic distribution, and certain
embryological characters in frogs of the genus Rana.

Moore 1942: Biol. Symp. 6:189.

Procedure: There are two distinct investigations included in this exercise:

1. Determination of the developmental rate at five different controlled temperature levels.
2. Effect on development of temporary exposure to a radically different temperature during certain critical stages of development.

RATES OF DEVELOPMENT AND TEMPERATURE

Data from these observations has practical value in that eggs inseminated at any particular time can be apportioned to the various temperatures at which the development is
known to be normal, and embryos of various stages will thereafter be available simultaneously. This is possible because within certain limits, acceleration and retardation
affect merely the rate of development.

DEVELOPMENTAL RATE OF RANA AT 19.8°C.*

STAGE OF DEVELOPMENT	R. pipiens	R. sylvatica	R. palustris	R. catesbiana
2 cells	0	0	0	0
Dorsal lip	20-24	16-20	20-24	23
Mid-gastrula	25	20-23	29	
Late gastrula	29-37	23-26	35	35
Neural plate	38-44	37	38-43	42
Neural folds	43-48	38	46-55	48-60
Rotation	50-54	40	55	60
Neural tube	51-58	40-45	61-64	
Tail bud	60-69		66-74	83
Muscular response	70-84	50	80-83	87-114
Heart beat	85-96	66	95-98	120
Hatching & gill circulation	95-103	72-87	105-106	131
Temp. tolerance	5-28°	2.5-24°	7-30°	15-32°

1. Place two finger bowls of medium at each of the five controlled temperatures (listed
    on preceding page) for 24 hours prior to beginning the observations. Into each place
    50 cc. of the appropriate medium for the embryos to be studied. Use Standard Solu-
    tion or Spring Water for Anura and Urodele Growing Medium for any Urodeles.

2. Inseminate eggs of Rana pipiens at laboratory temperatures (or, provide yourself
    with abundant eggs of any other species in pre-cleavage stage, if possible). Await
    the first cleavage (2½ hours) and then separate the eggs from the bottom of the finger
    bowl (by means of a clean section lifter) and allow the jelly to swell further. After
    about 10-15 minutes, cut the egg mass into groups of 5-10 eggs and place exactly 25
    eggs in each of the 10 finger bowls (2 each at 5 temperatures). See that the bowls are
    covered to reduce evaporation.

3. Consult the Shumway Table of Normal Stages for Rana pipiens, which is based on de-
    velopment at 18°C. At frequent intervals, particularly during the first 24 hours,
    examine eggs from each of the temperatures and determine the stage of development.
    Check the temperature of the medium, and record the stage of the group as the most
    advanced stage achieved by at least 50% of the eggs. It would be well also to note
    the extremes in development. The record should thereafter be taken at exactly 24
    hour intervals for a total of about 12 days, or until the embryos at the higher tem-
    perature level begin to require an external source of food.

*Modified from Moore '39, '40, '42, '49. Zero point is first cleavage or two cell stage.

The temperature tolerance of the Urodele eggs is generally at a lower range than for the Anuran eggs. Further, development at lower temperatures will be retarded for any embryos, within limits of viability. Record the data as follows:

DATA FOR SPECIES_____

STAGE (50% of eggs) at HOURS AFTER FIRST CLEAVAGE*

TEMP.	HOURS						DAYS					
4°C.												
10°C.												
20°C.												
ROOM TEMP.												
29°C.												

DATA FOR SPECIES_____

STAGE (50% of eggs) at HOURS AFTER FIRST CLEAVAGE*

TEMP.	HOURS						DAYS					
4°C.												
10°C.												
20°C.												
ROOM TEMP.												
29°C.												

DATA FOR SPECIES_____

STAGE (50% of eggs) at HOURS AFTER FIRST CLEAVAGE*

TEMP.	HOURS						DAYS					
4°C.												
10°C.												
20°C.												
ROOM TEMP.												
29°C.												

Stage data in the above tables represents the stage achieved by at least 50% of the eggs at each of the temperatures so recorded.

* Note: The final graph should be corrected by adding the time between insemination and placing the eggs at the various temperatures (2-1/2 hours or more).

THE EFFECT ON DEVELOPMENT OF
TEMPORARY DRASTIC TEMPERATURE CHANGE

Three temperatures are to be used for these observations, but two of them are to be beyond the normal range of viability. Prepare an incubator which is controlled at about 33° to 35°C. and a refrigerator at or near 0°C. Place four finger bowls, each with 50 cc. of the appropriate medium, at each of these temperatures. If possible, adjust the control temperature at 18°C. comparable to the Shumway series.

1. Pre-cleavage exposure to radical temperature: Inseminate healthy eggs of Rana pipiens and, after flooding and allowing them to swell (about 1 hour) cut them into clusters (5 to 10 each) and place 25 in each of the 10 finger bowls (4 at 0°C., 2 at 18°C., and 4 at 33°C.). Record the exact time on each bowl with China marking pencil. At exactly 1, 2, 6, and 24 hours thereafter remove one finger bowl from each of the two radical temperatures, and place it in the environment of the 18°C. control eggs (providing it is large enough and adequately controlled to take care of the drastic temperature invasion). Note the condition of the eggs in each bowl at the time of removal from the drastic temperatures, and the condition (stage) of the controls. Follow the subsequent development of all treated and control eggs to determine the effect of these radical temperatures at this early stage of development.

PRE-CLEAVAGE RADICAL TEMPERATURE TREATMENT

SPECIES_____ STAGE* AND CONDITION OF EGGS (EMBRYOS)										
HOURS / TIME / DAYS										
A - Controls										
B - Controls										
C - At 0° 1 hour										
D - At 0° 2 hours										
E - At 0° 6 hours										
F - At 0° 24 hours										
G - At 33° 1 hour										
H - At 33° 2 hours										
J - At 33° 6 hours										
K - At 33° 24 hours										

* 50% of eggs.

2. Subjection of pre-gastrula stage to radical temperatures: The forces involved in gastrular movements are no doubt at work prior to any indication of these morphogenetic movements. It is necessary, therefore, in this study to secure eggs (Rana pipiens) at stage #8 or #9 and place these eggs at the supra-maximal and subminimal temperatures, as previously determined, to see whether gastrulation is subject to temperature interference.

In a manner similar to (1) on the preceding page, prepare 25 eggs per finger bowl of 50 cc. Standard Solution and leave them at the controlled room (18°C.) temperature until they reach stage #8 or #9. In the meantime, provide abundant Standard Solution at 4°C. and at 33°C., into which the eggs can be transferred for intervals of 1, 2, 6, and 24 hours. Record the effect on gastrulation and subsequent development in the following table.

PRE-GASTRULATION RADICAL TEMPERATURE TREATMENT

STAGE* AND CONDITION OF EMBRYOS												
SPECIES:_____												
TIME IN DAYS												
A_2 - Controls												
B_2 - Controls												
C_2 - At 0° 1 hour												
D_2 - At 0° 2 hours												
E_2 - At 0° 6 hours												
F_2 - At 0° 6 hours												
F_2 - At 0° 24 hours												
G_2 - At 33° 1 hour												
H_2 - At 33° 2 hours												
J_2 - At 33° 6 hours												
K_2 - At 33° 24 hours												

3. Effect of temperature change on subsequent rate of development: It has been suggested (Buchanan, 1940; Ryan, 1941) that when eggs or embryos are subjected to low (or high) temperatures, within the viable range, and then returned to the control (normal) temperature, that the effect on the rate of development is such that temporary cold retardation (for instance) causes subsequent acceleration so that the experimentals may even pass the controls. To test this concept, the following procedure is suggested.

* Most advanced stage of at least 50% of the embryos.

Provide adequate space at a controlled 18°C. environment for 10 finger bowls. Inseminate eggs of Rana pipiens, and at the 2-cell stage separate them into groups of 25 per
finger bowl of 50 cc. of Standard Solution at 18°C. Place two (2) of these finger bowls
at the control temperature and four each at the upper limit (29°C.) and at the lower limit
(10°C.). At intervals of 6, 24, 36, and 48 hours remove a finger bowl of eggs from each
of the extreme temperatures and place it at the control temperature of 18°C. There
should be no radical or sudden change in temperature, rather, a gradual adjustment within
the original medium. Record the stage of development of 50% of the embryos at daily
intervals up to about 12 days (when feeding begins).

EFFECT OF (VIABLE) TEMPERATURE CHANGE ON SUBSEQUENT DEVELOPMENT STAGE* AND CONDITION OF EMBRYOS

TIME IN DAYS**

A_3 - Controls													
B_3 - Controls													
C_3 - At 10° for 6 hours													
D_3 - At 10° for 24 hours													
E_3 - At 10° for 36 hours													
F_3 - At 10° for 48 hours													
G_3 - At 29° for 6 hours													
H_3 At 29° for 24 hours													
J_3 - At 29° for 36 hours													
K_3 - At 29° for 48 hours													

There is a second method of approaching this problem. The eggs can be left at the extreme temperatures from one stage to another, and then returned to the control environment and allowed to develop. The time factor would necessarily be so variable, with
three temperatures involved, that this procedure is impractical.

Development in all cases should be normal, particularly if the temperature shift back to
the control temperature is gradual. Note especially the relative stage of development at
the termination of the experiment (i.e., 12 days).

OBSERVATIONS AND TABULATION OF DATA:

1. The normal rates of development at five (viable) temperatures should be recorded
     and plotted on a separate graph for each different species used. Compare with
     (Moore) graphs reproduced in this exercise.

* Most advanced stage of at least 50% of the embryos.
** Time in days from time of insemination of the eggs.

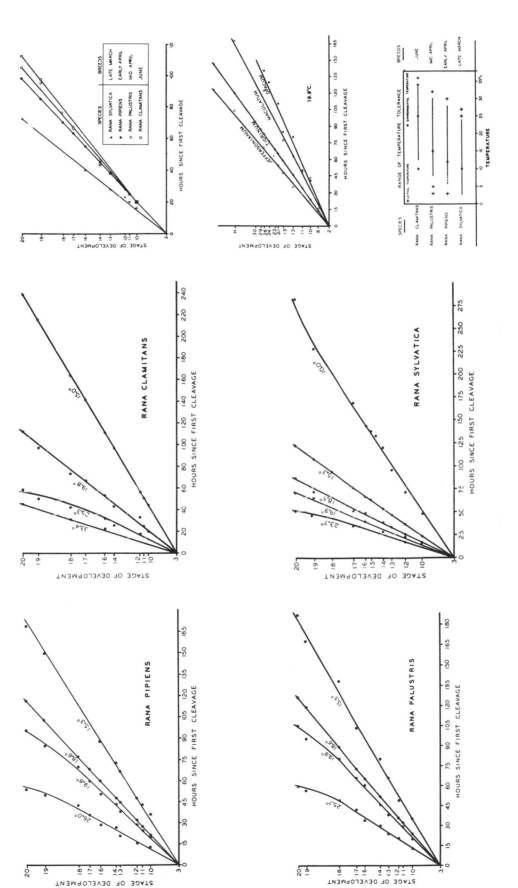

(Reprinted from Dr. J. A. Moore, Ecology, Vol. 20, October 1939)

2. Eggs exposed to extremes of temperature prior to the first cleavage are likely to
    show numerous abnormalities, and may (Witschi, 1930) even show some imbalance
    of the sex ratio if carried to the time of sex identification (i. e. , metamorphosis).

3. Subjection of the pre-gastrula embryos to extremes of temperature change is apt to
    interfere with the normal progress of gastrulation and may produce spina-bifida and
    other manifestations of interference with the "organizer" activity of the dorsal lip of
    the blastopore.

It seems possible to expand the normal temperature range by artificial means (Lillie and
Knowlton, 1896). Eggs of any species, reared at low normal temperatures, will tolerate
the sub-normal temperatures better than other eggs reared at higher, but normal temperatures. The range of Bufo lentiginosus was increased by as much as 3. 5°C. by such
acclimatization (Davenport and Castle, 1896). DuShane and Hutchinson (1941) have demonstrated that the development of form and the development of behavior are differentially
affected by temperature differences.

REFERENCES

ATLAS, M. , 1935 - "The effect of temperature on the development of Rana pipiens." Physiol. Zool. 8:290.

BELEHRADEK, J., 1935 - "Temperature and living matter." Protoplasma Monograph 8.

BUCHANAN, J. W. , 1940 - "Developmental rate and alternating temperatures." Jour. Exp. Zool. 83:235.

CONKLIN, E. G., 1938 - "Disorientations of development in Crepidula plana produced by low temperatures." Proc. Am. Phil-
    osophical Soc. 79:179.

CROZIER, W. J., 1926 - "On curves of growth especially in relation to temperature." Jour. Gen. Physiol. 10:53.

DAVENPORT, C. B. & W. E. CASTLE, 1896 - "Studies in morphogenesis. III. On the acclimatization of organisms to high tem-
    peratures." Arch. f. Ent. mech. 2.

DuSHANE, G. P. & C. HUTCHINSON, 1941 - "The effect of temperature on the development of form and behavior in amphibian
    embryos." Jour. Exp. Zool. 87:245.

HOADLEY, L., 1938 - "The effect of supra-maximum temperature on the development of Rana pipiens." Growth. 2:25.

KNIGHT, F C. E., 1938 - "Die Entwicklung von Triton alpestris bei verscheidenen Temperaturen mit Normentafel." Arch. f.
    Ent. mech. 137:461.

KROGH, A., 1914 - "On the influence of temperature on the rate of embryonic development." Zeit. f. Allg. Physiol. 16:163.

LILLIE, F R. & F. P. KNOWLTON, 1898 - "On the effect of temperature on the development of animals." Zool. Bull. 1:179.

MOORE, J A., 1939 - "Temperature tolerance and rates of development of eggs of Amphibia." Ecology. 20:459.

MOORE, J. A., 1940 - "Adaptive differences in the egg membranes of frogs." Am. Nat. 74:89.

MOORE, J. A., 1942 - "The role of temperature in speciation of frogs." Biol. Symp. 6:189.

MOORE, J. A., 1942 - "Embryonic temperature tolerance and rate of development in Rana catesbiana." Biol. Bull. 83:375.

MOORE, J. A., 1949 - "Patterns of evolution of the genus Rana." in "Genetics, Paleontology, and Evolution." Jepson et al (eds)
    Princeton Univ. Press.

OLSON, J. B., 1942 - "Changes in body proportions produced in frog embryos by supra-normal temperatures." Proc. Soc. Exp.
    Biol. & Med. 51:97.

POLLISTER, A W. & J. A. MOORE, 1937 - "Tables for the normal development of Rana sylvatica." Anat. Rec. 16:144.

RYAN, F. J., 1941 - "The time-temperature relation of different stages of development." Biol. Bull. 81:432.

RYAN, F. J., 1941 - "Temperature change and the subsequent rate of development." Jour. Exp. Zool. 88:25.

SCHECHTMANN, A. M. & J. B. OLSEON, 1941 - "Unusual temperature tolerance of an amphibian egg (Hyla regilla)." Ecology.
    22:409.

WITSCHI, E., 1930 - "Sex reversal in female tadpoles of Rana sylvatica following the application of high temperatures." Jour.
    Exp. Zool. 52:267.

>   "No concrete argument can be advanced to separate form and function in
> their essence. "   Dalcq
>
>   "Nature is never more perfect than in small things. "   Pliny

12. HETEROPLOIDY INDUCED BY VARIATIONS IN TEMPERATURE

PURPOSE: To intercede in the kinetic movements of maturation and amphimixis by utilizing extremes (high and low) of temperatures on amphibian eggs immediately after insemination, thereby producing variations in the numbers of chromosome sets within the somatic nuclei (i.e., heteroploidy).

MATERIALS:

    Biological: Recently layed eggs of Urodeles; ovulating Anura and mature males of the same and different species.

    Technical: Refrigeration controlled at 0.5°C. to 3.0°C., and 34°C. to 37°C. Histological technique equipment listed under "Tail Tip Chromosomes."

METHOD:

    Precautions:

        1. The transfer of eggs to and from the extremes of temperature must be abrupt.
        2. The eggs must be cold (or heat) treated prior to the normal completion of maturation. This means immediately upon egg-laying (for the Urodeles) or within 20 minutes of insemination (for the Anura).
        3. Heteroploids (particularly haploids) are less viable than diploids, and must be given special care.

    Controls: These consist of eggs from the same source, fertilized in the same manner, but kept within the temperature range for normal development. For Urodeles this is generally between 15° and 20°C. and for the Anura between 18°C. and 23°C.

    Procedure:

    The procedure is very simple, but it varies slightly with the different species and the temperature used. In general, a short exposure at the higher temperatures is equivalent (and often better) than a long exposure at the lower temperatures. Triturus viridescens is better than T. pyrrhogaster, which, in turn, is better than the white Axolotl. The Anura have not been used in this type of experiment until recently (Briggs, 1947), partly because their tail-tips do not yield such satisfactory chromosome figures as do the tail-tips of most Urodeles (the Axolotl is the poorest: Fankhauser & Humphrey, 1942). The second polar body is given off from the Anuran egg about 25 to 30 minutes after insemination while it seems to take about 1 hour to emerge from the Urodele egg (Griffith, 1940). The extreme of temperature used supposedly suppresses this second polar body formation.

FOR URODELA

Urodele eggs are layed singly, and are fertilized as layed by spermatozoa within the female genital tract. They should be picked off of the greens (Elodea, etc.) and transferred individually to the low (or high) temperature in a marked #2 Stender. After the prescribed exposure, transfer the eggs directly to another container at a temperature of 15° to 20°C. The culture medium is generally Urodele Growing Medium, or Spring Water. Do not crowd the eggs, allowing about 5 cc. of medium per egg.

FOR ANURA

Anuran eggs should be secured from an ovulating female, pituitary-induced.
The eggs should be inseminated in the normal manner, flooded within 5 minutes,
and transferred abruptly to the low (or high) temperature in Standard Solution or
Spring Water. The eggs will stick to the bottom of the container (e. g. , finger
bowl or Petri dish) and the water may be poured off, and the water of a different
temperature added directly. The Anuran eggs need not be separated until after
the drastic temperature treatment, but at that time they must be separated into
finger bowls containing no more than 25 eggs per 50 cc. of medium, kept at temperatures of 18°C. to 23°C.

TEMPERATURES AND EXPOSURE PERIODS

Species	Temperature Range	Time	Reference	Chromosome (2N) number
T. viridescens	0. 5° - 3. 0°C.	16 - 26 hours.	Griffiths 1940	
"	" "	5 hours	" 1941	22
"	0. 0° - 6. 38°C.	5 - 24 hours	Fankhauser &	
"	0. 0° - 4. 0°C.	5 hours	Watson 1942	
Axolotl	1. 0° - 3. 0°C.	9 - 24 hours	Fankhauser & Humphrey 1942	28
T. viridescens	34. 2° - 37. 2°	5 - 50 min.	Fankhauser & Watson 1942	
"	35. 0°C.	10 - 19 min.	"	
"	37. 0°C.	5 min.	"	
R. pipiens	37. 0°C.	4 min.	Briggs 1947	26

The time/temperature ranges for optimum results (highest heteroploidy with lowest mortality) have not been determined. However, for the Urodele eggs an exposure of about 5
hours at about 3. 0°C. or an exposure of about 15 minutes at 35. 0°C. may be considered
as optimum until exact data are available. For the Anura, the only reference is Briggs
(1947) who suggests that 4 minutes at 37. 0°C. seems to be highly productive of triploidy.

Rostand (1933, 1934, 1936) found that hybrids between Hyla, Bufo, and Rana which normally go to pieces during cleavage or early blastula stages, will respond to the cold treatment by producing some larvae. This type of experiment indicates that the Anura (as well
as the Urodela) will react to low temperatures by altering the chromosomal conditions
and thereby obviate the deleterious effects of foreign chromosomes. If various genera
(or species) of Anura are available, such attempts should be made to carry normally non-
viable hybrids past the critical stage of gastrulation.

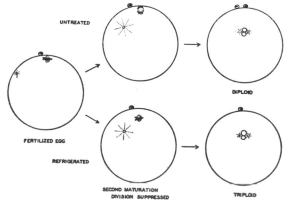

Diagram of hypothetical effect of low temperature
treatment on freshly fertilized salamander eggs. At
the time of fertilization, the amphibian egg has given
off the first polar body; the second maturation division
has reached metaphase and remains in this stage until
fertilization occurs. Refrigeration presumably sup-
presses the second maturation division and produces a
diploid egg nucleus.

From Fankhauser 1942: Biol. Symposia 6:21

METHODS FOR OBTAINING HAPLOID EMBRYOS

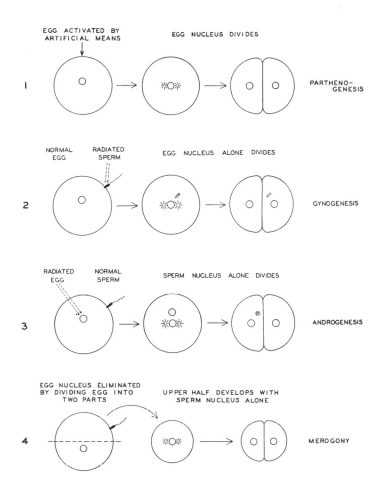

FOUR WAYS OF PRODUCING HAPLOID EMBRYOS

Above are shown diagrammatically the ways of producing embryos having
only one set of chromosomes instead of the two sets found ordinarily in
the higher plants and animals.

From Fankhauser 1937: Jour. Heredity 28:1

OBSERVATIONS AND TABULATION OF DATA:

A complete record must be kept of the number of eggs treated, the exact time (in relation
to maturation) and duration of exposure, the number of eggs that cleave, and the number
of eggs that reach the various stages of early development. The final test of heteroploidy
rests with the cytological analysis of the tail fin (tip). For the Urodela the tail tip is in
its best state for study at from 2½ to 3 weeks (just before the exhaustion of the reserve
yolk at the third finger-bud stage), and for the Anura some time after the external gills
have been resorbed.

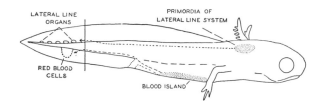

Diagrammatical drawing of a salamander larva to show the
origin of the rudiments of the lateral line organs and of the
red blood cells which are present in the tailtip. The amputated tailtip includes cells from widely separated regions of
the embryos.

From Fankhauser 1938:
Proc. Am. Philosoph. Soc. 79:715

Fix the tail tip in Bouin's fluid (it is not necessary to kill the larva) after clipping it off about 1/3 the distance from the tip to the base of the body. After about 4 hours, wash in the usual manner (decolorize in 0.5% NH_4OH), wash in running tap water to neutralize the tissue, and then stain for 7 to 10 minutes in about 33% Harris' acid haemalum (freshly acidified). Blue in tap water (alkaline), then dehydrate in the usual manner, mount, and study. The percentage of cells showing chromosome figures will be small, best in Triturus viridescens and poorest in the Axolotl and Rana. Drawings and photographs of chromosome groups constitute the record, in addition to which drawings and photographs of haploid, diploid, and triploid larvae, their chromatophores and relative cell sizes would be convincing (See figures on following page).

DIRECT EVIDENCE OF HAPLOIDY

Diagrammatic drawing of the metaphase chromosomes of a dividing epidermal cell from the amputated tail tip of 19-day haploid larva. The haploid chromosome number in this species is twelve; normal diploid tissue having twelve pairs of chromosomes.

(Triturus pyrrhogaster)

From Fankhauser 1937: Jour. Heredity 28:1

ABNORMALITIES FOUND IN HAPLOID
EMBRYOS AND LARVAE OF AMPHIBIANS

	Species	Author
Broader head and body	Triton taeniatus	P. Hertwig, 1916, Baltzer, 1922, Fankhauser, 1937a (Fig. 6)
	Triton palmatus	Fankhauser, 1937a (Fig. 7)
Dorsal flexure of body, widening of tail	Rana pipiens	Rugh, 1939
Shorter gills	Bufo, Rana	G. Hertwig, 1913
	Triton taeniatus	O. Hertwig, 1913, P. Hertwig, 1923
	Triturus viridescens	unpublished
Deformed lower jaw	Triturus viridescens	unpublished
	Triturus pyrrhogaster	Fankhauser, 1937a, Kaylor, 1940a
Circulation seldom functional	Rana pipiens	Porter, 1939
Neural plate one-third shorter	Rana pipiens	Porter, 1939
Microcephaly	Rana fusca	Dalcq, 1932
	Rana pipiens	Rugh, 1939
Abnormal development of brain	Rana pipiens	Porter, 1939
	Triton taeniatus	P. Hertwig, 1923
Small or abnormal eyes	Rana pipiens	Porter, 1939
	Rana fusca	Dalcq, 1932
	Triton taeniatus	P. Hertwig, 1923, Book, 1941
	Triton palmatus	Fankhauser, 1937a

Table from Fankhauser 1945: Quart. Rev. Biol. 20:20

DISCUSSION:

Heteroploidy in plants has long been recognized but not until recently has its normal incidence among animals been determined (See Fankhauser's excellent review in 1945 Quart. Rev. Biol. 20:20). It is now believed that triploidy in Triturus viridescens occurs naturally to an extent of about 0.7%. Some batches of eggs (or, more accurately, eggs from certain females) will respond to cold treatment by producing almost 100% triploids, among those which survive the treatment. It must be emphasized that the mortality of all eggs, treated by these extremes of temperature, is very high, often as much as 50%. It is now believed that the temperature shift at this particular time in maturation affects the kinetic movements of maturation so that the formation of the second polar body is suppressed. It is difficult to explain the infrequent haploids achieved by this treatment, but the vast majority of aberrations are in the direction of triploidy, tetraploidy, etc. The survival of Rostand's (1936) hybrids beyond the normal stage of termination of development, following exposure to cold, fits in perfectly with the concept of polar body retention and the further possibility that amphimixis (in this case, with the foreign sperm) is prevented. If the drastic temperature treatment is delayed for more than 30 minutes (Triturus viridescens) the larvae which result are all diploid.

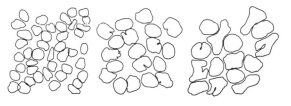

Metaphase chromosomes from epidermal cells of a haploid, a diploid and a triploid tail-tip (11, 22 and 33 chromosomes). Tracings of enlarged photomicrographs.

Nuclei of epidermis cells from a haploid, a diploid and a triploid tail-tip. The size of the nuclei is roughly proportional to the number of chromosomes they contain. Camera lucida drawings.

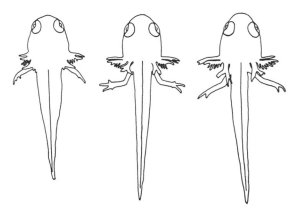

Pigment pattern on the head of a haploid, a diploid and a triploid larva, 4 weeks old. Tracings of enlarged photomicrographs.

The same larvae as shown in Figure 3. The haploid larva (left) is dwarfed and edematous, the triploid is slightly larger than the diploid. Tracings of enlarged photomicrographs.

TRITURUS VIRIDESCENS

From Fankhauser 1939: Proc. Nat. Acad. Sci. 25:233

Fankhauser and his students have analyzed the nucleoli, nuclei, cells, and organs of the heteroploids. They find that when there are extra sets of nucleoli and of chromosomes, that the increase in nuclear and cell size is compensated for by a corresponding decrease in cell number. This decrease must occur early, for in the later stages of development the mitotic rate of diploids and triploids seems to be much the same. There are corresponding differences in organ size except for the gonads and the notochord. Further "The diameter of the wall of the pronephric tubules and pronephric ducts, and the thickness of the epithelium of the lens of the eye thus remain about the same from the haploid to the pentaploid levels." and "These observations show that in the amphibian embryo both cell number and cell shape may be modified to allow the formation of organs of normal size and structure. This indicates that both are subject to some control by the developing organism." (Fankhauser, 1945). There is evidence that triploidy affects the females only, the triploid larvae being undifferentiated or males.

This field of investigation is extremely important from the physiological, morphological, and genetical points of view.

REFERENCES

BARBER, H. N. & H. G. COLLAN, 1943 - "The effects of cold and colchicine on mitosis in the newt." Proc. Roy. Soc. London B. 131:258.

BEAL, J. M., 1942 - "Induced chromosomal changes and their significance in growth and development." Am. Nat. 76:239.

BEETSCHEN, Jean-Claude, 1960 - "Recherches sur l'heteroploidie experimentelle chez un amphibien urodele Pleurodeles waltii." Michoh., Bull. Biol. 93:1-127.

BOOK, J. A., 1940 - "Induction of haploidy in a cold treatment experiment with egg cells of the salamander Triton taeniatus." Kungl. Fysiogr. Sallsk, Lund. Forh. 11, #12:1 (See also 1940 Hereditas 26:107).

BRIGGS, R. W., 1947 - "The experimental production and development of triploid frog embryos." Jour. Exp. Zool. 106.

COSTELLO, D. P., 1942 - "Induced haploidy and triploidy in the California Triturus." Anat. Rec. 84: suppl. 60.

DALCQ, A., 1932 - "Contribution a l'analyse des fonctions nucleaires dans l'ontogenese de la grenouille. IV. Modifications de la formule chromosomiale." Arch. Biol. 43:343.

DERMEN, H., 1938 - "A cytological analysis of polyploidy." Jour. Heredity. 29:211.

FANKHAUSER, G., 1937 - "The production and development of haploid salamander larvae." Jour. Heredity. 28:3.

FANKHAUSER, G., 1945 - "Maintenance of normal structure in heteroploid salamander larvae through compensation of changes in cell size by adjustment of cell number and cell shape." Jour. Exp. Zool. 100:445.

FANKHAUSER, G., 1945 - "The effects of changes in chromosome number on amphibian development." Quart. Rev. Biol. 20:20.

FANKHAUSER, G. & R. R. HUMPHREY, 1943 - "The relation between the number of nucleoli and number of chromosome sets in animal cells." Proc. Nat. Acad. Sci. 29:344.

FANKHAUSER, G. & R. WATSON, 1942 - "Heat-induced triploidy in the newt, Triturus viridescens." Proc. Nat. Acad. Sci. 28:436.

GALLIEN, L. P., 1959 - "Recherches sur quelques aspects de l'heteroploidie experimentale chez le Triton pleurodeles waltii." Jour. Emb. Exp. Morph. 7:380-393.

GRIFFITHS, R. B., 1941 - "Triploidy (and haploidy) in the newt, Triturus viridescens, induced by refrigeration of fertilized eggs." Genetics. 26:69.

HEILBORN, O., 1934 - "On the origin and preservation of polyploidy." Hereditas. 19:233.

HERTWIG, G. & P. HERTWIG, 1920 - "Triploide Froschlarven." Arch. mikr. Anat. 94:34.

HUMPHREY, R. R. & G. FANKHAUSER, 1946 - "Tetraploid offspring of triploid axolotl females from matings with diploid males." Anat. Rec. 94:suppl. 95.

HUSKINS, C. L., 1941 - "Polyploidy and mutations." Am. Nat. 75:329.

KAYLOR, C. T., 1940 - "Studies on experimental haploidy in salamander larvae. I. Experiments with eggs of the newt. Triturus pyrrhogaster." Biol. Bull. 79:397.

PARMENTER, C. L., 1933 - "Haploid, diploid, and tetraploid chromosome numbers and their origin in parthenogenetically developed larvae and frogs of Rana pipiens and Rana palustris." Jour. Exp. Zool. 66:409.

ROSTAND, J., 1936 - "Gynogenese par refroidissement des oeufs chez Hyla arborea." Comp. rendu. Soc. Biol. 122:1012.

VANDEL, A., 1937 - "Chromosome number, polyploidy and sex in the animal kingdom." Proc. Zool. Soc. London. 107A:519.

13. THE SPACE FACTOR AND THE RATE OF GROWTH AND DIFFERENTIATION

PURPOSE: To determine the relation of the single factor of space (lebensraum) to the rate of growth and differentiation of the tadpole.

MATERIALS:

Biological: Ovulating female, and males of Rana pipiens (or any Anuran).

Technical: Slate bottom aquaria measuring 12 x 24 x 4 inches, sub-divided by fine-meshed wire (galvanized) screen into 6 compartments measuring 8 x 6 x 4 inches. The screen may be held in place by paraffin, permoplast, or slit rubber tubing. The purpose is to provide free circulation of food, respiratory gases, and waste matter throughout the entire aquarium. The medium and all faecal material must be drained off by siphoning at increasingly frequent intervals as development progresses. (Other types of aquaria, such as enamel pans, can be adapted to this experiment.)

METHOD:

Precautions:

1. Make the compartments escape-tight, so that swimming tadpoles cannot move from one compartment to another. Wire mesh must have smaller holes than the diameter of the eggs used.
2. With some crowding, it will become increasingly important to change the medium frequently. A gauze-covered siphon tube may be used to remove the water, but when the faecal matter is abundant, it may be necessary to remove the tadpoles from a compartment and use the uncovered siphon. Remove dead animals immediately.

Control: The variations in numbers in the different compartments will include what may be considered the control, i. e., that compartment in which there is maximum or most rapid growth.

Procedure:

1. Ovulate the female in the usual manner, fertilize the eggs and allow them to cleave. At the 2-cell stage remove eggs from the cluster and place them in groups of no more than 5 in each of the compartments, the total number per compartment being indicated in the diagram below.

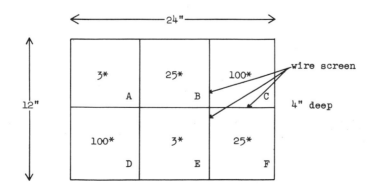

*Number of animals per compartment

2. The depth of the culture medium (Spring Water or Standard Solution) must be maintained constant. If there is evaporation, this loss should be replaced with glass distilled water. The water need not be changed until the tadpoles hatch, unless it becomes turbid. If the aquarium is covered with a glass plate and is placed in uniform light and heat, it will require no care until after the beginning of feeding. (Remove all dead eggs and embryos, recording the fact.)

3. After the absorption of the external gills, begin to feed the tadpoles on the standard diet of washed and softened spinach. The green leaves should be washed in running water, and softened by par-boiling. Tadpoles must be cleaned and fed daily thereafter. On occasion it may be necessary to remove all tadpoles to marked crystallizing dishes for a few minutes while giving the aquarium a thorough cleaning, to avoid bacterial contamination.

OBSERVATIONS AND EXPERIMENTAL DATA:

In the beginning the record will consist merely of staging the embryos under the various space conditions. After the tadpoles hatch, it will become necessary to make three records from each of the groups of tadpoles at each reading. It is suggested that the readings be taken at weekly intervals. The three records will be (a) size of the largest tadpole (b) size of the smallest tadpole (c) average of five sizes. Such size readings can be made quickly in Petri dishes over scaled graph paper, and are total length. After about $2\frac{1}{2}$ months (at ordinary laboratory temperatures and adequate feeding) the forelimb emergence will be detected in some specimens. This may be taken as the final step in the experiment, i.e., when 50% of the tadpoles reach forelimb emergence. Record the data in the following manner: (See record on following page.)

DISCUSSION:

During the early cleavage stages there may be no detectable difference in the rate of development under the various conditions of reduced crowding. As soon as there is freedom of movement the tadpoles must seek out their food and, in doing so, encounter each other and they are thereby stimulated to further activity, and we begin to find differences in growth rate. Even in the same clutch of eggs there may be genetic differences which might explain differences in growth rate, hence it is important to compare the averages and the composite averages from the compartments of the same number. The groups are so arranged to minimize any differences relative to the accumulation of metabolites and faecal waste. The single variable in this experiment is supposed to be the available space per tadpole, all other factors of oxygen, food, light, temperature, etc. being equal for all specimens. The surface area is identical for all compartments, and presumably the dissolved oxygen is the same, particularly if the activity of the tadpoles causes sufficient agitation of the medium to circulate all dissolved gases to an homogeneous condition. Lynn and Edelman (1936) have carried this experiment to metamorphosis and find that crowding not only affects the rate of development but the success of achieving metamorphosis. The optimum conditions for development, at least in the pre-feeding stages, is a ratio of 1 tadpole per 2 cc. of medium in a total of 50 cc. per finger bowl. After feeding begins, this ratio would be considered as definitely crowding the tadpoles and development would be consequently retarded.

Date of Fertilization of Eggs: _____

Species Used: _____

DATE IN WEEKS

Compartment	#Animals	Sizes MM.	1	2	3	4	5	6	7	8	9	10	11	12	13	14	15	16
A		Largest																
		Smallest																
		Average (5)																
B		Largest																
		Smallest																
		Average (5)																
C		Largest																
		Smallest																
		Average (5)																
D		Largest																
		Smallest																
		Average (5)																
E		Largest																
		Smallest																
		Average (5)																
F		Largest																
		Smallest																
		Average (5)																
DATE:																		
CULTURE TEMPERATURE:																		

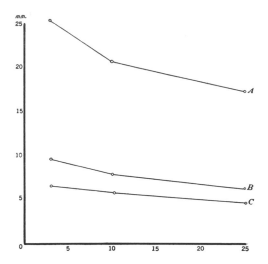

Growth rates of tadpoles with different numbers per
unit of space.   A - total length (body and tail);
B - body length;   C - body breadth.

Pairs of experimental tadpoles taken at random
from compartments containing 3, 10 and 25
tadpoles each.

From Rugh 1934: Ecology. 15:407

REFERENCES

ADOLPH, E. F., 1931 - "The size of the body and the size of the environment in the growth of the tadpoles." Biol. Bull. 61:350.
ALLEE, W. C., 1931 - "Animal Aggregations." Chicago Univ. Press.
BILSKI, F., 1921 - "Uber den Einfluss des Lebensraums auf das Wachstum der Kaulquappen." Pfluger's Arch. 188:254.
DEMPSTER, W. T., 1933 - "Growth in Amblystoma punctatum during the embryonic and early larval period." Jour. Exp. Zool.
    64:495.
GOETSCH, W., 1924 - "Lebensraum und Korpergrosse." Biol. Zentralbl. 44:529.
HUTCHINSON, C., 1939 - "Some experimental conditions modifying the growth of amphibian larvae." Jour. Exp. Zool. 82:257
    (See also 1938: Anat. Rec. 71:69).
KRIZENECKY, J., 1928 - "Studien uber die Funktion der im Wasser gelosten Nahrsubstanzen im Stoffwechsel der Wassertiere."
    Zeit. vergl. Physiol. 8.
LYNN, W. G. & A. EDELMAN, 1936 - "Crowding and metamorphosis in the tadpole." Ecology. 17:104.
MERWIN, R. M. & W. C. ALLEE, 1943 - "The effect of low concentrations of carbon dioxide on the cleavage rate in frog's eggs."
    Ecology. 24:61.
MERWIN, R. M., 1945 - "Some group effects on the rate of cleavage and early development of the frog's egg." Phys. Zool.
    18:16.
RUGH, R., 1934 - "The space factor in the growth rate of tadpoles." Ecology. 15:407.
RUGH, R., 1935 - "The spectral effect on the growth rate of tadpoles." Physiol. Zool. 8.
SHAW, G., 1932 - "The effect of biologically conditioned water upon the rate of growth in fishes and amphibia." Ecology.
    13:263.
YUNG, E., 1885 - "De l'influence des variations der milieu physicochemique sur le developpement des animaux." Arch. des
    Phys. et Nat. 14:502.

*"The organism and the environment interpenetrate one another through and
through - the distinction between them is only a matter of convenience."*
F. N. Sumner 1922 Sc. Monthly 14:233.

14. NUTRITION AND GROWTH OF AMPHIBIAN LARVAE

PURPOSE: To determine the effect on the rate of growth and of differentiation of various diets used with amphibian larvae.

MATERIALS:

<u>Biological</u>: Feeding larvae of Anura or Urodela.

<u>Technical</u>: Foods

For the Anura:

1. Spinach: fresh, green, washed, par-boiled. (Briggs & Davidson, 1942.)
2. Lettuce: fresh, green, washed, par-boiled. (Hyman, 1941.)
3. Cabbage: fresh, young green leaves, washed, par-boiled. (Borland, 1943.)
4. Banana: very ripe.
5. Liverwurst; or boiled, dried, and powdered beef liver.
6. Egg yolk, bacto-beef extract mixed with whole wheat flour.
7. Raw meat (fresh chopped hamburger).
8. Wheat mixture: (Pratt, 1940)

Ground yellow corn	46 parts
Wheat bran	13 parts
Wheat middlings	13 parts
Alfalfa meal	5 parts
Meat scrap	10 parts
Dried skim milk	10 parts
Salt	1 part
Sardine oil	2 parts

9. Wheat mixture free of vitamin-E (Pratt, 1940)
   Treat the above #8 mixture with 1% ferric chloride dissolved in ether, soaking it for 12 hours. Distill off the ether and add another portion of sardine oil to replace the vitamin A which is oxidized by the ferrous salts.
10. Synthetic vitamin E deficient diet: (Pratt, 1940)

Casein	25%
Corn starch	54%
Lard	15%
Salt mixture	4%
Yeast	1.5%
Cod liver oil	0.5%

11. Liver food (Briggs & Davidson, 1942)
    Liver, whole wheat, flour, milk.

For the Urodela:

1. Daphnia, small and large depending upon stage of larvae. Protozoa.
2. Enchytrea (white worms); small and large, depending upon size of larvae.
3. Tubifex (red worm). Generally not very clean.
4. Frog tadpoles, various sizes.
5. Meal flies, meal worms, wax moths (Galleria), fruit flies (Drosophila), plant lice, small ants.
6. Raw meat (liver strips).
7. Earthworms (after metamorphosis of the Urodele larvae).

8. Semi-synthetic diet (Patch, 1941)*
   Purified casein........................ 45%
   Powdered whole milk 37%
   Cooked cornstarch.....................
   Cod-liver oil.........................
   Baker's yeast ....

Amino acids for growth and differentiation of Anura: (Gudernatsch & Hoffman, 1936)**

Glycine ⎫
Alanine ⎬——————— for maintenance
Leucine ⎭

Aspartic acid ——————— toxic, but may support maintenance
Glutamic acid

Arginine ⎫
Lysine ⎬——————— for growth
Cystine ⎭

Phenylalanine ⎫
Tyrosine ⎬——————— for differentiation
Tryptophane ⎭

Histidine ——————— toxic but may support differentiation
Proline

METHOD:
Precautions:
1. Any food, particularly those which become acidic, will be a source of bacterial contamination. It will be necessary therefore to change the culture medium, and add fresh food on alternate days at first, and finally, every day.
2. Overfeeding is not possible, but maximal feeding will be achieved only by providing excess food. Experience alone will determine for any group of tadpoles the amount of food which is just in excess of maximal.
3. Green vegetables must be washed to free them of arsenic used by gardeners to get rid of insects.

Control: A variety of foods should be tried, and that which provides the most rapid and normal growth may be considered the control diet. All other conditions of space, medium, light, temperature, etc. must be the same for all embryos.

Procedure:
1. Provide uniform containers, each with a measured volume of the culture medium. Regulation finger bowls holding 5 tadpoles or Urodele larvae and 50 cc. of medium will prove satisfactory. The large (12 inch) crystallizing dishes may be used with 50 tadpoles and 100 cc. of medium. Mark the containers adequately, and place them in a uniform environment. The temperature should be about 14°-18°C. for Urodeles and about 5°C. higher for the Anura.
2. Select three distinctly different diets, such as carbohydrate, protein, and some synthetic mixture for comparison. Set up at least 5 finger bowls (or 2 crystallizing dishes) for each diet offered, using a minimum of 25 tadpoles (or larvae) for each diet.

---

* Note: This diet produced cataracts in 40% of A. trigrinum larvae living 2 months, but this effect was counteracted by adding 1.25% of the total protein of cystine.)

** Note: The best acid of each group is in the lowest, or most advanced position. Most of these acids are expensive, and their use in experimental analysis of protein nutrition is prohibitive, but the paper by Gudernatsch and Hoffman should be studied for its remarkable findings.)

3. The larvae may be carried to and through metamorphosis (Anura) which takes
    from $2\frac{1}{2}$ months to longer, depending upon temperature, space, and food.
    In this experiment, with temperature and space controlled, the emergence of
    the forelimb can be regarded as the beginning of metamorphosis and a ter-
    minal point for the nutrition experiment.

OBSERVATIONS AND EXPERIMENTAL DATA:

Growth measurements should be taken at weekly intervals to determine the relative value
at different stages of the different nutritional offerings. These readings may be taken
rapidly by placing a piece of calibrated graph paper beneath a Petri dish, and the tadpoles
transferred to this dish for direct size readings.

DIET	INITIAL SIZE	Species:	BODY LENGTH - MM. (Snout to end of tail) WEEKLY MEASUREMENTS (Average of 5 Specimens)															
			1	2	3	4	5	6	7	8	9	10	11	12	13	14	15	16
1.																			
2.																			
3.																			

DISCUSSION:

Feeding of amphibian larvae is not necessary for several days after the mouth opens as
there is at that time still some reserve yolk which can be utilized. For the Anura feeding may begin at stage #25 and for the Urodela at stage #40. A varied diet is generally
considered the best, and the Anura are thought of as herbivores and the Urodeles as
carnivores, although they may both be omnivores. Certainly the frog tadpoles, when
they are short on rations, will eat dead tadpoles, worms, and other organisms. In fact,
there is some evidence of cannibalism among the frog tadpoles. The elongated intestine
of the Anuran tadpole is associated with its vegetarian diet and those forms raised entirely on a protein or non-vegetarian diet tend to have shorter intestines.

The Anura do better on food with a green color while the Urodela do better on living,
moving food such as Daphnia, worms, and small tadpoles. When crowded and underfed,
the Urodela will snip off each others tails, and growing appendages.

TABLE 1

Incidence of kidney stone in tadpoles reared on spinach and
non-spinach diets. See text for more detailed explanation.

DIETS	NUMBERS OF TADPOLES WITH		
	Very numerous kidney stones	"Normal" kidneys (12 small stones or less)	Normal kidneys (no stones)
Spinach and liver food	306 (92%)	27 (8%)	0 (0%)
Spinach	13 (93%)	1 (7%)	0 (0%)
Liver food	0 (0%)	0 (0%)	13 (100%)
Lettuce and liver food	0 (0%)	32 (10%)	277 (90%)
Lettuce	0 (0%)	0 (0%)	15 (100%)

From Briggs & Davidson, 1942: Jour. Exp. Zool 90:401

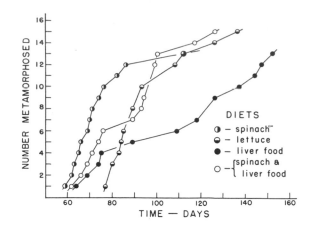

Effect of diet on time of metamorphosis. The number
of completely metamorphosed tadpoles is plotted against
time in days after fertilization.

From Briggs & Davidson 1942: Jour. Exp. Zool. 90:401

The kidney stones produced from oxalic acid of spinach and found commonly among the
frog tadpoles at metamorphosis (Briggs & Davidson, 1942) are not seriously damaging,
and spinach seems to carry the forms to metamorphosis more rapidly than any other
diet.   Daphnia and then Enchytrea have proven to be the best for Urodele larvae, with
small strips of liver being offered after metamorphosis.

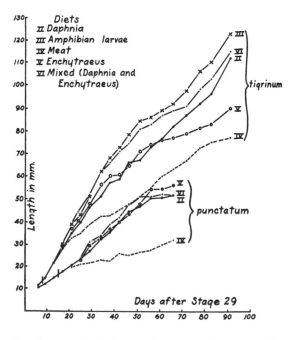

Growth curves for tigrinum and punctatum larvae raised
under similar environmental conditions but on different
diets. Vertical lines indicate the beginning of feeding.

From Hutchinson & Hewitt 1935: Jour. Exp. Zool. 71:465.

REFERENCES

ALLEE, W. C., R. B. OESTING W. H. HOSKINS, 1936 - "Is food the effective growth-promoting factor in homotypically conditioned water?" Physiol. Zool. 9.
BORLAND, R., 1943 - "The production of experimental goitre in Rana pipiens tadpoles by cabbage feeding and methyl cyanide." Four. Exp. Zool. 94:115.
BRIGGS, R & M. DAVIDSON, 1942 - "Some effects of spinach-feeding on Rana pipiens tadpoles." Jour. Exp. Zool. 90:401.
DORRIS, F., 1935 - "The development of structure and function in the digestive tract of Amblystoma punctatum." Jour. Exp. Zool. 70:491.
EVANS, H M. & K. S. BISHOP, 1922 - "On the existence of a hitherto unrecognized dietary factor essential for reproduction." Science 56:560 (also Jour. Am. Med. Ass'n. 81:889).
GUDERNATSCH, F., 1912 - "Feeding experiments on tadpoles." Arch. f. Ent. mech. 35:457.
GUDERNATSCH, F. & O. HOFFMAN, 1936 - "A study of the physiological value of a-amino acids during the early periods of growth and differentiation." Arch. f. Ent. mech. 135:136.
HOFFMAN, O. & F. GUDERNATSCH, 1935 - "Further studies on amino acids in development. VIII. On the physiological value of the amino acids of glutathione and of some proteins in amphibian development." Proc. Am. Physiol. Soc. 47th An. Meeting.
HOWES, N. H., 1938 - "Anterior pituitary and growth in the axolotl (Amblystoma tigrinum) the neotonic form. II. The effect of injection of growth-promoting extracts upon the utilization of food." Jour. Exp. Bio. 15:447.
HUTCHINSON C., 1939 - "Some experimental conditions modifying the growth of amphibian larvae." Jour. Exp. Zool. 82.
HUTCHINSON C. & D. HEWITT, 1935 - "A study of larval growth in Amblystoma punctatum and Amblystoma tigrinum." Jour. Exp. Zool. 71:465.
HYMAN L H., 1941 - "Lettuce as a medium for the continuous culture of a variety of small laboratory animals." Am. Microscopical Soc. 60:365.
JANES, R. G., 1939 - "Studies on the amphibian digestive system. IV. The effect of diet on the small intestine of Rana sylvatica." Copeia. 3:134.
McCURDY, M. B. D., 1939 - "Mitochondria in liver cells of fed and starved salamanders." Jour. Morph. 64:9.
MORGAN, ANN H. & M. C. GRIERSON, 1932 - "Winter habits and yearly food consumption of adult spotted newts, Triturus viridescens." Ecology. 13:54.
MORRILL, C. V., 1923 "The peculiar reaction of the common newt to a liver diet." Anat. Rec. 26:83.
PATCH, E. M., 1941 - "Cataracts in Amblystoma tigrinum larvae fed experimental diets." Proc. Soc. Exp. Biol. & Med. 46:205.
PRATT, E. M., 1940 - "The effects of vitamin E deficiency on the tadpole of Rana pipiens." Univ. Illinois Pub. Zoology.
TWITTY, V. C. & L. E. DeLANNEY, 1939 - "Size-regulation and regeneration in salamander larvae under complete starvation." Jour. Exp. Zool. 81:399.
TWITTY, V. C. & W. J. van WAGTENDONK, 1940 - "A suggested mechanism for the regulation of proportionate growth, supported by quantitative data on the blood nutrients." Growth. 4:349.

"Maintenance, growth, and differentiation are the three visual expressions of the metabolic processes which go on in the developing organism."
and
"In development, we are dealing with several concurrent processes which, though advancing synchronously, nevertheless are independent of each other."
J. F. Gudernatsch 1934

"The proportions of the human body prove to us that profound internal laws of harmony regulate the formation of the body. They also reveal to us the mystery of human beauty. We regard as beautiful those individuals in whom these proportions are embodied as purely as possible..."
Fritz Kahn, "Man in Structure and Function", 1943 A. A. Knopf

15. MECHANICAL SEPARATION OF GROWTH AND DIFFERENTIATION

PURPOSE: To inhibit growth (increase in mass) by limitation of the physical environment and the determination of the effect of such limitation upon differentiation.

MATERIALS:

Biological: Eggs and early embryos of Anura and Urodela.

Technical: Agar, 1% to 3% concentrations made up in appropriate culture media for the forms used. Petri dishes and #2 Stenders.

METHOD:

Precautions:

1. Bacterial contamination may appreciably shorten the duration of this experiment. It might be effective to use 0.5% sodium sulfadiazine in the agar mixture to cut down on the incidence of certain bacteria. This drug is non-toxic to embryos.
2. Avoid drying up of the agar through unnecessary exposure to warm or dry air. The containers should be covered during the experiment, and the agar should be submerged in the appropriate culture medium.

Control: This consists of similar stage and age embryos kept under unrestricted conditions in the normal culture medium, in similar containers.

Procedure: (Best results will be achieved with Amblystoma)

1. Divest the eggs or early embryos of their membranes and place them in sterile, slightly hypertonic culture medium. This will partially dehydrate them before the immersion in agar.
2. Prepare several Petri dishes or #2 Stenders with the agar mixture (above), using only enough agar to just cover the embryos to be studied. When the temperature reaches a tolerable level for the embryos and when the agar begins to gel, transfer an embryo to the agar by means of a wide-mouthed pipette, and a minimum of sterile medium. Gently press the embryo (with hair loop) into the agar until it is submerged.
3. As soon as the agar is jelled, cover it with about $\frac{1}{2}$ inch of the sterile culture medium used to make up the agar mixture. This can also contain 0.5% sodium sulfadiazine.
4. With older embryos (i.e., neurula or tail bud) place the specimen so that the gill, limb, or eye anlagen are uppermost and near the surface of the agar. When jelled, and submerged in culture medium, examine under a dissection microscope and scrape away the agar immediately covering one of these organ anlage thereby releasing it from mechanical restriction but retaining the balance of the embryo under restriction. This should allow differential growth of the exposed area.
5. If the agar is sufficiently concentrated, it may be cut into rectangular blocks, each containing an embryo, parts of an embryo, or even isolated cells. These blocks may be transferred to larger volumes of the culture medium and are very convenient to handle in that they may be turned over and the embryo be examined from various aspects. With the tail bud or later stages the partial dehydration by pre-treatment with hypertonic medium seems not to be so essential.

OBSERVATIONS AND EXPERIMENTAL DATA:

Record by a series of drawings and/or photographs, the changes that seem to occur
during each day following the embedding of the embryo in the agar. If free of bacteria
some of these embryos may survive for 10-12 days, particularly at temperatures
slightly below those of the laboratory.

DISCUSSION:

Whitaker and Berg (1944) first suggested this method of separating the processes of determination, growth, and differentiation, using the Fucus egg. Recently (1945) Holtfreter
has made a similar study on the amphibia with very instructive results. He says: "Embryonic development is brought about by the integrated cooperation of various chains of
biological processes, such as cell multiplication, morphogenetic movements, histological
differentiation, differential changes of size and form of the embryo, etc., each of which
has been given ample attention in analytical research while information on the relationship of these processes with each other is scarce and has been the by-product rather than
the aspired aim of experimental work." He says, further, that "Instances have been recorded where cytological differentiation occurred without cleavage, growth without differentiation, tissue formation without morphogenetic movements, metabolism without growth
or differentiation."

The agar medium provides an isotonic but restrictive environment where there may be
relatively free exchange of respiratory gases but which prevents expansive growth or the
acquisition of body cavities (neurocoel, archenteron, coelom). Such pressure as is exerted is due to the forces of expansive growth of the embryo, for it is first exactly fitted

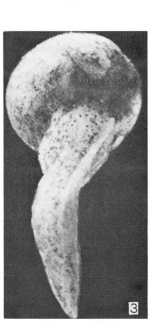

Figs. 1-4. Embryos of Amblystoma punctatum of equal age, which have been embedded for 10 days
in agar. According to whether they were included completely or partially, they exhibit
total or local growth inhibitions respectively. Cytological differentiation has not been
affected. Figure 4 shows the agar matrix still present.

From Holtfreter, 1945: Anat. Rec. 93:59.

into a relatively fluid agar medium.   Such uniform restriction does not impede the formation of neural folds, or of other invaginations such as the stomodeum, proctodeum, olfactory pits, etc.   The total volume of the egg (or embryo) remains almost static.   The
evaginations, such as the optic vesicles, gills, balancers, and limb-buds are apt to be
restricted.   Intra-cellular imbibition are limited and concern particularly the mesenchyme.   It is not yet known whether mitosis is in any way inhibited, but certainly morphogenetic movements are not.   While the general shape and size (growth factors) of the
embryo remains much as they were at the time of embedding, there is not present a
parallel restriction of differentiation.

REFERENCES

ADOLPH, E. F., 1931 - "Body size as a factor in the metamorphosis of tadpoles." Biol. Bull. 61:376.
BARNES. M. R., 1944 - "The metabolism of the developing Rana pipiens as revealed by specific inhibitors." Jour. Exp. Zool.
    95:399.
BRAGG, A N., 1938 - "The organization of the early embryo of Bufo cognatus as revealed especially by the mitotic index."
    Z. Zelif. mirk. Anat. Berlin. 28:154 (see also 1939; Bio. Bull. 77:268).
BRIGGS, R., 1946 - "Effects of the growth inhibitor, hexenolactone, on frog, embryos." Growth. 10:45.
BRIGGS, J. B. & R. W. BRIGGS, 1943 - "The effects of water-soluble carcinogen on early frog development." Cancer Research.
    3:1.
BROWN, L. A., 1927 - "On the nature of the equation for growth processes." Jour. Gen. Physiol. 11:37.
BROWN. M. G. & V. HAMBURGER, 1941 - "Density studies on amphibian embryos with special reference to the mechanism of
    organizer action." Jour. Exp. Zool. 88:353.
BUCHANAN, J. W., 1938 - "Differential acceleration following inhibition." Jour. Exp. Zool. 79:111 (see ibid, 1940: vol.
    83:235).
BURT, A. S., 1943 - "Neurulation in mechanically and chemically inhibited Amblystoma." Biol. Bull. 85:103.
COPENHAVER, W. M. & S. R. DETWILER, 1941 - "Developmental behavior of Amblystoma eggs subjected to indolebutyric acid."
    Anat. Rec. 79:247.
CROZIER, W. J., 1926 - "On curves of growth, especially in relation to temperature." Jour. Gen. Physiol. 10:53.
DALCQ, A. & J. PASTEELS, 1937 - "Une conception nouvelle des bases physiologiques de la morphogenese." Arch. de Biol.
    48:669.
DAWSON, A. B., 1938 - "Effects of 2,4-dinitrophenol on the early development of the frog. Rana pipiens." Jour. Exp. Zool. 78.
DEMPSTER, W. J., 1933 - "Growth in Amblystoma punctatum during the embryonic and early larval period." Jour. Exp. Zool.
    64:495.
DENT, J. N., 1942 - "The embryonic development of Plethodon cinereus as correlated with the differentiation and functioning of
    the thyroid gland." Jour. Morph. 71:577.
EAKIN, R. M., 1939 - "Further studies in regulatory development of Triturus torosus." Univ. Calif. Pub. Zool. 43:185.
GILCHRIST, F. G., 1928 - "The time relations of determinations in early amphibian development." Jour. Exp. Zool. 66:15.
HAMILTON, W. J., 1934 - "The rate of growth of the toad Bufo americanus under natural conditions." Copeia. p. 88.
HAMMETT, F S., 1946 - "What is growth?" Scientia April-June, 1946.
HOLTFRETER, J., 1945 - "Differential inhibition of growth and differentiation by mechanical and chemical means." Anat. Rec.
    93:59.
HUTCHINSON, C., 1939 - "Some experimental conditions modifying the growth of amphibian larvae." Jour. Exp. Zool. 82.
NEEDHAM, J., 1937 - "On the dissociability of the fundamental processes in ontogenesis." Biol. Rev. 8:180.
PATCH, E. M., 1927 - "Biometric studies upon development and growth in Amblystoma punctatum and tigrinum." Proc. Soc.
    Exp. Biol. & Med. 25.
PIKE, F. H., 1923 - "The effect of the environment in the production of malformations." Ecology. 4:420.
RANEY, S. C. & W. M. Ingvar, 1941 - "Growth of tagged frogs (R. catesbiana and R. clamitans) under natural conditions." Am.
    Midland Nat. 26:20.
REIMAN, S. P., 1947 - "Growth." Ann. Rev. Physiol. 9:1.
ROBB, R. C., 1929 - "On the nature of hereditary size limitations. II. The growth of parts in relation to the whole." Br. Jour.
    Exp. Biol. 6:311.
SHAW, G., 1932 - "The effect of biologically conditioned water upon the growth in fishes and amphibia." Ecology. 13:263.
STOCKARD, C. R., 1921 - "Developmental rate and structural expression." Am. Jour. Anat. 28:115.
THOMPSON, D. A. W., 1917 - "Growth and Form." Cambridge Univ. Press.
TWITTY, V. C., 1942 - "The role of genetic differentiation in the embryonic development of Amphibia." Biol. Symposium.
    6:291.
TYLER, A, 1947 - "An auto-antibody concept of cell structure, growth, and differentiation." Growth Symposium. 7-19.
WEISS, P., 1940 - "The problem of cell individuality in development." Am. Nat. 64:34.

WEISS, P., 1947 - "The problem or specificity in growth and development." Yale J. Biol. & Med. 19:235.

YOUNGSTROM, K. A., 1938 "On the relationship between choline esterase and the development of behavior in Amphibia." Jour. Neurophysiology. 1:357.

YUNG, E., 1885 - "De l'influence des variations due milieu physicopchemique sur le developpement des animaux." Arch. des Sci. Phys. et. Nat. 14:502.

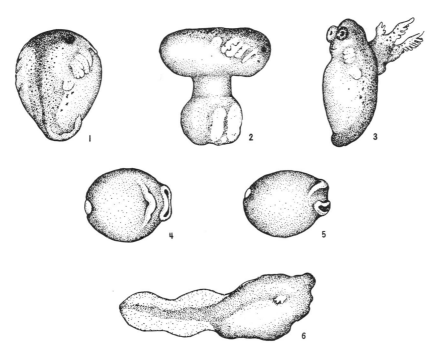

Fig. 1. -   Embryo embedded in the late gastrula stage exhibits, 8 days later, the original egg shape but has developed stunted external organs.

Fig. 2. -   The ventral portion of an embedded neurula has grown through a hole in the agar investment, while the upper portion has not increased in volume but continued differentiating.

Fig. 3. -   The embryo has for 12 days retained the general shape existing at the time of embedding. Left nasal placode and right gill region form abnormal extensions into holes cut into the agar matrix.

Figs. 4, 5, 6. - Differential inhibition of development in blastulae of Rana fusca that have been kept for 3 days closely packed in between other eggs. The frontal portion which alone had free access to the immersion fluid is least inhibited showing a medullary head fold and a sucker (Figs. 4-5). In the absence of exogastrulation such eggs develop into microcephalic larvae (Fig. 6).

(From Holtfreter, 1945: Anat. Rec. 93:59)

*"The determination or chemo-differentiation of any given part (i.e.,
the decision as to what any cell or group of cells shall develop into) takes
place invisibly some time prior to the process itself."*

H. Spemann

16. CHEMICAL ALTERATION OF GROWTH AND DIFFERENTIATION

PURPOSE: The study of the effect of a specific chemical, Lithium Chloride, on early amphibian development.

MATERIALS:

Biological: Early gastrula stages of Anura (stage #9) and Urodela (stage #10).

Technical: Various solutions as follows:*

1. Balanced lithium solution (Hall, 1942):
   Lithium chloride .... 1.12 gr.
   Lithium sulphate .... 1.5 gr.
   Calcium chloride .... 0.15 gr.
   Potassium biphosphate .... 0.04 gr.
   Sodium bicarbonate .... 0.5 gr.
   Glass dist. water...................... 1000.0 cc.

2. Unbalanced lithium solution (Hall, 1942):
   Lithium chloride .... 1.09 gr.
   Lithium sulphate .... 1.5 gr.
   Sodium bicarbonate .... 0.11 gr.
   Glass dist. water...................... 1000.0 cc.

3. Unbalanced sodium solution (Hall, 1942):
   Sodium chloride .... 1.5 gr.
   Sodium sulphate .... 1.97 gr.
   Sodium bicarbonate .... 0.25 gr.
   Glass dist. water...................... 1000.0 cc.

4. Pure lithium chloride solutions:
   (a) 1.9 grams LiCl in 1,000 cc. of glass distilled water.
   (b) 1.9 grams of LiCl in 250 cc. of glass distilled water.

5. Control solutions:
   For Anura: Standard (Holtfreter's) solution
   For Urodela: Urodele Growing Solution

METHOD:

Precautions:
1. Glass distilled water should be used, if possible, to make up the experimental solutions to avoid even the minutest traces of metallic or other ions.
2. In returning the exposed (experimental) gastrulae to the normal medium, it is wise to pass them through several changes to remove all adherent Lithium.

Control: This consists of similar gastrula, similarly denuded of their membranes, but kept in control media. Conditions of temperature, light, etc. must be identical.

Procedure:
1. Prepare 12 finger bowls, each with 50 cc. of solution as follows: Two finger bowls (a and b) each, of solutions 1, 2, 3, 4, and the appropriate control 5. Cover them and keep them at a cool temperature. (About 18°C. for Anura or 14°C. for Urodela.)

---

*Note: Effects similar to those produced by Lithium Chloride may be produced by unbalanced solutions of NaCl, NaOH, ethyl alcohol, NH_4OH, $MgCl_2$, $Mg(NO_3)_2$, ether, chloroform, and by x-rays.

2. Strip eggs (Anura or Urodela) of their jelly membranes. Do not attempt to remove the vitelline membranes, particularly of the Anura. The stages should be the same and in early gastrula (Anura #9 and Urodela #10). A total of at least 300 undamaged eggs should be quickly prepared. (Since it takes 5 hours to reach stage #10 in the Anura, at least this much time should be allowed for the denuding.)

3. Place 25 gastrulae in each of the finger bowls, and record the exact time and stage.

4. After 24 hours, pour off all experimental media and wash twice with control medium. Finally place the embryos in 50 cc. of the control medium.

5. Allow the embryos to develop under controlled conditions to Anura stage #22 or Urodela stage #40 (swimming), examine, and fix in 10% formaldehyde. (Various degrees of exo-gastrulae, monorhyny and cyclopia will be found.)

6. The long exposure of 24 hours may prove to be too drastic for the species used, as evidenced by the mortality and teratoligies of the experimental embryos. For those solutions which produce such drastic effects, reduce the exposure to 6 or even to 2 hours.

DISCUSSION:

Experiments in animalization and vegetalization have been standardized for the Echinodermata but Adelmann, Lehmann, and Hall have each demonstrated that Lithium Chloride will effect the medium strip of organizer material of Amphibia resulting in exo-gastrulae, which have faulty inductions (in consequence). A large variety of substances interfere with gastrulation, but Lithium Chloride seems most satisfactory in the uniformity and reproducibility of its effects.

Hall (1942) has shown that even with Lithium Chloride the results will depend upon a number of factors such as (a) concentration of Lithium (b) duration of exposure to the salt (c) phase of development of the embryo (d) temperature of medium (e) presence of other salts. The effect on differentiation is due to upsetting the delicately balanced developmental factors that are so important at the time of gastrulation, and the manifestations relate largely to the head and the tail organizers. By applying the Lithium Chloride for 6 hour exposures at different stages of development, Lehmann has determined a shift in susceptibility with progressive development. The effects are lessened at the lower temperatures, and in the presence of calcium and the salts of the control medium.

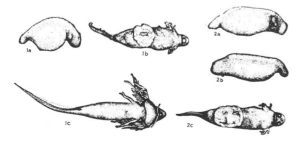

Figs. 1a. embryo of 32 somites; 1b. embryo of 8 mm.;
   1c. embryo (in Mg) of about 12 mm.
Figs. 2a. embryo of 31 somites; 2b. embryo of 5.5 mm.;
   and 2c. embryo of about 9.5 mm.

All but 1c from lithium treatment. The "1" group exhibit cyclopia complete and the "2" group exhibit cyclopia incomplete.

   From Adelmann 1934: Jour. Exp. Zool 67:217

CYCLOPIA IN AMBLYSTOMA
PUNCTATUM EMBRYOS

Histological examination is desirable but not necessary to identify the various types of developmental abnormalities. Material may be fixed in Bouin's for sectioning, or in 10% formaldehyde for dissection.

There is a current interest in mitotic inhibitors such as colchicine and the nitrogen mustards, which indirectly affect development. It is expected that within the next few years the chemical separation of ontogenetic processes will be extended to great lengths by the use of such and related chemical substances on the amphibian embryo.

REFERENCES

ADELMANN, H. B., 1936 - "The problem of cyclopia." Quart. Rev. Biol. 11:161 & 284.

BELLAMY, A. W., 1919 - "Differential susceptibility as a basis for modification and control of early development in the frog." Biol. Bull. 37:312.

BURT, A., 1943 - "Neurulation in mechanically and chemically inhibited Amblystoma." Biol. Bull. 85:103.

CHILD, C. M., 1940 - "Lithium and echinoderm exo-gastrulation; with a review of the physiological gradient concept." Physiol. Zool. 13:4.

COHEN, A., 1938 - "Myotome fusion in the embryo of Amblystoma punctatum after treatment with lithium and other agents." Jour. Exp. Zool. 79:461.

GREENE, H.S.N., 1955 - "Attributes of embryonic tissues after growth and development in heterologous hosts." Cancer Res. 15:170-172.

GURWITSCH, A., 1895 - "Ueber die Einwirkung des Lithionchlorids auf die Entwicklung der Frosch- und Kroteneier (R. fusca und Bufo vulgaris)." Anat. Anz. 11B;65 (See also 1896 Arch. f. Ent. mech. 3.)

HALL, T. S., 1942 - "The mode of action of lithium salts in amphibian development." Four. Exp. Zool. 89:1.

HENLEY, C., 1946 - "The effects of lithium chloride on the fertilized eggs of Nereis limbata." Biol. Bull. 90:188.

HERBST, C., 1943 - "Die Bedeutnungen der Salzversuche fur die Frage nach der Wirkungsart der Gene. Zusammenschau einer Hydrationsbzw. Mikrolaboratorien theorie der Genwirkung." Arch. f. Ent. mech. 142:319 (See ibid 1896, 2:455).

HOLTFRETER, J., 1943 - "A study of the mechanics of gastrulation." Jour. Exp. Zool. 94:261.

LEHMANN, F. E., 1937 - "Regionale Verschiedenkeiten des Organisators von Triton, insbesondere in der vorderen und kinteren Kopfregion, nachgewiesen durch phasenspezifische Erzeugung von Lithium-bedingten und operativ bewirkten Regionaldefekten." Arch. f. Ent. mech. 138:106.

LINDAHL, P. E., 1940 - "Neue Beitrage zur physiologischen Grundlage der Vegetativisierung des Seeigelkeimes durch Lithium-ionen." Arch. f. Ent. mech. 140:168.

PASTEELS, J., 1942 - "Les effets du LiCl sur le developpement de Rana fusca." Bull. de la Classe de Sci., Belgique. 27:605 (See also 1945, Arch. Biol. 56:105).

RANZI, S., 1942 - " Naturwiss. 30:329 (See also Pubbl. Staz. Napoli. Zool. 9:81).

RAVEN, C. P., 1942 - "The influence of lithium upon the development of the pond snail, Limnaea stagnalis." Proc. Nederl. Akad. von Wetens. 45:856.

RUUNSTROM, J., 1935 - "An analysis of the action of lithium on sea urchin development." Biol. Bull. 68:378.

SPIEGELMAN, S. & F. MOOG, 1945 - "A comparison of the effects of cyanide and ozide on the development of the frog's egg." Biol. Bull. 89:122.

STOCKARD, C. R., 1921 - "Developmental rate and structural expression; an experimental study of twins, double monsters and single deformities, and the interaction among embryonic organs during their origin and development." Am. Jour. Anat. 28:115.

TONDURY, G., 1938 - "Weitere Beitrage zur Frage der Kopfentwicklung dei Urodelen. II. Erzeugung von Mikrokephalie durch Einwickung von Lithium chlorid auf die Gastrula von Triton alpestris." Arch. f. Ent. mech. 137:510.

von UBISCH, L., 1929 - "Ueber die Determination der larvalen Organe und der Imaginanlage bei Seeigeln." Arch. f. Ent. mech. 117:80.

WATERMAN, A. J., 1937 - "Effects of salts of heavy metals on development of the sea urchin, Arbacia punctula." Biol. Bull. 73:401.

WOLSKY, A., M. A. TAZELAAR, J. S. HUXLEY, 1936 - "Differential acceleration in frog development." Physiol. Zool. 9"265.

"If there be a better way of securing understanding than by the method of science, human history and human experience have not yet revealed it."

A. J. Carlson

17. THE EMBRYO AND NARCOSIS, OR THE SEPARATION OF FORM AND FUNCTION

PURPOSE: To determine the efficiency of various depressants as embryonic narcotics, and to utilize such narcotics in an attempt to separate the development of form from function.

MATERIALS:

Biological: Early Anuran or Urodele embryos through stages of (muscular) motility, (Anura stage #17, Urodela stage #27).

Technical: Various known depressants: (None of these except freezing affect the cilia)

Acetanilid - 1/1,000 (lethal at 1/200) Rapid recovery
Alypin
Amyl alcohol - 0.15%
Barbital sodium - 1/100 (lethal at 1/15) Slow recovery
Borocaine
Butyl alcohol - 0.5%
Chloral hydrate - 0.1% or 1/500. Rapid recovery
*Chloretone - 0.2 to 0.9% or 1/20,000 (lethal at 1/2000) Rapid recovery
Chloroform - 0.05% Rapid recovery
CO_2 gas
Cocain
Diethyl ether - 1.4%
*Ethyl alcohol - 4.6% or 1/50 Rapid recovery
Ethyl chloride - 0.046 moles/liter
*Ethyl urethane - 2.0% (Not suitable for prolonged exposure unless in weaker concentrations, i.e., 1.0%.)
Freezing
Methyl alcohol - 6.4%
*MS 222 (M-Amino-Ethyl-Benzoate) - 1/3000. Can be autoclaved. **
Nembutal - 1/750 Slow recovery
Novocaine
Panthesine
Paraldehyde - 1/400 (lethal at 1/100)
Propyl alcohol - 1.5%
Stovaine
Tutocain

METHOD:

Precautions:
1. To function as an anesthetic, a drug must interfere with some physiological process such as respiration or enzyme activity. The action of untested drugs must not be prolonged beyond the stage of total anesthesia unless testing for its persistent effect or lethality.
2. All depressants are immediately lethal in high concentrations. In very low concentrations, and repeated immersion, the embryo may become increasingly resistant to narcosis.

---

* Suitable for these experiments.
** Available through M. Sandoz & Co., 68 Charlton St., New York City.

Controls: The controls consist of untreated embryos of the same age and stage, kept under identical conditions except for the drug being tested on the experimentals.

PROCEDURE:

EFFECT ON THE SPERM AND FERTILIZATION

1. Prepare an ovulating female, Rana pipiens.
2. Prepare two sperm suspensions (Rana pipiens), as follows:
   a. Control - 2 pairs of testes in 10 cc. of Spring water.
   b. Experimental - 2 pairs of testes in 10 cc. of Spring water containing 1/3,000 MS 222. Examine a drop of this suspension just before stripping the eggs into it to determine whether the sperm are motile.
3. Fertilize eggs from the same female in the two sperm suspensions. Flood in 15. minutes with more of the same solutions used to make the suspensions.
4. After 1, 3, and 5 hours remove eggs from the Experimental mass and place them in pure Spring Water. Label the container, and make a further change in Spring Water in 5 minutes. Allow these eggs to develop under the same conditions as the controls. Observe frequently.
5. Observe the development of the eggs remaining in the MS 222.

RECORD OF FERTILIZATION DATA (Species_____)

Condition	Total # Eggs	% Cleave	% Blastula	% Gastrula	% Neurula	% Hatch
Control						
MS 222-1 hr.						
MS 222-3 hrs.						
MS 222-5 hrs.						
MS 222- hrs.						

EFFECT ON EARLY MOTILE STAGES
Anura St. #17-#25: Urodela St. #27-#35

1. Select a large number of embryos of the same age, stage, and species. There should be evidence of motility. Anura stages #21-25, Urodela Stages #31-#35 are best.
2. Prepare finger bowls or Petri dishes of MS 222 in 1/3,000 concentration.
3. Place the embryos, 5 at a time, in a finger bowl of anesthetic and, with a stop watch and 2-second interval stimulations, determine the time of the first and the last of the 5 embryos to lose their responsiveness to tactile stimulation. It is best to use a hair loop and stimulate the same region, i.e., the side of the body. Mark each finger bowl with the exact time of anesthesia.
4. At intervals of 1, 6, 24, 36, and 48 hours (or approximately similar hours) transfer the anesthetized embryos from one of the finger bowls to pure Spring Water. With a stop watch and 2-second interval stimulations (as above) determine whether short or long anesthesia has any effect on the period of recovery. Note, incidentally, whether there has been any injury to the experimental embryos as evidenced by abnormal movements.

RECORD OF ANESTHESIA TIME IN MS 222

Time in seconds for total anesthesia

EMBRYOS (Species_____)

	A	B	C	D	E	Average Time
Group 1						
Group 2						
Group 3						
Group 4						
Group 5						

RECORD OF RECOVERY TIME FROM MS 222

Time in seconds or minutes for total recovery

EMBRYOS (Species_____)

	A	B	C	D	E	Average Time
Group 1						
Group 2						
Group 3						
Group 4						
Group 5						

Total Time Under Anesthesia_____

DEVELOPMENT OF FORM WITHOUT FUNCTION

Anesthetics knock out the normal functioning of the nervous and/or the muscular system but seem to have no effect on ciliary motion. It is instructive to determine to what extent the muscular and the nervous systems can develop (normally) although the embryo is under the continued influence of an anesthetic.

Select a group of embryos of the same species and at an age and stage prior to the initiation of muscular movement (see exercise on "Behavior Patterns"). In fact, the best stage to begin narcosis for this observation is #14 for the Anura and #17 for the Urodela, when there are as yet no somites. Place them, five to a finger bowl of 50 cc. total volume, in 1/10,000 MS 222 freshly made up in Spring Water for the Anura and Urodele Growing Medium for the Urodela. Keep controls under the same conditions except for the anesthetic, and allow the embryos to remain undisturbed for periods ranging from 1 day to 2 weeks, at appropriate temperatures for the species considered. The Anura will do well at laboratory temperatures but the Urodela should be kept at temperatures below 18°C. For the extended observations, replace the experimental medium with fresh experimental medium every 4-5 days, since there is some loss of potency of the MS 222 in solution.

Upon returning the embryos from prolonged narcosis to normal medium, determine the speed of recovery of response but more particularly compare the stage of development with that of the controls. Note any morphological and behavior variations when compared with the untreated controls. Have the muscles developed normally in spite of total anesthesia?

DISCUSSION:

There are three major theories regarding the mechanism of narcosis. They are the permeability theory of Lillie and Winterstein; the adsorption theory of Warburg; and the lipoid theory of Meyer-Overton. According to Henderson (1930) the Meyer's theory is the most plausible but "No theory of anesthesia," says Henderson, "will prove acceptable which is based on a proof of a depression of the resting oxidation of the cell."

Moog (1944) found a smooth rise in the normal respiration of Rana pipiens eggs from fertilization to the heart-beat stage (#19) and that chloretone, from 0.03% to 0.09%, had a small but increasing effect on that respiration through late gastrula. The gastrula seemed to be resistent to chloretone. After neurulation the effect was more pronounced, weak chloretone effects being reversible, stronger ones producing various permanent abnormalities, and still stronger ones causing disintegration and cytolysis. On the basis of differential reaction at different stages, Moog postulates two separate chloretone-sensitive respiratory systems, one related to "activity" and the other to "maintenance".

Karczmar and Koppanyi (1947) in brief notes list a large group of anesthetics which were used with larval salamanders. They classify the drugs as to the rapidity with which they bring on immobilization and from which the larvae recover. The precise mechanism of narcosis has not been determined, and therefore it is unlikely that the action of these various depressants can be directly compared. However, from the point of view of practicality, a reliable, non-toxic, non-injurious anesthetic is necessary for many of the procedures in experimental embryology. Thus far MS 222 has proven to be the most satisfactory of all. It is nevertheless recommended that the student test the value of other depressants, particularly chloretone, chloroform, chloral hydrate, ethyl alcohol, and freezing.

This exercise throws light on the relation of the development of structure in relation to function, since the larvae are immobilized during the development of the musculature.

REFERENCES

ANDERSON, B. G. & G. J. JACOBS - "The apparent thresholds of narcosis and toxicity for some normal aliphatic alcohols and their isomers." Anat. Rec. 99: suppl. 43.

BANCROFT, W. D. & G. H. ROCHTER, 1931 - "The chemistry of anesthesia." Jour. Phys. Chem. 35:215.

CLARK, A. J., 1937 - "The action of narcotics on enzymes and cells." Trans. Faraday Sic. 33:1057.

FISHER, K. C., 1942 - "Narcosis." Canadian Med. Ass'n. Jour. 47:414.

FOX, D. L., 1933 - "Carbon dioxide narcosis." Jour. Cell. Comp. Physiol. 5:75.

GREIG, M. E., 1946 - "The site of action of narcotics on brain metabolism." Jour. Pharm. Exp. Therap. 87:185.

HENDERSON, V. E., 1930 - "The present status of the theories of narcosis." Physiol. Rev. 10:171.

HILLER, ST., 1924 - "Influence de l'alcool ethylique sur le developpement de Rana fusca." Bull. de l'Acad. Polonaise des Sc. et des Lettres. B. 623.

JOHNSON, F. A., D. BROWN, D A. MARSLAND, 1942 - "A basic mechanism in the biological effects of temperature, pressure, and narcotics." Science. 95:200.

JOWETT, M., 1938 - "The action of narcotics on brain respiration." Jour. Physiol. 92:322.

KARCZMAR, A. G. & T. KOPPANYI, 1947 - "The effect of stimulant drugs on overt behavior." Anat. Rec. 99: suppl. 64.

KOPPANYI, T. & A. G. KARCZMAR, 1947 - "The effect of depressant drugs on overt behavior." Anat. Rec. 99: suppl. 64.

MATHEWS, S. A. & S. R. DETWILER, 1926 - "The reactions of Amblystoma embryos following prolonged treatment with chloretone." Jour. Exp. Zool. 45:279.

McELROY, W. D., 1947 - "The mechanism of inhibition of cellular activity by narcotics." Quart. Rev. Biol. 22:25.

McGOVERN, B. H. & R. RUGH, 1944 - "Efficacy of M-Amino-Benzoate as an anesthetic for amphibian embryos." Proc. Soc. Exp. Biol. & Med. 57:127.

MICHAELIS, M. & J. H. QUASTEL, 1941 - "The site of action of narcotics and respiratory processes." Bioch. Jour. 35:518.

MOOG, F., 1944 - "The chloretone sensitivity of frog's eggs in relation to respiration and development." Jour. Cell. & Comp. Physiol. 23:131.

NARINS, S. A., 1930 - "A quantitative study of the effect of chloroform on oxygen consumption of the tadpole (Rana clamitans). Physiol. Zool. 3:519.

PARKER, G. H., 1939 - "General anesthesia by cooling." Proc. Soc. Exp. Biol. & Med. 42:186.

PARNAS, J. K., & S. KRASINSKA, 1921 - "Uber den Stoffwechsel der Amphibien larven." Biochem. Zeitschr. 116:108.

PRASLICKA, M., 1955 - "The influence of the simultaneous effect of x-ray irradiation and some narcotics and stimulants on the mortality of tadpoles." Folia Biol. (Prague) 1:3750380.

RIDEAL, E. K., 1945 - "Surface chemistry in relation to biology." Endeavor. 4:83.

ROBLIN, R. O., Jr., 1946 - "Metabolite antagonists." Chem. Rev. 38:255.

ROTHLIN, E., 1932 - "MS 222 (losliches anaesthesin) ein Narkotikum fur Koltbluter." Schweiz. und. Wchnschr. 62:1042.

TWITTY, V. C., 1935 "Nature of paralysis produced in Amblystoma by Triturus transplants." Proc. Soc. Exp. Biol. & Med. 32:1283.

VALKO, E. I., 1946 - "Surface active agents in biology and medicine." Ann. N.Y. Acad. Sci. 46:451.

●

"Life has been compared to a beautiful tapestry, woven in intricate design of many threads and colors. By means of physics, chemistry, physiology, anatomy, embryology and genetics we unravel this texture, separate its constituent threads and colors, but lose the pattern as a whole. These analytical sciences have enormously increased our knowledge of life's constituent elements and processes, but the pattern of the tapestry is usually neglected or ignored."

"Living things are analyzed into organs, tissues, cells, chromosomes, genes, and their functions into tropisms, reflexes and forced movements, while the synthesis of all of these elements into the broader aspects of the organism and its relation to environment are too much neglected. Of course, analysis is necessary, but so also is synthesis if we are to see organisms as living beings. We lose sight of these larger aspects of life in the process of analysis, unless we reverse this procedure from time to time and consider organisms and environment synthetically".

". . . no philosopher, scientist, or average human being can avoid asking the question WHY, or fail to feel that the end, goal, meaning or purpose of any phenomenon in nature is the most significant inquiry that can be made about it. . . . In his 'De Patibus Animalium' (Aristotle) maintained that the essence of a living animal is found not in <u>what</u> it is, or <u>how</u> it acts, but <u>why</u> it is as it is and acts as it does."

E. G. Conklin 1944 Trans. N.Y. Acad. Sci. 6:125

18. EXPERIMENTS WITH THE AMPHIBIAN GERMINAL VESICLE

PURPOSE: To study the living but isolated nucleus of the amphibian egg, with special emphasis on the chromosome structure and the effects on the chromosomes of various environmental variables.

MATERIALS:
    <u>Biological</u>: Ovaries of any Anuran or Urodele.

    <u>Technical</u>: Stenders, Syracuse dishes, depression slides, medicine droppers, electrical apparatus (diagram on p. 175), and various solutions:
        <u>Phenol red</u> as pH indicator.
        <u>Nuclear medium</u> (N-medium) which is Ca-free Ringers solution made up with glass distilled water as follows:
            NaCl .... 0.66 gms.
            KCl .... 0.014 gms.
            Water .... 100 cc (pyrex distilled)
            Buffer: Unnecessary, but with small nuclei can reduce pH to 5.9
        <u>Fixatives</u>: Bouin, $HgCl_2$ sat. aq., 4% formalin, aceto-orcein.
        <u>Stains</u>: Mayer's Haemalum, 1% crystal violet in N-medium; aceto-orcein (45% glacial acetic acid and 0.5% orcein), 1% methyl green in 1% acetic acid.
        <u>General</u>: 0.1 N-$NaHPO_4$
            0.001 N, 0.003 N, and M/100 HCl
            0.001 N, 0.003 N, and M/100 NaOH

METHOD:
    <u>Precautions</u>:
        1. All glassware is to be thoroughly washed and rinsed at least once with glass distilled water to remove all traces of metallic ions.
        2. Glass distilled water must be used to make up all solutions, particularly N-medium. Ordinary distilled water often contains traces of copper which are deleterious.
        3. Calcium and all heavy metals must be avoided. (N-medium is calcium-free).
        4. Reduce to a minimum the amount of light, carbon dioxide, and bacteria.
        5. Keep the isolated germinal vesicle beneath the surface of the solution at all times to avoid contact with air, air bubbles, surface films, and dust particles.

    <u>Controls</u>:
        1. The standard control is the fixed and stained germinal vesicle.
        2. Where environmental variables are used the environment of the nuclear (N) medium is to be considered as the control environment.
        3. Where the ⁻OH ions are used, the +H ions may be used for contrast; where an electric current is used, it may be reversed.

---

* This exercise has been organized with the generous aid of Dr. W. R. Duryee.

Procedure:

Where possible, use the eggs of some Urodele for in these the germinal vesicles are relatively larger and the chromosomes are the more easily studied than in the eggs of other amphibia. However, since the frog (Anura) is more readily available, the following description will be concerned with the germinal vesicles of Rana pipiens.

A. REMOVAL OF THE GERMINAL VESICLE

Remove the ovary of a sexually mature and hibernating female frog and place it in Amphibian Ringer's solution in a finger bowl. Wash free any adherent blood. This ovary will remain healthy for about 24 hours at 20°C. or for about 4 days at 10°C.

Cut off a small portion of the ovary (20 to 30 eggs) and transfer to a #2 Stender containing Nuclear Medium. Pour off this solution after a few minutes and replace with fresh N-medium. Cut this piece of ovary into smaller pieces each containing 3 to 4 eggs and transfer one such cluster of eggs to a Syracuse dish containing N-medium.

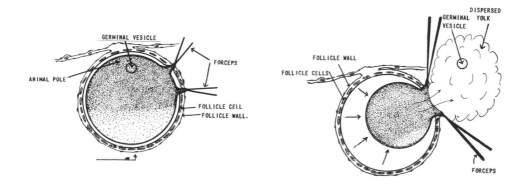

REMOVAL OF THE AMPHIBIAN GERMINAL VESICLE

With very sharp forceps and under the low magnification of the microscope, make a small tear at a point in the follicle sac and egg wall in the region of the animal hemisphere but close to the margin of the vegetal material. The germinal vesicle is located in the center of the animal hemisphere. The tear should not be larger than 1/3 the diameter of the egg. The egg substance will immediately flow out, carrying with it the rather large and spherical germinal vesicle. When working with the smaller, immature oöcytes, a needle puncture may suffice to liberate the vesicle.

Using a clean medicine dropper, force a gentle flow of N-medium over the isolated germinal vesicle to wash away the yolk globules which are adherent to it. This will become increasingly difficult with time so that the cleaning procedure should immediately follow the liberation of the vesicle. The clean germinal vesicle should appear as a clear spherical sac without visible contents.

The chromosomes cannot be seen at low magnification. Transfer the germinal vesicle to fresh N-medium in another Syracuse dish for further cleaning. The transfer can be made by sucking up a small amount of fluid into the medicine dropper and then drawing up the vesicle, followed by more of the same fluid. The transfer must be made in nuclear fluid to a position beneath the surface of the fluid in the new container. The vesicle must not come into contact with air. Re-examine the vesicle and clean it further if necessary. The yolk actions tend to coagulate the vesicle and must be removed entirely. A medicine dropper with diameter slightly greater than the diameter of the vesicle can be used to suck the vesicle in and out (gently), the edges of the dropper thus scraping off the adherent yolk.

B. EXAMINATION OF THE GERMINAL VESICLE

Place a small amount of Permoplast on each of the four corners of a small, square coverslip (a quarter size coverslip is satisfactory). Add equal amounts of Permoplast to each of the corners but only enough to elevate the coverslip a bit more than the diameter of the vesicle. Now transfer the germinal vesicle, in a drop or two of N-medium, to a clean slide and gently cover with the coverslip. Add more N-medium from the side of necessary. The advantage of a small coverslip is that various reagents may be added readily from the side.

OBSERVATIONS AND EXPERIMENTS:

1. NORMAL APPEARANCE OF THE GERMINAL VESICLE
   a. The isolated germinal vesicle should appear exactly as it does in the egg except for a very slight swelling.
   b. The hyaline condition of the ground substance should persist for several hours.
   c. The nucleoli and the hyaline chromosomes should maintain their relative central positions in respect to each other.
   d. Fixation pictures are distinctly different.

To see the chromosomes within the central chromosome core it will be necessary to add a drop of 0.1-N $NaHPO_4$ or a small amount of calcium (as in normal Ringer's solution). The chromosomes may then be stained with 1% Crystal Violet or with Aceto-orcein and studied under high power magnification. With Aceto-orcein, which is a combination fixative and stain, the vesicle is permanently fixed.

The germinal vesicles of large, medium, and small ovarian eggs are structurally different and should be studied in detail before applying any of the experimental procedures. The smaller eggs are relatively more transparent, due to the lack of yolk or pigment. The general characteristics of the three types are as follows:

Large egg vesicle (nucleus)
   1. Nuclear membrane has outside sac-like bulges (see photographs).
   2. Nucleoli clusters appear in the center.
   3. The chromosome frame appears in the center of the ring of nucleoli. This is a gel structure which gives rise to the first maturation spindle.
   4. Very small contracted chromosomes appear on the framework. The diploid numbers of a few of the common forms are as follows:

Bufo (various species)	- 22 chromosomes
Rana esculanta	- 24
Rana pipiens, R. fusca	- 26
Rana catesbiana	- 28 (26?)
Hyla arborea	- 24
Triturus (various species)	- 24
T. viridescens	- 22
Desmognathus	- 24
Salamandra	- 24
Amblystoma tigrinum	- 28 (axolotl 16, 24, 28, 30)
Plethodon	- 24

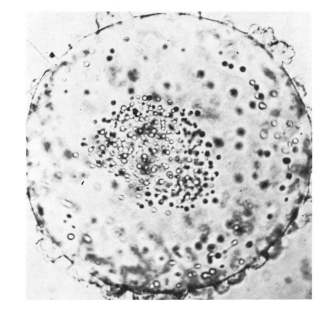

GERMINAL VESICLE
OVARIAN EGG
OF
ANURAN

CHROMOSOME CORE
IN CENTER: SACS
ON SURFACE: COLLOID
GROUND SUBSTANCE

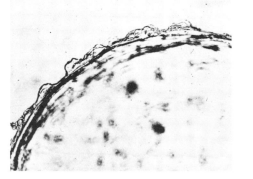

GERMINAL VESICLE
STUDIES

(Courtesy Dr. W. R. Duryee)

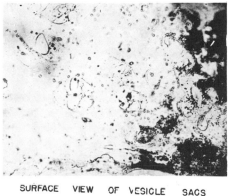

SIDE VIEW VESICLE SACS & MEMBRANE

SURFACE VIEW OF VESICLE SACS

TEMPORARIA CHROMOSOME IN 0.1% NACL

R. PIPIENS CHROMOSOMES IN
GERMINAL VESICLE

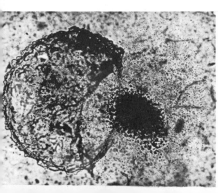

OUTWARD FLOW OF
COLLOID UPON TEARING
NUCLEAR MEMBRANE:

SHRINKAGE (70%)
DURING FIXATION OF
OF T. PYRRHOCASTER
GERMINAL VESICLE

NUCLEAR SUBSTANCE A GEL.

Half or medium-sized egg vesicle (nucleus)
  1. Nuclear sacs small.
  2. Nucleoli are next to nuclear wall.
  3. Chromosome frame fills the entire nucleus.
  4. Chromosomes are spread out to their maximum extension, and possess large lateral loops.

Small-sized egg vesicle (nucleus)
  1. Nuclear sacs barely visible.
  2. Nucleoli peripheral.
  3. Chromosome frame fills the entire nucleus.
  4. Chromosomes are much smaller than in the larger nuclei.

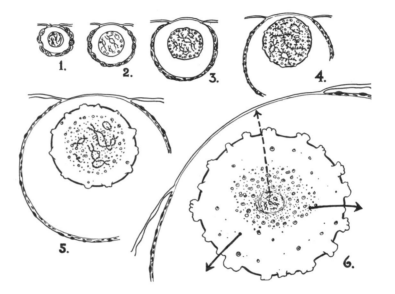

Normal nuclear growth cycle of the ovum of Rana pipiens. (Stage 1) Smallest follicle in which the chromosomes within the germinal vesicle can be seen. (Stage 2) The paired chromosomes are barely visible, embedded in a nucleoplasmic gel. Egg diameters less than 200 microns. (Stage 3) Eggs measuring from 200 to 500 microns in diameter, more detail visible through the transparent theca cells. Lateral loop production begins. Zone of large irregular nucleoli may be seen just beneath the nuclear membrane. (Stage 4) First development of yellow-brown color and yolk. Eggs range in size from 500 to 700 microns in diameter. Chromosomes attain length of about 450 microns. For salamanders of comparable stage chromosomes measure 700 microns in length. (Stage 5) Chromosome frame begins contraction while the nucleus continues to grow in eggs ranging in diameter from 750 to 850 microns. This is approximately half the ultimate size. Chromosomes shorten and have fewer and smaller loops. The major nucleolar production continues and sacs appear on the surface of the nuclear membrane. (Stage 6) Egg diameter about 1.8 millimeters and germinal vesicle is of maximum size. Chromosome frame now about 1/1000 of the nuclear volume, coated by a denser substance which can be coagulated by the calcium ion. Chromosomes have shortened to 40 microns or less and have lost all large and small hyaline bodies called loop fragments.

Heavy arrows indicate the mixing of nuclear material in the cytoplasm after the breakdown of the germinal vesicle. The dotted arrow indicates migration of the central chromosomal mass toward the animal pole to become the maturation spindle for the first polar body. (From W. R. Duryee, 1950, Ann. N.Y. Acad. Sci., 50, Art. 8.)

2. PERMANENT FIXATION AND STAINING OF THE GERMINAL VESICLE

The student is again cautioned about the use of fixatives in the laboratory where living material is also to be kept. Further, fixation artifacts are most readily apparent in germinal vesicle fixation, hence this section should be treated as a further study of the germinal vesicle and its reactions to environmental factors. This in addition to acquaintance with methods of providing permanent preparations.

A rather new fixative-stain is recommended (see La Cour, 1941) in which aceto-orcein is applied directly to the isolated vesicle. This stain consists of 45% acetic (glacial) acid and 0.5% orcein into which the vesicle is placed for 30-60 seconds. It is then run up rapidly through the alcohols (in which some of the dye will dissolve out) and into an alcohol-free mounting medium. A stain of 1% Methyl Green (acidified) acts in much the same manner. Other permanent mounts may be made with Bouin's fixation followed by Mayer's fixation followed by Mayer's haemalum stain.

A study of the action of fixatives on the vesicle is very profitable. Isolate 20 to 30 full-sized vesicles in N-medium and, while observing them under low-magnification of the microscope (under elevated coverslips) add singly such fixatives as Bouin's, 4% formalin, saturated $HgCl_2$ in water, etc. Immediate changes in size and consistency of the vesicle should be noted. Since Bouin's contains an acid, follow the Bouin-fixation with some alkaline treatment to attempt to counteract the acid factor in this fixation.

A study of the fixed germinal vesicle raises the legitimate question as to how far we may assume that fixed material accurately represents the structures of the living germinal vesicle. Probably the more accurate picture is a composite one, arrived at by the study of both fresh and fixed material.

3. IONIC EFFECTS

A visible iso-electric point can be demonstrated passing through the germinal vesicle by the addition, to one side of the coverslip, of a small drop of dilute HCl. If a slow reaction is desired, use 0.001N-HCl; if a fast reaction is desired, use 0.003N-HCl. The germinal vesicle is negatively charged. Note the Brownian movement of granules. The diffusion of weak acids through the germinal vesicle gives an effect known as the "Ring Phenomenon". As proteins within the vesicle reach the iso-electric point (I.E.P., hereafter) they become insoluble and appear as floccules. The size of the floccule is relative to the speed of the acid penetration. If penetration is fast, the floccules will be small; if penetration is slow, they will aggregate and be large. Observe the fusion of micelles to build up the so-called "linin reticulum".

The chromosomes will appear and become distinct only when the solution immediately around reaches the I.E.P. of the chromosomes. Watch the I.E.P. passing to the center of the germinal vesicle and the subsequent swelling of the outer colloidal area, which becomes positively charged and reverses its reaction.

When the germinal vesicle in weak acid clears, add a similar amount of weak alkali (NaOH) and the reactions will be reversed. In NaOH alone the germinal vesicle will burst. If a very dilute base is used, this swelling can be compensated by acid shrinking. The reactions can be made to go back and forth under experimental control.

4. ELECTRICAL CHARGE AND THE REACTION OF THE GERMINAL VESICLE

An electrical set-up has been devised by means of which a known current may be sent through the germinal vesicle and then reversed. A brief description of the apparatus is given below. The equipment consists of a 45-volt dry cell, a reversing switch, key, platinum electrodes mounted in glass, with voltmeter and milli-ammeter in the circuit as shown in the accompanying diagram on the following page.

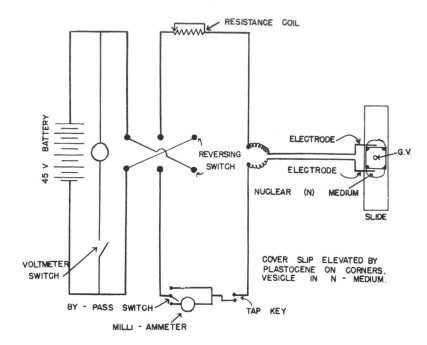

ELECTRICAL STIMULATING — EQUIPMENT FOR GERMINAL VESICLES

Study the electrical set-up before attempting to use it, making particular note of the various switches. The milli-ammeter and the voltmeter must be out of circuit at all times and are to be used only by the instructor to check the apparatus. The student should use only the reversing switch and the tap key. The reversing switch will reverse the direction of the current and the tap key will complete the circuit between the points of the platinum electrodes providing there intervenes a conducting (salt) medium.

Germinal vesicles should be placed on slides in such a manner as to allow a small amount of fluid to flow beyond each side of the Permoplast supported coverslip. The platinum electrode must be immersed in the fluid on each side of the coverslip, and consequently on each side of the germinal vesicle. When the object is in focus beneath the compound microscope, press the tap key down and hold it as long as you want the current to pass through the solution. To reverse the current simply throw the reversing switch. (See Findlay: "Practical Chemistry" p. 153 for comparable set-up.)

a. Sign of Nuclear Charge: Use the germinal vesicle of half-sized eggs in which the chromosomes are relatively large. When the vesicle is in position, press the tap key for two-second contact and observe the substance of the vesicle piling up on the positive (+) side, indicating a negative (-) charge. Watch the migration of the nuclear substance and the effect of the release of the current.

b. Reactions of Chromosomes: If copper (Cu) electrodes are used, which give off hydrogen ions, sustain the current and note that the chromosomes will pile up at the positive (+) pole while the wall of the germinal vesicle will burst toward the negative (-) pole, due to the release in that direction of hydroxyl (OH) ions. It would be well to add a drop of phenol red to this solution prior to initiating the current, in order to detect these changes in pH. (It is important that after each experiment the copper electrodes be thoroughly cleaned with cotton and acid alcohol, followed by distilled water, since they will corrode.)

c. Combined Acid and Electric Current" Use the set-up as in b. above but before passing the current through the solution containing the germinal vesicle, add to the N-medium, at a point opposite yourself, a small drop of 0.001N-HCl. This will bring in the hydrogen ion effect at right angles to the direction of the current. As the I.E.P. passes over the germinal vesicle, apply the current in short shocks. A continuous current will produce an irreversible coagulum. Movement inside the vesicle will be oriented within the imposed electrical field.

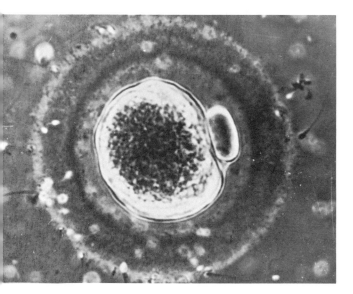

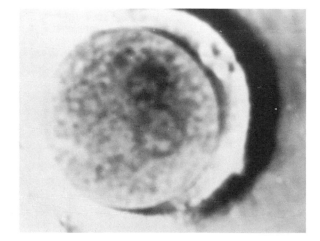

Fertilization of the human ovum. Note extruded polar body and unsuccessful surrounding spermatozoa. (Courtesy Dr. L. B. Shettles, from "Ovum Humanum", Hafner, Pub. N.Y.)

Human ovum showing two extruded polar bodies and two pronuclei, one from the ovum and the other from the penetrated spermatozoan. From "Ovum Humanum", Dr. L. B. Shettles courtesy. (Pub. Hafner, N.Y.)

REFERENCES

BRACHET, J., 1939 - "Quelques proprieties chimiques de la vesicule germinative isolee." Arch. f. exper. Zellforsch. 22:541.

BRIGGS, R., T. C. KING - "Factors affecting the transplantability of the nuclei of frog embryonic cells. Jour. Exp. Zool. 122:485.

DURYEE, W. R., 1938 - "A microdissection study of amphibian chromosomes." Biol. Bull. 75:345.

DURYEE, W. R., 1949 - "The nature of radiation injury to Amphibian cell nucleus." Jour. Nat. Cancer Inst. 10:735-793.

LA COUR, L., 1941 - "Aceto-orcein: a new stain-fixative for chromosomes." Stain Techno. 16:169.

MOORE, B., 1957 - "Chromosomal vesicles and double nuclei in amphibian embryos." Jour. Morph. 101:209-223.

NEBEL, B. R., 1939 - "Chromosome structure." Bot. Rev. 5:563.

OGUMA, K. & S. MAKINO, 1937 - "A new list of the chromosome numbers in Vertebrata." Jour. Fac. Sci. Hakkaido Imp. Univ. Japan. 5:297.

SAMBUICHI, H., 1957 - "The roles of the nucleus and the cytoplasm in development." Jour. Sci. Hiroshima Univ. Ser. B., 17:33-46.

SHETTLES, L., 1960 - "Ovum Huminum". Hafner Pub. Co., New York City. 79 pages.

STRAUB, J., 1943 - "Chromosomenstructur." Naturwiss. 31:97.

WADDINGTON, G H., 1939 - "The physico-chemical structure of the chromosomes and the gene." Am. Nat. 73:300.

19. ANDROGENESIS

PURPOSE: To study the variations in early development of the embryo under the influence of the haploid set of chromosomes from the sperm nucleus alone.

MATERIALS:
Biological: Recently inseminated eggs of any Amphibian, preferably Triturus or Rana.

Technical: Glass needles and needle holder; micro-pipette (0.16 mm. in diameter) with attached rubber tubing; #2 Stenders with covers.

METHOD:
Precautions:
1. Since the polar bodies are very small and not distinctly colored, it is important that maximum spot-lighting be achieved. The heat of the light must be absorbed, preferably by water-filled Florence flask. The overhead and other lights should be off to reduce extraneous sources of light.
2. The time of oviposition must be known because the egg nucleus is to be removed as it comes to the surface of the egg to give off the second polar body. In Rana pipiens this occurs from 15 to 35 minutes after insemination.
3. A minimum of cytoplasm and yolk is to be removed with the egg nucleus.
4. Haploid eggs and embryos are less viable than controls, and must be given special post operative care.

Controls:
1. Control eggs should be punctured in a manner identical with the experimentals, but at a point well removed from the position of the maturation spindle of the egg nucleus. The same amount of yolk should be removed.
2. Some untreated eggs should be allowed to develop to determine whether they are otherwise entirely normal.

Procedure:
Provide yourself with optimum lighting conditions. This includes a spot light directed at the eggs from a 45° angle in order to shine on the upper surface of each egg and to cast a shadow from the first polar body and, by contrast, to reveal the polar body pit. Low power magnification will be adequate after the polar bodies and pits are recognized.

It is necessary here to give a brief description of the amphibian egg nucleus at the time of oviposition, and during the few minutes after insemination. The nucleus of the ovarian egg of the hibernating and non-ovulating amphibian is in the germinal vesicle stage, prior to any maturation divisions. This germinal vesicle breaks down at the time of ovulation (liberation from the ovary) so that coelomic eggs show neither a vesicle nor chromosome figures. As the egg enters the oviduct (within 2 hours) the metaphase figure of the first maturation division appears, and as the egg progresses through the upper third of the oviduct it extrudes the first of two polar bodies. The egg nucleus remains near the periphery and about the time the egg reaches the uterus, the metaphase figure of the second maturation division will appear. The egg remains in this condition until it is fertilized (or dies). The procedure described below takes advantage of the peripheral position of the egg nucleus, removing it before it has a chance to fuse with the sperm nucleus entering the egg at another point.

---

* The author acknowledges, with appreciation, the help of Dr. K. R. Porter in organizing this exercise.

Fertilization of the egg and the removal of the female nucleus (androgenesis) in Triturus viridescens.

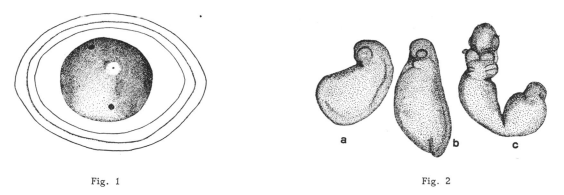

Fig. 1   Fig. 2

Fig. 1.   Drawing of an egg in its capsule about 12 minutes after deposition, showing two dark sperm marks and the lightly pigmented polar area containing in its center the second maturation spindle, marked by a small pigmented spot.

Fig. 2.   Diagram of the pipette, needle, and an egg in position for puncturing.

Androgenetic embryos of Triturus viridescens compared with control and younger diploid embryos.

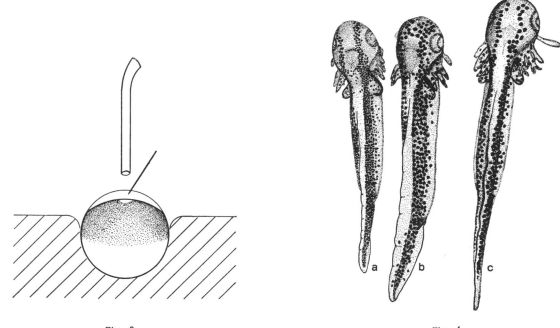

Fig. 3   Fig. 4

Fig. 3.   Androgenetic embryo 7 days old (b), the diploid control of the same age and from the same female (c), and a younger diploid embryo (a), of about the same stage of development as the androgenetic embryo. The head and eye vesicles of the androgenetic embryo are smaller than those of either one of the two diploid embryos.

Fig. 4.   Androgenetic larva 12 days old (a), the diploid control of the same age of (c), and younger diploid larva (b), of about the same stage of development and from the same female as the androgenetic larva. The differences in the size of the gills as well as the size of the pigment cells of the haploid and the two diploid larvae are very noticeable. The haploid larva is also shorter than both diploid larvae.

(Kaylor, 1937: Jour. Exp. Zool. 76:375)

REMOVAL OF THE FEMALE NUCLEAR ELEMENTS

An ovulating female frog is secured and concentrated frog sperm suspensions are prepared as thin films in 4 Syracuse dishes. When the optical equipment is adjusted, strip
a few of the eggs from the female into one of the Syracuse dishes. At 10 minute intervals
strip additional eggs into other Syracuse dishes, marking the exact time of insemination
on each dish. Within 3 to 5 minutes after insemination, flood each dish with Spring Water
(or Standard Solution) so that the eggs are completely covered. The other dishes are to
be similarly flooded at comparable intervals thereafter. The water on the eggs may be
changed to clear it of excess spermatozoa.

The nucleus is to be pulled out by means of a glass needle. This needle should be made
of soft glass but must have a sharp and rigid point. A large number of needles should
be made available with an appropriate needle holder.

When the egg is inseminated the first polar body is already located between the egg and
the vitelline membrane. This small gray bead representing an extruded nucleus may
sometimes be located on the animal pole surface, near its center. One must focus very
sharply onto this animal pole surface, and use light coming onto the egg from an angle,
in order to see the very small polar body and its shadow.

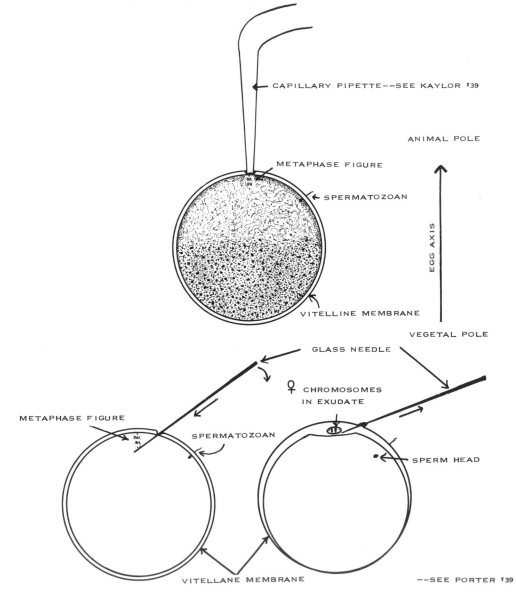

From 7 to 10 minutes after insemination there will appear a small depigmented area near the center of the animal pole, and within this area will develop a pin-point depression. This is caused by a temporary retraction of the surface coating just above the forming second maturation spindle.

Insert the tip end of a glass needle just below this polar body depression at such an angle that it will extend below the spindle and with a very slight withdrawing and upward motion, bring the spindle out with an exudation mass of yolk. This mass will necessarily be somewhat larger than the size of the first polar body, but with practice its size may be reduced and yet include the whole second spindle. Since there are a total of 4 Syracuse dishes of eggs which were inseminated at 10 minute intervals, the second dish will be ready about the time the first dish of eggs has been experimentally treated.

ANDROGENESIS IN THE URODELE EGG

The eggs of Triton, Triturus pyrrhogaster and T. viridescens have been used successfully in androgenesis. The salamander egg is generally fertilized as it passes through the genital tract of the female where spermatophores are stored for variable periods. Ovulation can be induced by anterior pituitary injection (see section on Induced Breeding).

Since the eggs are fertilized shortly before they are deposited by the female, it is important (when using Urodele eggs) to note the exact time of oviposition of each egg. The removal of the maturation spindle must occur within 30 minutes after oviposition.

Urodele eggs are normally polyspermic and the multiple sperm entrance points can be identified by dark spots caused representing the accumulation of pigment. Toward the center of the animal hemisphere will be seen a clear area, considerably larger than a sperm entrance spot, marking the position of the metaphase spindle. With watchmaker's forceps remove the several layers of jelly but avoid the vitelline membrane. With a wide-mouthed pipette transfer the egg to a Syracuse (operating) dish in which there is a wax depression appropriately molded to fit the egg. Use Urodele Growing Solution or Spring Water as the medium.

The Urodele maturation spindle may be removed by the needle method, as described above. Another method, developed by Kaylor (1937), involves sucking out the nuclear elements with a micro-pipette. The egg must be oriented with the animal hemisphere dorsal in position. Then, with a fine glass needle (1 to 2μ in thickness) rupture the vitelline membrane, but avoid injury to the egg cortex, at several points directly above the position of the spindle. Attach a micro-pipette to a small bore rubber tubing, the tapered end of the pipette having a diameter of not more than 0.16 mm. Place the end of the rubber tubing in your mouth, hold the pipette firmly in one hand, and with the other hand adjust the low power microscope and the operating dish. Bring the open end of the micro-pipette down directly onto the vitelline membrane just above the region of the spindle and with negative pressure (gentle suction) draw the entire spindle out of the egg. A small amount of cytoplasm and yolk will be included, and this must be kept at a minimum. Transfer the operated egg to a covered #2 Stender with fresh Urodele Growing Solution or Spring Water and keep it at a constant temperature in the vicinity of 15° to 18°C.

CARE OF MATERIAL:

Operated eggs should be examined within several hours to determine whether they are cleaving. Such eggs as seem to be developing, and show operation exudates, should be isolated in #2 Stenders with the appropriate medium and should be kept at the cooler temperatures within the normal range. Controls must be kept at the same temperatures and under the same conditions of medium and space.

OBSERVATIONS AND TABULATION OF DATA:

There are two criteria for successful androgenetic operations.

1. <u>Delay in cleavage and early development.</u> The first cleavage may be delayed as much as 45 minutes (at 22°C.) and development through neurulation will tend to be delayed. After hatching, the embryo will manifest those characteristics normally associated with experimentally induced haploidy such as in artificial parthenogenesis. These include stunting, dorso-ventral thickening, dorsal flexion of the head and tail, oedema, reduction of the gills, etc. (see photographs of abnormalities in development and haploid larva in section on Artificial Parthenogenesis). Make drawings of androgenetic embryos and tadpoles.

2. <u>Chromosome count which should be haploid.</u> This can be determined in the neurula stage either by sectioning and staining the material, or by making coverglass smears of neural crest cells (see Culturing Isolated Embryonic Cells) and staining them with Harris' haematoxylin. Those tadpoles which survive for 10 days or more can have their tails clipped and examined (see Tail Tip Chromosome Technique) for chromosome figures, without killing the tadpole.

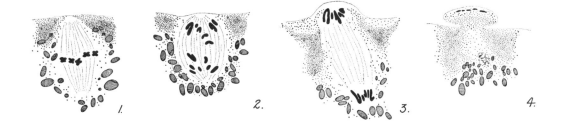

POLAR BODY FORMATION: RANA PIPIENS

(From Porter, 1939: Biol. Bull. 77"233)

Figs. 1-4.   Semi-diagrammatic representations of four stages in second polar body formation of R. pipiens eggs. Drawings were made with camera lucida and give exact distribution of pigment granules, yolk platelets and chromosomes, only part of which are shown. Selected from considerable material sectioned at 10 μ. (Eggs inseminated and kept at 12°C.) 1125 X.

Fig. 1.   Division spindle as in egg at time of insemination.

Fig. 2.   Anaphase of maturation division. Stage at which spindle can be seen from exterior of egg as small black dot. Egg fixed 35 minutes after insemination.

Fig. 3.   Early telophase. Egg fixed 50 minutes after insemination.

Fig. 4.   Polar body just forming. Egg fixed 56 minutes after insemination.

REFERENCES

BALTZER, F. & V. de ROCHE, 1936 - "Uber die Entwicklungsfahigkeit haploiden Triton alpestris." Rev. Suisse de Zool. 43:495.
BRIGGS, R., T. KING, 1953 - "Factors affecting the transplantability of nuclei of frog embryonic cells." Jour. Exp. Zool. 122:485.
EAST, E. M., 1934 - "The nucleus-plasma problem." Am. Nat. 68:289 & 402.
FANKHAUSER, G. & C. MOORE, 1941 - "Cytological and experimental studies of polyspermy in the newt, Triturus viridescens. II. The behavior of the sperm nuclei in androgenetic eggs (in the absence of the egg nucleus)." Jour. Morph. 68:387.
KAYLOR, C. T., 1941 - "Studies in experimental haploidy in salamander larvae. II. Cytological studies on androgenetic eggs of Triturus viridescens." Biol. Bull. 81:402.
MOORE, B., 1957 - "DNA in diploid and androgenetic amphibian hybrids." Jour. Morph. 101:227-274.
PORTER, K. R., 1941 - "Diploid and androgenetic haploid hybridization between two forms of Rana pipiens Schreiber." Biol. Bull. 80:238. (see also Biol. Bull. 77:223).

20. ARTIFICIAL PARTHENOGENESIS *

PURPOSE: To repeat the earlier experiments, using modern methods of inducing ovulation and of equipment, in an attempt to initiate the development of the amphibian egg
by artificial means (i. e. , without benefit of spermatozoa).

MATERIALS:

Biological: Uterine eggs from an ovulating anuran: Rana or Bufo. Blood from a
second non-ovulating female anuran, same species.

Technical: Slides, Petri dishes, finger bowls, #2 Stenders, moist chamber, section lifter, sharp-pointed (3 to 9 μ) glass or platinum (20 to 30 μ) needles, and china marking pencil.

METHOD:

Precautions:
1. All articles and female frogs must be kept sperm-sterile. The instruments
and glassware may be boiled for 5 minutes or immersed in 70% alcohol and
air dried.
2. The female frog which produces the eggs for the experiment should be isolated from all males for several days prior to the experiment and should be
washed off with tap water and dried before stripping.

Controls: Two types of controls are necessary for this experiment.
1. Some eggs are to remain untreated, but should be placed side-by-side with
the eggs experimentally treated. This provides identical environmental conditions for the experimentals and the controls, with but a single variable.
2. The eggs should be tested to determine whether they are in fertilizable condition. Following the conclusion of the experiment, some of the uterine eggs
should be normally inseminated by frog spermatozoa, of the same species,
in another laboratory. There must be no possible contamination of the experimental eggs with spermatozoa.

Procedure:
1. Adjust a low-power microscope so that the heat-absorbed light will strike
the eggs from a 45° angle from above. A lantern slide cover glass might be
used to protect the microscope stage from water.
2. Place 10 clean microscope slides, a slight distance apart, on clean paper
towelling. On the upper left hand corner of each mark "C" (for controls) and
below on the lower left hand corner of each slide mark "X" (for experimentals), using a china marking pencil. Number the slides in sequence.
3. Strip a single row of eggs from the uteri of an ovulating female, placing
them along the length of the slide opposite "C" and then another opposite "X".
Try to strip eggs in a single row so that they will not lie over each other,
and will adhere to the slide. Place all 10 slides of eggs in a moist chamber
where they may remain for an hour or more without deleterious effects.
(The chamber should have stood for at least an hour so that the contained air
is completely saturated with water vapor.) Such eggs will lose their CO_2
and thereby facilitate their physiological maturation (Bataillon & Tchou-Su,
1930).
4. Pith a non-ovulating female frog; lay it on some paper towelling; cut through
the leg muscles to prevent further reflex movements; open the abdomen and

---

* This laboratory procedure has been organized with the very generous help of Dr. C. L. Parmenter. The results could also be
called "gynogenetic haploidy."

expose the heart. With the frog on its back cut off the tip end of its ventricle and allow the blood to flow freely into the body cavity, mixing there with the coelomic fluid. Keep the abdomen closed until ready to use the blood.

5. Remove one slide from the moist chamber. Take a small strip of abdominal muscle from the non-ovulating female, draw it through the mixture of blood and coelomic fluid, and gently pass it over each of the two rows of eggs. Avoid any pressure on the eggs but see that each egg is provided with a partial coating of blood and coelomic fluid.

6. Cortical stimulation. Gently but firmly prick each egg with a sharp point of a glass or platinum needle. The puncture should be applied within the animal hemisphere but not in its exact center where the second maturation spindle is likely to be located. Leave the eggs in row "C" untouched as controls.

7. Immediately after pricking the experimental row of eggs, immerse the slide in Spring Water or Standard Solution in which normal development is known to occur. It is best to use Petri dishes and only about 2 cm. depth of medium to cover.

8. Repeat the above procedure with 4 other slides from the moist chamber.

9. Follow the above procedure with the remaining 5 slides from the moist chamber but limit the pricking to the vegetal hemisphere of the egg. Mark these slides to indicate location of stimulation.

If time permits, the same procedure should be followed with single variations which might increase the incidence of successful stimulation. Such variables are as follows:

a. Allow the eggs to remain within the uterus at 10°C. for 5 days before stripping (Zorzoli and Rugh, 1941). Such aged eggs must be allowed to come to the laboratory temperature before stimulation.

b. Keep the female at refrigerator (4°C.) temperature, and in the moist chamber provided with ice cubes, to determine whether a lower temperature alone would increase the sensitivity of the egg to artificial stimulation.

c. Omit the use of blood or serum (Guyer, 1907; Bataillon, 1911 and 1919).

d. Vary the depth of cortical injury, deep or shallow pricking.

e. Allow the eggs to dry (partially) on the slide before pricking.

f. Allow the jelly to swell in water to various degrees, before stimulating. The cortical pricking will be a bit more difficult through swollen jelly.

g. Follow the artificial stimulation of the egg by immersion in media of various osmotic conditions.

h. Determine the role of the presence and the absence of calcium (using oxalates and citrates) in the response to parthenogenetic stimulation.

OBSERVATIONS AND TABULATION OF DATA:

Record the data from your experiment in tabular form on the following page.

Total experimentals should include all eggs stimulated. The pseudo-cleavages include irregular cleavages and superficial indications of attempts at cleavage. Along with these data, include a statement regarding the exact method of stimulation, instrument used, and any variations in the prescribed technique. If, perchance, you achieve an unusually high percentage of cleavages, you will want to be able to repeat the procedure in every detail.

There are qualitative aspects of the problem which should be recorded under:

1. Pattern of cleavage when it is not normal. Is the injury point in any way related to the position of the cleavage furrow or the position of the grey crescent?

CONDITION   NUMBER & PERCENTAGE

	Total Controls	Total Experimentals	Pseudo-Cleavages	%	Cleavages	%	Blastula	%	Gastrula	%
Animal Pole										
Vegetal Pole										
Aged Eggs										
Frozen Eggs										
Deep Injury										
Dried Eggs										
Eggs with Swollen Jelly										

2. Rate of cleavage. This observation will have value only if the temperature for the experimentals and controls is identical.
3. Analysis of haploid characteristics of the tadpoles which develop. These include microcephaly (due to sluggish or incomplete gastrulation); dorsal flexion of head and tail; increased number of cells per unit area (except the notochord); and frequent oedema which is thought to be due to the malfunctioning of the excretory system of haploid tadpoles. Oedema alone is not an adequate criterion for there are many environmental factors which will cause this condition in normally diploid tadpoles.
4. Fix and stain tail tips of parthenogenetic tadpoles 9 to 10 days old to make chromosome counts. (See under Tail Tip Technique.)

Many of the parthenogenetically activated eggs will proceed to early stages of development and then cytolyze. It would be instructive to make a rapid preparation of a healthy neurula stage to determine whether the cells are truly haploid, using the method of Tyler (1946). This simply involves placing the neurula on a coverslip; separating or teasing apart its cells in a minimum amount of culture medium, possibly with the aid of 0.1% KOH; inverting the coverslip over a second coverslip on which is placed a large drop of Bouin's fixative. The edges of the upper coverslip should cross the corners of the lower coverslip so that they can be separated the more easily after fixation. If the coverslips are moved over each other slightly, this will separate the cells of the neurula and they will become fixed and most of them will become attached to one of the coverslips. After 5 minutes, place the paired coverslips in a Syracuse dish of Bouin's fluid and gently tease them apart with needles. Allow the fixative to act another 5 minutes. From this point on the coverslips may be treated as any mounted cytological preparation, and may be stained for chromosomes. It should be possible to locate some mitotic figures in the neural crest cells which will answer the question relative to ploidy.

In general the frog's egg lends itself admirably to this type of experiment. The results should give from 0% to 18% cleavages, with the average about 6%. The eggs which show relatively normal cleavages should be isolated and given special care in the hope that some may develop into tadpoles.

REFERENCES

BATAILLON, E., 1929 - "Analyse de la fecondation par la pathenogenese experimentale." Arch. f. Ent. mech. 115:711.

DALCQ, A., 1928 - "Les Bases Physiologiques de la Fecondation et de la Parthenogenese." Les Problemes Biologiques, Paris.

HARVEY, E. B., 1940 - "Development of half-eggs of Arbacia punctualata obtained by centrifuging after fertilization, with special reference to parthenogenetic merogony." Biol. Bull. 78:412.

JUST, E. E., 1939 - "The Biology of the Cell Surface." Blakiston.

KAWAMURA, T., 1940 - "Artificial parthenogenesis in the frog." Jour. Sci. Hiroshima Univ. Ser. B. 8:117.

LILLIE, R. S., 1941 - "Further experiments on artificial parthenogenesis in starfish eggs with a review." Physiol. Zool. 14:239.

LOEB, J., 1921 - "Further observations on the production of parthenogenetic frogs." Jour. Gen. Physiol. 3:529.

PARMENTER, C. L., 1940 - "Chromosome numbers in Rana fusca parthenogenetically developed from eggs with known polar body and cleavage histories." Jour. Morph. 66:241.

PINCUS, G. & H. SHAPIRO, 1940 - "The comparative behavior of mammalian eggs in vivo and in vitro. VII. Further studies on the activation of Rabbit eggs." Proc. Am. Phil. Soc. 83:631.

ROSTAND, J., 1938 - "La Parthenogenese des Vertebres." Actualities Scientifiques er Industrielles. 651:3 (Herman er Ci, Paris).

TCHOU-SU, M., & CHEN, CHAO-HSI, 1940 - "The technique of Professor Bataillon and some three year old parthenogenetic frogs." Chinese Jour. Exp. Biol. 1:303.

TYLER, A., 1941 - "Artificial Parthenogenesis." Biol. Rev. 16:291.

ZORZOLI, A. & R. RUGH, 1941 - "Parthenogenetic stimulation of aged anuran eggs." Proc. Soc. Exp. Biol. & Med. 47:166.

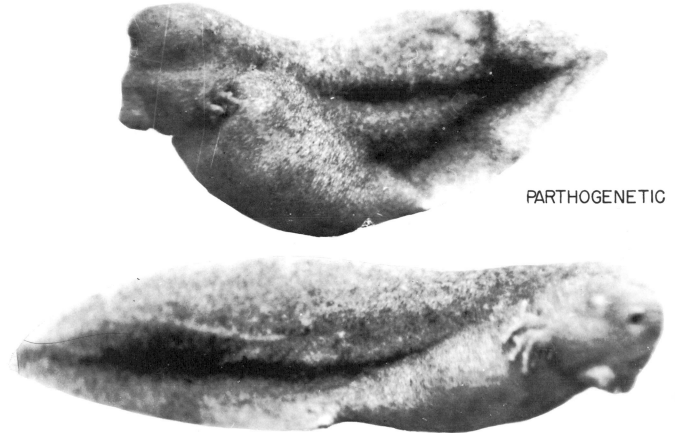

PARTHOGENETIC

CONTROL

RANA PIPIENS

"It is the thought-transmitting propotency of the human species, more than any other, that gives it a superlative lead over all the creatures of the globe."   *A. J. Lotka 1925*

21. PRESSURE EFFECTS ON CLEAVAGE

PURPOSE: To determine the effect of altering the yolk-cytoplasmic axis on cleavage and on the subsequent development of the embryo. Specifically, to attempt to shift the third cleavage from the equatorial to the meridional plane by the application of unequal pressure.

MATERIALS:

    <u>Biological</u>:   Fertilized eggs of any Amphibian.

    <u>Technical</u>:   Petri dishes, glass tubing 2.0 mm. in diameter.

METHOD:

    <u>Precautions</u>:

        1. Do not crowd the eggs; allow sufficient medium for appropriate aeration.

        2. Separate and remove the eggs whose cleavage plane has been altered, placing them in #2 Stenders where they may be given special care.

    <u>Controls</u>: Eggs fertilized at the same time, from the same female, but not subjected to any pressure.

    <u>Procedure</u>:

        1. Strip some uterine eggs into a sperm suspension in an inverted <u>cover</u> of a Petri dish. Gently shake them so that they spread out into a single layer of eggs. Flood with Spring Water or Standard Solution in 5 minutes. Mark the time of insemination on the dish.

        By $2\frac{1}{2}$ hours after insemination these eggs should be in the 2-cell stage, and 1 hour later ($3\frac{1}{2}$ hours after insemination) most of them should be in the four cell stage. The first two cleavages are normally vertical (meridional) and generally bisect each other in the center of the animal pole. The third cleavage is horizontal but slightly above the true equator of the egg, at right angles to both the first and the second cleavages.

        As soon as most of the eggs are in the 4-cell stage, place the <u>bottom</u> of the same Petri dish over the eggs and, while observing them under low power magnification, add water to the upper dish until pressure is exerted on the eggs to such an extent that they are definitely distorted but not ruptured. The bottom of the Petri dish partially filled with water provides the pressure, and this pressure can be controlled by adding or removing water. The dish also acts as a pseudo-lens so that the eggs beneath can be observed directly and at all times. The pressure must be maintained from before the initiation of and through the time of the third cleavage of both the experimentals and controls.

        2. A second method of applying pressure is to draw up the eggs with their jelly into glass tubing which has a diameter slightly less than that of both the egg and its jelly. This will be about 2.0 mm. for Rana pipiens eggs. The eggs should be drawn up by suction at the 4-cell stage, and observed through the side of the tubing, under water. The eggs will be considerably distorted and sketches should be made while the eggs are under pressure and immediately thereafter.

OBSERVATIONS AND TABULATION OF DATA:

The observations here are purely qualitative and a series of sketches or photographs should be made of several eggs whose cleavage planes have been altered. Then the eggs, properly identified with their sketches, should be isolated in #2 Stenders and allowed to develop as far as they will normally. Any variations from the controls should be indicated by parallel sketches of experimentals and controls.

DISCUSSION:

Pfluger (1884) was probably the first to discover that vertically applied pressure will alter the normally horizontal third cleavage plans of the frog's egg and will make it vertical, as are the first two cleavages. This means that in the 8-cell stage, all eight cells extend from the animal to the vegetal pole. Driesch (1892) applied pressure to the cleaving sea-urchin egg in an attempt to alter its cleavage plane. Born (1893) and O. Hertwig (1893) repeated and refined the work on the frog's egg. None of these investigators left series-sketches to indicate whether the grey crescent was involved, and the effect on subsequent cleavages. Their concern was primarily with whether succeeding development would be normal.

The first cleavage in the frog's egg occurs about $2\frac{1}{2}$ hours after insemination, the second about 1 hour later and the third about $\frac{1}{2}$ hour after the second. There is an acceleration of cleavages. Each of the cleavages is at right angles to the preceding cleavage, and the spindle axis lies in the longest protoplasmic axis (see the laws of Hertwig, Sachs, and Balfour in the Glossary). The third cleavage is normally horizontal (equatorial), and the fourth is again meridional (vertical).

If the protoplasmic axis of the blastomeres is shifted at the 4-cell stage, the cleavage plane will be shifted. If the third cleavage, under pressure, is shifted to the vertical, and the egg is then released from pressure, the next cleavage (normally vertical) will tend to be horizontal.

Generally eggs which have been subjected to this type of unequal external pressure will survive perfectly well and will develop quite normally providing the pressure is not maintained too long and it does not rupture the surface coating of the egg. Such a shift in cleavage pattern as generally occurs means a shift in the distribution of nuclei. Since abnormal embryos are not generally produced by altering one of the cleavage planes, it must be assumed that there is no qualitative distribution of the nuclear material in these early blastomeres.

REFERENCES

BORN, G., 1894 - "Ueber neue Compressionversuche an Froscheiern." Jahresbericht der Schlesischen Gesellschaft fur waterlandische Cultu. Zool. Bot.
DRIESCH, H., 1892 - "Zur Verlagerung der Blastomeren des Echinodeneies." Anat. Anz. 8:348.
HERTWIG, O., 1893 - "Ueber den Werth der ersten Furchungszellen fur die Organbildung des Embryo." Arch. Mikr. Anat. 42.
MARSLAND, D. A., 1956 - "Protoplasmic contractility in relation to gel structure." Int. Rev. Cytology. 5:199.
MORGAN, T. H., 1910 - "The effects of altering the position of the cleavage planes in eggs with precocious specification." Arch. f. Ent. mech. 29. (See also "Experimental Embryology:, 1927.)
PFLUGER, E., 1884 - "Ueber die Einwirkung der Schwerkraft und anderer Bedingungen auf die Richtung der Zelltheilung." Arch. Ges. Physiol. 34.
ROUX, W., 1895 - "Gesammelte Abhandlungen uber Entwicklungsmechanik der Organisman." Leipzig.

"Treasure your exceptions"
Bateson

22. THE EFFECT OF CENTRIFUGATION ON DEVELOPMENT

PURPOSE: To determine the susceptibility of various stages (from the unfertilized egg to the neurula stage) to centrifugal force, and the types of abnormalities produced by a shifting of the egg or embryo contents.

MATERIALS:

Biological: Ovulating female frogs (Rana pipiens), sexually mature males (Rana pipiens) and early developmental stages of Amblystoma.

Technical: Centrifuge with large tubes, controlled speed, and brake.
Nujol.

METHOD:

Precautions:

1. Calculate centrifugal force in terms of gravity, using the formula

$$F = \frac{mv^2}{r}$$

where F is the gravitational force; r is the radius from the center of the centrifuge to the rotational position of the biological material; m is the total mass in grams; and v is the velocity as determined by 2π x revolutions per minute. In general the R.P.M. figure is somewhat greater than the force times gravity. In every instance, record exactly the value for r and m and the number of revolutions per minute so that computations can be checked if necessary. If the same apparatus is used throughout, the relative values of R.P.M. will be adequate. (See Costello, Science, May 2, 1947, p. 474 for a criticism of centrifugation experiments.)

2. Crowding must be limited to the duration of centrifugation, and the controls should be similarly crowded for a corresponding period. As soon as possible after treatment, the eggs or embryos should be given optimum conditions of volume, and temperature.

Control: Eggs from the same source, untreated by centrifugation but otherwise kept under conditions identical with the conditions of the experimentals.

Procedure:

A. CONSTITUENTS OF THE AMPHIBIAN EGG

1. Apply a very thin coat of albumen-water to several microscope slides. Open a sexually mature female Rana pipiens and excise several ovarian eggs. Place a single egg (within its capsule) on each of the five slides, and rupture it with watchmaker's forceps, allowing the contents to flow freely over the dried albumen-water. With the edge of a coverslip, the egg contents may be spread evenly and thinly over the egg-albumen base.

   a. Examine one of the egg smears under the microscope before it has dried. Note the yolk granules of various sizes. Can you identify any other formed structures?

   b. Expose two of the slides (after they have become dried) to formaldehyde or osmic vapors to fix the egg contents, and then stain with an alcoholic solution of Sudan III. This dye is specific for fat.

   c. When thoroughly dried, apply the plasmal test to the other two slides (see section on Chemistry of the Embryo).

2. Dissect the ovaries from a sexually mature female frog and crush them in a mortar, (in an ice bath if available). The crushing may be accomplished the better with a small amount of clean sand.

   a. To half the egg brei add 10 volumes of cold phosphate buffer (M/200 at pH 7), mix well, and centrifuge for 10 minutes at 3,000 R. P. M. The amphibian egg contains fat, translucent protoplasm, heavy yolk, pigment granules, and a germinal vesicle. The pigment will be found at the centrifugal pole, and the so-called microsome layer will be found between the fat and the pigment, as a cloudy layer. The translucent protoplasm comprises the middle layer and the centripetal pole will have the whitish, opaque cap of hyaloplasm. With micropipette, remove material from each of these layers and examine immediately under high magnification of the microscope. (Do not expect to find an intact germinal vesicle.)

   b. To the other half of the egg brei add 10 volumes of cold phosphate buffer (M/200 at pH 7), mix well, and centrifuge for 10 minutes at 3,000 R. P. M. Before there has been any opportunity for mixing of the various layers, remove each with micropipette into separate homopathic vials. Biochemical tests should be applied to these isolated egg constituents, particularly to the microsome layer which can be identified as the cloudy layer between the fats and pigment.

   Place the microsome layer in a centrifuge tube and centrifuge for 20 minutes at 12,500 R. P. M. (ultracentrifuge). Note the supernatant fluid and the pellets. To the latter apply the following tests: indophenoloxidase; peroxidase; -SH; and plasmal. (See section on Biochemistry of the Embryo.)

B. RESISTANCE OF EMBRYONIC STAGES TO CENTRIFUGATION DAMAGE

There are two aspects of this study: (A) The ability of various stages to survive centrifugation damage and (B) The variety of abnormalities produced by standard centrifugation at different stages of development.

The stages that are to be used are: Uterine eggs, recently fertilized (but uncleaved) eggs; blastulae; and gastrulae. With the large International Centrifuge the approximate speed to be used should range from about 1500 to 3000 R. P. M., but the data should be recorded in terms of the value times gravity (see formula on preceding page). The duration should be from 1 to 10 minutes, the shorter interval at the higher speeds. (For example, a speed of 180 times gravity for 10 minutes to 1800 times gravity for 1 minute might be the extremes tested.) If but one speed and time are used, the lower force for the longer interval is recommended for all stages.

It has been suggested (Brachet) that if the eggs are centrifuged immediately after fertilization, the eggs that do not develop fail because all of the ribonucleic acid is carried to one pole, opposite that of the yolk. Centrifugation at later stages (e. g., blastula) may produce triploid embryos because of the excessive concentration of ribonucleic acid in specific areas.

The effect of fertilization can be tested very simply by stripping several hundred eggs from an ovulating female into a concentrated sperm suspension. The female is then to be opened and the uteri tied off above and below, and removed as a double sack full of eggs. The two uterine sacks may then be separated and placed directly into a centrifuge tube, previously coated (internally) with Nujol (paraffin oil). In a balancing tube, place the fertilized eggs, and centrifuge simultaneously. All eggs will be from the same female and the only difference will be that one group are fertilized. The unfertilized eggs should be fertilized immediately upon removal from the centrifuge, by cutting open the uteri and stripping the eggs into a concentrated sperm suspension.

The later stages of development, such as the blastula and gastrula, are to be centrifuged within their jelly membranes and in the Standard Solution.

Record the data in the following tables:

TABLE I: CENTRIFUGATION_____ X GRAVITY

	# EGGS	% DEVELOPED AFTER CENTRIFUGATION	% NORMAL	TYPES OF ABNORMALITIES
Unfertilized				
Fertilized				
Blastula				
Early Gastrula (Crescent Lip)				
Late Gastrula (Yolk Plug)				

TABLE II: CENTRIFUGATION_____ X GRAVITY

	# EGGS	% DEVELOPED AFTER CENTRIFUGATION	% NORMAL	TYPES OF ABNORMALITIES
Unfertilized				
Fertilized				
Blastula				
Early Gastrula (Crescent Lip)				
Late Gastrula (Yolk Plug)				

Some of the types of abnormalities produced by centrifugation are: depigmentation, permanent blastulae; inhibition of gastrulation, anaxial and hypaxial conditions, doubling of embryos, spina bifida, head defects, and accessory appendages. These should be photographed or sketched below, always with a record of the stage and conditions of centrifugation.

REFERENCES

BANTA, A. M. & R. A. GORTNER, 1915 - "Accessory appendages and other abnormalities produced in amphibian larvae through the action of centrifugal force." Jour. Exp. Zool. 18:437.
BEAMS, H. W. & R. L. KING, 1938 - "Pigmentation changes in tadpoles of Rana pipiens following centrifugation during the early gastrula." Jour. Morph. 63:477.
BRACHET, J., 1947 - "Localisation de l'acide ribonucleique et des proteines dans l'avaire de Grenouille normal et centrifuge." Experientia III/8.
COSTELLO, D. P., 1940 - "The fertilizability of nucleated and non-nucleated fragments of centrifuged eggs." Jour. Morph. 66:99.

HARVEY, E. N., 1934 - "The air turbine for high speed centrifuging of biological material, together with some observations on centrifuged eggs." Biol. Bull. 66:48.

HEILBRUNN, L. V., 1927 - "The viscosity of protoplasm." Quart. Rev. Biol. 2:230.

JEENER, R., 1946 - "Essai de fractionnement des proteines du noyau cellulaire par ultra-centrifugation." Compt. rendu. Soc. Biol. 140:1103.

JENKINSON, J. W., 1915 - "On the relation between the structure and the development of the centrifuged egg of the frog." Quart. Jour. Micr. Sci. 60:61.

KOSTOFF, D., 1937 - "Chromosome alterations by centrifuging." Science. 86:101.

LUYET, B. J., 1935 - "Behavior of the spindle fibres in centrifuged cells." Proc. Soc. Exp. Biol. & Med. 33:163.

PASTEELS, J., 1953 - "Les effets de la centrifugation sur la blastula et la gastrula des Amphibien." Jour. Emb. Exp. Morph. 1:125-145.

SCHECHTMAN, A. M., 1937 - "Mechanism of anomaly induction in frogs eggs by means of the centrifuge." Proc. Soc. Exp. Biol. & Med. 37.

TCHOU-SU, M., 1936 - "Embryons double obtenus par la centrifugation d'oeufs d'Anoures recemment fecondes. Origine des localisations germinales." Comp. rendu. Soc. Biol. 24:1043.

WHITAKER, D. M., 1937 - "Determination of polarity by centrifuging eggs of Fucus furcatus." Biol. Bull. 73:249.

"The campaign must begin with the study of developmental biology, for we have hardly begun to understand the forces and reactions that drive and guide the development of the fertilized ovum into a human infant. Embryology of the classical morphological type, experimental embryology, cytology, histochemistry, all have their contribution to make. The genes, and the whole sequence of events by which they determine the infinite detail of bodily structure, await new discoveries. There are countless unsolved questions in the physiology of reproduction, touching on the maternal environment of the embryo and its control by hormones and other chemical agents of the body. The chemistry of respiration and nutrition must be called upon to explain the marvelous homeostatic balances through which, after all, the child generally enters the world sound and healthy. Microbiology must detect for us all the various pathogenic organisms which invade and damage the fetus in utero; clinical medicine and obstetrics must teach us what illnesses of the mother may affect her offspring in the susceptible earliest days of development."

G. H. Corner, 1960, First Int. Conf.
Congenital Malformations, London.

23. THE PRODUCTION OF DOUBLE EMBRYOS

A. DOUBLE EMBRYOS BY INVERSION

PURPOSE: To produce double monsters by inverting the egg in a gravitational field at the two-cell stage, shifting the egg deutoplasm and thereby affecting subsequent gastrulation.

MATERIALS:

Biological: Ovulating Rana pipiens and adult males of the same species; Urodele eggs in the 2-cell stage.

Technical: Standard equipment.

METHOD:

Precautions:

1. Avoid excess handling of eggs and embryos.
2. Avoid desiccation of eggs, crowding, and heat.
3. Practice adhering eggs to filter and glazed paper before experimenting.

Controls: Eggs from the same source as the experimentals, in the same stage of development, adhered to the same kind of paper and in the same manner but without sufficient tension to prevent rotation of the egg within its membranes. These controls may be inverted along with the experimentals, but they must be able to rotate within their membranes.

Experimental Procedure:

Ovulate a female Rana pipiens and fertilize the eggs about 2 hours before the time of the experiment. Cut some clean paper (both filter paper and white, smooth glazed paper) into 1 inch squares and practice adhering eggs with their jelly capsules to this paper. Place one egg only on each piece of paper. The egg is transferred to the square of paper with a minimum of water. Then, using a scalpel, spread the egg jelly down onto the paper in all directions in such a manner that the drying jelly will hold the egg firmly to the paper. Allow the jelly to dry slightly, in air. Test by inverting the paper and the attached egg over a finger bowl of culture medium for 2 minutes and then re-examine to determine whether the egg has rotated or has been held firmly in the inverted position. Remember that there must be some tension to hold the egg sufficiently to prevent rotation.

Prepare several finger bowls of culture medium and quickly adhere 2-cell stages to the single pieces of paper in the manner described. In all cases orient the egg so that the animal pole is uppermost. After making certain that there is sufficient tension to prevent rotation, invert the paper, with adherent egg, in the finger bowl of culture medium and leave it undisturbed through at least the two subsequent cleavage as determined by parallel-developing control eggs. If eggs are mounted separately they may be examined briefly after the completion of the second cleavage, and those which do not remain inverted should be so marked or discarded. The pieces of paper float and the eggs are adequately submerged in the medium.

After the 8-cell stages has been achieved by the controls (about 4 hours after insemination) carefully remove all of the experimental eggs from their paper squares and place them separately in #2 Stenders. If particular eggs did not remain inverted, or were distorted by the jelly-tension, it would be well to make a sketch record in order to have a possible explanation of later developmental monstrosities.

The original method of placing the eggs between glass plates (glass slides) and compressing them sufficiently to prevent rotation when the plates are inverted, can be attempted. The objection to this method is simply that the pressure factor is not uniform and should be taken into consideration.

The first cleavage normally occurs 2 hours after the eggs are inseminated, and the second cleavage follows within 1 hour. It is important that the eggs be inverted immediately after the completion of the first cleavage and not later. It would be well, therefore, to segregate eggs inverted at various stages of the first cleavage development to determine the effect of this variable on double monster production.

B. DOUBLE EMBRYOS BY CONSTRICTION

PURPOSE: To determine the ability of single blastomeres of the 2-cell stage to develop complete embryos, following accentuation of the first cleavage furrow.

MATERIALS:
    Biological: Urodele eggs in the 2-cell stage. Amblystoma eggs may be collected in nature (see section on Breeding Habits) or Triturus eggs may be layed in the laboratory as a result of anterior pituitary stimulation (see Induced Ovulation).

    Technical: Standard Solution for Anura and Growing Medium for Urodela.
    0.1% KOH in appropriate medium.
    Hair loops, silk fibers, operating glass needles.

METHOD:
    Precautions:
        1. Avoid over-exposure to the KOH solution (see section on Isolation of Embryonic Cells).
        2. After separating the blastomeres, keep specimen in adequate medium and at a cool temperature.

    Controls: These will consist simply of eggs from the same clutch, kept under identical conditions except for the separation of the blastomeres.

    Procedure:
        Prepare simple loops of fine (blonde) baby's hair so that each loop is slightly greater than the diameter of the egg and its jelly capsule. Prepare several Syracuse dishes with Permoplast base and depressions calculated to hold the 2-cell stage and its jelly capsule. Fill with appropriate medium and then select eggs in the two cell stage for constriction.

        By placing these eggs for a brief period in 0.1% KOH (made up in the same culture medium) the surface coat will be weakened and the cleavage furrow will be accentuated. Remove the egg and pass it through three changes of culture medium before the furrow has progressed very far. This should be practiced, for it may not be easy to stop the KOH action as abruptly as desired.

        Remove the 2-cell stage to the Syracuse dish with Permoplast depression and press the hair loop into the bottom of the depression (two ends above the depression) and maneuver the egg into the depression and loop so that the cleavage furrow lies directly parallel to the loop. With practice one can determine whether

it is best to anchor one end of the loop in the nearby Permoplast, leaving but a
single loose end to tighten as the egg is held in position by forceps. It may also
help to build up the Permoplast about the egg to hold it the better. When secure,
use watchmaker's forceps and tighten the loop so that it constricts the 2-cell
stage between the blastomeres, through the jelly capsule and all. It may be
necessary to re-orient the egg after the hair loop has attained a grip on the
capsule. The blastomeres can be separated without rupturing the fertilization
(vitelline) membrane.

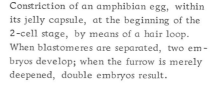

Constriction of an amphibian egg, within
its jelly capsule, at the beginning of the
2-cell stage, by means of a hair loop.
When blastomeres are separated, two embryos develop; when the furrow is merely
deepened, double embryos result.

The loop should hold as a result of friction and the egg can be removed to an
appropriate #2 Stender for continued development and observation. However,
very fine hair or individual fibers of silk can sometimes be looped twice, resulting in ever better (friction) holding. The degree of constriction can be controlled with practice.

A second method but one which aims at complete separation of the blastomeres
is to remove the jelly capsule and separate the blastomeres (through the fertilization membrane) by means of a cutting movement of the side of a glass needle.
This can be done without rupture of the membrane. Controls for this consist
simply of eggs deprived of their jelly.

OBSERVATIONS AND TABULATION OF DATA:

1. Make sketches of any changes in the superficial pigmentation of the inverted eggs, as
   compared with the controls. Determine whether these changes are carried over to
   the period of gastrulation. Sketch at periodic intervals.

2. During neurulation it should be possible to select those embryos which will, in all
   probability, develop into double monsters. Keep accurate and periodic records of
   developmental changes in specific eggs of this category. It is most important that
   any sequence of sketches represent the changes in a single egg.

REFERENCES

FANKHAUSER, G., 1948 - "The organization of the amphibian egg during fertilization and cleavage." Ann. N.Y. Acad. Sci.
    49:684.
HADORN, E., 1937 - "Die entwicklungsphysiologische Auswirkung der disharmonischen Kern-Plasma-Kombination beim Bastard-
    Merogon Triton palmatus x T. cristatus." Arch. f. Ent. mech. 136:400.
HARVEY, E. B., 1940 - "A new method of producing twins, triplets, and quadruplets in Arbacia punctulata, and their develop-
    ment." Biol. Bull. 78:202.

HINRICHS, M. A. & I. J. GENTHER, 1931 - "Ultra-violet radiation and the production of twins and double monsters." Physiol. Zool. 4:461.

LYNN, W. G., 1938 - "Conjoined twins and triplets in trout." Anat. Rec. 70:597.

MANGOLD, O., 1921 - "Situs inversus bei Triton." Arch. f. Ent. mech. 48:505.

NEWMANN, H. H., 1940 - "The question of mirro imaging in human one-egg twins." Human Biology. 12:21.

PASTEELS, J., 1933 - "Recherches sur les facteurs initiaux de la morphogenese chez les amphibienes anoures. I. Resultates de l'experience de Schultze et leur interpretation." Arch. Biol. 49:629.

PENNERS, A. & W. SCHLEIP, 1928 - "Die Entwicklung des Schultzeschen Doppelbildungen aus dem Ei von Rana fusca." Zeit. f. Wiss. 130:306. (Also ibid. 131:1.)

SCHWIND, J. L., 1942 - "Spontaneous twinning in the Amphibia." Am. Jour. Anat. 71:117.

SPEMANN, H., 1901 - "Entwicklungsphysiologische Studien am Triton-Ei." Arch. f. Ent. mech. 12:224 (See also 15:448; 16:551).

SPEMANN, H., 1938 - "Embryonic development and induction." Yale Univ. Press.

SPEMANN, H. & H. FALKANBERG, 1919 - "Ueber asymmetrische Entwicklung und Situs inversus viscerum bei Zwillingen und Doppelbilungen." Arch. f. Ent. mech. 45:371.

STRETT, J. C. Jr., 1940 - "Experiments on the organization of the unsegmented egg of Triturus pyrrhoghaster." Jour. Exp. Zool. 85:383.

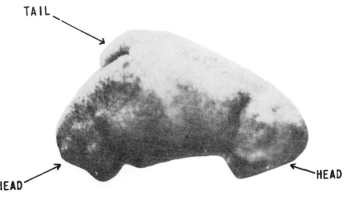

TAIL

HEAD

HEAD

CHIMERA - fusion of anterior ends of
Rana pipiens embryos.

"If there is one broad principle which emerges clearly from experimental teratology, it is that all anomalies can no more be treated as a single universe than can all rashes or all tumors."

Ingalls

"The course from the primary cause of a malformation to the observed defect frequently is not predictable. As Eerhardt wrote, the same 'inciting event' may produce several different defects, and similar defects may result from dissimilar agents or events. Some embryos exposed to a given 'insult' may die and be aborted, yet others may go to term and survive despite a gross malformation."

James D. Ebert, 1961 Jour. Chron. Dis. 13:91.

D. Experiments on the Early Embryo
24. THE ORGANIZER AND EARLY AMPHIBIAN DEVELOPMENT *

PURPOSE: To test the organizing potencies of the dorsal lip of the blastopore when transplanted, or when introduced into the blastocoel of another embryo. Also, to test the inductive capacities of other regions, and other (non-living) substances.

MATERIALS:
    Biological: Urodele* gastrula, stage #10.

    Technical: Syracuse dishes with agar bases and standard operating equipment.

METHOD:
    Precautions:
        1. Blastula and early gastrula stages are very delicate and must be handled with extreme caution. A soft agar base is best. Avoid shaking or jarring after the membranes have been removed.
        2. The membranes may be removed in 10% Standard Solution, or even easier in hypotonic media, but the operation is to be performed in full-strength Standard Solution. After the wound has healed and the transplant has become incorporated in the host, gradually return the Urodele embryo to the Urodele Growing Medium.
        3. Use sterile instruments throughout.

    Control: The control for dorsal-lip transplantation or implantation is the use of a comparable sized piece of tissue from the same donor, but from a region other than that of the dorsal lip.

    Procedure: The student should be thoroughly acquainted with the morphology and with the morphogenetic movements of the late blastula and the early gastrula before attempting these delicate operations. To do this it will be necessary to dissect the various stages, to locate and identify the blastocoel, the early gastrocoel, and the surrounding yolk and cell layers. It will further familiarize the student with the conditions of the early gastrula if he removes the membranes and hardens some of the specimens in 10% formalin for 24 hours and then dissects some and cuts others in sagittal and other planes. (Avoid contamination of usual dissecting instruments with fixative.) (See the section on "Morphogenetic Movements and Vital Staining.")

The jelly and vitelline membranes are to be removed from the early gastrula while it is in 10% Standard Solution over the agar base in a Syracuse dish. Do not use as hosts any embryos which have been injured unintentionally. Place the denuded embryo in a depression in the agar, and orient it with a hair loop in anticipation of one of the following operational procedures. (Remember that the embryo is alive and that during delayed preparations the embryo may progress from stage #10 to stage #11.)

A. INJURY EFFECTS AND REGENERATION OF THE DORSAL LIP

With sharp pointed glass needles and a hair loop, remove a rectangular group of cells from the mid-dorsal region, just anterior to the dorsal lip. Vary the size and the shape of the excisions in different gastrulae, but sketch each embryo immediately after the

---

* The Anuran embryos are not as satisfactory as the Urodele embryos for these experiments. ·See the next exercise and page 207.

operation and put it aside (carefully) in a separate #2 Stender with sterile medium and allow it to regenerate. (See section on "Wound Healing") If there is incomplete regeneration there should be incomplete or abnormal induction of parts of the medullary plate, determined within about 3 days at laboratory temperatures. (If there are abundant embryos, remove sections of the lateral marginal zone and observe for regeneration and effect on neurulation.)

B. IMPLANTATION OF THE DORSAL LIP MATERIAL

Having become acquainted with the size, location, and extent of the blastocoel of the Urodele, the student will now attempt to place a dorsal-lip (from stage #11) within the blastocoel of an otherwise complete blastula of about stage #7 or #8. This can be accomplished best by making the transfer in a small-bore pipette (see p. 6, 8, 9, 199) and allowing gravity to carry the cells through the roof of the blastula into the blastocoel. The terminal bore of the pipette should be just large enough to hold the group of dorsal lip cells to be implanted. Spemann's pipette with a side hole covered with a thin rubber tubing, with pressure controlled by gentle thumb pressure over the covered hole, has proven to be very satisfactory. The cells tend to fall apart and the "organizer" region becomes highly disorganized when the implantation is attempted with forceps or needles.

It must be remembered that the blastocoel is filled with a fluid and that any pressure exerted on the fluid by contents of the pipette will tend to "blow up" the entire blastula.

When the donor cell area has been excised, suck up a small amount of medium into the transfer pipette, then pick up the dorsal lip cells, and before the transfer is made (under water at all times) it will be noted that the dorsal lip is pulled by gravity to the tip of the pipette. It will therefore be necessary only to penetrate the roof of the blastocoel and the cells to be implanted will drop in. Slowly and carefully withdraw the pipette, aided (if necessary) by a hair loop. Allow the wound to heal and then do not disturb for 3 days or more.

If the student becomes proficient in the above, it is suggested that he coagulate several gastrulae in hot water, excise the dorsal lip and make a similar implantation to determine the relative "organizer" and "inductor" effects of the dorsal lip areas.

C. EXPLANTATION OF THE DORSAL-LIP MATERIAL

When the belly ectoderm of the neurula (stage #15) is peeled off as a sheet of cells, it will normally round up in the form of a tube. It is possible to take advantage of this fact by prior excision of the dorsal-lip material and placing it on the inside of such a sheet of cells so that the "organizer" will become wrapped up within indifferent ectoderm. The whole may then be treated as the above operated gastrulae and observed for inductions during 3 to 4 days.

D. TRANSPLANTATION OF THE DORSAL-LIP

Select two early gastrulae (stage #10) and place in Syracuse operating dish over agar and in 10% Standard Solution. After removing the membranes, select the best specimen to be the host. From the prospective host remove a small rectangular piece of ectoderm from the presumptive flank or belly region. From the donor quickly excise a similarly sized piece including the dorsal-lip, and transfer it on the point of a needle, under water, to the wound on the host. This is a difficult procedure because the host must be oriented and kept in position within the agar depression, and also because mitosis is so rapid, the cells are so large, and cell movements are so extensive that the transplants are often

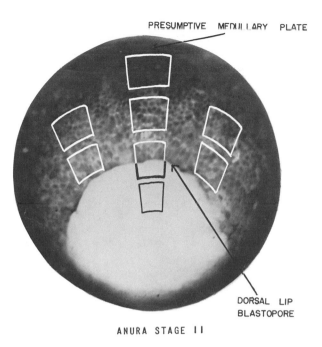

ANURA STAGE II

SHOWING REGIONS TO BE EXCISED OR TRANSPLANTED

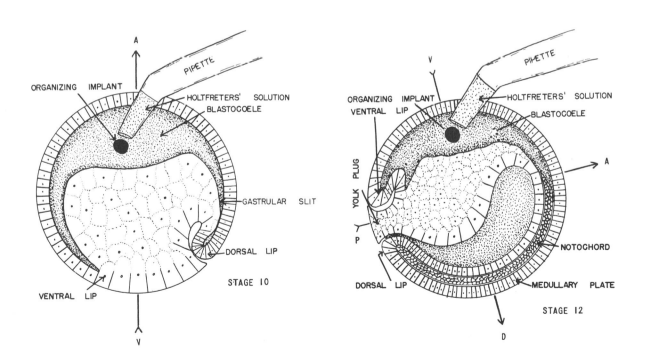

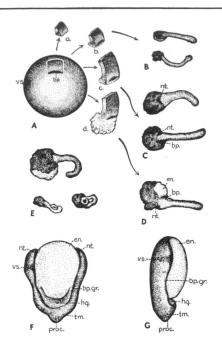

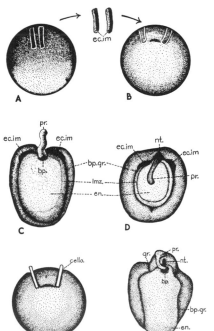

Fig. 2:

A. Incision made in order to explant the dorsal lip together with a large amount of presumptive ectoderm.

B. The explant fastened to wax substrate.

C.D. Explants after 16 hours of culture. The explant shown in C included a larger amount of entoderm than the one shown in D.

E. Diagrams showing successive stages (a-d) in the development of the explants shown in B, C.D. ch., presumptive chorda (coarse stippling); dl., dorsal lip; ec., presumptive ectoderm; en., presumptive entoderm (sparsely stippled); g., tinfoil girder; hm., presumptive head mesoderm (fine stippling); nt., neural tissue; pr., presumptive chordal projection.

Fig. 1:

A - Various types of explants involving the dorsal lip.

    a - dorsal lip without circumblastoporal material

    b - dorsal lip with circumblastoporal material

    c - dorsal lip with circumblastoporal material and more presumptive ectoderm

    d - dorsal lip with more presumptive ectoderm and endoderm

B, C, D - Explants after 14 to 16 hours of culture.

E - Explants after 18 to 24 hours of culture.

F, G. - Ring embryo produced by removal of the dorsal lip as seen from above (F) and from the side (G).

    bp. - blastopore

    bp.gr. - blastoporal groove

    en. - endoderm

    hg. - hindgut endoderm

    nt. - neural tissue

    proc. - proctodeum

    tm. - tail mesoderm

    vs. - vital-stain mark (A, F, G)

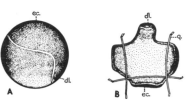

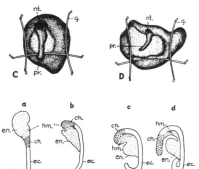

Fig. 3:

A, B - Implantation of strips of presumptive ectoderm (ec. im.) into slits made through the marginal zone on both sides of the dorsal lip.

C, D - Two types of ring embryos resulting from the foregoing operation.

E - Insertion of two strips of cellophane (cello.) into slits made through the marginal zone on both sides of the dorsal lip.

F - Ring embryo resulting from the foregoing operation.

    ec. im. - ectodermal implant

    en. - endoderm

    gr. - groove left by cellophane

    lmz. - exposed portion of lateral marginal zone

    nt. - neural tissue

    pr. - presumptive chordal projection

(Schechtman: 1942 Univ. Calif. Pub. Zool. 51:1)

Fig. 4:

    A. Explantation of dorsolateral and lateral blastoporal lips; at extreme right the explants (enlarged) after 16 hours of culture.

    B. Insertion of strips of presumptive ectoderm (ec.im.) into slits made through the lateral and ventrolateral marginal zones.

    C. Ring embryo resulting from the foregoing operation. bp.gr., blastoporal groove; ec.im., presumptive ectodermal implant; en., presumptive entoderm; nt., neural tissue; pr., presumptive chorda projection; vs., vital-stain mark.

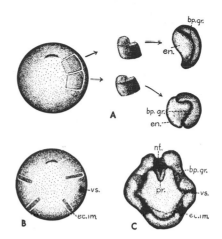

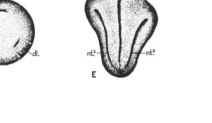

Fig. 6:

    A.C.E. Implantation of strips of presumptive ectoderm into slits cut through the marginal zone at various distances from the dorsal lip.

    B.D.F. Neurulae resulting from the foregoing operations, A, C, E, respectively. ec.im., ectodermal implant; nt., neural plate; pr., projection.

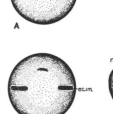

Fig. 5:

    A.B. Transplantation of dorsal lip (dl.) from one egg (A) into presumptive ectodermal region of another egg (B).

    C. The implant has developed a blastoporal pocket (bp.) on one side of the presumptive chordal projection (pr.), and a patch of neural tissue (nt.) on the opposite side.

    D. Implantation of two dorsal lips (dl.) into the ventrolateral marginal zones.

    E. Embryo resulting from the foregoing operation (D, above). nt., primary neural plate; nt.^{1}. and nt.^{2}, secondary neural plates. See figure 5, plate 7, for cross section.

(Schechtman: 1942 Univ. Calif. Pub. Zool. 51:1)

pushed out of the wound before they have a chance of becoming adherent. It may be necessary to use a glass bridge or Brücke to hold the transplant in position for 30 to 45 minutes during the healing process. Such a cover cannot be used longer because it interferes with respiration. Observe the healing process and re-examine during 3 days.

E. TRANSPLANTATION TO THE DORSAL-LIP REGION

As in "D" above, select two embryos at stage #10 and remove the membranes. The transplantation is to be made from the presumptive flank region of the donor to a position just anterior to the dorsal lip of the host. Since the dorsal lip cells move rapidly it is necessary to:

1. Make the excision from the donor first.
2. Make the host wound with the donor material nearby, and complete the transfer as quickly as possible. The host wound must be sufficiently anterior to the forming dorsal-lip so that the transplant will "take" well before it reaches the level of involution.

A variation on this procedure is recommended for those students who prove to be proficient in the first part. The donor may be previously stained with Nile blue sulphate (1 part in 500,000) so that the transplant will be identifiable. After it has become attached to its new location (i.e., the dorsal lip region of the host) for about 4 hours, remove it (without bothering to protect the host), brush away all host cells with a hair loop, and then implant the stained cells into the blastocoel of another embryo at stage #7. Examine during 3 days for evidence of "organizer" activity acquired by the usually indifferent flank ectoderm temporarily transplanted and located in the dorsal lip environment.

F. INDUCTIVE CAPACITY OF THE NOTOCHORD OR ARCHENTERIC ROOF

Dissect living embryos at stages #13 and #14 to locate the notochordal tissue directly ventral to the neural folds. Remove, and clean strips of notochord by means of a hair loop and watchmaker's forceps. Such notochordal tissue may be implanted into the blastocoel ("B") or explanted ("C") to determine organizer or inductive capacity. The notochord is derived from cells involuting over the dorsal-lip and it is of interest to determine how long the notochordal cells will maintain their influential activity. If possible, determine the portion of the notochord used, whether anterior or posterior. Similarly, the archenteric roof may be identified (generally grayish cells) and parts of it may be implanted and explanted to test the duration of inductive capacity. The original experiments of this nature led to the concept of "individuation". (See glossary.)

G. EVOCATION BY INORGANIC SUBSTANCES

This portion of the exercise constitutes essentially the control experiments for "B" above, the implantation of the living dorsal lip material.

Obtain the smallest particles of silicon (Okada, 1938) or pieces of cellophane previously soaked in 1/10,000 methylene blue (Waddington, et al 1936) and dried. Insert these small inorganic masses into the blastocoel of stages #7 or #8 and observe during 3 days for evidence of inductions.

Sterols, saponins, glycogen, cephalin, oestrogenic and carcinogenic substances, dead tissues from a variety of animal sources, and tissue extracts from worms to mammals have been used to successfully cause significant changes in contiguous but otherwise indifferent ectoderm. (See Waddington, 1940.)

OBSERVATIONS AND EXPERIMENTAL DATA:

The post-operative care of the embryos generally includes returning them to their normal growing medium after the healing of the wounds in the operating medium. Specimens
should be kept in separate #2 Stenders or finger bowls, properly marked for identification, and placed at cool temperatures to reduce bacterial growth.

The maximum duration of observations for these experiments is about 4 days after the
operation. Sketches and photographs at the time of the operation, with similar records
at appropriate intervals, and finally, histological confirmation of the macroscopic effects
are recommended. The results are qualitative in that no two experiments could possibly
be alike, hence complete and accurate records of each specimen are most important.

(The student should study the Glossary to learn the distinction between organizer, inductor, and evocator as illustrated in the above experiments.)

REFERENCES

BARTH, L. C. & S. GRAFF, 1943 - "Effect of protein extracts of neural plate plus chordamesoderm on presumptive epidermis. "
     Proc. Soc. Exp. Biol. & Med. 54:118.
BAUTZMANN, H., 1932 - "Experimentelle analyse des organisatorischen Geschehens in der Primitiventwicklung von Amphibian:
     Determinationszustand und Aufgabenverteilung der Randzonenanlagen im Organosationsprozess." Verh. der Anat. Gesell. 75:221.
BOELL, E. J., J. NEEDHAM, 1939 - "Morhogenesis and metabolism: studies with the Caryesian diver ultramicromanometer. "
     Proc. Roy. Soc. London B, 127:363.
BOSE, A., 1959 - "X-ray effects in the secondary organizer action.' Die Naturwissenschaften. 46:563.
BRACHET, J., 1939 - "Etude du metabolisme de l'oeuf de grenouille (Rana fusca) au cours du developpement. V. Le metabolisme
     proteique et hydrocarbone de l'oeuf en relation avec le probleme de l'organisateur. " Arch. Biol. 50:233.
BROWN, M. G., 1941 - "Collapse of the archenteron in embryos of Amblystoma and Rana. " Jour. Exp. Zool. 88:95.
CHILD, C. M., 1946 - "Organizers in development and the organizer concept. " Physiol. Zool. 19:89.
DETWILER, R. S., 1917 - "On the use of Nile blue sulphate in embryonic tissue transplantation." Anat. Rec. 13:493.
GOERTTLER, K., 1925 - "Die Formbildung der Medullaranlage beu Urodelen. " Arch. f. Ent. mec. 106:503.
GOERTTLER, K., 1931 - "Desorganization durch Einwirkung von Organisatoren auf organisierendes Materiel. " Verh. Anat. Ges.
     37:132 (Also Anat. Anz. 71:132)
GOODALE, H. D., 1911 - "The early development of Sperlepes bilineatus. " Am. J. Snat. 12:173.
HARRISON, R. G., 1945 - "Relations of symmetry in the developing embryo. " Conn. Acad. Arts & Sci. 36:277.
HOLTFRETER J., 1945 - "Neuralization and epidermization of gastrula ectoderm. " Jour. Exp. Zool. 98:161.
JAEGER, L., 1945 - "Glycogen utilization by the amphibian gastrula in relation to invagination and induction. " Jour. Cell. &
     Comp. Physiol. 25:97.
LEHMANN, F. E., 1926 - "Entwicklungsstorungen in der Medullanlage von Triton, erzeugt durch Unterlagerungs-Defekte. " Arch.
     f. Ent. Mech. 108:243.
LEHMANN, F. E., 1938 - "Regionale Verscheidenheiten des Organisators von Triton. " Arch. f. Ent. mech., 138.
NAKAMURA, O., 1938 - Tail formation in the urodele". Zool. Mag. Tokyo. 50:442.
NEEDHAM, J., 1940 - "Biochemical aspects of organizer phenomena. " Growth Suppl. p. 45.
OPPENHEIMER, J., 1936 - "Structures developed in amphibians by implantation of living fish organizer. " Proc. Soc. Exp. Biol.
     & Med. 34:461.
PASTEELS, J., 1942 - "New observations concerning the maps of presumptive areas of the young amphibian gastrula. " Jour. Exp.
     Zool. 89:255.
SCHECHTMAN, A. M., 1932 - "Movement and localization of the presumptive epidermis in Triturus torosus. " Univ. Calif. Pub.
     Zool. 36:325.
SHEN, S. C., 1939 - "A quantitative study of amphibian neural tube induction with a water-soluble hydrocarbon. " Jour. Exp.
     Zool. 16:143.
SPEMANN, H., 1938 - "Embryonic development and induction. " Yale Univ. Press.
SPEMANN, H. & H. MANGOLD, 1924 - "Uber Induktion von Embryonalanlagen durch Implantation artfremder Organisatoren. "
     Arch. f. mikr. Anat. u. Ent. mech. 100:599.
VINTEMBERGER, P., 1938 - "Sur les resultats de la transplantation d'organisateurs d'entendues differentes chez Rana fusca, dans
     la region blastoporale ventrale. "
VOGT, W., 1925 - "Gestaltungsanalyse am Amphibienkeim mit örtlicher Vitalfarbung, I. Methodik." Arch. f. Ent. Mech. 106:542.
VOGT, W., 1929 - "Gestaltungsanalyse am Amphibienkeim mitortlicher Vitalfarbung." Arch. f. Ent. mech. 120.
WADDINGTON, C. H., 1940 - "Organizers and genes. " Cambridge Univ. Press.
WEISS, P., 1935 - "The so-called organizer and the problem of organization in Amphibian development. " Physiol. Rev. 15:639.
WOERDEMAN, M. W., 1938 - "Embryonale Induktion und Organization." Inst. Internat. Emb., London, Aug. 1938.

25. MORPHOGENETIC MOVEMENTS AS DETERMINED BY VITAL STAINING

PURPOSE: To stain the early embryo with vital dyes by means of which movements of various cell areas can be followed to their final location in organogenesis. (See frontispiece)

MATERIALS:

Biological: Blastula stages of Anura and Urodela.

Technical: Powdered or crystalline agar, cellophane, and vital dyes (Nile blue sulphate and neutral red, preferably Gruebler's).

METHOD:

Precautions:

1. These vital dyes are water-soluble. It is therefore wise to soak the pieces of stained agar or cellophane in distilled water briefly before using them for staining embryos, to remove excess dye.
2. The smallest pieces of stained medium should be used. These can be prepared in the dry state by cutting into small beads beneath a dissection microscope.
3. While being stained the embryo should be as dry as is compatible with the maintenance of normal conditions.
4. All membranes except the vitelline membrane must be removed. The vitelline membrane can be punctured if it is otherwise difficult to hold the embryo in position.
5. The Permoplast or soft paraffin base must be rigid enough to hold the egg in place for 45 to 60 minutes without applying abnormal pressure.

Control: This is an exploratory and qualitative type of experiment so that controls are not possible. Localized injury of cell areas could be used to impede such cell movements as seem evident from the vital staining observations.

Procedure:

PREPARATION OF STAINING MEDIUM

Bring 100 cc. of distilled water* to a boil in each of 2 Erlenmeyer flasks. To each, add 2 grams of pure powdered or shredded agar, and dissolve completely by further boiling. Avoid burning by constantly stirring with a glass rod.

To one flask add 1 gram of Nile blue sulphate (Gruebler's) and to the other add 1 gram of Neutral Red (Gruebler's). Heat gently until the solutions are homogeneous.

Tilt some clean lantern slide covers (or other glass plates) slightly on paper towelling, and pour the warm and stained agar mixture onto the plates so that there is a thin and even layer. Allow the agar to dry thoroughly in a dust-free environment, and then wrap the plates in white typewriter paper and label for future use. (See Vogt, 1925.)

Generally the thin layer of stained and dried agar can be chipped off of the glass plate with a scalpel, but if this proves difficult, simply add a drop of distilled water to the edge of the agar film and allow it to swell, after which it is possible to cut out a small strip of stained agar. This can be further subdivided with sharp scissors.

---

* Culture media contain salts which may precipitate the dyes.

A recent modification of this original procedure is to use the thinnest sheets of cellophane or pliofilm which take up the stain and can be cut into small pellets. Such pieces of stained cellophane can be kept in envelopes until needed.

The staining dishes are generally Syracuse dishes provided with Permoplast or soft paraffin bases. Permoplast is softer and easier to mould than paraffin, but it is apt to crumble when left in water for any length of time. It is well to prepare 10 to 12 dishes well in advance of these experiments, each provided with depressions of various sizes in anticipation of various sized embryos. Depressions can be made easily in a paraffin base by means of a warmed ball-tip, while the dish is partially filled with water.

STAINING PROCEDURE*

It is not always possible to stain an exact area with a particular dye. The usual procedure is to place various small vitally stained pellets within the wall of a depression in the Permoplast (or paraffin) and in the appropriate medium and then to fit the egg or embryo into the depression, moulding the material to hold the embryo firmly in place. It is not particularly important to use any special configuration as long as a record is made, immediately after staining, of the exact distribution of the stained areas on the egg or embryo.

Remove the jelly membranes from the egg, or embryo, and place it in the depression. Gravity will orient the egg so that the vegetal pole takes most of the stain in any depression. This position can be varied by holding the egg in position with a hair loop while building up a closely confining cover of the Permoplast (or paraffin) with a ball tip. If the colored pellets are properly alternated within the depression, and properly spaced, the transferred marks on the embryo will not become confluent. Cover the egg or embryo with Standard Medium and leave undisturbed for 45 to 60 minutes at the laboratory temperature. Gently uncover the embryo and shake it out of the depression.

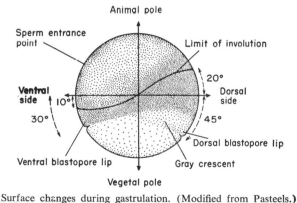

Surface changes during gastrulation. (Modified from Pasteels.)

STAGES AND AREAS TO BE STAINED

1. Grey Crescent: Within 20 to 30 minutes after insemination a grey crescent will appear between the animal and the vegetal hemispheres of the frog's egg, the more pronounced the longer the eggs are aged in the uterus. Using but a single (Neutral Red) pellet, attempt to orient the grey crescent region adjacent to the dye and allow it to stain for half an hour.

---

* Either Anuran or Urodele eggs (or embryos) may be used, but the latter are preferred, because of the reduced natural pigmentation.

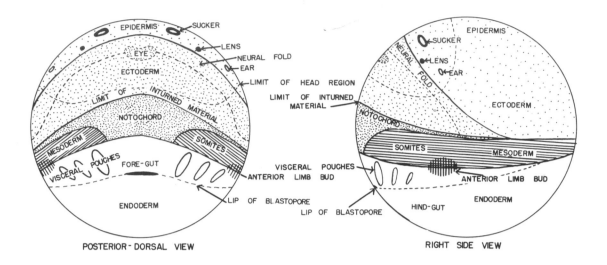

PRESUMPTIVE REGIONS OF ANURAN BLASTULA

(ADAPTED FROM VOGT: 1929)

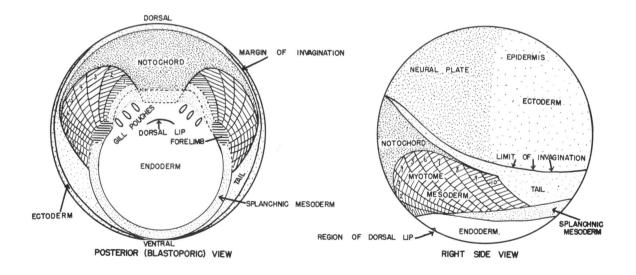

PRESUMPTIVE REGIONS OF URODELE BLASTULA

(ADAPTED FROM VOGT: 1929)

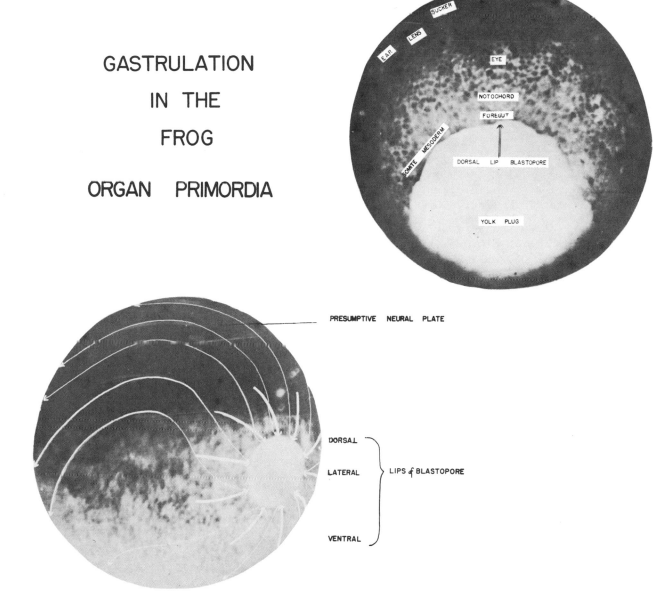

GASTRULATION

IN THE

FROG

ORGAN   PRIMORDIA

SUCKER
LENS
EAR
EYE
NOTOCHORD
FOREGUT
SOMITE   MESODERM
DORSAL   LIP   BLASTOPORE
YOLK   PLUG

PRESUMPTIVE   NEURAL   PLATE

DORSAL

LATERAL   LIPS of BLASTOPORE

VENTRAL

LATE GASTRULA—STAGE

(MODIFIED   FROM   VOGT   1929)

Paths of displacement in
gastrulation. Based on Vogt.

(From Ward's Natural Science
Establishment Inc. Dr. J.
Mueller)

A second method of staining the grey crescent is to utilize the jelly of the egg by spreading it gently onto a small square of filter paper just enough to hold the egg firmly in place. Take a stiff piece of dry and colored agar pellet held with forceps and, using it as a pencil, mark the region of the grey crescent by applying and holding the dye against the egg for as long a period as possible. (Do not overstain.)

Study the movement of the stained grey crescent, and determine its relation to the first cleavage furrow and to the subsequent position of the initial involution of gastrulation.

2. Blastula Stage: At about the 64-128 cell stage (stage #8 Rana) apply 4 stain marks of two colors around the germ ring, alternating the colors. These spots should appear circumferentially placed. On other blastulae of similar stage, apply a line of alternating colors from the germ ring of one side, through the dorsal hemisphere, to the germ ring of the other side.

These stained areas should not only move but should change shape, depending upon their location in relation to the morphogenetic movements of gastrulation. (See Goerttler, 1925 and Vogt, 1925.)

3. Gastrula Stage: At the first indication of gastrulation (stage #10) mark the dorsal, the lateral, and the (presumptive) ventral lip regions of the future blastopore. If you are successful in this work, attempt to repeat Goerttler's work of staining a line of spots both dorsal and ventral to the initial involution of the blastopore. (See Hamburger '60)

4. Yolk Plug Stage: (stage #11 Rana or Amblystoma)
   a. Presumptive notochord: Carefully apply a stain to the medium upper lip of the early blastopore. When this embryo has reached the tail-bud stage (Rana, stage #17 or #18) dissect it with needles to locate the position of the invaginated colored cells.
   b. Presumptive medullary plate: Locate a region about 2/3 of the distance from the dorsal lip of the early blastopore to the center of the animal pole, and mark with Neutral Red. This region should not invaginate and may be followed until it becomes enclosed in the neural folds.

5. The Somite Area of the Blastula: Using the map of Vogt (derived by the vital dye method) locate the presumptive somite area (dorso-lateral to the crecentric blastopore) and stain (on either side) with Neutral Red. When the embryo reaches the tail-bud stage (stage #17 or #18) dissect it with needles and a hair loop to expose the somites beneath the dorso-lateral ectoderm.

6. Presumptive Eye-forming Areas: This can be accomplished best by using stage #13 of Amblystoma and consulting the exercise on Eye Field Operations to determine the presumptive area to be stained. With Urodele material either Nile blue sulphate or Neutral Red may be used, since there is less pigment than in the Anural egg.

The presumptive eye-forming areas will be incorporated within the brain to give rise to the optic vesicles. The stain must be applied anteriorly over the transverse neural folds. Embryos thus stained should be dissected at stages #20, #26, and #30 to locate the position of the previously stained areas.

7. Lateral Line Organs: Select specimens of Amblystoma punctatum at stage #30, when the otic (auditory) vesicles begin to form. There may be some muscular activity making it necessary to confine the embryo more rigidly, or even to cover it with a piece of cover glass during the staining. Locate the otic vesicles, just above the second visceral arch. Apply the dye to the otocyst and to the epidermis just posterior to it for about 30 minutes.

The lateral line organs may be followed superficially from their point of origin into the tail, hence this part of the exercise requires a series of drawings to indicate the path of the dye as it moves posteriorly with the development of the lateral line system. The dye should pass posteriorly across the somites, and subsequently a smaller line may be seen passing dorsal to the somites, both reaching the tail (see Stone, 1933).

8. Specific Organ Anlagen: Consult the accompanying figures and photographs for the presumptive areas for the nasal placodes, balancers, lens, gills, etc. (also see Carpenter, 1937) and stain any specific area to check the "fate-maps" that have derived by this procedure.

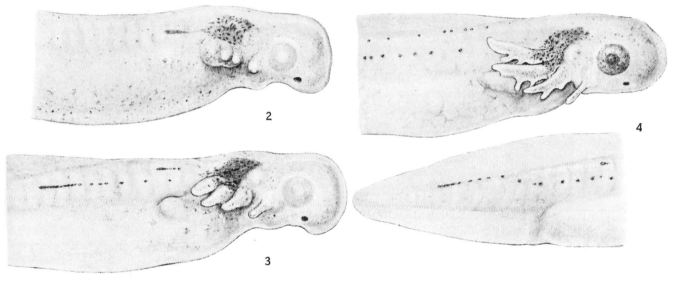

Fig. 1. Camera-lucida drawing of a living Amblystoma punctatum embryo, made 1 day after operation. Nile-blue stained graft (shaded) as excised from the same area in the donor as it now occupies in the recipient. The operation was made at Harrison stage 30. The specimen is now about stage 31. For following stages see Figures 2, 3, and 4.

Fig. 2. Same living specimen as in Figure 1, shown second day after operation. The shaded elongated club-shaped structure growing posteriorly from ectoderm of graft (shaded) is the blue migrating mid-body lateral-line primordium. Specimen is about stage 36.

Fig. 3. Same specimen as in Figures 1 and 2, shown third day after operation. Note beaded appearance of mid-body line primordium which has left in its trail blue clumps (shaded) of cells that are forming lateral-line organs. The short primordium of the dorsal body line (above limb region) from the graft is also laying down segments for sense organs. Ectoderm of graft (shaded) is still seen above second and third gill buds. Specimen is stage 37.

Fig. 4. Same specimen as in Figures 1, 2, and 3, shown fourth day after operation. Mid-body line primordium has bent dorsally (the normal course) above and behind anal region and has moved caudally on the tail. The tear-shaped dorsal body line primordium (second portion of figure) has not quite reached the position dorsal to the anal region where it normally terminates. It did so later. The blue mid-body primordium, about 3 days later, reached the tip of the tail and laid down a terminal blue organ at Harrison stage 44 (a larva with bidigitate fore limb and open mouth). Note in organs the dark ring about a light center and a peripheral light border. For a later stage see Figure 13. Specimen is stage 39.

Development of the lateral-line organ system as indicated by Nile Blue Sulphate-stained graft of the anlage.

(From Stone, 1933: Jour. Comp. Neur. 57:507)

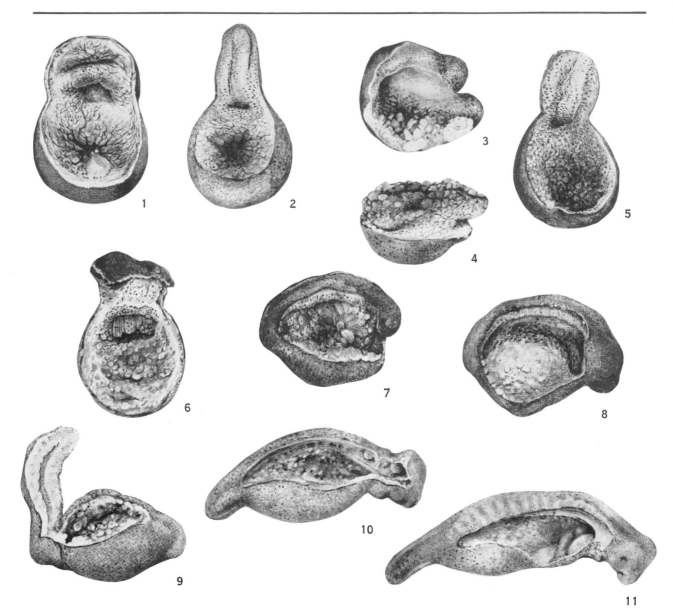

BLASTULATION IN AMBLYSTOMA FOLLOWED BY MEANS OF STAINING AT STAGES 3 OR
4 WITH NILE BLUE SULPHATE AND DISSECTION OF EMBRYOS AT STAGES 11 TO 33.

(J. S. Nicholas 1945: Jour. Exp. Zool. 100:265)

1. Intense stain applied at stage 3; polar ingression; no stain coming through blastopore. Dissected at stage 11.
2. Light stain applied at stage 2; polar ingression; stain covers whole area with greatest intensity near center of archenteron.
   Compare with fig. 1 where intercellular material has been stained.
3. Polar ingression with secondary transmission of stain applied at stage 4. Blastocoelic concentration of stain visible. Dorsal
   lip stained, lateral lips unstained. Dissected at stage 12.
4. Polar ingression with secondary transmission of stain applied at stage 4. Thin band of material from the yolk endoderm
   extends forward and meets the primary stream. Dorsal lip stained, lateral lips unstained. Dissected at stage 12.
5. Medium-heavy stain applied at stage 5. During staining the vegetal region was eccentric and lateral lip material was
   stained, the central chordal region was not stained. Dissection at stage 13.
6. Stain applied at stage 8. All of the stain coming into the archenteron through the blastopore. Dissection at stage 12.
7. Heavy stain applied at stage 4. Barker mass blackened represents the results of the primary, the posterior the secondary stain
   path. The apparent diffusion of the secondary stain is due to the dissection in which the gut canal was opened. Dissection
   at stage 24.
8. Medium stain applied at stage 3. The gut canal has been opened. The stain is in the lining and the inner layer of the gut
   cells. Dissection at stage 26.
9. Medium stain applied at stage 4. Gut canal opened. Dissection at stage 27.
10. Medium stain applied at stage 3. Gut canal opened, dissection at stage 30.
11. Light stain applied. Stain in liver region, partial diffusion. Lateral dissection at stage 33.

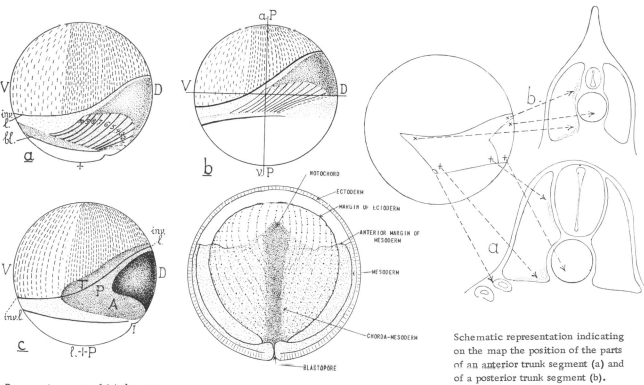

Presumptive maps of (a) the young gastrula of Triton (Vogt, '29); (b) the early blastula of Triton (Vogt, '29); (c) of the young gastrula of Triturus pyrrhogaster (Nakamura, '38).

Composite drawing to illustrate germ-layer relations in the late gastrula of an Anuran. Medullary plate (ectoderm) not indicated.

Alternate dots and dashes - endoderm
Heavy stippling - notochord
Sparse stippling - mesoderm
Cellular markings - ectoderm

Schematic representation indicating on the map the position of the parts of an anterior trunk segment (a) and of a posterior trunk segment (b).

(From Pasteels, 1942: Jour. Exp. Zool. 89:255)

OBSERVATIONS AND DATA

This is strictly a qualitative, observational type of experiment and it will be necessary to keep separate and periodic records of each stained egg or embryo. The significance of the experiment will depend upon the accuracy and the completeness of the record. The embryos should be kept in Standard Solution, in separate #2 Stenders, properly marked for identification. When the dye is moved internally, it can be traced by dissection of the living embryo. It must be remembered, however, that the dyes are soluble and some will diffuse out of the embryo and also into surrounding cell areas.

It is possible to preserve the Nile blue sulphate for histological examination by using the following procedure: (Stone, 1932)

a. Fix in Zenkers-acetic for 2 hours.
b. Wash in tap water.
c. Place in 1% Phosphomolybdic acid for 2 hours.
d. Transfer to dioxan to which 0.1% Phosphomolybdic acid has been added - for 2 two-hour changes.
e. Transfer to cedar oil plus 0.1% Phosphomolybdic acid until clear.
f. Embed in paraffin, 3 baths of about 15 minutes each.
g. Section and mount in xylol-clarite.

(It is the Phosphomolybdic acid which keeps the Nile blue sulphate in position.)

⬤ *"All these observations taken together illustrate emphatically the integration of all gastrulation movements, the uniformity of the process as a whole, whose basic trends -- elongation, convergence, divergence, etc. -- transcend the border lines of invaginating and non-invaginating areas and of the prospective germ layers." Hamburger 1960, p. 59.*

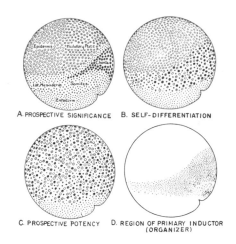

A. PROSPECTIVE SIGNIFICANCE   B. SELF-DIFFERENTIATION

C. PROSPECTIVE POTENCY   D. REGION OF PRIMARY INDUCTOR (ORGANIZER)

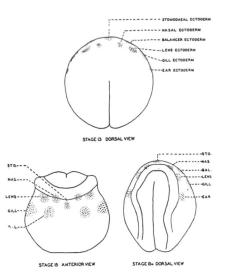

STAGE 13 DORSAL VIEW

STAGE 15 ANTERIOR VIEW   STAGE 15a DORSAL VIEW

A. profile view of the early gastrula showing the prospective areas as revealed by the vital staining method. B. similar view showing power of self-differentiation of small pieces when isolated. C. showing prospective potency (powers of differentiation under various tried conditions). D. showing the primary inductor area; stippled area, head organizer; area with dashes, trunk-tail organizer. After Holtfreter (1936).

(From Harrison 1945: Trans. Conn. Acad. Arts & Sci. 36:277)

The relative position of the presumptive ecto-dermal organ rudiments of the head in early neurula stages of Amblystoma punctatum.

(From Carpenter 1937: Jour. Exp. Zool. 75:103)

REFERENCES

ADAMS, A. E., 1928 - "Paraffin sections of tissue supravitally stained." Science, 68:303.

BANKI, O., 1927 - "Die Lagebeziehungen due Spermium-Eintrittsstelle zur Medianebene und zur ersten Furche, nach Versuchen mit orlichen Vitalfarbungen Axolotei." Anat. Anz. 63:198.

CARPENTER, E., 1937 - "The head pattern in Amblystoma studied by vital staining and transplantation methods." Jour. Exp. Zool. 75:103.

CONN, H. J. & R. S. CUNNINGHAM, 1932 - "The use of dyes as vital stains." Stain Technology. 7:81.

CUNNINGHAM, R. S. & H. J. CONN, 1932 - "Methods for the preservation of supravitally stained material." Stain Technology. 7:15.

DETWILER, S. R., 1937 - "Application of vital dyes to the study of sheath cell origin." Proc. Soc. Exp. Biol. & Med. 37:380 (See Detwiler, 1917, Anat. Rec. 13:493).

FRANKSTON, Jane E., 1940 - "The photodynamic action of neutral red on Triturus viridescens." Jour. Exp. Zool. 83:161.

GOERTTLER, K., 1925 - "Die Formbildung der Medullaranlage bei Urodelen. Im Rahman der Verscheibungsvorgange von Keimbezirken wahrend der Gastrulation und als entwicklungs-physiologisches Problem." Arch. f. Ent. mech. 106:503.

HAMBURGER, V., 1960 - "Description of Gastrulation in Urodeles." in "A Manual of Experimental Embryology." p. 47, Univ. Chicago Press.

HARVEY, E. B., 1941 - "Vital staining of the centrifuged Arbacia punctulata eggs." Biol. Bull. 80:114.

PASTEELS, J., 1942 - "New observations concerning the maps of presumptive areas of the young Amphibian gastrula (Amblystoma and Discoglassus)." Jour. Exp. Zool. 289:255.

STONE, L. S., 1933 - "The development of lateral line sense organs in amphibians observed in living and vital stained preparations." Jour. Comp. Neur. 57:507.

VOGT, W., 1929 - "Gestaltungsanalyse am Amphibienkeim mit ortlicher Vitalfarbung. II. Gastrulation und Mesodermbildung bei Urodelen und Anuran." Arch. f. Ent. mech. 120:384.

VOTQUENNE, M., 1934 - "Experiences de Destruction des Micromeres dorsaux de l'oeuf de Rana fusca stad VIII, et interpretation des Resultats par la Methode des Colorations vitales localisees." Arch. de Biol. 45:80.

ZORZOLI, A., 1946 - "Effects of vital dyes on the early development of the amphibian embryo." Proc. Soc. Exp. Biol. & Med. 63:565.

26. THE BEHAVIOR OF ISOLATED EMBRYONIC CELLS

PURPOSE: To determine the structure and the behavior of embryonic cells isolated from each other, with particular emphasis on their motility, adhesiveness, phagocytosis, and differentiation.

MATERIALS:

    Biological: Urodele embryos from cleavage to neurula. Anuran eggs and embryos can be used but are not as satisfactory.

    Technical: Operating needles, slides, coverslips, depression slides.
                Carbon and carmine particles, finely divided.
                Nile blue sulphate: 1/750,000 in Standard Solution.
                Solutions:

                      Standard Solution - both hypo- and hypertonic concentrations.
                      Standard Solution plus 1% KOH, freshly made up and adjusted to pH. 9.0 - 11.0
                      Standard Solution made up without the $CaCl_2$ (Ca-free Standard).
                      Potassium oxalate (0.4%) and sodium citrate (0.4%), used to oppose the solidifying action of calcium.
                      KCN: M/40 to M/640 made up in Standard Solution.

METHOD:

    Precautions: Use reasonably aseptic conditions, particularly in the differentiation observations. Sterilization is not generally necessary.

    Controls: None are possible in this type of qualitative experiment.

    Procedure:

MOTILITY

1. Remove the bulk of the jelly from a blastula or gastrula stage, leaving the fertilization (vitelline) membrane intact. Place the embryo in 1% KOH in Standard Solution and observe continually under the low power magnification. When the cellular mass has become disarranged, remove it (within the membrane) to fresh Standard Solution (without KOH). After a few minutes change again to fresh Standard Solution. Now rupture the fertilization membrane with sharp watchmaker's forceps. This will liberate the cells which may then be picked up with a fine pipette and transferred to a microscopic slide for examination beneath a coverslip elevated by two hairs or glass slivers. Study under both low and high magnification and note internal Brownian movement, pseudopodial formation, and general activity. (Compare with accompanying figures from Holtfreter's paper.)

2. Stain an entire embryo at any early stage, using Nile blue sulphate. Allow the embryo to remain in the vital dye until its surface is distinctly blue in color. Now follow directions under "1" above. The peripherally exposed parts of cells will be stained the more heavily and motility can be studied in relation to the original polarity or axis of the cell.

---

* The author acknowledges with pleasure the suggestions made by Dr. Holtfreter in organizing this exercise. See new section #28 on "Dissociation and Reaggregation of cells."

3. Repeat either "1" or "2" but place the disarranged cells in calcium-free Standard Solution and note the effect on amoeboid movement as well as cellular aggregation.

4. Cells may be separated from each other mechanically, with fine glass needles. This should be attempted, particularly with the later (neurula) stages where the germ layers can be distinguished.

5. Separate the cells of a neurula within its external membranes by means of the KOH Standard Solution. This should require from 10 to 60 minutes. When the cells are fully separated, return the neurula to Standard Solution and observe at intervals over a period of 2 or 3 days. Frequently there will be complete re-organization of the neurula and development will be normal.

6. Other solutions to be tested against neurulae to determine their ability to separate cells in a manner similar to KOH. Such solutions as K oxalate, Na citrate, Ca-free Standard, and M/64 KCN might be tried.

FRAGMENTATION

Isolated embryonic cells can be caused to fragment or pinch off knobs of protoplasm or form blister-like protrusions by a variety of means.

1. Observe an amoeboid embryonic neural plate cell which shows a passing wave of constriction along its main axis. Gently handle this cell with a glass needle and often the wave-like constriction will cut the cell into two.

2. Chemical fragmentation of cells may be accomplished by means of hypertonic (Standard) solutions; alkaline media; pure sodium chloride solutions (isotonic); and a variety of agents such as cysteine and alloxan. Such fragments should be returned to Standard Solution and observed for the duration of activity, which may be as long as 7 days.

    The best results will be achieved by treating the cells with KOH in Standard Solution where the pH is raised to 10 or 11.

ADHESIVENESS

Embryonic cells are most adhesive immediately after their isolation or separation from each other. This adhesiveness is gradually lost even in Standard Solution. (See the Glossary under such terms as cytotaxis, cytolisthesis, cytotropism.) The developmental stage of the cell and its histological type will also affect the degree of adhesiveness.

Following the above procedure of isolating embryonic cells, place the isolated cells in each of the following media to determine the effect of the medium on the tendency of cells to stick together.

1. Calcium-rich Standard Solution.
2. Calcium-free Standard Solution.
3. 10% Standard Solution (hypotonic).
4. Alkaline Standard Solution with pH above 9.6.
5. Neutral Standard Solution with pH at 7.0 to 9.0.

PHAGOCYTOSIS

This observation is rather difficult, but can be observed if the student has abundant patience and can concentrate on endoderm, mesenchyme, endothelial cells and neuroblasts.

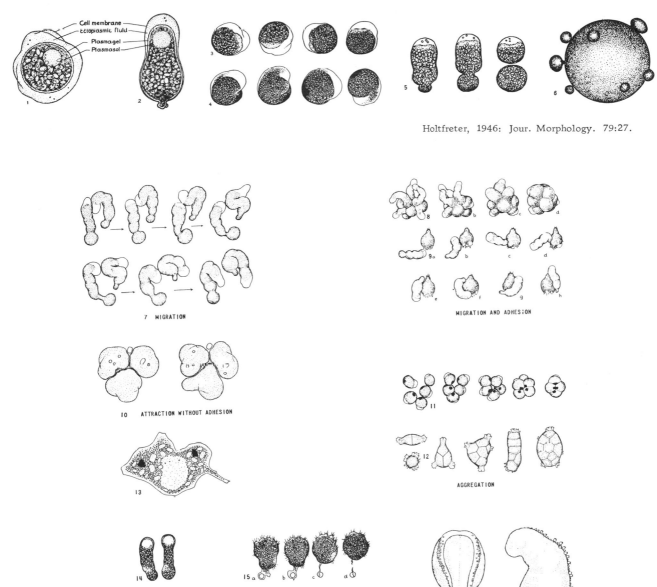

Holtfreter, 1946: Jour. Morphology. 79:27.

Holtfreter, 1947: Jour. Morphology. 80:57.

Fig. 1.   Isolated amphibian gastrula cell.

Fig. 2.   Ectoplasmic movements in isolated Embryonic Cell.

Rotating movements in the absence of (Fig. 3), and in the presence of endoplasmic sol-gel formation (Fig. 4).

Fig. 5.   Fission of a cell into unequal halves.

Fig. 6.   Unfertilized frog egg budding off spherical fragments.

Fig. 7.   Migrating vermiform cells, isolated from the medullary plate, failing to aggregate.

Fig. 8.   Cells from the medullary plate becoming adhesive to each other while changing from a cylindrical into a spherical shape, the intervals between each picture being about 5 minutes.

Fig. 9.   Successive phases of kinetic relations between a sessile and a migrating neuroblast.

Fig. 10. Three ectoplasmic cell fragments exhibiting reciprocal attraction, but no adhesion.

Fig. 11. Ectodermal cells in the process of aggregating, the whole process taking about 20 minutes.

Fig. 12. Aggregations comprising various numbers of cells, some of which are at the same time spreading on glass.

Fig. 13. Spreading embryonic cell containing 2 particles of carbon.

Fig. 14. Cylindrical cell having ingested a drop of paraffin oil.

Fig. 15. Neuroblast attempting but failing to incorporate a droplet of paraffin oil.

Fig. 16. Neuroblasts leaving an embryo which has been exposed to a hypertonic salt solution.

The cells of a neurula should be isolated with 0.1% KOH in Standard Solution and then transferred to fresh Standard Solution (without KOH) to which some carbon or carmine particles have been added. Occasionally one will see the amoeboid-type of ingestion of the foreign particles, a process similar to normal phagocytosis.

DIFFERENTIATION

The neurula-stage isolated embryonic cells in Standard Solution may be placed in a culture dish or a depression slide and sealed with a rim of vaseline around the cover or coverslip. All conditions must be aseptic. The cells will often survive from 2 to 7 days and many will differentiate.

If one can select a mesectoderm cell for particular study, the differentiation is most graphic. These mesectoderm cells can be isolated from the closed neural tube stage by temporary immersion in hypertonic solutions. (See figures from Holtfreter's paper.)

The chemical isolation of neurula-stage cells may require several hours of exposure. The isolation of blastula stage cells takes from 3 to 5 minutes.

A rapid cytological examination of normal but isolated blastula, gastrula, or neurula cells and of isolated cells of the neurula which have differentiated, can be achieved by the technical procedure recommended by Tyler (1946). The isolated cells are placed on the center of a coverslip and inverted (in the hanging drop) over another coverslip on which there is a drop of Bouin's fixative. If the edges of the upper coverslip are placed across the corners of the lower coverslip, they can later be separated the more easily. The Bouin's fixative should be allowed to act for 5 minutes, and then the coverslips are together immersed in a Syracuse dish of Bouin's fixative and the upper coverslip is gently separated from the lower one by means of a needle. Allow the Bouin's fixative to act on the cell smears for another 5 minutes, then transfer to 70% alcohol in a Columbia staining dish made for coverslips. From this point on the usual cytological procedures can be followed, staining the smears with Feulgen for thymonucleic acid; Harris' haematoxylin for gross chromosome structure; pyronin for ribosnucleic acid, etc.

DISCUSSION:

This exercise has been organized from a series of investigations by Holtfreter (1943-1947) which represent a new approach to the problems relating to morphogenetic movements. Holtfreter has shown that up to a certain stage, any isolated cell of the embryo is ready to unite with any other similar cell, provided the cells face each other with their uncoated surfaces. Such isolated cells show an inherent tendency to movement due to the autonomous activity of the cell membrane and not to any activity of the endoplasmic core. There are wave-like contractions of the plasmalemma and an internal shifting of a clear fluid mass which often results in the formation of lobopodia. Aggregation of cells results in the reduction of exposed surface tension. (See Section 28 on page 224).

The general cytology of the amphibian cell is remarkably like that of the Amoeba. There are four major parts:

1. Central core of semi-liquid endoplasm (plasmosol) which contains the nucleus, yolk, lipo-protein granules, melanin granules, and cytoplasmic ground substance.

2. Capsular wall of endoplasm, the plasmogel.

3. Outer shell of fluid ectoplasm which contains smaller particles. This is generally miscible with water, and is rather thick.

4. Thin refractive surface membrane, the plasmalemma, which forms irregular surface bulges. This is semi-solid. Movements are initiated and executed by forces localized in this layer or membrane but "they may be associated with local solation and re-gelation of that portion of the endoplasm which underlies a fully developed ectoplasmic bulge." (Holtfreter)

The adhesiveness of isolated embryonic cells is associated with the fluid environment, the developmental stage of the cells, and the cytological type of cell involved. Cells in isolation tend to lose their adhesiveness, and the hyaline bulges of the moving cells are less adhesive. Adhesion is definitely toward other cells rather than toward the substratum such as glass. Cytolizing cells become non-adhesive and are generally expelled from an aggregation of cells.

Any living cell which exhibits amoeboid movement, forming lobopodia, would be expected to phagocytize particles from the environment. Some of these embryonic cells are more efficient than others, the difference being the more apparent in cells from the neurula stage.

Holtfreter has been able to keep isolated embryonic cells of the Amphibia alive and active for weeks. There is around each cell an elastic surface coat whose strength increases during development (differentiation) and whose existence is important in the behavior, survival, and differentiation of that cell. As long as this surface membrane is intact the cell is protected.

REFERENCES

BUTSCHLI, O., 1892 - "Untersuchungen uber mikroscopische Schaume und das Protoplasma." Leipzig.
CHAMBERS, R., 1943 - "Electrolytic solutions compatible with the maintenance of protoplasmic structure." Biol. Symp. 10:91.
CONKLIN, E. G., 1933 - "Development of isolated and partially separated blastomeres of Amphioxus." Jour. Exp. Zool. 64:303.
HOLTFRETER, J., 1943 - "Properties and functions of the surface coat in amphibian embryos." Jour. Morph. 93:251.
HOLTFRETER, J., 1946 - "Structure, motility, and locomotion in isolated embryonic amphibian cells." Jour. Morph. 79:27.
HOLTFRETER, J., 1947 - "Observations on the migration, aggregation, and phagocytosis of embryonic cells." Jour. Morph. 80:25 and 57.
HOLTFRETER, J., 1947 - "Changes of structure and the kinetics of differentiating embryonic cells." Jour. Morph. 80:57.
LEWIS, W. H., 1939 - "Some contributions of tissue culture of development and growth." Growth Symposium. 1939.
ROUX, W., 1894 - "Uber das Cytotropismus der Furchungszellen des Grasfrosches (Rana fusca)." Arch. f. Ent. Mech. 1:161.
SEIFRIZ, W., 1945 - "The physical properties of protoplasm." Ann. Rev. Physiol. 7:35.
SIMON, P., 1961 - "Association de blastodermes d'oiseaux en culture in vitro. Application de cett methode a la migration des gonocytes primaires d'un embryon, a un autre embryon". Coll. Int. du Centre. Nat. de la Recherche Scientifique. 101:269-275.
TYLER, A., 1946 - "Rapid slide making method for preparation of eggs, Protozoa, etc." The Collecting Net 19.

(See also sections on Culture of Isolated Anlagen, p. 218; Dissociation and Reaggregation of Cells, p. 224; and Tissue Culture Techniques, p. 229).

"A graduate from one of our larger universities, when asked why he changed from Biology to Philosophy, said: "Well, I found that there was so much to be learned in Biology that I had no time to think, so I took up Philosophy, where there is nothing to be learned and I had all my time to think".

E. M. East

27. THE CULTURE OF ISOLATED AMPHIBIAN ANLAGEN

PURPOSE: To test the self-differentiating capacities of the constituents of the various organ anlagen of the early amphibian embryo.

MATERIALS:
   Biological: Anuran (stage #18) and Urodele (stage #28) embryos.

   Technical:
      1. Culture media:
         a. Amphibian Ringer's solution.
         b. Standard (Holtfreter's) solution.
         c. Standard (Holtfreter's) solution plus frog blood plasma, lymph, coelomic fluid, or crushed embryo extracts.
         d. Urodele growing medium plus Urodele coelomic fluid.
         (Note: Media #1 and #2 may be autoclaved and kept in ampoules.   Medium #3 should be made up with sterile Standard Solution and #4 with sterile Urodele growing medium.   Sodium sulfadiazine 0.5% may be added to give further protection against bacterial contamination.)

      2. Depression slides, watchglasses, Syracuse and Petri dishes.   Circular coverslips, cellophane tubing (Visking cellulose sausage casings of minimum diameter).

METHOD:
   Precautions:
      1. While amphibian tissues do not require the asepsis required by avian tissues, aseptic conditions will undoubtedly prolong the development in isolation. The operating instruments may be boiled (glassware) or dipped in 95% alcohol.   Large glassware may be autoclaved.   Culture media which do not contain body fluids (lymph, plasma, etc.) may also be autoclaved.   Otherwise, 0.5% sodium sulfadiazine can be added without any effect but an aid to asepsis.
      2. Moist chamber conditions should be provided since evaporation changes the concentration of the constituents of the medium.
      3. If embryos which are to contribute the anlagen are divested of their membranes and are then passed through several changes of sterile Standard Solution (for the Anura) of Urodele Growing Medium (for the Urodela) most of the adherent bacteria will be removed.
      4. The isolates should be kept at temperatures near the lower limit of viability of the species under investigation.   This will retard development but also the incidence of infection.
      5. Large amounts of culture medium may be placed in ampoules and autoclaved, to be used when needed.   The 0.5% sodium sulfadiazine may be added before autoclaving, for it is not altered by this treatment.

   Controls: There are two types of controls: (1) Isolates other than those under immediate investigation.   For instance, the experimental isolate might be the gill or limb anlagen and the control could be tail ecto- and mesoderm.   (2) If but a single anlage is removed from an embryo, the bilaterally located mate anlage may be considered the control organ, or embryos of identical stage may be cultured under parallel conditions of temperature, etc. for direct comparison of the isolate with the intact anlage.

Procedure:
1. Prepare 2 culture media at least. For Anura use Standard Solution and for Urodela use Growing Medium, each of which should be sterilized by boiling or autoclaving. Boiling must be brief to avoid changing the salt concentration. The second type of culture medium should be either of the above (depending upon whether Anura or Urodela are used) to which is added peritoneal fluid. This can be done by injecting about 3 cc. of the salt solution into the body cavity of adults of the same species, preferably females and then removing it, with the same hypodermic, after a few minutes in the body cavity. This second medium cannot be boiled, but the 0.5% sodium sulfadiazine should be added.
2. Prepare the culture dishes:
   a. Place a layer of absorbent cotton on the bottom of a Petri dish, and then mould a place in the center of the cotton for a small watchglass. Place on the cover and sterilize in the autoclave. Allow it to air cool. Just before placing the culture medium and the explant in the watchglass, it will be necessary to moisten the cotton with sterile distilled water. Avoid placing any water in the watchglass, and undue exposure to the bacteria of the air.
   b. Wrap some depression slides individually in white paper, and heat sterilize (at 150°C.) for 15 minutes. Circular coverslips may be autoclaved in a #2 covered Stender, or sterilized in 95% alcohol.
3. Prepare the explants:
   The following anlagen make excellent explants:
   Gill - try ectoderm alone, ecto- and mesoderm, and then include the pharyngael endoderm. (See Moser, 1940)
   Limb - try ectoderm alone, then include underlying mesoderm. (See Harrison, 1928)
   Balancer (Urodele) - use both ecto- and mesoderm components.
   Sucker (Anura) - use both ecto- and mesoderm components.
   Olfactory placode - use ectoderm alone.
   Eye - use optic vesicle, with and without overlying ectoderm. (See Filatow, 1926)
   Tail - include both ecto- and mesoderm.
   Heart - remove ventral ectoderm and allow it to wrap itself around some of the heart mesenchyme. (See Stohr, 1924)
   Neural crest - peel off the dorsal ectoderm and isolate the cord and attached crest alone (see section on "Neural Crest Origin of Pigment").

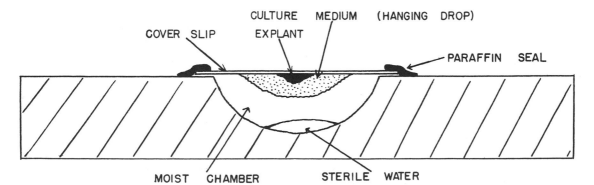

SCHEMATIC SECTION THROUGH
DEPRESSION SLIDE WITH EXPLANT

(Note: If one treats the early post-neurula embryo as a mosaic of many
organ anlagen, explantation of a variety of structures may be studied.
It should be recorded, however, exactly what germ layers are included in each explant.)

The embryo is first passed through several changes of sterile culture medium to remove adherent bacteria, and then the anlagen are removed by means
of iridectomy scissors, lancets, glass needles, etc. and are transferred to
the culture medium by means of an adequately wide-mouthed, sterile pipette.

4.   Culturing of the explants:
The explant may be placed directly into the appropriate medium in the watchglass surrounded by a moat of distilled water which provides a moist chamber when the Petri dish cover is replaced.

An alternative method* is to prescribe a small ring with a sterile glass rod
dipped into soft paraffin, ** the ring being about half the diameter on the sterile coverslip. When this is cool, place 2 drops of sterile culture medium in
the center of the ring (on the coverslip) and then add the excised explant to
the medium. Place a drop or two of sterile distilled water in the depression
slide and a ring of vaseline or petroleum jelly around the margins of the depression. Quickly invert the coverslip and place it over the depression,
thereby providing the explant with an air-tight moist chamber. In some instances, it will be better to omit the distilled water in the depression, and
to use more culture medium and turn the slide (and attached coverslip) upside down so as to bring the explant against the coverslip to which it will become adherent within a day or so. The depression slide may then be re-in-
verted, and the explant examined directly (through the coverslip) within the
hanging drop of culture medium under a dissection or regular microscope.

Urodele explants should be kept at temperatures of 10° to 15°C. and Anuran
explants will do better at 15° to 18°C.

OBSERVATIONS AND EXPERIMENTAL DATA:

Avoid any unnecessary disturbance of the cultures during the first 24 hours. During subsequent examinations avoid drastic changes in temperature as from the microscope lamp.

It is obvious that the radical change to which the organ anlagen are subjected in this type
of experiment make it imperative that the material be observed at frequent intervals. In
the space below:
1.   Compare the changes in the explant with corresponding changes in the same area
of unoperated animals of the same age, and with the control explants.
2.   Make day-to-day sketches of observable changes under the microscope.
3.   If the explant seems to be healthy, attempt to renew the culture medium after 3 to
4 days, and continue it as long as possible. (Remember Carrel's chick heart
fibroblasts which lasted over 25 years!).
4.   At the conclusion of the experiment, section, stain, and study the differentiation.

---

* Or white vaseline.

** Seamless cellophane tubing of small diameter is available in 100 foot rolls and can be cut and tied off into short culture tubes
which can be immersed in any constant temperature bath. If about 25% of the space is air, the culture will survive for several
days before a change is necessary.

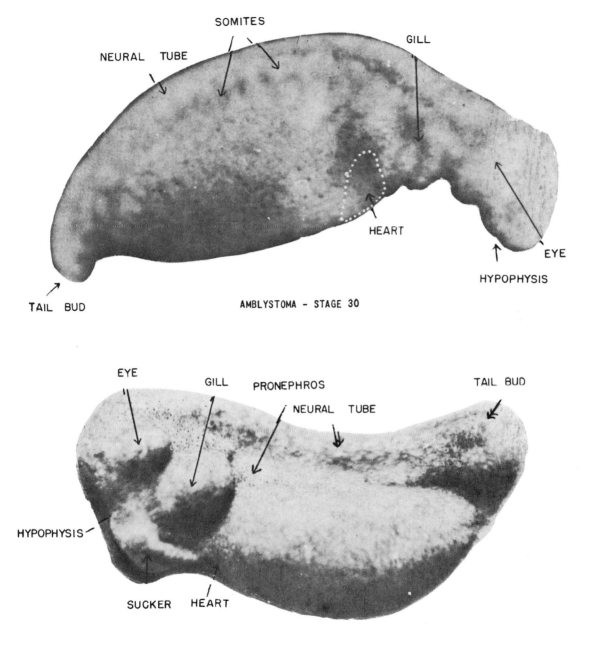

AMBLYSTOMA - STAGE 30

RANA - STAGE 18 - 19

ANLAGE: TO BE CULTURED AS EXPLANTS

Progressive development of gill anlagen
of Amblystoma in isolation.

(From Moser, 1940: Jour.
Morph. 66:261)

DISCUSSION:

This type of experiment simply tests the self-differentiating capacity of a germinal fragment and is to be compared with the transplantation of the same fragment to a living host,
particularly to heterotopic positions.   In the isolated condition the explant must be provided with an adequate culture medium, it must supply its own energy for growth and development, and if it is to differentiate it must have acquired some pattern influence before
excision.   It is this pattern which is the interest of this experiment.

No synthetic medium has yet been devised which is perfect enough to satisfy living cells
so that they can differentiate normally for an indefinite period.   In the younger explants
there is apt to be greater survival because the cells possess yolk reserves upon which
they may call.   Nevertheless, morphogenetic differentiation in such explants is rare because they have not received inductive influences from their surrounding areas, but cellular and even histological differentiations in such early explants may be seen.

The most instructive aspect of this exercise will relate to the determination of the value
of the various germ layers in the differentiation of specific organs.   It should be determined, for instance, to what extent the ecto-, meso-, and endoderm are related to the
development of the gills, which structure in the normal embryo is composed of all three
germ layers.

REFERENCES

BAKER, L. E., 1938 - "The secretion of iodine by thyroid glands cultivated in the Lindbergh pump." Sc. 88:479. (See also
    Science 83:605, 1936).
BAUTZMANN, H., 1929 - "Uber debeutungsfremde Selbstdifferenzierung aus Teilstucken des Amphibienkeime." Naturwiss. 17:818.
BLOOM, W., 1937 - "Cellular differentiation and tissue culture." Physiol. Rev. 17:589.
BRACHET, J. & RAPKINE, 1939 - "Oxydation et reduction d'explantats dorsaux et ventraux de Gastrulas (Amphibien)." Comp.
    rendu. Soc. Biol. 131:789.
DORRIS, F., 1938 - "Differentiation of the chick eye in vitro." Jour. Exp. Zool. 78:385. (See also 1940: Pro. Soc. Exp. Biol.
    & Med. 44:286.)
ERDMANN, W., 1931 - "Uber das Selbstdifferenzierungsvermogen von Amphibienkeimteilen bekannter prospektiver Bedeutung
    im Explantat." Arch. f. Ent. mech. 124:666.
ESAKI, S., 1929 - "A sure method for the elective staining of neurofibrillae in tissues cultivated in vitro." Ztschr. f. wiss.
    Mikrosk. 46:369 (See also Comp. rendu. Soc. d. Anatom. 24:223).
FELL, H. B. & R. ROBISON, 1930 - "The development and phosphatase activity in vivo and in vitro of the mandibular skeletal
    tissue of the embryonic fowl." Bioch. Jour. 24:1905.

FILATOW, D., 1926 - "Uber die Entwicklung des Augenkeimes einiger Amphibien in vitro." Arch. f. Ent. mech. 107:575.

FISCHER, I., 1938 - "Uber die Differenzierung Melanophoren und Lipophoren in Extoderm-explantaten von Amblystoma." Arch. f. Exper. Zellforsch. 22:55.

FOOTE, C. L., F. M. FOOTE, 1960 - "Maintenance of gonads of Xenopus laevis in organ culture." Proc. Soc. Exp. Biol. &. Med. 105:107-108.

FOSTRECT, G., 1939 - "Preliminary in vitro studies of melanophore principle activity of the pituitary gland." Proc. Soc. Exp. Biol. & Med. 40:302.

GOERTTLER, K., 1928 - "Die Bedeutung der ventralateralen mesodermbezirke fur die Herzenanlage der Amphibienkeime." Verh. Anat. Ges. 37:132.

HADORN, E., 1934 - "Uber die Entwicklungsleistungen bastardmerogonischen Gewebe von Triton palmatus x Triton cristatus im Ganzkeim und als Explantat in vitro." Arch. f. Ent. mech. 131:238.

HARRISON, R. G., 1928 - "On the status and significance of tissue culture." Arch. f. Zellforsch. 6:4.

HETHERINGTON, D. C. & J. S. CRAIG, 1939 - "Effect of frozen-dried plasma and frozen-dried embryo juice on tissue cultures." Proc. Soc. Exp. Biol. & Med. 42:831.

HITCHCOCK, H. B., 1939 - "The behavior of adult amphibian skin cultured in vivo and in vitro." Jour. Exp. Zool. 81:299.

HOGUE, M. J., 1932 - "The reaction of tissue-culture cells to barium (x-ray) sulphate." Anat. Rec. 54:307.

HOLTFRETER, J., 1931 - "Uber die Aufsucht isolierter des Amphibienkeimes." Arch. f. Ent. Mech. 124:404.

HOLTFRETER, J., 1938 - "Differenzierungspotenzen isolierter Teile der Urodelengastrula." Arch. f. Ent. Mech. 138:522 (See also ibid 138:657).

LAZARENKO, T., 1931 - "Ein Beitrage zur Morphologie des Wachstums von embryonalem Nervengewebe in vitro." Arch. f. Exper. Zellf. 11:555.

LEVI, G., 1934 - "Explantation, besonders die Struktur und die biologischen Eigenschaften der in vitro gezuchteten Zellen und Gewebe." Ergebn, Anat. u. Entw. Gesch. 31:125.

LEWIS, M. R. & W. H. LEWIS, 1924 - "Behavior of cells in tissue cultures." General Cytology, Sec. 7:384.

LONG, J. A., 1939 - "A pulsating circulation apparatus for tissue cultures, embryos, and small organs." Univ. Calif. Pub. Zool. 43:211.

MAXIMOW, A., 1925 - "Tissue cultures of young mammalian embryos." Pub. Carnegie Inst. Washington, #361, p. 47.

MAY, R. M., 1936 - "Les substances embryonnaires de croissance. Leur rapport avec la culture des cellules embryonnaires." Bull. de la Soc. Philomathique de Paris, 119:15.

MOSER, F., 1940 - "The differentiation of isolated gills of the amphibian embryo." Jour. Morph. 66:261.

MURRAY, M. R. & A. P. STOUT, 1942 - "Characteristics of human Schwann cells in vitro." Anat. Rec. 84:275.

NICHOLAS, J. S. & D. RUDNICK, 1934 - "Development of rat embryos in tissue culture." Proc. Nat. Acad. Sci. 20:656.

NIU, M. C., V. C. TWITTY, 1953 - "The differentiation of gastrula ectoderm in medium conditioned by axial mesoderm." Proc. Nat. Acad. Sci. 39:985.

ONO, Y., 1927 - "The behavior of cells in tissue cultures of Oryzias latipes with special reference to the ectodermic epithelium." Annot. Zool. Japan 11.

PARKER, R. C., 1938 - "Methods of tissue culture." New York.

PERRI, T., 1934 - "Ricerche sul compartamento dell'abbozzo oculare di Anfibi in condicioni di espianto." Arch. f. Ent. Mech. 131:113.

PORTER, K. R., A. CLAUDE, & E. F. FULLUM, 1945 - "A study of tissue culture cells by electron microscopy." Jour. Exp. Med. 81:233.

PRESTON, M. M'E., 1948 - "Amphibian tissue cultures for biophysical research." Nature, 161:203.

RAYLE, J., 1945 - "Some effects of hexenolactone on tissue cultures." Growth. 9:275.

RUDNICK, D., 1938 - "Differentiation in culture of pieces of the early chick blastoderm". Jour. Exp. Zool. 79:399.

SPRATT, N. T., Jr., 1940 - "An in vitro analysis of the organization of the eye-forming area in the early chick blastoderm." Jour. Exp. Zool. 85:171.

STEINBERG, M., 1957 - See chapter in Carnegie Institute Washington Year Book #56 (p. 437)

STILWELL, E. F., 1947 - "The influence of temperature variation upon the occurrence of multipolar mitoses in embryonic cells grown in vitro." Anat. Rec. 99.

STOHR, Ph. Jr., 1924 - "Experimentelle Studien an embryonalen Amphibienherzen. I. Uber Explantaten embryonaler Amphibien-herzen." Arch. mikr. Anat. u. Ent. Mech. 102:426.

TOMPKINS, E. R., B. B. CUNNINGHAM, & P. L. KIRK, 1947 - "Mitosis, cell size and growth in culture of embryonic chick heart." Jour. Cell. & Comp. Physiol. 30.

TOWNES, P. L., H. HOLTFRETER, 1955 - "Directed movements and selective adhesion of embryonic amphibian cells." Jour. Exp. Zool. 128:53.

TWITTY, V. C. & D. BODENSTEIN, 1939 - "Correlated genetic and embryological experiments in Triturus. IV. The study of pigment cell behavior in vitro." Jour. Exp. Zool. 81:357.

VOIGTLANDER, G., 1932 - "Untersuchungen uber den Cytotropismus der Furchungszellen." Arch. f. Ent. Mech. 127:151.

WEISS, P., 1940 - "Functional properties of isolated spinal cord grafts in larval Amphibians." Proc. Soc. Exp. Biol. & Med. 44:350.

WELLS, E. A. & A. CARMICHAEL, 1930 - "Microglia; An experimental study by means of tissue culture and vital staining." Brain. 53:1.

WOERDEMAN, M. W., 1930 - "Versuche zur verringerung der Sterblichkeit nach mikrochirurgischen Enigriffen an Amphibienkeimen." Arch. f. Ent. Mech. 121:524.

28. THE DISSOCIATION AND REAGGREGATION OF EMBRYONIC CELLS*

PURPOSE: To separate differentiating embryonic cells from each other by disrupting the intercellular matrix, and observing the reaggregation of similar and dissimilar cells.

MATERIALS: Early organ rudiments and tissues of embryos such as the chick and mouse.

Technical materials are the same as for tissue culture procedures, in addition to which the solutions listed below.

METHOD: Since Moscona has shown that tissues from various warm-blooded vertebrates can be dissociated by trypsinization and the cells may then reaggregate along lines of prospective differentiation rather than generic source, the general method of preparing the separated cell masses will be given so that the investigator may try the process on other forms as well as repeat those reported. It is obvious that those with prior experience in tissue culture methods and cell physiology will, most likely, be the most successful. While Moscona and others report their researches in a way which might convey the impression that the technique is simple, one should not be misled. However, the results are so rewarding and so significant that anyone so inclined to work should be encouraged.

Freshly dissected fragments of early differentiating embryonic tissue, measuring no more than 1 mm in diameter, are collected in small centrifuge tubes and incubated (warm-blooded animals) for 10 minutes in calcium and magnesium free solution (CMF) at 37°C. and at a pH. of 7.2 under a mixture of 5% CO_2 and 95% air.

CMF Solution

NaCl - 8.0 gr.	KH_2PO_4 - 0.025 gr.
KCl - 0.30 gr.	$NaHCO_3$ - 1.00 gr.
$NaH_2PO_4 \cdot H_2O$ - 0.05 gr.	Glucose - 2 gr.

Glass Dist. Water - 1,000 cc.

The fragments are then transferred to trypsin in CMF at 37°C. for 15-20 minutes, also under the CO_2-air mixture. The trypsin is a crystallized, lyophilized preparation (Worthington Co., Freehold, N.J.) made up as a 1% solution in CMF. Also use crystalline soybean trypsin inhibitor which is non-toxic in concentrations of 1 mgm per 5 ml of culture medium.

The fragments are then gently rinsed several times with CMF, avoiding disruption or disaggregation at this time by careful handling. The purpose of the rinsing is to free the fragments of adherent and excess trypsin. It is the tryptic degradation of the intercellular mucoproteins which brings about the separation of the cells without their destruction. But the tryptic action must not be allowed to go far enough to destroy the cells. To each fragment add 1 cc of the culture medium kept at room temperature, and, with tapered pipette, disperse the cell masses into single cells by flushing the fragments in and out briskly through the tip of the pipette without frothing. This could be done under the dissecting microscope with the pipette containing no air, only the medium used.

---

*This exercise has been organized with the generous cooperation of Dr. A. Moscona.

STANDARD CULTURE MEDIUM (MOSCONA)

Eagle's basal medium* 1% glutamine; with 10% unfiltered and sterile

Horse serum 2% fresh chick embryo extract,
        (10 day chick embryos and Tyrode's solution 1:1); and

1% penicillin-streptomycin mixture (50 units each per cc.)

Equal portions of the cell suspensions are distributed into sterile, 25 cc. Erlenmayer flasks each containing 3 cc. of the standard culture medium. The flasks are gassed with the CO_2-air mixture (5%/95%), tightly stoppered, and placed on a gyratory table shaker with a 3/4 inch eccentric rotary motion of 70 r.p.m. at $38^{\circ}C$. constant temperature. Aggregates may be collected after 24-48 hours for analysis, and others may be further cultured on plasma clots or in roller tubes using the culture medium as a liquid phase.

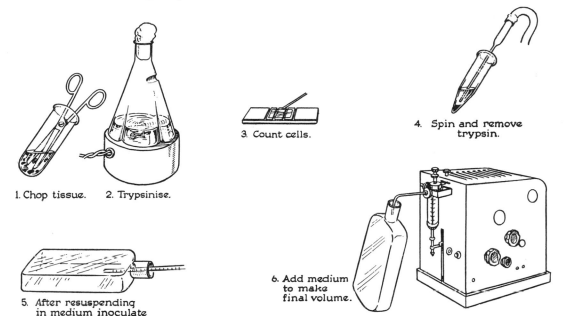

1. Chop tissue.   2. Trypsinise.

3. Count cells.

4. Spin and remove trypsin.

5. After resuspending in medium inoculate vessels.

6. Add medium to make final volume.

TRYPSINISATION OF FRESH TISSUE

Figure reproduced with permission from J. Paul's "Cell and Tissue Culture" 1960, E. & S. Livingston, Pub., Edinburgh.

The shape, number, size distribution and internal structure of aggregates formed under a set of specific conditions within 24 hours is known as the aggregation pattern of the cells in testing. Different cell types or cell populations produce different aggregation patterns. Under constant conditions the patterns are highly reproducible. Even slight variations in any of the conditions (i.e. changes in culture medium, temperature, rotation, shape of flask) may affect them. Cell cohesiveness is probably the major force which aids in the formation of aggregates. According to Moscona ('60) "In suspensions of freshly dispersed embryonic cells, a characteristic course of events takes place, as a result of which the cells convene and aggregate into clusters and reestablish tissue-like continuity".

* Obtainable from The Microbiological Association, Bethesda, Maryland.

DISCUSSION: When embryonic cells are disassociated by trypsinization there appears to
form a viscous extracellular material derived from these disassociated cells, possibly a mucoprotein, which aids in the process of re-aggregation. This extracellular material (ECM) may, in fact, be a variant of the ground substance which
binds together intact cells in tissues. Moscona says (1960) that this ECM may be
"elaborated in response to specific environmental situations by cells denuded of
their original matrix; that it provided cells with a controllable microenvironment, a
physiologically active intermediary zone between cells and culture medium, an operational framework related to their native matrix yet adjusted to the particular
physical and metabolic conditions encountered. "

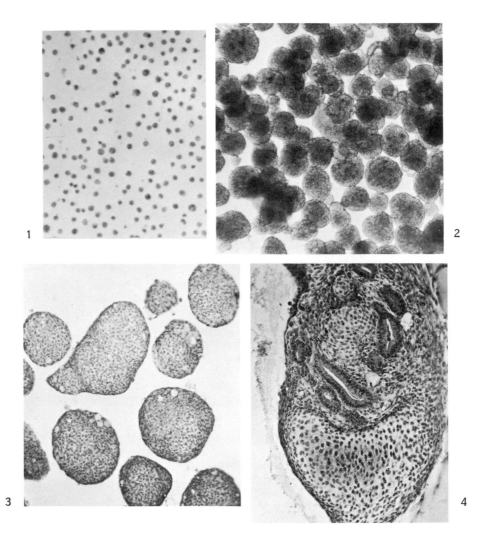

Fig. 1 - Smear of dissociated limb-bud cells from a 4-day chick
         embryo.
Fig. 2 - Aggregates of chick limb-bud cells at 24 hours obtained
         by rotation-culture of the cell suspension at 70 rpm.
Fig. 3 - Aggregates at 48 hours of chondrogenic cells showing
         early cartilage formation.
Fig. 4 - Aggregates of intermingled cells from embryonic chick
         limb-buds (4-day embryos) and mesonephros (7-day
         embryos), showing mixture of cartilage and nephric
         tubules.

(These available through courtesy of Dr. A. Moscona)

Dissociated embryonic cells tended to re-aggregate when their concentration (numbers) reached a certain minimal level. When organ rudiments of chick and mouse embryos were disassociated together into mixed suspensions, there was ready re-aggregation to form chimeric tissues, often with histotypical differentiation. This occurred even when such divergent types of cells as cartilage, nerve, liver, and melanotic cells were intermixed. When similar (tissue) type cells from mouse and chick were intermixed, the reconstituted mass included cells from both generic origins. When the intermixed cells were from dissimilar tissue origins (i.e., chick kidney and mouse cartilage) there was a clear-cut separation of the re-aggregates. There was demonstrated, therefore, preferential re-aggregation according to the original identities of the embryonic differentiating cells, rather than to generic origin.

RESULTS: This exercise is perhaps more difficult than the above description suggests. Nevertheless, it is recommended that the student, after he has mastered most of the other procedures of this book, and the basic procedures of tissue culture (isolation culture) work, attempt to repeat one or another of Moscona's described experiments. The rewards will far out-weigh the effort, and the results will contribute to one's concept of organismic influences in development. (See also - section #26 on "Behavior of Isolated Embryonic Cells.")

REFERENCES

ANDRES, G., 1953 - "Experiments on the fate of dissociated embryonic cells (chick) disseminated by the vascular route. II. Teratomas." J. Exp. Zool. 122:507-539.

AUERBACH, R., C. GROBSTEIN, 1958 - "Inductive interaction of embryonic tissues after dissociation and reaggregation." Exp. Cell Res. 15:384-397.

BARTH, L. G., & L. J., 1959 - "Differentiation of cells of Rana pipiens gastrula in unconditioned medium." J. Emb. Exp. Morph. 7:219-222.

BLOOM, W., 1937 - "Cellular differentiation and tissue culture." Physiol. Rev. 17:589-617.

BORGHESE, E., 1955 - Lo sviluppo di organi embrionali isolati." Atti. Soc. Tal. Anat. XVI Convegno sociale, Pisa. 1954, p. 1-92.

BORGHESE, E., 1958 - "Organ Culture Methods" in "Chemical Basis of Development." McElea and Glass, Eds.

DAY, T. D., 1947 - "The nature and significance of the cementing substance in interstitial connective tissue." J. Path. Bacteriol. 59:567-573.

DAY, T. D., 1949 - "The mode of reaction of interstitial connective tissue with water." J. Physiol. 109:380-389.

DREW, A H., 1923 - "Growth and differentiation in tissue cultures." Brit. J. Exp. Path. 4:46-52.

EDDS, M. V., 1958 - "Origin and structure of intercellular matrix." in The Chemical Basis of Development, eds. McElroy & Glass, Johns Hopkins Univ. Press, Baltimore.

FELL, H. B., 1940 - "The application of tissue culture in vitro to embryology." J. Roy. Microscop. Soc. 60:95-108.

FELL, H. B., 1954 - "The effect of environmental factors on the differentiation of allantoic endoderm in organ culture." J. Embryol. & Exp. Morph. 2:348-352.

FELL, H. B., 1957 - "The future of tissue culture in relation to morphology." J. Nat. Cancer Inst. 19:643-662.

GAILLARD, P., 1942 - "Hormones regulating growth and differentiation in embryonic explants." Hermann, Paris.

GALTSOFF, P. S., 1925 - "Regeneration after dissociation". Jour. Exp. Zool. 42:183.

GERSH, I., & H. R. CATCHPOLE, 1949 - "The organization of ground substance and basement membrane and its significance in tissue injury, disease and growth." A. J. Anat. 85:457-522.

GLUCKSMANN, A., 1952 - "The response of human tissues to radiation with special reference to differentiation." Brit. J. Radiol. 25:38-43.

GROBSTEIN, C., 1954 - "Tissue interaction in the morphogenesis of mouse embryonic rudiments in vitro." in Aspects of Synthesis and Order in Growth., XIII Growth Symposium, Princeton Univ. Press. p. 233-268.

GROBSTEIN, C., 1956 - "Inductive tissue interaction in development." Advances in Cancer Research. 4:187-236.

GROBSTEIN, C., & E. ZWILLING, 1953 - "Modification of growth and differentiation of chorio-allantoic grafts of chick blastoderm; pieces after cultivation at a glass-clot interface." J. Exp. Zool. 122:259-284.

GROBSTEIN, C., & G. PARKER, 1954 - "In vitro induction of cartilage in mouse somite mesoderm by embryonic spinal cord." Proc. Soc. Exp. Biol. & Med.. 85:471-481.

GROSS, J., 1956 - "The behaviour of collagen units as a model in morphogenesis." J. Biophys. Biochem. Cytol. 2:Suppl. 274.

HANKS, J. H., J. H. WALLACE, 1958 - "Determination of cell viability!" Proc. Soc. Exp. Biol. & Med. 98:188-192.

HARRISON, J. R., 1954 - "Morphogenesis of chick embryo in vitro after exposure to lowered temperature in ovo." Physiol. Zool. 30:187-197.

HARRISON, R. G., 1928 - "On the status and significance of tissue culture." Arch. Exp. Zellforsch. Gewebezucht. 4:4-27.

HARRISON, R. G., 1933 - "Some difficulties in the determination problems." Am. Nat. 67:306-321.

HOLTFRETER, J., 1947 - "Observations on the migration, aggregation, and phagocytosis of embryonic cells." J. Morph. 80:25-56.

HOLTFRETER, J., 1948 - "Significance of the cell membrane in embryonic processes." Ann. N. Y. Acad. Sci. 49:709-760.

HOLTFRETER, J., 1951 - "Some aspects of embryonic induction." Growth 15, Suppl. 117-152.

HOLTFRETER, J., & V. HAMBURGER, 1955 - In "Analysis of Development", eds. Willier, Weiss, & Hamburger, W. B. Saunders, p. 230-296.

MARKERT, C. L., 1958 - "Chemical concepts of cellular differentiation." In The Chemical Basis of Development, eds. McElroy & Glass, Johns Hopkins Univ., Baltimore.

MOSCONA, A., 1952 - "Cell suspensions from organ rudiments of chick embryos." Exp. Cell. Res. 3:535-539.

MOSCONA, A., 1956 - "Development of heterotypic combinations of dissociated embryonic chick cells." Proc. Soc. Exp. Biol. & Med. 92:410-416.

MOSCONA, A., 1957 - "The development in vitro of chimaeric aggregates of dissociated embryonic chick and mouse cells." Proc. Nat. Acad. Sci. 43:184-194.

MOSCONA, A., 1957 - "Formation of lentoids by dissociated retinal cells of the chick embryo." Science 125:598-599.

MOSCONA, A., 1958 - "Keratinization in vitro of chorionic epithelium of the chick embryo." Proc. Soc. Exp. Biol. & Med. 98:757-759.

MOSCONA, A., 1960 - "Rotation-mediated histogenetic aggregation of dissociated cells: A quantitative approach to cell interactions in vitro." Exp. Cell. Res. 20:1.

MOSCONA, A., H. MOSCONA, 1952 - "The dissociation and aggregation of cells from organ rudiments of the early chick embryo." J. Anat. 86:287-301.

NIU, M. C., V. C. TWITTY, 1953 - "The differentiation of gastrula ectoderm in medium conditioned by axial mesoderm." Proc. Nat. Acad. Sci. 39:985.

OKADA, T. S., 1959 - "Tracer study on the reconstitution of cartilage from dissociated cells." Exp. Cell Res. 16:437-440.

RINALDINI, L. M., 1959 - "An improved method for the isolation and quantitative cultivation of embryonic cells." Exp. Cell. Res. 16:477.

ROMANOFF, A. L., 1952 - "Membrane growth and function." Ann. N. Y. Acad. Sci. 55:288-301.

ROSE, S M., 1957 - "Cellular interaction during differentiation." Biol. Rev. 32:351-382.

SHAFFER, B. M., 1956 - "The culture of organs from the embryonic chick on cellulose-acetate fabric." Exp. Cell. Res. 11:244-248.

SHAFFER, B. M., 1957 - "Aspects of aggregation in cellular slime moulds. I. Orientation and chemotaxis." Am. Nat. 91:19-35.

STEFANELLI, A., & A. M. ZACCHEI, 1958 - "Sulle modalita di aggregazione di cellule embrionali Pollo disaggregate con tripsina." Acta Emb. Morph. Exp. 2:1-12.

STEINBERG, M. S., 1958 - "On the chemical bonds between animal cells." A mechanism for type-specific association." Am. Nat. 92:65-81.

SUSSMAN, M. & R. R. SUSSMAN, 1956 - "Cellular interactions during the development of the cellular slime moulds." in Cellular Mechanisms in Differentiation and Growth, XIV Growth Symp. Princeton Univ. Press. p. 125-154.

TOWNES, P. L. & J. HOLTFRETER, 1955 - "Directed movements and selective adhesion of embryonic amphibian cells." J. Exp. Zool. 128:53-120.

TRINKAUS, J. P., 1956 - "The differentiation of tissue cells." Am. Nat. 90:273-289.

TRINKAUS, J. P., & P. W. GROVES, 1955 - "Differentiation in culture of mixed aggregates of dissociated tissue cells." Proc. Nat. Acad. Sci. 41:787-795.

WEISS, P., 1933 - "Functional adaptation and the role of ground substance in development." Am. Nat. 67:322-340.

WEISS, P., 1945 - "Experiments on cell and axone orientation in vitro: the role of colloidal exudates in tissue organization." J. Exp. Zool. 100:353-386.

WEISS, P., 1949 - "The problem of cellular differentiation." Proc. Nat. Cancer Congr. 1949, p. 20-60.

WEISS, P., 1950 - "Perspective in the field of morphogenesis." Quart. Rev. Biol. 25:177-198.

WEISS, P., 1953 - "Some introductory remarks on the cellular basis of differentiation." J. Emb. Exp. Morph. 1:181-211.

WEISS, P., 1958 - "Cell contact." Int. Rev. Cytol. 7:391-422.

WEISS, P., & G. ANDRES, 1952 - "Experiments on the fate of embryonic cells (chick) disseminated by the vascular route." J. Exp. Zool. 121:449-487.

WEISS, P. & R. JAMES, 1955 - "Skin metaplasia in vitro induced by brief exposure to vitamin A." Exp. Cell. Res. Suppl. 3:381-394.

WEISS, P. & A. MOSCONA, 1958 - "Type-specific morphogenesis of cartilage developed from dissociated limb and scleral mesenchyme in vitro." J. Emb. Exp. Morph. 6:238-246.

WILLMER, E. N., 1958 - "Tissue culture." Metheun, London.

WILSON, H. V., 1911 - "On the behaviour of the dissociated cells in Hydroids, Alcyonaria and Asterias." J. Exp. Zool. 11:281-338.

WOLFF, E., 1954 - "Potentialites et affinities des tissus, revelees par la culture in vitro d'organes en associations heterogenes et xenoplastiques." Bull. Soc. Zool. (France) 79:357-368.

ZWILLING, E., 1954 - "Dissociation of chick embryo cells by means of a chelating compound." Science. 120:219.

ZWILLING, E., 1959 - "Some aspects of differentiation: Disaggregation and reaggregation of early chick embryos." Jour. Nat. Cancer Inst. Monogr. No. 2 from Symp. Normal and Abnormal Differentiation and Development, p. 19-39.

29. AN INTRODUCTION TO TISSUE CULTURE TECHNIQUES

Since the technique of tissue culture (i.e. the growth of cells or tissues apart from their normal environment) is receiving accelerated attention, it is proposed here to summarize the essentials of the procedures, followed by a reference list of books and papers which will allow the qualified student to pursue the subject further.

Tissue culturing developed from experimental embryology, particularly with poikilother-mic forms, although the original study was by Roux in 1885 with chick medullary plate. Harrison (1907) sustained frog medullary tubes in frog lymph. This nutritional medium was supplanted by the plasma clot, then by tissue and embryonic extracts and synthetic media. It was Carrel who sustained chick cells in vitro over many years. The current trend is combining in vitro and in vivo studies, particularly in relation to the development of cancer.

To maintain a cell or cells for any length of time, there are a number of basic require-ments. There must be regulation of the temperature, osmotic pressure, pH and other inorganic ion control, adequate and varied metabolites must be available, and vitamins, enzymes, and substrates in proper balance, and a matrix within which the cells can grow. In other words, the living cell must be given an environment approximating that of its natural environment as closely as possible in order to survive.

The medium for culturing must be very carefully selected with respect to the type of cell or cells to be studied. There is no universal medium satisfactory for all cells or organs, even among the cold-blooded animals. There are, in general, three types of media: the plasma coagulum, biological fluids, and tissue or embryonic extracts. For the plasma coagulum, blood is generally taken from the wing, carotid artery or heart of the hen and prevented from coagulating either with anti-coagulating agents or by the prevention of contamination. Rat-tail collagen has recently been used instead of the plasma clot and agar is sometimes satisfactory. For the biological fluid, serum is the most satisfactory and may be obtained from horse, calf, or human placental cord or even adult blood. The serum is obtained by allowing natural clotting of the whole blood and filtering and steriliz-ing the exuded serum. Bovine amniotic fluid is also used, as is the aqueous humor. For the tissue extracts, the embryo has traditionally been used but this may soon be replaced by synthetic media, for some tissues at least. Autologous and heterologous sources of serum or extract may or may not be toxic, the test must be empirical. Culture media may be chosen for short or long term survival of cells, for slow or rapid growth, or even indefinite growth and also for certain specialized functions. Since there is a variety of combinations of the essential salts which will allow survival for warm or for cold-blooded cells or organ explants, the most frequently used formulae will be presented below. There are many synthetic media which include various organic acids, vitamins, and hormones which are used in special instances (see Paul '60). One of these, for instance, is known as Eagle's medium consisting of 33 different compounds.

In all tissue culture work the prime requisite is absolute cleanliness because bacteria, fungi and viruses can quickly ruin any culture. Further, chemical contamination is also a constant threat because even some of the so-called cleaning fluids are so tenacious that they also kill the living cells which constitute the culture. The glassware and bottle stop-pers are also a source of contamination. Thus, there is coming into use polystyrene, perspex, cellophane, and other plastics which can be purchased sterile to be discarded after a single use. The sulfur in rubber stoppers and tubing is also toxic and must be washed off completely. Silicone stoppers are now replacing rubber stoppers. Instru-ments must always be sterile, as must the hands and air surrounding the cultures.

Cleaning may be with alkalies, detergents, or with various oxidizing agents, and sterilization may be by dry or moist heat; by antiseptics and/or antibiotics; and, to some extent by washing, centrifugation and filtration. Ionizing radiations are not recommended because of the high level of exposure necessary to attain real sterilization but ultra-violet light appears to be effective.

Once complete asepsis is attained, then possible contamination by the worker must be examined and prevented. Aseptic techniques are learned in any good bacteriological laboratory, but perfected only with hard experience and practice. The bacterium has it all over the investigator, lurking everywhere ready to invade and contaminate. Thus, the design of any culture laboratory is of paramount importance.

The tissues to be used in tissue culture studies may come from adults, although among such tissues only the tumorous ones grow readily. The adult tissues appear to elaborate toxins which make them incompatible in gross transplants, and non-viable in tissue or cell transplants. However, some tumors grow readily, especially the malignant types. Tissues from embryos, coming from a naturally sterile source and being very active mitotically, are often found to be the best for such studies. Embryonic tissues may be obtained from any amphibian, fish, chick, mouse or human source. Certain of the embryonic tissues appear to grow more readily and survive longer, and some tend even to differentiate without resorting to the prior embryonic state. This variation enlivens the field of the tissue culture approach to experimental embryology.

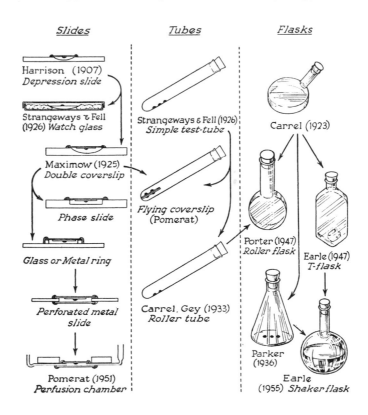

Vessels used for culturing cells and tissues

(Figure reproduced with permission from
J. Paul's "Cell and Tissue Culture" 1960,
E. & S. Livingston, Pub., Edinburgh.)

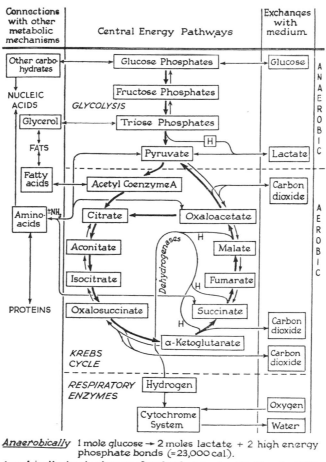

Connections with other metabolic mechanisms	Central Energy Pathways	Exchanges with medium

Other carbo-hydrates → Glucose Phosphates ← Glucose

NUCLEIC ACIDS

GLYCOLYSIS

Fructose Phosphates

Glycerol → Triose Phosphates

FATS

Pyruvate ← Lactate

Fatty acids ← Acetyl CoenzymeA → Carbon dioxide

±NH₃

Amino-acids → Citrate ← Oxaloacetate

Aconitate — Malate

Isocitrate — Fumarate

PROTEINS — Oxalosuccinate — Succinate

Dehydrogenases

α-Ketoglutarate → Carbon dioxide / Carbon dioxide

KREBS CYCLE

RESPIRATORY ENZYMES — Hydrogen

Cytochrome System ← Oxygen / Water

ANAEROBIC / AEROBIC

Anaerobically 1 mole glucose → 2 moles lactate + 2 high energy phosphate bonds (=23,000 cal.).

Aerobically 1 mole glucose + 3 moles O_2 → 6 moles CO_2 + 6 moles H_2O + ca 40 high energy phosphate bonds (=460,000 cal.)

Interrelationships between the main metabolic pathways in animal cells

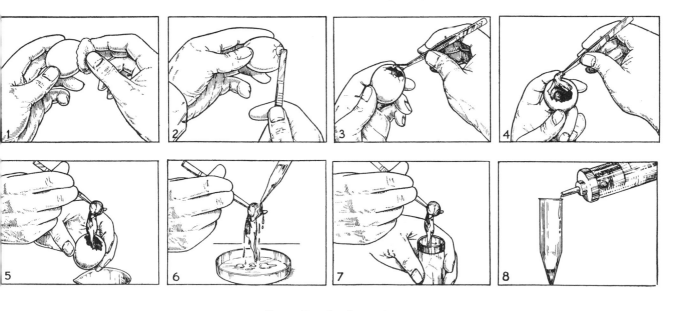

Preparation of embryo extract

(Figures reproduced with permission from
J. Paul's "Cell and Tissue Culture" 1960,
E. & S. Livingston, Pub., Edinburgh.)

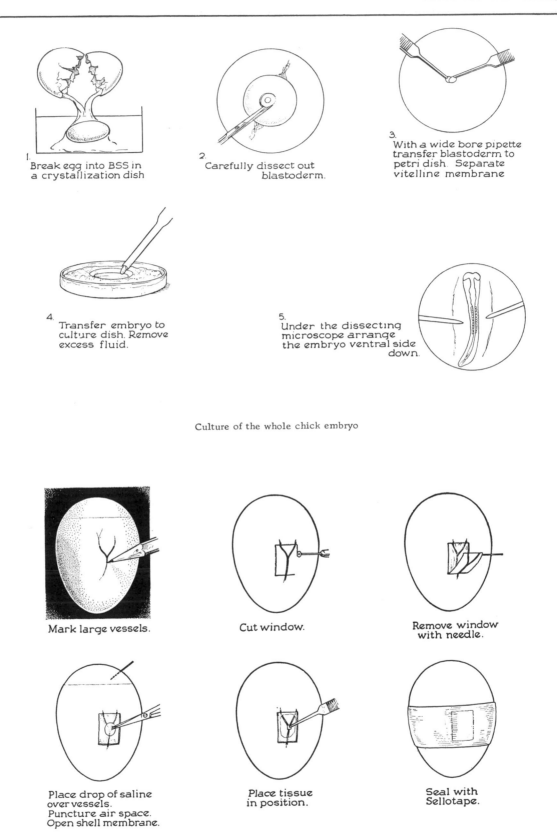

1. Break egg into BSS in a crystallization dish

2. Carefully dissect out blastoderm.

3. With a wide bore pipette transfer blastoderm to petri dish. Separate vitelline membrane

4. Transfer embryo to culture dish. Remove excess fluid.

5. Under the dissecting microscope arrange the embryo ventral side down.

Culture of the whole chick embryo

Mark large vessels.

Cut window.

Remove window with needle.

Place drop of saline over vessels. Puncture air space. Open shell membrane.

Place tissue in position.

Seal with Sellotape.

Cultivation of tissue on the chorio-allantoic membrane of the fertile egg

(Figures reproduced with permission from
J. Paul's "Cell and Tissue Culture" 1960,
E. & S. Livingston, Pub., Edinburgh.)

Cell cultures may be maintained on slides which are generally sealed off from the air.
Such cultures must be sub-cultured at frequent intervals to supply oxygen and to replen-
ish the nutrients. Fresh explants may be maintained in Carrel flasks which are so constructed as to minimize the probability of contamination, and still allow the transfer of
tissues. Test-tube cultures are a modification of the Carrel method, but somewhat more
easily handled. In such test tubes coverslips bearing the culture may be protected and,
to some extent, observed without contamination. Aggregates of cells or even organs may
be cultured, on either solid or fluid media, and generally in depression slides where
they may be continually observed if necessary. Possibly the least fruitful (thus far) and
yet the most promising material for the future may be the ova and very early embryos of
mammals.

This very brief summary of the major ideas in tissue culture work is meant only to be
suggestive to those qualified and experienced students who show aptitude in this direction.
The following reference list includes the most recent paper or book by each of the major
research workers in the field today. The student is referred to any of the multitudinous
sources for detailed information.

While tissue culture methods are extremely varied with respect to specific tissues and
aims, a single procedure will be described here which allows for the fast, undifferentiated growth of small fragments of animal tissues, known as explants, placed upon a
glass substrate with or without the plasma clot. This procedure was devised by Dr.
Jewel Plummer Cobb and Dorothy Walker (Jour. Nat. Cancer Inst. 1958, vol. 21:263-
278).

MATERIALS:
Instruments and glassware:
   Porter flasks, approximately 1 3/8 inches in diameter (Karl Schuman, Cliffside,
      N.J. 681 Jefferson Ave.)
   Coverglasses, No. 0, size 11 x 22 mm.
   Silicone stoppers to fit Porter flasks, sterilized in dry heat oven. (The West
      Co., Phoenixville, Pa.)
   Cataract knives or Bard-Parker blades attached to handles
   Fine curved forceps
   Cornman roller knife (Aloe Scientific Co., 5655 Kingsbury St., St. Louis, Mo.)
   Graduated pyrex pipettes (6) cap. 1.5 ml. (Bellco Glass Inc., Vineland, N.J.)
      plugged with cotton and attached to 2 ml. cap. amber rubber bulbs (A.A.
      Henning Co., 16 E. 23rd., N.Y.C.).
   Glass depression slides (6)
   Pyrex petri dishes (6) measuring 150 mm diam., for instruments.
   Lipless pyrex test tubes (6) measuring 25 x 100 mm (A.H. Thomas Co., Phil-
      adelphia, Penn.)
   Metal test tube rack for slanted large test tubes (Arista Surgical Co., 67 Lex-
      ington Ave., Bethesda, Md.)
   Touch-o-matic Bunsen burner for flaming under hood (Microbiological Asso-
      ciates, 4846 Bethesda Ave., Bethesda 14, Md.)

Biological materials: There are several chemically defined nutrient media which,
   when supplemented with 10% horse or human serum, provide an optimum fluid
   environment for growth. A few examples of good media follows:
   1. Tissue culture medium 1066, available from Connaught Medical Research
      Laboratories, Univ. Toronto, Toronto, Canada
   2. Raymond and Parker's Mixture 199, available from Difco Co., Detroit,
      Mich. or Microbiological Associates, 4846 Bethesda Ave., Bethesda, Md.
   3. Eagle's Basal Medium (E.B.M.) available from Microbiological Associates.

BALANCED SOLUTIONS FOR WARM AND COLD BLOODED ANIMALS, THEIR TISSUES AND CELLS

Chemical	WARM BLOODED ANIMALS								COLD BLOODED ANIMALS			
	Ringer	Locke	Tyrode 1910	Glucosol	Gey 1945	Simms 1941	Earle 1943	Hanks 1946	Holtfreter's*	*Ringer**	Locke***	Carlson****
NaCl	9.00	9.00	8.00	8.00	8.00	8.00	6.80	8.00	3.50	6.50	9.00	7.00
KCl	0.42	0.42	0.20	0.20	0.375	0.20	0.40	0.40	0.05	0.14	0.42	0.20
$CaCl_2$	0.25	0.24	0.20	0.20	0.275	0.147	0.20	0.14	0.10	0.12	0.25	0.02
$MgSO_4 \cdot 7H_2O$							0.10	0.10		0.20		
$MgCl_2 \cdot 6H_2O$					0.210	0.20		0.10				0.10
$NaH_2PO_4 \cdot H_2O$			0.05	0.05	0.150	0.21	0.125					0.20
$Na_2HPO_4 \cdot 2H_2O$					0.025			0.06				0.20
KH_2PO_4								0.06				
Glucose			1.00	1.00	2.00	1.00	1.00	1.00			2.50	0.80
Phenol red						0.05	0.05	0.02				
$NaHCO_3$		0.20	1.00		0.250	1.00	2.20	0.35	0.20		0.20	0.05
Gas phase						2% CO_2 air	5% CO_2 air					

* Holtfreter's is a modified Ringer's suitable for Amphibia and Fish.

** Cold-blooded Ringer's is used largely for Amphibia, but Holtfreter's is preferred.

*** Locke's for cold blooded animals may be used for insects.

**** Carlsons is specifically for grasshoppers.

(See Paul, J., 1960 "Tissue and Cell Culture" Williams & Wilkins for other and more complicated formulae).

4. Rooster plasma obtained frozen in 15 ml vials from Microbiological Associates.

5. Chick embryo extract. 50% obtained from 9-11 day old chick embryos minced in suitable balanced salt solution.

(Also have available penicillin-streptomycin mixture to be used as 50-100 units per ml of culture medium as standard prophyllactic)

All glassware and instruments are to be wrapped in aluminum foil and sterilized at 150°C in dry heat oven for one hour. All synthetic media are to be sterilized by filtration through ultrafine porosity fitted glass filter. Plasma and embryo extracts are obtained from the animal source under sterile conditions.

METHOD:

Mouse heart fragments may be obtained from various strains in utero. One mm³ fragments are embedded in a soft coagulum consisting of fowl plasma and chick embryo extract on double cover slips on Maximow slides. One drop of nutrient medium (consisting of 90% Eagle's basal medium (EBM) and 10% nondialyzed human or horse serum) is added to each coverslip. This medium is withdrawn and new medium added twice weekly.

Human neoplastic tissue may be cultured on coverslips inserted into Porter flasks, and may be obtained sterile from the operating room. One ml of EBM nutrient medium is supplemented with 10% nondialyzed serum in each flask. Pleural or ascitic-effusion samples may be centrifuged, supernatant removed, and cells placed in 0.2 ml aliquots in several Gey roller-tubes or Porter flasks, without plasma. The nutrient medium for these cells is better made of 50% EBM and 50% autologous clear pleural or ascitic fluid. The pH is adjusted to 7.2 and medium changed twice weekly.

RESULTS:

The growth rate is defined as the average distance cells migrated from the explant and/or the average density of the cell population at 72 hour intervals. The extent of outgrowth is defined as the total distance the cells emigrated, expressed in microns. The cell population density may be determined by inserting a Howard grid in the eyepiece and estimating the number of cells in two representative fields. Cells may be stained with May-Grunwald-Giemsa for best differentiation*.

Tissue cultures are studied for long-term survival, for growth rate and type, and for the effects of added drugs which might accelerate or decelerate growth. Obviously parallel controls are necessary although they are difficult in that identical conditions for simultaneous cultures may not be obtained. Since Carrel was able to maintain chick heart cells for many times the life of the species itself, the range of biological possibilities in this field is limitless.

REFERENCES FOR TISSUE CULTURE TECHNIQUES

It is recognized that tissue culture techniques are so specialized and require a background in biochemistry, cytology, physiology and related subjects, that it would be impossible to provide any student with adequate direction for success within the limits of a single volume, let alone a chapter. However, organ culture in poikilothermic forms is not difficult and those who are successful may wish to continue in the direction of tissue culture experimentation. To aid in such interest there is listed here some of the best current titles in the field, concentrating on techniques, which the ambitious investigator may wish to study.

---

* See Hanks et al, "A Introduction to Cell and Tissue Culture". p. 120, app. IV. (See also sections #26 and #28)

REFERENCES

ATKINS, A. J. B., 1959 - "Tools of Biological Research". 183 pgs., C. C. Thomas, Springfield, Ill.

BIGGERS, J. D., M. WEBB, R. C. PARKER, G. M. HEALY, 1957 - "The cultivation of embryonic chick bones on chemically defined media." Nature 180:825.

BOSS, J., 1954 - "Mitosis in cultures of newt tissues." III. Cleavage and chromosome movements in anaphase. Exp. Cell Res. 7:443.

BRYANT, J. C., E. L. SCHILLING, W. R. EARLE, 1958 - "Massive fluid-suspension cultures of certain mammalian tissue cells." I. General characteristics of growth and trends of population. J. Nat. Cancer Inst. 21:331.

CAMERON, G., 1950 - "Tissue Culture Technique." Academic Press, N.Y.

CARREL, A., 1923 - "A method for the physiological study of tissues in vitro." Jour. Exp. Med. 38:407.

CHANG, S. L., G. BERG, et al, 1958 - "Application of the 'most probable number' method for estimating concentrations of animal viruses by the tissue culture technique." Virology 6:27.

CHEN, J., 1954 - "The cultivation in fluid medium of organized liver, pancreas, and other tissues of foetal rats." Exp. Cell. Res. 7:518.

CHU, E. H. Y., N. H. GILES, 1959 - "Human chromosome complements in normal somatic cells in culture." Am. Jour. Human Genetics. 11:63-79.

COOPER, P. D., A. M. BURT, J. N. WILSON, 1958 - "Critical effect of oxygen tension on rate of growth of animal cells in continuous suspended culture." Nature. 182:1508.

EAGLE, H., S. BARBAN, Mina LEVY, H. O. SCHULZE, 1958 - "The utilization of carbohydrates by human cell culture." J. Biol. Chem. 233:551.

EARLE, W. R., 1957 - "Comments in discussion on tissue culture in the study of animal and human tumors." J. Nat. Cancer Inst. 19:781.

EVANS, V. J., 1957 - "Probable future trends in the nutrition of tissue cultures." J. Nat. Cancer Inst. 19:539.

FELL, H. B., 1940 - "The application of tissue culture In vitro to embryology." J. Roy. Micr. Soc. 60:95.

FELL, H. B., 1953 - "Recent advances in organ culture." Science Prog. 162:212.

FELL, H. B., 1957 - "The effect of excess vitamin A on cultures of embryonic chick skin explanted at different stages of differentiation." Proc. Roy. Soc. B., 146:242.

FORD, C. E., P. A. JACOBS, L. B. LAJTHA, 1958 - "Human somatic chromosomes." Nature. 181:1565.

FORD, D. K., G. YERGANIAN, 1958 - "Observations on the chromosomes of Chinese hamster cells in tissue culture." J. Nat. Cancer Inst. 21:393.

GAILLARD, P. J., 1957 - "Morphogenesis in animal tissue cultures." J. Nat. Cancer Inst. 19:591.

GAILLARD, P. J., 1957 - "Parathyroid gland and bone in vitro." Schweiz. Med. Wochensch. No. 14:217.

GEY, G. O., 1933 - "An improved technique for massive tissue culture." Am. Jour. Cancer. 17:752.

GEYER, R. P., 1958 - "Nutrition of mammalian cells in tissue culture." Nutrition Rev. 16:321.

GOLDRING, I. P., 1956 - "The effects of x-rays on the growth of spinal ganglion from 6- and 12-day embryos in tissue culture." Rad. Res. 5:390-403.

GRAFF, S., K. S. McCARTY, 1957 - "Sustained cell culture." Exp. Cell Res. 13:348.

HANKS, J. H., J. H. WALLACE, 1958 - "Determination of cell viability." Proc. Soc. Exp. Biol. (N.Y.) 98:188.

HARRISON, R. G., 1907 - "Observations on the living developing nerve fiber." Proc. Soc. Exp. Biol., N.Y. 4:140.

HEALY, G. M., D. C. FISHER, R. C. PARKER, 1955 - "Nutrition of animal cells in tissue culture. X. Synthetic medium N. 858." Proc. Soc. Exp. Biol. & Med. 89:71.

HSU, T. C., 1960 - "Mammalian chromosomes in vitro." XIII. Cyclic and directional changes of population structure. J. of Nat. Cancer Inst. 25:1339-1354.

KAHN, R. H., 1958 - "Organ culture in experimental biology." Univ. Michigan M. Bull. 24:242.

LASNITISKI, I., 1956 - "The effect of 3-4 benzpyrene on human fetal lung grown in vitro." Brit. J. Cancer. 10:510.

LEWIS, W. H., 1922 - "The importance of dextrose in the medium of tissue cultures." J. Exp. Med. 35:317.

LIEBERMAN, I. P. OVE, 1958 - "Enzyme activity levels in mammalian cell cultures." J. Biol. Chem. 233:634.

MARCUS, P. I., S. J. CIECIURA, T. T. PUCK, 1956 - "Clonal growth in vitro of epithelial cells from normal human tissues." J. Exp. Med. 104:615.

MARTINOVITCH, P., 1951 - "Culture of infantile endocrine glands of rats by watch glass technique in a moist chamber." in Methods in Medical Research, Vol. 4:237-240. Year Book Pub., Chicago.

MAXIMOW, A., 1925 - "Tissue cultures of young mammalian embryos." Contr. Embryol. Carnegie Inst. 16:49.

MERCHANT, D. J., R. H. KAHN, W. H. MURPHY, 1960 - "Handbook of Cell and Organ Culture." Burgess Publ. Co., Minneapolis.

MORGAN, J. F., H. J. MORTON, R. C. PARKER, 1950 - "Nutrition of animal cells in tissue culture." Proc. Soc. Exp. Biol. & Med. 73:1.

MORGAN, J. F., 1958 - "Tissue culture nutrition.", Bact. Rev. 22:20.

MOSCONA, A., H. MOSCONA, 1952 - "The dissociation and aggregation of cells from organ rudiments in the early chick embryo." J. Anat. London. 86:287.

MURRAY, M. R., G. KOPECH, 1953 - "A bibliography of the research in tissue culture." 2 vols. Academic Press, N.Y.

MURRAY, M. R., 1951 - "Tissue culture procedures in medical installations." Meth. Med. Res. 4:211.

NITZIMA, M., 1956 - "Tissue culture studies on amphibian metamorphosis." I. Growth patterns of tadpole tissue. Folia Anat. Jap. 28:59.

NUI, M. C., 1954 - "Further studies on the origin of amphibian pigment cells." J. Exp. Zool. 125:199.

OISHI, Y., 1956 - "Effects of antibiotics and chemotherapeutics on the growth of fibroblasts from chick-embryo heart in the simplified replicate tissue culture." Jap. J. Exp. Med. 26:159.

PARKER, R. C., 1950 - "Methods of Tissue Culture." Cassell & Co., London.

PARKER, R. C., 1957 - "Contribution to discussion on nutrition and metabolism of animal tissue cultures." J. Nat. Cancer Inst. 19:502)

PAUL, John, 1959 - "Cell and Tissue cultures." Livingston, London.

PEER, L. A., 1959 - "Transplantation of tissues." William & Wilins Co.

PERRY, V. P., K. K. SANFORD, V. J. EVANS, G. W. HYATT, W. R. EARLE, 1957 - "Establishment of clones of epithelial cells from human skin." J. Exp. Med. 104:427.

POMERAT, C. M., 1951 - "Tissue culture methods." In Med. Res. ed. M. B. Visscher. Chicago: Year Book Publ.

PUCK, T. T., S. J. CIECIURA, H. W. FISHER, 1957 - "Clonal growth in vitro of human cells with fibroblastic morphology." J. Exp. Med. 106:145.

PUCK, T. T., S. J. CIECIURA, A. ROBINSON, 1958 - "Genetics of somatic mammalian cells." III. Long-term cultivation of euploid cells from human and animal subjects." J. Exp. Med. 108:945.

SANFORD, K. K., W. R. EARLE, G. D. LIKELY, 1948 - "The growth in vitro of single isolated tissue cells." J. Nat. Cancer Inst. 9:229. (see also ibid, 15:215, 1954)

SCHENCK, Dorothy M., M. MOSKOWITZ, 1958 - "Method for isolating single cells and preparation of clones from human bone marrow cultures." Proc. Soc. Exp. Biol. (N.Y.) 99:30.

SCHERER, W. F., 1955 - "An Introduction to Cell and tissue culture." Minneapolis: Burgess.

SHAFFER, B. M., 1956 - "The culture of organs from the embryonic chick on cellulose-acetate fabric." Exp. Cell. Res. 11:244.

STRANGWAYS, T. S. P., H. B. FELL, 1926 - "Experimental studies on the differentiation of embryonic tissues growing in vivo and in vitro." Proc. Roy. Soc. B. 100:273.

SWANN, M. M., 1958 - "The control of cell division: A review." II. Special mechanisms. Cancer Res. 18:1118.

TOOLAN, Helene, W., 1954 - "Transplantable human neoplasms maintained in cortisone-treated laboratory animals." Cancer. 14:660.

TROWELL, O. A., 1959 - "The culture of mature organs in a synthetic medium." Exp. Cell. Res. 16:118.

VOGT, M., 1958 - "A genetic change in a tissue culture line of neoplastic cells." J. Cell. Comp. Physiol. 52:271-285.

WALLACE, J. H., J. H. HANKS, 1958 - "Agar substrates for study of microepidemiology and physiology in cells in vitro." Science. 128:658.

WENIGER, Jean-Pierre, 1958 - "Culture in vitro et differeniation de tres jeunes gonades d'embryon de poulet." C. R. Soc. Biol. 152:647.

WHITE, P., 1949 - "Prolonged survival of excised animal tissues in vitro in nutrition of known constitution." J. Cell. Comp. Physio. 24:311.

WHITE, P. R., 1954 - "The cultivation of animal and plant cells." Ronald Press, N.Y.

WHITTEN, W. R., 1956 - "Culture of tubal mouse ova." Nature. 177:96.

WILLMER, E. N., 1945 - "Tissue culture; the growth and differentiation of normal tissues in artificial media. Methuen's monographs on Biological subjects." 2nd ed. London: Methuen. New York: Wiley.

WOLFF, E. M., 1955 - "Les besoins specifiques en acides amines de la syrinx de l'embryon de poulet cultivee in vitro sur un milieu entierement synthetique." C. R. Acad. Sci. (Paris) 240:1016.

"The cells of the cerebral cortex are the most unnecessary of all the cells of the body. A creature can live without a cerebral cortex, but in these cells that are unnecessary for life the creature becomes conscious of its own self and the world; with them it recognizes and enjoys, it gathers memories and experiences, thinks and feels, speaks and writes, makes music and paints, dreams and loves - and suffers. They are life, knowledge, feeling, and enjoyment; they are the I, the personality. We is the sum total of the cortical cells of our brain; our I is the giant concert which is the greatest of all radio stations, this station of microscopic tubes, antennas, coils, condensers, and transformers, broadcasts as thought and feeling to the microcosmos of the cell body, and as word and deed to the wide world."

Fritz Kahn 1943 in "Man in Structure and Function", A. Knopf.

30. OSMO-REGULATION

PURPOSE: To determine:
1.   The ability of eggs and embryos to tolerate various osmotic conditions.
2.   The ideal concentration (isotonic medium) for the various stages.
3.   The ability of the various stages of development to adjust to anisotonic conditions.

MATERIALS:

Biological: Ovulating female and mature male frogs; Urodele embryos.

Technical: Various salt solutions listed below.
Fine-lined graph paper mounted on underside of Petri dish.

METHOD:

Precautions:
1.   Prevent evaporation from containers by properly covering them during the course of the experiment.   If evaporation does occur, replace the lost volume with glass-distilled water.
2.   Avoid crowding.   The number of eggs or embryos must be the same in all of the containers, and should not exceed 25 per finger bowl of 50 cc. fluid.

Controls:
1.   For frog's eggs and embryos, consider Spring Water or Standard Solution as the control medium.
2.   For Urodele eggs and early embryos, consider Urodele Growing Solution as the control medium.

Procedure:
Prepare the following media for use in this experiment:
1.   Distilled water, hypotonic medium.   (Glass distilled water if possible)
2.   Half Standard, hypotonic.   (50% Holtfreter's equal to 0.192% salt)
3.   Spring Water, isotonic.   (Great Bear Spring Water)
4.   Standard Solution (Holtfreter's) equal to 0.385% salt, isotonic.
5.   Standard X $1\frac{1}{2}$, hypertonic.   Equal to 0.57% salt.
6.   Frog Ringer's, equal to 0.72% salt.
7.   Double Standard hypertonic (2 X Holtfreter's) equal to 0.77% salt.

PROCEDURE WITH ANURAN EGGS

The Anura are particularly suitable for this type of investigation for the eggs and embryos are available in quantity and under controlled conditions.   It is recommended that the following stages be tested against the various solutions:

1.   Body cavity eggs possessing vitelline membranes only.
2.   Unfertilized uterine eggs possessing vitelline membranes, jelly, and all being in metaphase of the second maturation division.   These may be transferred from the opened uterus to the appropriate solution by means of a wide-mouthed pipette moistened with Nujol.
3.   Fertilized eggs, transferred to the experimental media 30 minutes after insemination.   This is about $1\frac{1}{2}$ to 2 hours before the first cleavage.
4.   Early cleavage: 4 to 8 cell stages.
a.   Jelly intact.
b.   Jelly removed (with sharp watchmaker's forceps).
5.   Beginning of gastrulation - slit blastopore stage.
6.   Beginning of neurulation - medullary plate stage.

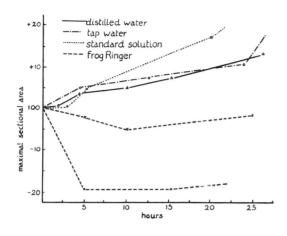

The relative size of unfertilized eggs of R. pipiens, expressed as percentage increase or decrease from the initial size (indicated by 100), after exposure to salt solutions of varying osmotic pressure. 21 to 24°C.

	DIS-TILLED WATER	TAP WATER	PHYSIOLOGICAL SALT SOLUTIONS				
			0.20%	0.38%	0.57%	0.68%	0.76%
Viscosity of the cytoplasm	<	<	<	<	<	<	<
Elasticity of the surface coat	+++	+++	++	+	(+)	— —	— —
Surface sticky to glass	— —	— —	— —	(+)	+	+	++
Aggregation of uncoated cells	— —	— —	+++	++	+	— —	— —
Cleavage in isolated blastomeres	— —	— —	(+)	+++	(+)	— —	— —
Isolated cells die after	10–15 min.	10–15 min.	20–60 min.	days, weeks	3–6 hours	1–2 hours	30–60 min.
Cells swell	+	+	↑	— —	— —	— —	— —
Cells shrink				— —	↑	+	+
Embryo gastrulates	+	+	+	(+)	— —	— —	— —
Neuralplate closes	+	+	+	(+)	— —	— —	— —
	Hypotonic			Isotonic	Hypertonic		

Effects of various osmotic pressure upon amphibian cells up to the neurula stage. pH 7.6 to 8.2.

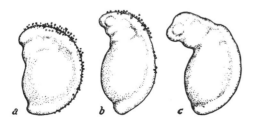

Neurulae of Triturus torosus exposed (a) to Ringer, (b) to standard solution, (c) to tap water display varying degrees of retarded development and lose mesoctoderm cells.

From Holtfreter, 1943. Jour. Exp. Zool. 93:251.

PROCEDURE WITH URODELE EGGS

Salamander eggs and embryos are not generally available in abundance as Anuran eggs, nor can they be secured in identical stages of development in any suitable quantities. Such embryos as are available may be segregated into stages and if there are sufficient numbers, some may be deprived of their jelly and vitelline membranes. So far as possible test the covered and nude eggs against the same media, using identical and sufficient numbers in each medium so that the results may be considered statistically valid. It is of utmost importance that all conditions of relative volume of medium per egg, temperature, etc. are identical.

EXPERIMENTAL PROCEDURE:

Prepare 2 finger bowls for each of the media, each of which should receive 50 cc. of the solution to be tested. Place 25 eggs or embryos in each finger bowl, all of the same stage of development. The ratio must be 2 cc. of medium per egg or embryo. With Urodele material, which is less abundant, the volume of medium need not be reduced but the number of embryos per container may be less than 25 but must remain the same for all. The environmental conditions of temperature, light, etc. must be identical for all so that the only variable is the medium being tested against embryonic development.

Eggs and embryos that are to be deprived of their jelly and vitelline membranes should first be placed in the test medium and then denuded.

OBSERVATIONS AND EXPERIMENTAL DATA:

There are three sets of observations to be made:

1. The survival of eggs or embryos allowed to remain in the various media, beginning at different stages of development. These data will have significance not only in relation to isotonicity but also to tolerance, at the various embryonic stages. Duration of observation: one week.

2. The developmental rate in anisotonic solutions as compared with the controls. These data will be significant only under the condition that the temperature is very accurately controlled.

3. The diameter readings, or swelling and shrinking of the eggs and embryos. These readings can be taken directly by placing fine-lined graph paper beneath the finger bowl containing the eggs and determining the relative values against the graph paper. Readings should be taken along two axes, at right angles to each other, since some eggs may be ovate. The average of the two readings would then be taken as the value for any particular egg.

    This type of observation has relative value only, and can be used on body cavity eggs, aged eggs, and early cleavages up to but not including the gastrula stage. Gastrulation involves the development of internal cavities which would render these readings invalid.

If time permits, two additional sets of observations should be made:

4. The aged uterine egg of the Anuran shows cortical breakdown, beginning after about 5 days at 10°C., and earlier at the higher temperatures. Such an egg should react more with increasing age toward anisotonic media, eventually responding like any non-living osmometer. Readings may be made over rather short intervals of time.

5. The tolerance of the extremes in osmotic pressure by the various critical embryonic stages exposed for brief periods can be tested. For instance, recently inseminated eggs or eggs about to gastrulate might be exposed for a limited time to glass distilled water, or to double Standard Solution, or to both in succession before returning them to the control medium.

REFERENCES

ANDREASSI, G., 1939 - "Effect of saline solutions on the development of eggs of Amblystoma." Boll. Soc. Ital. Biol. Sperm. 14:195.

BACHMANN, E. L & J. RUUNSTROM, 1912 - "Der osmotische Druck wahrend der embryonalentwicklung von Rana temporaria." Pfluger's Arch. f. Ges. Physiol. 144:287.

HOLTFRETER, J., 1943 - "Properties and functions of the surface coat in amphibian embryos." Jour. Exp. Zool. 93:251.

KROGH, A., R. SCHMIDT-NIELSEN, & E. ZEUTHER, 1938 - "The osmotic behavior of frog's eggs and young tadpoles." Zeitschr. f. vergl. Physiol. 26:230.

McCUTCHEON, M. & B. LUCKE, 1926 - "The kinetics of osmotic swelling in living cells." Jour. Gen. Physiol. 9:697.

NEEDHAM J., 1931 - "Chemical Embryology." 3 vols. Cambridge.

PIIPER, E., 1933 - "The development of Rana temporaria under the influence of cane sugar solutions." Proc. Roy. Soc. B. 112:359.

RICHARDS, O. W., 1940 - "The capsular fluid of Amblystoma punctatum eggs compared with Holtfreter's and Ringer's solutions." Jour. Exp. Zool. 83:401.

RINGER, S. & A. G. PHEAR, 1894 - "The influence of saline media on the tadpole." Jour. Physiol. 17:423.

VOSS, H., 1926 - "Entwicklungsphysiologische Untersuchungen am Froschei (Rana fusca)." Arch. f. Ent. mech. 107:241.

TABULATION OF DATA

Species	Stage	Medium	Volume Change	Survival Time	Normality

"The value of a scientific hypothesis depends, it seems to me, first on the possibility of testing it by direct observation, or by experience; second, on whether it leads to advance; and, lastly, on its elimination of certain possibilities."

T. H. Morgan

31. WOUND HEALING IN EMBRYOS

DEFINITION: The ability of the interrupted living surface to close.

PURPOSE: To determine the ability and rate of wound closure of the egg, blastomere, and embryonic epidermis under various environmental conditions.

MATERIALS:
    Biological: Ovulating females and early developmental stages of any Anura or Urodela.

    Technical: Stock solutions (see below)
                 Glass needles, pointed lancet
                 Vital dyes: Nile blue sulphate (1/7500)
                                    Neutral red (1/2500)

METHOD:
    Precautions:
        1. Avoid infection. Sterilization of the instruments and solutions will not be necessary if ordinary care is observed.
        2. Keep eggs and embryos in separate #2 Stenders with covers, at room temperatures or below. Provide 10 to 20 cc. of solution per egg or embryo. This relatively large volume will reduce any effects from accumulating metabolites.
        3. In Ca-free experiments, wash the egg or embryo in several changes of Ca-free solution prior to making the incision. Adherent calcium or calcium diffused from the embryo may alter the results.

    Controls: Holtfreter (1943) says: "In an optimal medium, as represented by our Standard Solution, the healing faculty is extraordinary." We may therefore consider the healing process in this solution as the control situation with which the process, in other media, is to be compared.

    Procedure:
        Observations are to be made on wound healing of the following embryonic stages:
        1. Body cavity eggs, having vitelline membranes only.
        2. Recently fertilized eggs - 1 hour after insemination.
        3. The 4-cell stage, a single blastomere to be injured.
        4. Animal pole of early gastrula.
        5. Epidermis of neurula.

        The effect on wound healing of the following solutions is to be determined:
        1. Distilled water (glass distilled water preferred), - hypotonic.
        2. Standard Solutions diluted to 10%, - hypotonic.
        3. Standard Solution - isotonic.
        4. Standard Solution x 2: - hypertonic.
        5. Standard Solution plus 0.1% KOH - alkalinized. (Determine the pH.)
            (Standard Solution for this should be made without the buffer.)
        6. Standard Solution plus 0.1% HCl - acidified. (Determine the pH.)
            (Standard Solution for this should be made without the buffer.)

Prepare an ovulating female frog, Rana pipiens, about 48 hours before the time of the experimental work. The various solutions should be made up and distributed to labelled #2 Stenders ready for the introduction of eggs or embryos.

---

* This exercise has been organized with the generous aid of Dr. J. Holtfreter.

Wounds inflicted on the surface of a single cell will generally heal in a matter of minutes. The closure of a wound in a coated epithelium (ectoderm or endoderm) may take several hours, depending in part on the number of cells injured or removed.

To facilitate the observations of surface movements in relation to wound healing, it is advisable to pre-stain eggs or embryos with one of the vital dyes. Nile blue sulphate 1/7500 is toxic if the embryos are left in it very long but it can be used for rapid staining as in this experiment. A concentration of 1/750,000 of this vital dye is nontoxic and embryos may be left in it indefinitely (Zorzoli, 1946). The stages are to be immersed in the vital dye for a few minutes, or dye-stained agar or cellophane may be used for locally staining areas on the surface of the egg, (see section of "Vital Staining").

The wound is best made with a sharp-pointed glass needle or lancet. In the case of uncleaved eggs the needle may be inserted below the surface coating and the cut made by an upward movement, using the glass needle as a knife blade. The healing capacity of coated epithelia can be best observed in a neurula or somewhat older stage where part of the epidermis is peeled off by means of a pair of glass needles.

The wound should be inflicted while the specimen is immersed in the solution to be tested. For instance, a body cavity egg is transferred from the body cavity to Standard Solution and then the wound is inflicted. Since the healing process is rapid it will be necessary to observe the wound rather constantly for a period of minutes. This observation should be repeated 4 or 5 times for each stage and each solution.

There are several possible variations in the wound:
1. Compare the healing of wounds in the animal and the vegetal poles; dorsal and ventral epidermis of the neurula (where there is little and much yolk).
2. Inflict several wounds, some parallel and others at right angles to each other, and note the consequences on healing.
3. Inflict a wound on a single blastomere of a four-cell stage and allow its contents to escape. Note the effect on this and the other blastomeres.
4. Peel off from 1/4 to 3/4 of the epidermis of neurulae and later stages and determine the ability to recover.

There are environmental variables, aside from the osmotic conditions of the medium, which may well alter the wound healing process. Reference is made to:
1. Crowding, with the consequent accumulation of metabolites.
2. Increasing concentration of carbon dioxide (or even oxygen).
3. Temperature.
4. Presence of monovalent metallic ions.
5. Extremes of pH. The moderate shift in pH will be determined with solutions "e" and "f" above.

OBSERVATIONS AND THE TABULATION OF DATA:

The healing process as observed in the Standard Solution is to be considered the normal or control situation. It is important, therefore, to establish data in this solution for all stages and operating conditions first. Thereafter, comparisons are to be made with these data. If there is a limit in time and facilities, it is recommended that solutions "b" and "e" in the above list might be omitted.

Drawings made at the time of wound infliction, a minute thereafter, and at a stated subsequent interval will constitute the record for each of the above observations.

DISCUSSION:

The most recent and complete analysis of wound healing is contained in a 1943 paper by Holtfreter in which he says that "The coated surface layer is of predominant importance for the closing of wounds in single cells and in epithelia."

Sodium, Potassium, and Magnesium ions, hypertonicity, and alkalinity all cause lique-
faction and dispersion of the surface layer while Calcium, a slightly hypotonic medium,
and an intermediary pH, tend to counteract the effect of the former by binding and solidi-
fying the egg substances, thus favoring wound healing. Calcium, even in a concentration
of 1/100,000,000 is sufficient to aid the healing process and this amount may diffuse out
of the embryo from regions other than the wound area. The coated cells, in the wound
healing process, tend to spread over the uncoated ones.

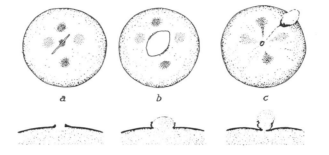

In an injured egg the edges of the coat at first retract, then
contract. Vital dye marks are dragged out centripetally.

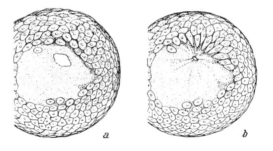

A wound inflicted within the unsegmented area pulls into
its orbit neighbouring cells by the expansion of the syncytial
coat.

The contraction of an epithelial wound orients the adjacent
cells like the petals of a daisy.

(Illustrations from Holtfreter: 1943. Jour. Exp. Zool. 93:251)

The wound healing of later embryonic stages is even more remarkable than that of single
cells. More than half of the epidermis of a neurula may be peeled off and within a day or
so the remaining epidermis will spread to form a very thin covering epithelium over the
exposed or uncoated endo-mesoderm. Cell multiplication plays no significant role in
this healing process. Former cylindrical cells of a spreading epithelium may become
flattened out into a squamous epithelium.

REFERENCES

AREY, L. B., 1932 - "Certain basic principles in wound healing." Anat. Rec. 51.

BAITSELL, G. A., 1916 - "The origin and structure of a fibrous tissue formed in wound healing." Jour. Exp. Med. 23:739.

BARBER, L. W., 1944 - "Correlations between wound healing and regeneration in fore-limbs and tails of lizards." Ant. Rec. 89:441.

BENTLEY, F. H., 1936 - "Wound healing in vitro." Jour. Anat. 70:498.

BURR, H. S., S. C. HARVEY, M. TAFFEL, 1938 - "Bio-electric correlates of wound healing." Yale Jour. Biol. & Med. 11:103.

BURR, H. S., M. T. TAFFEL, S. C. HARVEY, 1940 - "An electrometric study of the healing of wound in man." Yale Jour. Biol. & Med. 12:483.

EYCLESHYMER, A. C., 1907 - "The closing of wounds in the larvae Necturus." Am. Jour. Anat. 7.

HARRISON, Ross G., 1947 - "Wound healing and reconstitution of the central nervous system of the amphibian embryo after removal of parts of the neural plate." Jour. Exp. Zool. 106:27.

HARVEY, E. N. & G. FANKHAUSER, 1933 - "The tension at the surface of eggs of the salamander, Triturus viridescens." Jour. Cell. & Comp. Physiol. 3:463.

HOLTFRETER, J., 1943 - "Properties and functions of the surface coat in amphibian eggs." Jour. Exp. Zool. 93:251.

HOLTFRETER, J., 1943 - "A study of the mechanics of gastrulation." Jour. Exp. Zool. 94:261. (see page 292)

LAWRENCE, W., J. J. NICKSON, L. M. WARSHAW, 1953 - "Roentgen rays and wound healing." Surgery. 33:376-384.

TAFFEL, M., & S. C. HARVEY, 1938 - "Effect of absolute and partial vitamin C deficiency on wound healing." Proc. Exp. Biol. & Med. 38:518.

ZIMMERMAN, L. & R. RUGH, 1941 - "Effect of age of the development of the egg of the leopard frog, Rana pipiens." Jour. Morph. 68:329.

"The ground motive of science is a high order of curiosity, led on by ambition to overcome obstacles."

H. F. Osborne

"In science you must not talk before you know."
Ruskin

"It is deserving of emphasis that the function of imagination is not merely the conception of mythical creations, but also, and quite particularly, the presentation, to the mind, of realities. Hence, imagination plays an important role in the exact Sciences."

A. J. Lotka, 1925

"I am unwilling to accept the defeatism of the vitalist, so long as means of investigation by experiment are available."

R. G. Harrison, 1945

"Theory without fact is fantasy, but fact without theory is chaos. Divorced, both are useless; united, they are equally essential and fruitful."

C. O. Whitman

"The stabilization of our institutions rests ultimately upon our ability to know and to test assumptions, and upon willingness to revise them without partizanship, or bitterness, or distress."
Simpson, 1922, Am. Math. Month

"Man is the only animal who in any considerable measure bequeathed to his descendants the accumulated wisdom of past generations."

A. J. Lotka, 1925

"Truth comes out of error more readily than out of confusion."
Bacon

32. PARABIOSIS AND TELOBIOSIS

PURPOSE: To learn the technique of grafting embryos together in various positions, and to study the effect of such fusion on the behavior and the morphology of paired larvae. Pairs which survive metamorphosis may be studied for shared structures, and for hormonal relations.

MATERIALS:

 Biological: Anuran (stages #15 to #17) or Urodele (stages #22 to #29) larvae.

 Technical: Syracuse operating dishes with permoplast or paraffin bases.

METHOD:

 Precautions:

  1. Moderate precautions relative to sterile conditions will prove adequate.
  2. Embryos must be held together firmly but not so that there is displacement of organs or any incurred damage. The Permoplast may be built up around the pair, leaving small opening above for access to the medium and respiration.
  3. Operate in hypertonic or slightly alkaline media, or in a deficiency of Calcium to facilitate adhesion. Gradually return the pair to normal medium.

 Controls: Operated but not fused embryos constitute the controls, to determine whether the operation alone might account for any untoward results. For pairs that survive metamorphosis and are to be studied for hormonal relations, consult papers by Burns and by Witschi for adequate controls.

 Procedure: The method consists of simply removing the epidermis, some underlying mesoderm and yolk from a limited area on the mirror surfaces of two embryos of similar stages of development (early tail bud is the best) and bringing these injured surfaces together long enough to effect permanent fusion by healing. This may take as little as 20 minutes, or as long as 24 hours, depending a great deal on the temperature and the constituents of the medium.

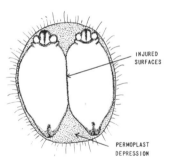

Diagram illustrating position of embryos (Amblystoma stage #22) being fused laterally in parabiosis, within a Permoplast depression. Injured surfaces healing together.

PARABIOSIS

Remove several embryos of corresponding age from their capsules and with a wide-mouthed pipette transfer them to the operating Syracuse dish with a base of Permoplast or very soft paraffin (containing some beeswax). Bring the two embryos together and estimate the size of the depression which must be moulded in the Permoplast to hold the two embryos closely side-by-side. Make such a depression with a ball tip.

In the vicinity of the depression, lay the two embryos on their sides, facing away from each other. With a sterile needle, or pair of forceps, outline an oval area covering the region just posterior to the gill anlagé on the left side of one and the right side of the other embryo. With scalpel, scissors, or forceps, excise this oval

FUSION OF EMBRYOS

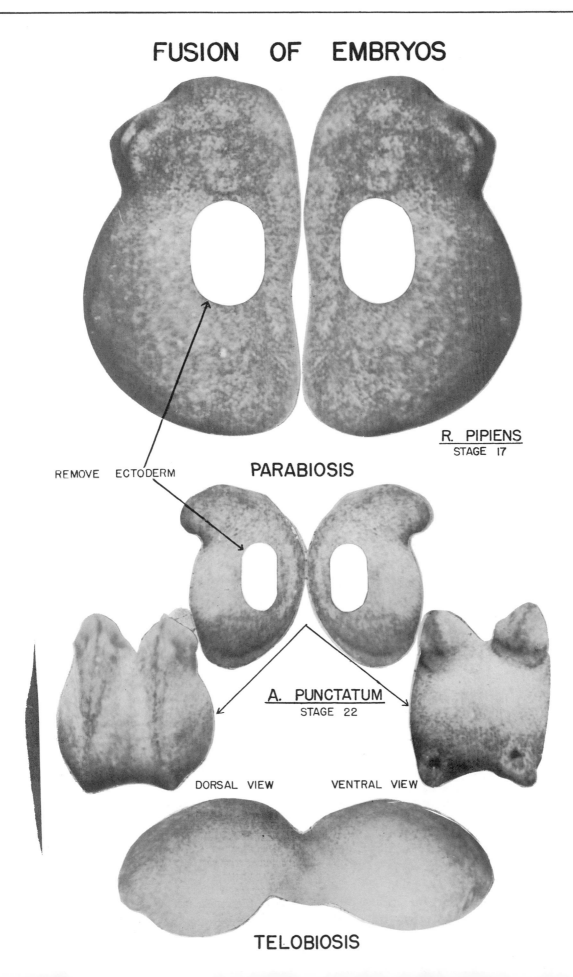

R. PIPIENS
STAGE 17

PARABIOSIS

REMOVE ECTODERM

A. PUNCTATUM
STAGE 22

DORSAL VIEW   VENTRAL VIEW

TELOBIOSIS

area of ectoderm, mesoderm, and some yolk from each of the embryos. Quickly maneuver the embryos together into the Permoplast depression, approximately their wounded areas. Build up the Permoplast around them in such a manner that they cannot move, but do not distort either embryo with excessive pressure. If the cilia are active, an adequate block in front of the pair will impede them sufficiently.

Parabiosis means lateral fusion. This may be side-to-side; back-to-back; belly-to-belly; or a combination of these. The side-to-side fusion is generally the best because the larvae are permitted to move about and to feed in quite a normal manner. The lateral fusion of three embryos has been achieved.

TELOBIOSIS

The technique of terminal fusion is identical with that above except that the Permoplast depression is long and narrow, and the injured areas are terminal rather than lateral. Simply cut off the tip end of the heads, tails, or combinations, using sharp and sterile scalpel or scissors. Bring the cut surfaces together and hold them approximated until healed. The relations may be head to head; tail to tail; or head to tail. Also, one of the embryos can be inverted.

OBSERVATIONS AND TABULATION OF DATA:

1. Determine the growth rate of paired embryos as compared with the controls.
2. Is there any evidence of dominance of one member of the pair over the other?
3. How large a discrepancy in stages can be used for successful parabiosis? Discrepancy in species? (See section on "Transplantations".)

The data should be recorded in the form of photographs or drawings, and preserved specimens which survive to the later stages.

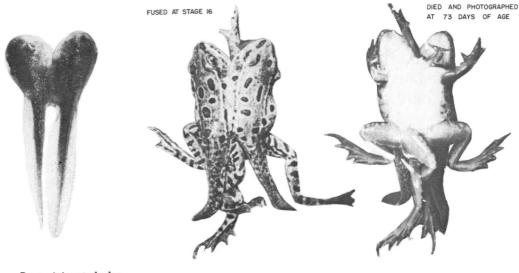

Rana pipiens tadpoles in parabiosis, fused at stage 16 photographed at stage 24.

PARABIOSIS IN METAMORPHOSED FROGS
(RANA PIPIENS)

Tulipan & Schreiber, 1942

REFERENCES

BALTZER, F., 1941 - "Untersuchungen an Chimaren von Urodelen und Hyla." Rev. Suisse de Zool. 48:413.

BURNS, R. K. Jr., 1935 - "The process of sex transformation in parabiotic Amblystoma. III. Conversion of testis to ovary in heteroplastic pairs of A. tigrinum and A. punctatum". Anat. Rec. 63:   .

FELS, E., 1929 - "Experimentelle Studien an Parabiose-Tieren uber Physiologie und Biologie der Sexualhormone." Arch. f. Gynakologie. 138:16.

FRITZ-NIGGLI, H., 1958 - "Radiation chimaeros and parabiosis". Strahlentherapie. 106:378-390.

GALLIEN, L. & M. R. COURRIER, 1960 - "Haploide par exerese du pronucleus femelle de l'oeuf feconde chez le Triton Pleurodeles waltii et elevage en parabiose des larves obtenues." C. r. l'Acad. des Sci. 250:4038.

GALLIEN, L. & J. C. BEETSCHEN, 1960 - "Differentiation sexuelle et gametogenese abotrive chez un male haploide d'Urodele eleve en parabiose." C. r. s. de l'Acad. des Sc. 251:1655.

HUMPHREY, R. R., 1936 - "Studies on sex reversal in Amblystoma. IX. Reversal of ovaries to testes in parabiotic A. tigrinum." Jour. Exp. Zool. 73:1.

HUMPHREY, R. R. & R. K. BURNS, Jr., 1939 - "An incompatability manifested in heteroplastic parabiosis or grafting in Amblystoma due to a toxin of cutaneous origin." Jour. Exp. Zool. 81:1.

KAYLOR, C. T., 1940 - "Experiments on the parabiotic union of haploid and diploid larvae of Triturus pyrrhigaster." Anat. Rec. 78:52 (suppl.).

SMITH, P. E., 1921 - "Some modifications induced by parabiotic union of the hypophysectomized to the normal tadpole." Anat. Rec. 21:83 (abs.).

STONE, L. S., 1934 - "Production and metamorphosis of chimeras in anurans and urodeles." Proc. Soc. Exp. Biol. & Med. 31:1084.

WITSCHI, E., 1937 - "Studies on sex differentiation and sex determination in amphibians.

WITSCHI, E., & H. M. M. McCurdy, 1943 - "Sex differentiation in heterogenous parabiotic twins (Amblystoma x Triturus)." Essays in Bio., Univ. of Calif. Press.

"Nature is never more perfect than in small things."
Pliny

"The species is contained in the egg of the hen as completely as in the hen, and the hen's egg differs from the frog's egg as the hen from the frog."
C. O. Whitman

"Between vitalism and mechanism there is a middle ground which may be called 'Organizationism' or 'Emergence', which holds that life, differential sensitivity and reactivity, fitness and psychic phenomena, are results of increasing organization, these properties 'emerging' as it were, by a process of creative synthesis."
E. G. Conklin, 1944

"It is the thought transmitting propotency of the human species, more than any other, that gives it a superlative lead over all the creatures of the globe."
A. J. Lotka, 1925

"Aristotle in his 'De Partibus Animalium' maintained that the essence of a living animal is found not in what it is, or how it acts, but why it is as it is and acts as it does."

33. EXTIRPATION EXPERIMENTS ON ORGAN ANLAGEN

PURPOSE: To remove organ anlagen and to determine the ability of the embryo to adjust to the loss.

MATERIALS:

    Biological: Various stages of Amblystoma as designated for each experiment.

    Technical: Standard equipment for operating on and caring for embryos.

METHOD:

    Precautions:

       1. The post operative care of embryos is important, for they are naturally susceptible to bacterial infection. This can be reduced somewhat by operating and healing in 0.1% sodium sulphadiazine, and keeping them in cool media.

       2. Remove only the areas and cell layers indicated, at the designated stage. Organ fields become contracted with succeeding stages.

       3. Study section on "Wound Healing", p. 242.

    Controls: The controls for extirpation experiments consist of the same operation but without the actual removal of the organ anlage.

    Procedure: Operate in 10% Standard Solution and transfer to full strength Standard Solution when the wound is fully healed.

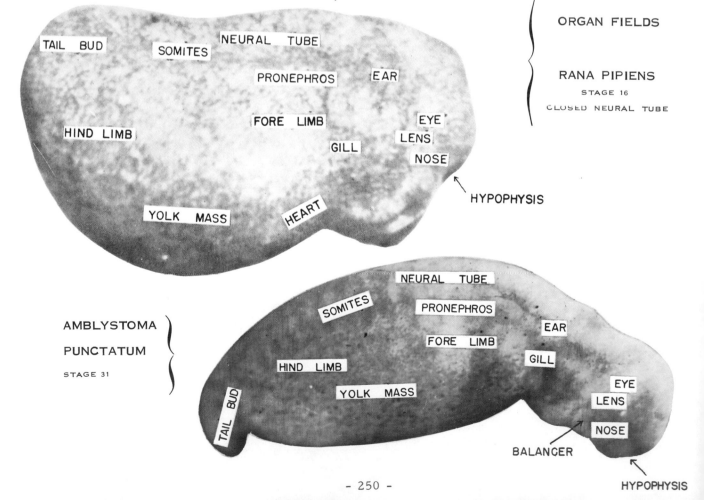

THE URODELE BALANCERS

The balancers are slender rod-like appendages which project from the side of the head, slightly posterior and ventral to the eyes, and which serve as supports to hold the head off the bottom and maintain balance in many Urodeles (see Amblystoma series stage #40). They are present in most species of Triturus, in Amblystoma punctatum (maculatum), jeffersonianum, microstomum and opacum but are absent in A. tigrinum. The club-shaped ends of the fully formed balancers are sticky, and this condition may be taken as a criterion of normal development.

Select Amblystoma punctatum or opacum at stages #28 to #32 and extirpate the balancer anlagé on the right side, leaving the left side as the control. Remove both the ectoderm and the underlying mesoderm from a circular area posterior and slightly ventral to the eye, on the mandibular arch. The dorsal margin of the balancer area is on a direct line from the dorsal border of the eye, and the area extends to a level below that of the eye. The area also extends from the posterior margin of the eye to the first gill slit.

THE EXTERNAL GILLS

Select Anuran embryos at stage #17 or #18 or Amblystoma embryos (any species) at stage #25 or #26 and locate the gill swellings. If available, study Anura stage #23 and Amblystoma stage #40 to see the position of the filamentous external gills which normally develop from the anlagen.

Since all three germ layers contribute to the formation of the external gills, it will be necessary to extirpate an adequate area of the ectoderm and a considerable amount of the underlying mesoderm of these early stages in order to make the operation complete. This may be done with glass needles, and deep excavation by means of a hair loop. The pharyngael cavity should be exposed. The gill anlagé on the right side may be removed and the left side left untouched for control comparison.

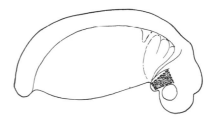

Position of the balancer anlagé (stippled) and posterior to it the gill swelling: Amblystoma stage #28.

THE EYE FIELD OF THE NEURULA

Manchot (1929), Adelmann (1930) and Mangold (1931) have shown that the two eye fields are located close together near the median line of the anterior medullary plate of stage #14 or #15 of the Urodela or stage #14 of the Anura. The eye field extends beyond the ultimately realized eye area, and extirpations and transplantations often result in producing accessory eyes.

Attempt to extirpate the eye forming area of the right eye alone. With glass needles cut deeply along lines indicated on the accompanying diagram, exposing the archenteron beneath. Remove the ectoderm and the substrate of this area while the embryo is in 10% Standard Solution and allow it to heal completely before gradually returning it to the full strength Standard Solution. It will be necessary to operate on a number of embryos because survival is low.

Variations of this extirpation should be in the direction of widening the area toward the left side; moving the area toward the mid-line; removing the epidermis with and without the substrate. (See section on Eye Field Operations.)

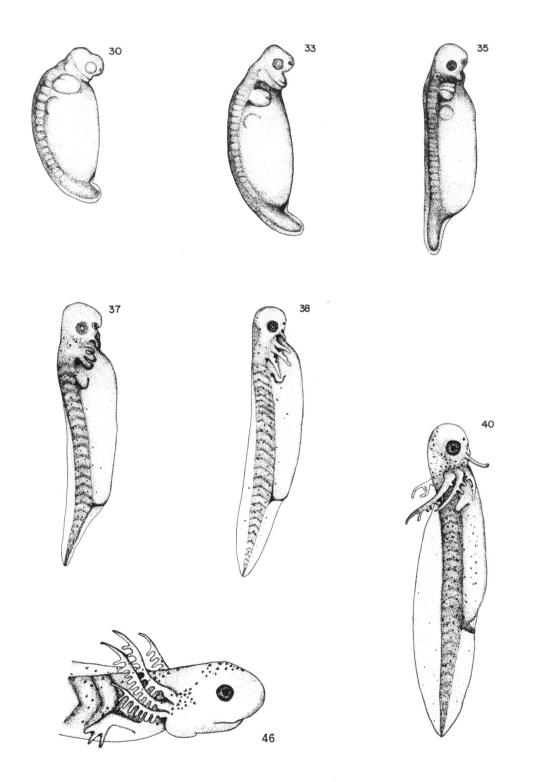

AMBLYSTOMA PUNCTATUM

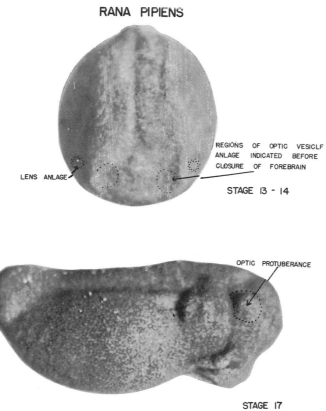

RANA PIPIENS

REGIONS OF OPTIC VESICLF
ANLAGE INDICATED BEFORE
CLOSURE OF FOREBRAIN

LENS ANLAGE

STAGE 13 - 14

OPTIC PROTUBERANCE

STAGE 17
(34 HRS. LATER)

THE OPTIC VESICLE

The optic vesicles of both the Anura and the Urodela are capable of regulation. This means that if the entire eye field is not removed, there may be a degree of restoration or regeneration of the excised parts. No regeneration occurs when the entire optic vesicle is removed, indicating that the eye-forming properties do not extend beyond the limits of the prospective eye forming area.

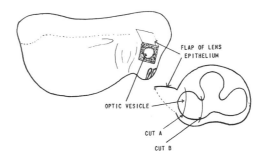

FLAP OF LENS
EPITHELIUM

OPTIC VESICLE

CUT A

CUT B

Extirpation of the retina and the entire optic vesicle Rana: stage #17

The above statements can be verified by removing only the outer retinal portion of the optic vesicle in some embryos and the entire optic vesicle in others, examining by dissection and by histological (sectioning) technique after a minimum of a week of recovery and development at laboratory temperatures.

The Anuran embryos at stage #17 (R. sylvatica and palustris preferable to pipiens) or the Urodele embryos at stage #25 or #26 may be used. Remove the membranes and place the embryo on its left side in a Permoplast or agar depression in a Syracuse dish. Locate the optic bulge and with a glass needle and hair loop cut a rectangular piece of epidermis directly over the eye, leaving the upper margin of the rectangle uncut (a hinge). Lift the flap of epidermis and locate the underlying optic vesicle.

1. In some embryos, take the hair loop and cut off the most lateral (outer portion) of the optic vesicle, that portion known to give rise to the retina.

2. In other embryos, excavate the entire optic vesicle, clipping it off at its base.

If the flap of epidermis is still intact, replace it over the wound. If it has been damaged, simply leave the embryo in 10% Standard Solution until the wound has closed completely by the spreading of adjacent epidermis, and then transfer to full strength Standard Solution. The extirpation of the optic vesicle does not do away with the eye muscles entirely but they are reduced in size and are atypical.

THE HEART ANLAGE

The partial or even the complete extirpation of the heart forming mesoderm of Amblystoma is generally followed by regeneration, which may mean the entire heart. The heart field extends well beyond the limits of the ultimate heart forming area so that even the extirpation of an area equivalent only to the ultimate heart may result in the formation of a small heart or hearts. With these facts in mind, derived from the work of Copenhaver, attempt to extirpate parts of the heart as follows:

Amblystoma stage #15 or Anuran stage #14 should be used, for the heart mesoderm is derived from two separate lateral primordia representing the free ventral margins of the two hypomeres. These fuse in the mid-line, ventral to the pharynx and just posterior to the thyroid anlagé to give rise to a single tubular heart. The two primordia meet ventrally at about stage #27 in the Urodeles and about stage #17 in the Anura.

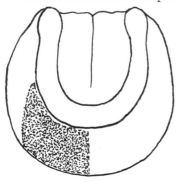

Medullary plate stage of an amphibian embryo showing the presumptive heart area to be extirpated (stippled).

Remove the membranes and orient the medullary plate stage with the right ventro-lateral side uppermost, in a depression in agar or Permoplast. The excision and healing should be in 10% Standard Solution. With sharp needles outline the heart area on the right side of the mid-ventral line and cut out a rectangular area deep enough to include all three germ layers (see figure). It may be necessary to excavate cells with a hair loop, and this should be done extensively on the right side. Keep the embryo in 10% Standard Solution until the wound is healed over and then gradually return to full strength Standard Solution.

Urodele embryos may be allowed to develop as long as possible because the heart development can be viewed through the thin covering ventral epidermis. The Anuran embryos should be dissected, or fixed, stained, and sectioned within about a week following the operation to determine the extent of damage or recovery of the above extirpation. (See section on Heart Field Operations.)

THE BRAIN

Amblystoma punctatum (or tigrinum) embryos should be freed from their jelly membranes at stage #14 to #16 and allowed to grow at about 18°C. in Urodele Growing Medium until they reach stage #32. At this time the primary brain vesicles have been developed and can be outlined from the exterior of the embryo.

AMBLYSTOMA

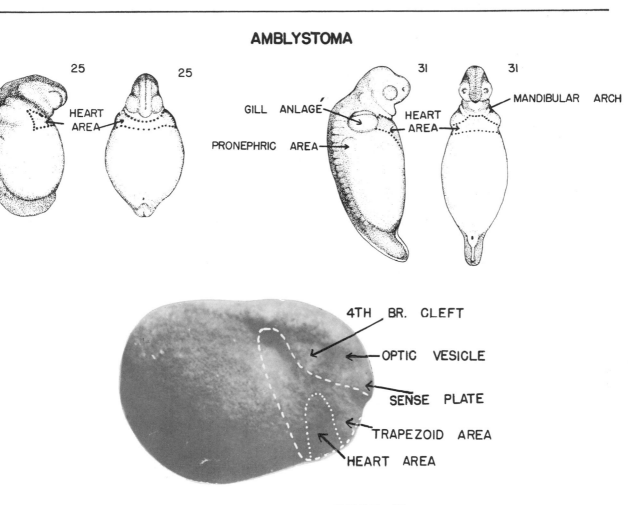

25   25   31   31

HEART AREA

GILL ANLAGE   MANDIBULAR ARCH

PRONEPHRIC AREA   HEART AREA

4TH BR. CLEFT

OPTIC VESICLE

SENSE PLATE

TRAPEZOID AREA

HEART AREA

RANA PIPIENS : STAGE 15

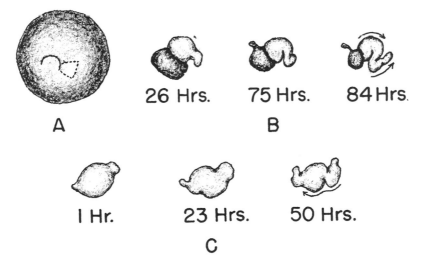

A   26 Hrs.   75 Hrs.   84 Hrs.
            B

1 Hr.   23 Hrs.   50 Hrs.
       C

Self-differentiation of presumptive heart material cultured in modified Holtfreter's solution. A, Amblystoma punctatum, stage 11. Explant of gastrula wall from outlined area lateral to the blastopore differentiates as shown in B. Arrows show direction of contraction wave at 84 hours after explantation. C, differentiation of presumptive mesoderm explanted from an embryo of stage 15, late medullary plate stage. (Redrawn after Bacon, '45.)

(Courtesy W. M. Copenhaver and W. B. Saunders Pub. Co., from
Willier, Weiss, Hamburger "Analysis of Development" 1955.)

Embryos of this stage show some movement and can be quieted in 1/3000 M.S. 222 freshly made up in Growing Medium. When fully narcotized, transfer to a Syracuse dish with bottom of soft paraffin or Permoplast and filled with Growing Medium saturated with sodium sulfadiazine. With a sharp scalpel make a single cut just anterior to the gill anlagen and the first somite, just posterior to the auditory vesicle. The head will be removed by such a cut, but particularly the entire brain. A sharp scalpel will bring the cut surfaces together and within 18-24 hours the wound should be entirely healed over.

The purpose of such an extirpation (or ablation) is to determine the degree of further differentiation without benefit of the brain and the three sets of sense organs. (See Detwiler's papers) Obviously such an embryo cannot feed so that its life span is determined by the amount of yolk available. However, the anlagen in the vicinity of the cut (gill and balancer fields) will be the most likely to show variations in the direction of size and number of parts. Such embryos will generally show full development of the heart and circulatory system; will respond to stimuli; but will be somewhat more difficult to anesthetize than the controls (Anagnostis, 1948 unpublished).

(Note: Extirpation of limb anlagen will be accomplished in connection with limb operations.)

OBSERVATIONS AND EXPERIMENTAL DATA:

Under each sub-heading for Extirpations, follow the development of each embryo with a series of sketches. The first drawing should be made immediately after the excision, and the last one after the excised area has been completely reformed, whether or not it is regenerated. The time elapsed (days) and, the medium and temperature should all be noted. (See section on "Wound Healing".)

REFERENCES

ADELMANN, H. B., 1937 - "The effect of the partial and complete excision of the prechordal substrate on the development of the eyes of Amblystoma punctatum." Jour. Exp. Zool. 75:199.

BODENSTEIN, D., 1943 - "An analysis of balancer development in Triturus torosus." Physiol. Zool. 16:44.

COPENHAVER, W. M., 1939 - "Initiation of the beat and intrinsic contraction rates in the different parts of the Amblystoma heart." Jour. Exp. Zool. 80:193.

DETWILER, S. R., 1946 - "A quantitative study of locomotion in larval Amblystoma following either midbrain or forebrain excision." Jour. Exp. Zool. 102:321.

EKMAN, G., 1929 - "Experimentelle Untersuchungen uber die fruheste. Herzentwicklung bei Rana fusca." Arch. f. Ent. Mech. 116:327.

HARRISON, R. G., 1924 - "The development of the balancer in Amblystoma, studied by the method of transplantation and its relation to the connective tissue problem." Jour. Exp. Zool. 41:349.

KOLLROS, J. J., 1940 - "The disappearance of the balancer in Amblystoma larvae." Jour. Exp. Zool. 85:33.

PETERSEN, H., 1923 - "Berichte uber Entwicklungsmeckanik. I." Ergebn. d. Anat. u. Entw'gesch. 24:327.

ROTMANN, E., 1935 - "Der Anteil von Induktor und reagierendem Geweb an der Entwicklung der Kiemen und ihrer Gefasse." Arch. f. Ent. Mech. 133:225.

SCHOTTE, O. E., & M. V. EDDS, 1940 - "Xenoplastic induction of Rana pipiens adhesive discs on balancer site of Amblystoma punctatum." Jour. Exp. Zool. 84:199.

SEVERINGHAUS, A. E., 1930 - "Gill development in Amblystoma punctatum." Jour. Exp. Zool. 56:1.

STOHR, P., 1929 - "Zur embryonalen Herztransplantation." Arch. f. Ent. Mech. 109:300.

"There is fundamentally a natural corrective for our inclination to allow likes and dislikes to influence our reason. This corrective is found in the instinct of curiosity, the faculty that impels men to seek the truth, even if it be unpalatable."

A. J. Lotka

34. TRANSPLANTATIONS

PURPOSE: To determine the ability of various organ anlagen to adjust to and differentiate within a new environment.

MATERIALS:

Biological: Early embryos of the various amphibia, Anura and Urodela. (See illustrations in previous section)

Technical: Standard equipment.

METHOD:

Precautions:
1. Remove and transplant only the area and the cells prescribed. This is very important because the areas may vary with the age of the donor, and the various germ layers may have different developmental relations to the organ.
2. Adequate excavation of the host site must be made, especially since there is very rapid healing of any embryonic wound.
3. The transplant must "take" (become firmly attached) before the host is moved to a new environment, or changed to a different medium.
4. Twitty (1937) and others, have found that the tissues of certain amphibia produce toxins which paralyze or kill the host (or transplant) in xenoplastic combinations. Triturus tissues are particularly potent when combined with Amblystoma. Therefore, in making xenoplastic transplants one must keep in mind the possibility of tissue in compatibility.

Controls: Since most of the organ anlagen that will be used are bilateral, the organ of the unoperated side of the host may be considered as the control organ.

Procedure: The following directions will be specific for each of the various organs. It is recommended that the student consult the Chapter in this Manual pertaining to the organ under study.

Where natural pigmentations can be used to identify and trace a transplant (graft) in the host environment one need not add any further marking. In homoplastic transplants it will be necessary to pre-stain the donor tissue (graft) in Nile Blue Sulphate or Neutral Red, in order to identify and follow the fate of the graft. Operated embryos should be allowed to recover in #2 Stender dishes with agar bases.

LIMBS
(see pages 85-87 and 273)

The forelimbs of Amblystoma punctatum (Texanum, jeffersonianum, opacum and Triturus torosus) are smaller and slower growing than those of A. tigrinum and A. mexicanum (axolotl). However, the A. punctatum anlagé appear early (Stage #37) and develop digits shortly thereafter (Stage #41), while the forelimb buds of the A. tigrinum do not appear until about the beginning of the larval period (when the yolk is resorbed). Detwiler (1938) states that the prospective limb material is determined as early as the late yolk-plug stage, and Swett has shown that the two axes of the limbs are laid down consecutively. (See exercise on Limb Fields.)

1. Remove the vitelline membranes of 10 specimens of Amblystoma (Stage #28) and place them in sterile 10% Standard Solution. If necessary, narcotize the embryos in 1/3000 MS 222. If the transplants are to be within the same species, pre-stain the donors in Nile Blue Sulphate.

2. Select a pair of embryos of similar developmental stage and place them side-by-side in an operating dish over soft paraffin or Permoplast. Mould a depression for the host, and place it in the depression with the right side uppermost.

3. Locate the forelimb anlagé. This will be found ventral to somites #3-#5, just posterior to the gill swelling and includes a portion of the ventral slope of the pronephric bulge.

4. Prepare the host by cutting a square hole with a glass needle (or a lancet) about 3 somites in diameter at the level of the pronephric bulge but just beneath the somites #8 to #10. The excavation must be deep enough to include some underlying mesoderm. This may be done with a hair loop.

5. Prepare the donor forelimb anlagé by excising the limb area, including the underlying mesoderm. This can be done by passing a glass needle from ventral to dorsal beneath the body ectoderm just posterior to the gill buds, and dorsal to (and including) the pronephric bulge. By bringing the needle upwards, the ectoderm will be cleanly cut. In a similar manner, make a parallel vertical cut beneath somite #5 at the posterior limit of the pronephric bulge. Then cut the third side of the square between the two ventral points of needle insertion. This will provide a flap of ectoderm which can be worked away from the neighboring tissues but with the underlying mesoderm attached. Finally, make the dorsal cut to free the graft and quickly transfer it (always under water) on the tip of a glass needle, into the previously made hole in the host. Note the orientation of the graft with respect to its original axes. It may be necessary to further enlarge the hole of the host, due to healing movements while preparing the graft. Gently press the graft into place with the hair loop and cover it with a piece of (chipped) cover slip or glass bridge. If the depression is properly made, the cover slip edges will rest on the Permoplast and its center will continually press the graft into place. Do not distort the host by excessive pressure.

6. After about half an hour gently remove the cover slip bridge and allow the embryo to adjust to the new situation. If the graft has not taken, replace the bridge. After another half hour gently shake the embryo from its depression, and transfer it to a #2 Stender (preferably with agar base) for further growth. If there are loose cells about the wound, clean them away with the hair loop.

Variations in the above procedure would include transplanting the limb ectoderm above or exchanging the limb ectoderm indifferent belly ectoderm before transplanting the whole anlagé, to determine the place of limb mesoderm in limb determination.

Record by drawings or photographs the condition of the graft at the time of the transplantation and during subsequent weeks. Xenoplastic transplants between A. punctatum and A. tigrinum are very instructive. (See section on Limb Field Operations for further details.)

THE GILLS

(See also page 251)

The external gills of the Anura appear as anlagen at stage #18 and in the Urodela at stage #26. In the Anura they develop as branched, and filamentous outgrowth by stage #22 and in the Urodela by stage #41 they are fully formed. Before operating it is well to become fully acquainted with the normal morphology and development of the external gills.

All three germ layers contribute to the formation of the external gills and Harrison (1921) has shown that the gills of Amblystoma punctatum are determined by stage #21, (see also Severinghaus, 1930 and Rotmann, 1935). Transplants can be varied to check the relative place of at least the ectoderm and the endoderm, it being rather difficult to isolate the intermediate mesoderm for such an experimental test, although it can be done.

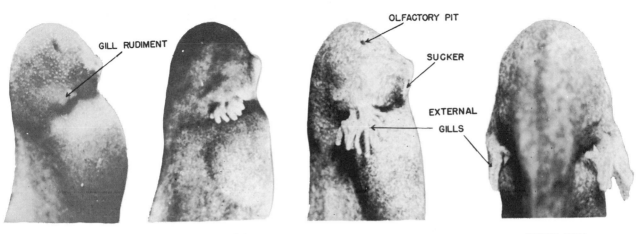

LATERAL VIEW   DORSAL VIEW

1. Select two embryos, Anura or Urodela, of the same age and size and place them in
    Standard Solution in a Permoplast or paraffin operating Syracuse dish. Prepare shal-
    low depressions to hold them right side uppermost. Remove all the membranes.

2. Prepare the host site by removing a piece of ectoderm and underlying mesoderm from
    different sites on different embryos, e.g., just posterior to the normal position of
    the gill anlagé; beneath somites 9 to 12; just posterior to the anterior limb bud; just
    anterior to the posterior limb bud; or in the position of the eye. Excavate deeply
    enough to provide adequate room for a transplant with considerable thickness.

Amblystoma tigrinum gill
anlagé transplanted to the
belly region of A. punctatum.

3. The gill swelling will be found in a line with the eye but beneath the first several
    somites. Its anterior extremity will be just posterior to the otic vesicle. With oper-
    ating glass needle and hair loop cut out the entire gill swelling, and include mesoderm
    and some of the pharyngeal endoderm. Keeping the piece intact, and properly oriented,
    transfer it on a needle to the prepared site on the host. Further excavate the host
    site to hold the transplant, and then hold it in place for 30 minutes by means of a
    coverslip bridge. Remove the bridge carefully, and clean away any sloughed off
    cells around the margin of the wound by means of a hair loop. After complete heal-
    ing transfer to the growing medium.

Variations in the above procedure not only include a different site on the host, but isolation of the germ-layer constituents of the anlage´ to determine (if any) their separate ability to develop into gills; rotation of the anlage´; and xenoplastic transplants between the
slow developing species (A. punctatum) and the rapidly developing species (A. tigrinum).

Make drawing or photographic records of individual transplants at appropriate intervals.

DORSAL VIEW   VENTRAL VIEW

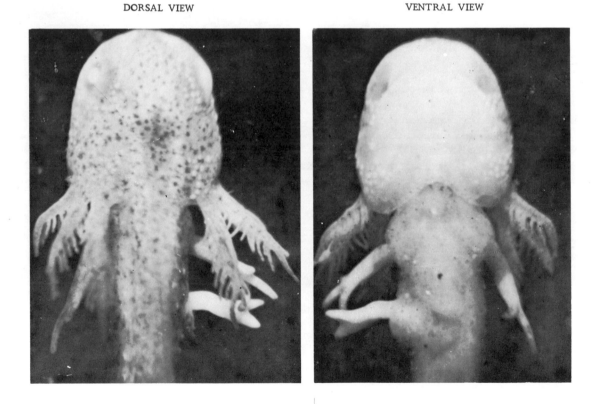

HETEROPLASTIC TRANSPLANTATION OF LIMB FROM A. TIGRINUM
TO RIGHT SIDE OF A. PUNCTATUM

THE EYE

(See also page 253 and 283)

The eye is a composite organ made up from brain (neural) ectoderm and head ectoderm (lens). Transplantations may be made at various stages, and of constituent parts, but it is the purpose of this exercise merely to determine to what extent the entire optic vesicle and overlying ectoderm can adjust to a new site on the host, a site devoid of the normal second cranial nerve.

1. Secure embryos (Anura stage #17 or Urodela stage #25) and place them in the operating Syracuse dish over Permoplast and in depressions, in Standard Solution. The
   optic vesicle protuberance can be easily located on the right side of the head. Prepare one embryo as the host by excavating a hole in the ectoderm and underlying
   mesoderm in the lateral body wall; just anterior to the position of the hind-limb bud;
   or in the tail bud.

2. Remove the entire optic vesicle on the right side of the donor, including a good portion of the diencephalon. With the overlying ectoderm intact, transfer the entire
   transplant on a needle to the host site and pack it into place with a hair loop, and hold
   it for 30 minutes with a piece of cover slip. The eye anlage is a rather compact unit
   and since there is less yolk and mesoderm around it than around other anlagen, it
   may not adhere so readily to the host site. For this reason the excavated site should
   be somewhat deeper than the thickness of the transplant, and the surrounding ectoderm should be allowed to partially close over the transplant.

This procedure can be varied in a number of ways. Extra eyes may be transplanted close to the site of the host eye to determine the degree of fusion or interference; an older anlage may be transplanted to a younger host (the reverse is likely to give negative re-sults); the eye may be so oriented that the optic vesicle faces inward (in which case an extra covering of ectoderm must be provided); and xenoplastic transplants should be at-tempted, particularly between species of Amblystoma. (See Hewitt, 1935, Jour. Exp. Zool. 69:235 for a study of xenoplastic transplants of eye rudiments between various Anura and Amblystoma.) (Some ingenious transplantations, rotations, and regenerations of older, larval eyes, have been made by Stone and Zaur, 1940.) (See exercise on Eye Field Operations and on Wolffian Regeneration.)

As in all transplant experiments, make drawings or photographs immediately after the operation and at appropriate intervals thereafter. Sectioned material at a later stage will answer the question relative to innervation.

THE BALANCERS

(See also page 85-87)

Balancers are paired, slender, rod-like appendages which project from the side of the head slightly behind and below the level of the eyes. They are found in Triturus and in Amblystoma, (except for A. tigrinum), but never in Rana. They serve as supports which hold the head off the bottom, preventing the larva from losing its balance before the de-velopment of functional forelimbs. They consist of an epithelial membrane whose glands secrete a mucoid substance at the tip and a mesodermal central core with a nerve and blood vessels (see Bodenstein, 1943).

1. Select two Urodele embryos of about stage #28 and shell them out of their membranes. Place them in a Syracuse operating dish with Permoplast base and partially filled with Urodele Operating Medium. Prepare depressions with ball tip, side-by-side and just adequate for the embryos.

2. Prepare the host embryo. Choose the site for the transplantation on one of the embryos. The most satisfactory positions are just posterior to the pronephros and in line with it, or just posterior to the otocyst. With glass operating needles cut out a rectangular piece of ectoderm about the size of two somites. This may be done by piercing the ectoderm with the point of the needle; pushing the needle forward, beneath and parallel to the ectoderm; allowing the needle to emerge at the upper level of the pre-chosen area, and then (if the needle is rigid) lifting it upward and thereby making a clean cut. If this seems impractical, rub a hair loop against the needle until the ectoderm is cut. Repeat this procedure along the parallel line of the pre-chosen area, then across the ventral and finally the dorsal edge. Lift out this ectoderm and discard. Excavate some underlying mesoderm.

3. Preparation of transplant. The balancer site is on the mandibular arch, just posterior to and slightly ventral to the eye. The dorsal limit of the balancer anlagé is on a level with the dorsal limit of the eye and the ventral limit on a line below the ventral limit of the eye. Anteriorly the balancer area touches that of the eye and posteriorly it is below the second gill slit.

In a manner similar to that of host ectoderm removal (above) remove the balancer ectoderm from the area indicated and on the tip of a needle (or hair loop) transfer it to the prepared (excavated) site on the host. Try to retain the same orientation of the transplant in the new, host environment, in respect to the original antero-posterior, dorso-ventral axes. (Do not rotate the transplant.) If the host implantation site has closed over in the interim, remove some mesenchyme cells with the hair loop and widen the hole to fit the transplant. Work as quickly as possible since the transplant is apt to fall apart. As soon as the transplant is in position, press it gently into place with the hair loop and lay over it a piece of coverslip (which will act as a bridge). The embryo should be left undisturbed for at least 30 minutes, in a cool, dark place.

After about 30 minutes if it seems that the transplant is not "taking", or has been moved, scratch the host site with a needle, replace the transplant and bridge, and await further healing. When the transplant is definitely attached, gently remove the bridge and allow the embryo to adjust to the new situation for a few minutes. Work the embryo out of its depression, by means of hair loops, shake it free, and (after about 1 hour or more) remove it with a large-mouthed, clean pipette to a #2 covered Stender provided with a sterile agar base. Place at a cool (18°C.) temperature.

It will be instructive to make the transplant between individuals of different ages, and also to rotate the transplant 90° or 180° in the host site to determine the degree of determination of the axes at the time of transplantation. Since a balancer does not normally develop on A. trigrinum, an heteroplastic transplant from any other species to A. trigrinum should be attempted.

Both donor and host may be kept in the same Stender, and the balancer site and anlagé of the other (bilateral) side of each may be considered as control.

Make drawing or photographic records of individuals at appropriate intervals.

OBSERVATIONS AND EXPERIMENTAL DATA:

Each experiment will be peculiar to itself in that it is impossible from a technical point of view, to exactly repeat any operation. For this reason it is important that the student make numerous records, drawings, or photographs, to indicate (a) the donor area (b) the depth of the donor tissue transplanted (c) the site on the host and the depth of the excavation (d) the orientation of the donor transplant in the host field (e) and periodic drawings or photographs of the success of the transplant. Only when a transplant might involve the central nervous system (e. g., the eye) should the material be sectioned to determine the nervous connections established. Space is provided with each section for such records.

DISCUSSION:

The value of these experiments is the establishment of the stage in development when various organ anlagen are determined, and the degree of determination. Detailed experiments on the limb and eye are provided elsewhere, but it is instructive for the student to determine for himself the fact that certain anlagen are exchangeable and that certain transplantations are perfectly viable while others (see Twitty, 1937, Humphrey and Burns, 1939, and Eakin and Harris, 1945) are not.

There are, of course, numerous other anlagen that can be used such as the sense plate (stage #14), the olfactory placode (stage #15), the lens (stage #16), the ear, parts of the nervous system (Detwiler, 1942), thyroid (Allen, 1918), pituitary (Blount, 1933), gonads (Burns, 1928, Humphrey, 1944), and heart (Copenhaver, 1945). The basic procedure can be established with the above four organ anlagen. (See sections on Eye, Heart, Limb.)

Heteroplastic grafting (graft location different from the graft source) is instructive in relation to growth and differentiation, and may give data on rate of growth, early and ultimate size factors, pigmentation, inhibitions found to exist in the normal environment but non-existent in the transplant environment, mutual compatibility, etc. The student should consult the Glossary for the distinction between the various types of transplants such as homoplastic, heteroplastic, heterotopic, xenoplastic, and the extreme case of the chimera (Baltzer, 1941).

REFERENCES

ALLEN, B. M., 1957 - "Effects of 60,000$_2$ gamma irradiation upon tissues of Bufo transplanted into unirradiated tadpoles." Anat. Rec. 127:394.

ALBRINK, W. S., H. S. N. GREENE, 1953 - "The transplantation of tissues between zoological species." Cancer Res. 13:64.

BILLINGHAM, R. E., L. BRENT, 1957 - "A simple method of inducing tolerance of skin homografts in mice." Transplant. Bull. 4:67.

BLOUNT, R. F., 1939 - "Heteroplastic transplantation of hypophysis between different species of Amblystoma." Proc. Soc. Exp. Biol. & Med. 40:212.

BORN, G., 1897 - "Uber Verwachsungsversuche mit Amphibienlarven." Arch. f. Ent. Mech. 4:349.

BRENT, L., 1958 - "Tissue transplantation immunity". Progro. Allergy. 5:271.

COPENHAVER, W. M., 1945 - "Heteroplastic transplantation of the sinus venosus between two species of Amblystoma." Jour. Exp. Zool. 100:203.

COPENHAVER, W. M., 1955 - "Growth of thyroid tissue in the gills of Amblystoma punctatum reared in propylthiouracil." Jour. Exp. Zool. 129:291-308.

DETWILER, S. R., 1938 - "Heteroplastic transplantation of somites." Jour. Exp. Zool. 79:361. (also Jour. Exp. Zool. 64:405)

DETWILER, S. R., 1942 - "Neuroembryology." MacMillan.

EAKIN, R. M. & M. HARRIS, 1945 - "Incompatibility between amphibian hosts and xenoplastic grafts as related to host age." Jour. Exp. Zool. 98:35.

EMERSON, H. S., 1944 - "Embryonic grafts in regenerating tissue. II. The behavior of the transplants during metamorphosis in Rana pipiens." Jour. Exp. Zool. 95:61.

GEINITZ, B., 1925 - "Embryonale transplantation zwischen Urodelen und Anuren." Arch. f. Ent. Mech. 106:357.

HANDLER, A. H., S. DABIS, S. C. SOMERS, 1956 - "Teterotranplantation experiments with human cancers." Cancer Res. 16:12.

HARRISON, R. G., 1935 - "Heteroplastic grafting in embryology." Harvey Lectures, p. 116.

HERTWIG, G., 1927 - "Beitrage zum Determinations-und-Regenerationsproblem mittels den transplantation Haploidkernigen Zellen." Arch. f. Ent. Mech. 111:292.

HEWITT, D. C., 1935 - "Xenoplastic transplantation of amphibian eye rudiments." Jour. Exp. Zool. 69:235.

HUMPHREY, R. R., 1944 - "The functional capacities of heteroplastic gonadal grafts in the Mexican axolotl and some hybrid offspring of grafted animals." Am. Jour. Ant. 75:263.

HUMPHREY, R. R. & R. K. BURNS, Jr., 1939 - "An incompatibility in heteroplastic parabiosis or grafting in Amblystoma due to a toxin of cutaneous origin." Jour. Exp. Zool. 81:1.

KOLLROS, J. J., 1940 - "The disappearance of the balancer in Amblystoma larvae." Jour. Exp. Zool. 285:33.

KORSCHELT, E., 1927 - "Regeneration und Transplantation." Berlin.

LOEB, L., 1930 - "Transplantation and individuality." Physiol. Rev. 10:547.

MEDAWAR, P. B., 1958 - "The immunology of transplantation" in The Harvey Lectures 1956-'57, Academic Press, N.Y.

NICHOLAS, J. S., 1924 - "The development of the balancer in Amblystoma. tigrinum". Anat. Rec. 28:317.

OPPENHEIMER, J., 1939 - "The capacity for differentiation of fish embryonic tissues implanted into amphibian embryos." Jour. Exp. Zool. 80.

PERRI, T., 1950 - "The biological action of x-rays on embryos of amphibians. Experiments on transplantations." Rev. Biol. 42:119-154.

PIATT, Jean, 1941 - "Grafting of limbs in place of the eye in Amblystoma." Jour. Exp. Zool. 86:77.

ROTMANN, E., 1935 - "Der Anteil von Induktor und reagierendem Gewebe an der Entwicklung der Kiemen ihrer Gefasse." Arch. f. Ent. Mech. 133:225.

SCHOTTE, O. E. & M. V. EDDS, 1940 - "Xenoplastic induction of Rana pipiens adhesive discs on balancer site of Amblystoma punctatum." Jour. Exp. Zool. 84:199.

SCHWIND, J. L., 1937 - Tissue reactions after homoplastic and heteroplastic transplantations of eyes in the anuran amphibia." Jour. Exp. Zool. 77:87.

SEVERINGHAUS, A. E., 1930 - "Gill development in Amblystoma punctatum." Jour. Exp. Zool. 56:1.

SIMONSEN, M., 1957 - "The impact on the developing embryo and newborn animal of adult homologous cells." Acta. Path. Microbiol. Scand. 40:480.

SNELL, G. D., 1957 - "The homograft reaction." Avv. Rev. Microbiol. II;439.

STONE, L. S., 1934 - "Production and metamorphosis of chimeras in anurans and urodeles." Proc. Soc. Exp. Biol. & Med. 31:1084.

STONE, L. S. & I. S. ZAUR, 1940 - "Reimplantation and transplantation of adult eyes in a salamander (Triturus viridescens) with return of vision." Jour. Exp. Zool. 85:243.

SWETT, F. H., 1937 - "Determination of limb-axes." Quart. Rev. Biol. 12:322.

TWITTY, V. C., 1934 - "Growth correlations in amphibia studied by the method of transplantations." Cold Spring Harbor Symposium Biology. 2:148.

TWITTY, V. C., 1937 - "Experiments on the phenomenon of paralysis produced by a toxin occurring in Triturus embryos." Jour. Exp. Zool. 76:67.

von UBISCH, L., 1931 - "Keimblattchimaren." Verhandl. du Deutsch Zool. Gesell. 178.

"Critical points occur during embryonic development, moments at which a given amount and intensity of interference by external agents will more easily put an end to the process or make it diverge from its normal course, than at other times."

C. R. Stockard

"The search for TRUTH is in one way hard and in another easy. For it is evident that no one can master it fully nor miss it wholly. But each adds a little to our knowledge of NATURE, and from all the facts assembled there arises a certain grandeur."

Aristotle

35. THE ORIGIN OF AMPHIBIAN PIGMENT

PURPOSE: To experimentally test the thesis, by excision, explanation, homoplastic and heteroplastic transplantation, that the amphibian pigment is derived from the neural crests.

MATERIALS:
  Biological: Urodele larvae stages #13 to #34
                Anuran larvae stages #14 to #18

  Technical: Standard operating equipment.
                Glass tubing measuring 0.25 to 0.45 mm. in diameter.
                Petri dishes, depression slides, cover slips.

METHOD:
  Precautions:
    1. Sterile precautions will insure greater success, although amphibian tissues are very hardy. This is particularly true of the isolation cultures. The media should be boiled or autoclaved; the instruments sterilized either by boiling or in alcohol; and the denuded embryos should be put through several changes of sterile medium to remove surface bacteria.

  Controls:
    1. For the excision experiments the control consists of excision of any region other than the neural crest.
    2. For isolation experiments of neural crest anlagé, the control likewise consists of the isolation of any region other than the neural crest, and the tissue may be taken from the same donor.
    3. For transplantation experiments the control consists of the transplantation of regions other than the neural crest to the same locality in the host as the experimental transplant.

  Procedure: The following descriptions will apply specifically to Amblystoma but may be followed with comparable stages of Anuran material.

EXCISION OF THE NEURAL CREST

The neural crest may be easily excised at the neural fold stage, before the folds have come together, at stage #15 for the Urodele embryo (or stage #14 for Anura).

1. Remove the membranes from Urodele larvae, stage #14-#15 as follows: Fresh clusters of Amblystoma eggs may be dipped briefly into 1% KOH, rinsed thoroughly, and quickly placed in isotonic medium (urodele medium, pond or spring water). With forceps or wide-mouthed pipette remove the individually capsulated embryos from their more inclusive but soft jelly masses. Then with pipette transfer these encapsulated embryos to 0.5% sodium-sulfadiazine (in pond or spring water or urodele medium) and leave them for 30 minutes. Finally, transfer the embryos to finger bowls with a ratio of 4 cc of medium per embryo (25 per finger bowl of 100 cc medium). Avoid unnecessary crowding. The embryos are then ready for the final decapsulation with sharp, watchmaker's forceps, in anticipation of the surgical procedures.

2. Place the embryo in a shallow depression in Permoplast or paraffin and, using a double-edged lancet or needles, excise the neural fold on the right side as indicated in the accompanying diagrams. Include the dorsal ectoderm.

3. Leave the embryo in Operating Medium until the wound closes over, then transfer it
    to Growing Medium at about 15°-18°C. and allow it to develop. A single specimen in
    a #2 Stender or finger bowl is best.

This operation will have the more graphic results in the more highly pigmented Amblystoma tigrinum or T. pyrrhogaster.

HOMOPLASTIC NEURAL CREST TRANSPLANTATIONS

Removal of neural crest material from the normal to a strange site should similarly
alter the final pigment pattern of the embryo. It is generally too drastic to make the
transplant on the same embryo, but comparable stages should be used or the donor material may be taken from an embryo slightly older than the host.

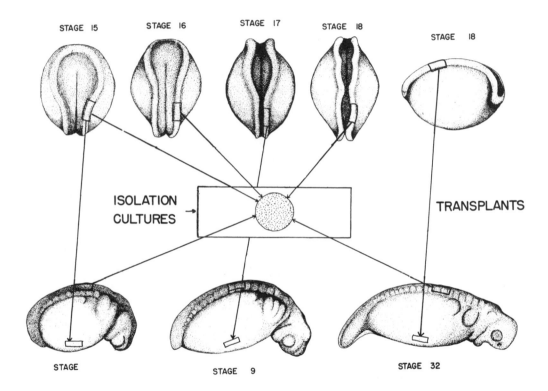

1. In Operating Medium, prepare a transplant site on the host embryo (stage #15) some-
    where in the lateral belly region, far removed from the host neural folds. The em-
    bryo should lie on its side in a Permoplast or paraffin depression deep enough so that
    the belly ectoderm is flush with the surface of the Permoplast.

2. Excise the neural fold of the right side from a similar embryo of stage #15 or older,
    and place it in the host wound, making the transfer on a needle point or by means of
    the hair loop. Hold it in place with a piece of cover slip (Brücke) for 30 minutes
    without disturbance.

3. Transfer the embryo by means of wide-mouthed pipette to Growing Medium at 18°C.
    or less for recovery and development.

Recently (1945) Twitty rotated the neural crest and adjacent somite material with interesting results (see accompanying figures). This operation should be attempted but might
be varied in respect to position on the host. If the somites and crest are reversed, it
would be significant to make the 180° rotation at the level of the hind- or forelimb to determine not only the lateration in pigment pattern but also in the muscular control of the
adjacent appendage.

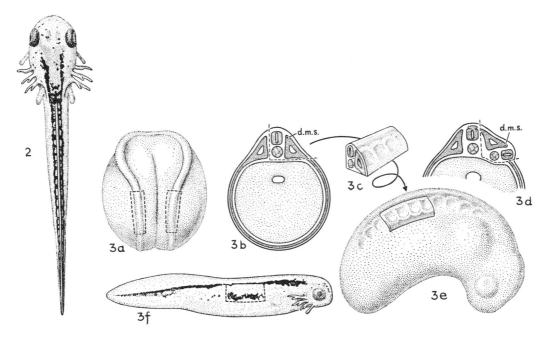

Fig. 2.   Dorsal view of Triturus torosus larva showing the transverse strands which connect the paired
          bands of melanophores located on the spinal cord.

Fig. 3.   (a) Extirpation of neural (trunk) folds.
          (b) Closure of "crestless" neural tube.
          (c) Block of tissue excised and grafted upside down in substitution of the somites of another
              embryo (d & c).
          (d) Diagram of transplant in host (d.m.s. - dorsal margin of myotome).
          (e) Inverted somites and neural crest in host.
          (f) Modified distribution of melanophores in host.

                        V. C. Twitty, 1945: Jour. Exp. Zool. 100:141.

HETEROPLASTIC NEURAL CREST TRANSPLANTATIONS

If Amblystoma punctatum and A. tigrinum larvae of stages #23 to #28 are available,
heteroplastic transplantations resulting in varied pigment patterns should be attempted.
If the white axolotl is available, the results are even more graphic. (See section on
"Transplantations" to determine the viable combinations.) When Urodeles of different
developmental rates are used, this factor must be considered. In general, the graft tissue should be from a donor slightly older than the host. Heteroplastic transplantations
are best made to the normal site, transferring dorsal ectoderm and ganglion crest, along
with some of the nerve cord, to insure presence of crest.

Some suggested combinations:
      Amblystoma tigrinum crest stage #24 to A. punctatum stage #23.
      Amblystoma punctatum crest stage #28 to A. tigrinum stage #23.

The transplant should be treated as in the homoplastic experiments, the operation being carried out in Urodele Operating Medium and after the graft has taken, transfer the host to Urodele Growing Medium for further development.

ISOLATION CULTURE OF THE NEURAL CREST

Pieces of embryonic neural tube (Urodele stages #23 to #26) are stripped of their dorsal ectoderm and then cut into small fragments, each with some neural crest, and are cultured in isolation (Twitty & Bodenstein, 1939, Twitty, 1945) to derive chromatophores. There are two methods, and several culture media.

The sterile culture media are: (1) Standard (Holtfreter's) Solution, in which the bicarbonate is dissolved separately from the other salts and the two volumes are mixed after boiling and cooling. (2) Coelomic Fluid which consists of fluid from the coelomic cavity of the adult of the same species, removed under sterile conditions by means of a sterile syringe. Twitty (1945) has found that females during the spawning season provide the most abundant coelomic fluid.

The culture methods are: (1) In a depression slide sealed over with a vaseline-ringed, coverslip. (2) On a coverslip inverted over a depression slide, the culture being in a hanging drop. (3) On a microscopic slide under coverslip slightly elevated by a ring of soft paraffin. In each instance, the isolated neural crest is in a liquid environment, protected against evaporation and extrinsic change, and provided with facilities for growth and expansion. The coelomic fluid is generally the best, for it provides more than just the isotonic salt requirements for maintenance and growth. Twitty and Bodenstein (1939) found that boiling did not destroy the effectiveness of peritoneal fluid in stimulating pigment development, but did reduce the risk of infection.

The most successful isolation cultures will probably be achieved if sterile coelomic fluid is used and the neural crest is isolated into this medium on a clean circular coverslip which is ringed with white vaseline. If the sterile inverted depression slide is brought down over the isolated tissue, pressed against the vaseline, and left in this position for 24 hours before re-inversion, the explant will become adherent to the coverslip so that when it (and the depression slide) is turned over, the neural crest and any derived cells

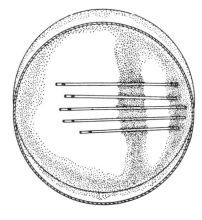

Place in Petri dishes filled with Holtfreter's solution, the tubes containing the explants are held in position by partly imbedding them in a row ridge of vaseline. The end near which the explant lies is left open; the opposite end is plugged with vaseline to prevent any flow of fluid through the tube which might be created by tipping or disturbance of the dish. Semi-diagrammatic drawing.

A semi-diagrammatic drawing to represent the differential onset of melanization within cultures of embryonic pigment cells developing in capillary tubes.

From Twitty, 1944: Jour. Exp. Zool. 95:259.

will be merely the thickness of the coverslip away from microscopic examination. Such cultures should last for 8-10 days, or longer at lower temperatures.

Recently (1944) Twitty cultured pigment cells from neural crests within capillary tubes measuring 0.25 to 0.45 in diameter. The neural crests were drawn into the tubes by oral suction, while submerged in sterile Standard (Holtfreter's) Solution, and the tubes were tilted slightly (within the Standard Solution) and the end of each tube farthest away from the end containing the explant was embedded in non-toxic vaseline. This vaseline acted as a plug, and at the same time held the tube in place. The tilting was achieved by a mid-way ridge of vaseline, but this could be accomplished equally well with a knotched paraffin ridge. The free end, i.e., where the explant is located, was open to the culture medium. During examination, the curved sides of the capillary tube acts somewhat as a lens, magnifying the contained neural crest and pigment cells. Twitty found that pigment formation in the capillary tubes was dependent upon substances diffusing from the nervous tissue of the explant, and that the first cells to become pigmented were those found deepest within the tube. He attributed this to regional differences in the concentration of oxygen and pigment precursors or oxidases essential to melanin formation.

The record for this experiment will consist of a series of daily drawings or photographs of the explants and the cells (pigmented and otherwise) which are derived therefrom

SELECTIVE STAINING OF IN-VIVO NEURAL CREST DERIVATIVES

In transplantation and isolation experiments there is always the question as to whether the derivatives of the excised anlage are the same as they would have been in the original site of the donor. Stone (1932) refined a method of preserving the vital dye Nile Blue Sulphate in the fixed embryo so that it could be located in sectioned material. It is therefore in the nature of a confirmatory experiment that the following procedure is given.

1. Select Urodele embryos of stage #23, and remove all of their membranes in Growing Medium. Place them in an operating dish with a Permoplast or soft paraffin base, and mould depressions to hold them with the neural folds uppermost.

2. Cut a piece of Nile Blue dyed agar (0.1 gr. Nile Blue Sulphate in 2% agar in 100 cc. of distilled water, dissolved by heating, and poured, while hot, onto glass plates covered with a very thin layer of glycerine. When dried, the agar can be peeled off of the plate in thin sheets of any size or shape (e.g., the shape and size of the neural fold). Place this minute piece of agar flat on a piece of coverslip and pass the coverslip through a flame. This will cause the agar to melt slightly, and become adherent to the coverslip chip. With practice one can provide a marker of the exact shape and size of the neural fold.

3. After the neurula stage (#23) is firmly placed within the depression, in Standard Solution, bring the (inverted) coverslip chip into position so that the Nile Blue Agar will make precise contact with one of the neural folds. Press it against the embryo, and anchor the edges of the glass chip in the surrounding Permoplast. Hold the neurula in this position for 20-30 minutes, while the dye is being transferred to the neural fold, and then gently remove it without tearing away any of the cells of the embryo.

4. Transfer the embryo to Urodele Growing Medium for development until stage #28 or later. The dye will remain for a long time and spread with the cells it has invaded, so that it may be found even after the pigment has begun to appear.

5. (a) Fix the embryo in Zenker-acetic for two hours; wash in running tap water 1 hour.
   (b) Place in 1% aqueous solution of phosphomolybdic acid for 2 hours (Lehmann, 1929).
   (c) Transfer for half hour periods through the ascending alcohols to each of which has been added 0.1% phosphomolybdic acid. This acid preserves the dye.

(d) Transfer for one-half hour to a mixture of equal parts of 100% alcohol, (containing 0.1% phosphomolybdic acid) and cedar oil. Then place in pure cedar oil until clear (overnight).

(e) Embed in three changes of paraffin-Bayberry-beeswax mixture (90 - 5 - 5) and, when hardened, section at 10 microns. The sections may be treated in the usual way (with xylol) and mounted under clarite. If the tissues are not passed through any water they will retain the Nile Blue Sulphate dye in the cells which were originally stained, and with appropriate lighting the demarcation between stained and unstained areas can be made out easily.

OBSERVATIONS AND TABULATION OF DATA:

The data for these experiments are qualitative rather than quantitative. Histological sections, when possible, will confirm the macroscopic analyses. (See DuShane, 1935: Jour. Exp. Zool. 72:1 for cytological procedures relative to the various types of chromatophores.)

DISCUSSION:

The neural crest arises as a strip of cells lying between the neural plate and the dorsal ectoderm, this plate being separated from both of these structures during the closure of the neural folds. It is now established that the neural crest is the principal and probably the sole source of all pigment cells (except the tapetum) in all of the vertebrates that have been studied (DuShane, 1943). Melanophores are found in the epidermis and dermis, meninges, visceral mesenteries, peritoneum, and in close association with the blood vessels throughout the body. This means that from the original source of such pigment cells there has been very extensive migration. The forces involved in this migration are illustrated in the capillary-tube isolation experiments of Twitty (1944). But the pre-migratory neural crest cells cannot be distinguished from their neighbors because they show no pigment differentiation until about the time they reach their normal destination. Such pigment cell differentiation includes:

Melanophores - wide distribution, cells with brown to black melanin.
Lipohores - dermis and epidermis, having diffuse yellow pigment (lipochrome) in solution.
Guanophores - pericardium and most lateral line organs, highly refractive, granular, golden yellow guanin crystals with metallic lustre.

The pigment pattern may be used to identify different species of Amblystoma or Triturus and frequently in heteroplastic transplantations there is evidence that both genetic and environmental factors (such as humoral or contiguous cell influences) may be important in directing ultimate cellular differentiation. In Amblystoma punctatum there is even distribution of melanophores while the lipohores are fused to give a continuous sheet within the dermis. In A. tigrinum the melanophores are large and dark and are arranged in groups, as are also the lipohores. The time of melanophore appearance is species specific. In A. punctatum the first melanophores appear at stage #34 lateral to the medulla, beneath the epidermis, and by stage #36 they have reached the level of the pronephros. The lipohores begin to appear at stage #28. Potential melanophores from various species manifest different abilities to develop in isolation, and even in the normal environment there are melanophores which are dependent upon the presence of pigmented epidermis to produce melanin. Other derivatives of the neural crest may include chromaffin tissue, mesenchyme, sheath cells, visceral cartilages, spinal ganglion (neuroblast) cells, sympathetic ganglia, and adrenal medulla.

Twitty and Bodenstein (1939) found that pigment appears in the isolated chromatophores when cultured in Standard (Holtfreter's) Solution later than in peritoneal fluid, they darken less rapidly, and the melanophores become more widely dispersed. The active migration of melanoblasts in vitro is confined to the period before the pigmentation is established, in both species of Triturus studied, although migration does not preclude the possibility of further melanization. They found, in general, that when the volume of the culture medium was kept low that pigment development was the better, and small drops of peritoneal fluid were the best. Xanthophores appear more frequently in cultures of Amblystoma than in cultures of Triturus crests.

Szepsenwol (1945) found that the eyes of larvae (Amblystoma and Rana) effect the body color either by a humoral substance (early in development) or reflexly (later in development), when the nervous control of the melanophores dominates the humoral. These observations resulted from parabiotic union studies in which the eyes of one or both members of the pair were excised, and subsequent pigment pattern studies were made.

REFERENCES

ADLER, A., 1939 - "Melanin pigment in the central nervous system of vertebrates." Jour. Comp. Neur. 70.

ATWELL, W. J., & E. HOLLEY, 1936 - "Extirpation of the pars intermedia of the hypophysis in the young amphibian with subsequent silvery condition and metamorphosis." Jour. Exp. Zool. 73:23.

BALTZER, F., 1941 - "Untersuchungen an chimaren von Urodelen und Hyla. I. Die Pigmentierung chimarischer Molch-und Axolotllarven mit Hyla-Ganglienleiste." Rev. Suisse de Zool. 48:413.

BARDEN, R. B., 1942 - "The origin and development of the chromatophores of the amphibian eye." Jour. Exp. Zool. 90:479 (See ibid. 92:171).

BEAMS, H. W. & R. L. KING, 1938 - "Pigmentation changes in tadpoles of Rana pipiens following centrifugation during the early gastrula." Jour. Morph. 63.

BYTINSKI-SALZ, H., 1939 - "Chromatophorenstudien II. Struktur und Determination des adepidermalen Melanophorennetzes bei Bombina." Arch. f. Zellforsch. 22:123.

DALTON, H. C., 1946 - "The role of nucleus and cytoplasm in development of pigment patterns in Triturus." Jour. Exp. Zool. 103:169.

DANNEEL, R., 1957 - "Die ersten Melanoblasten der Neunaugenlarvae" Naturwissen. 2:46-47.

DAWES, Ben 1941 - "The melanin content of the skin of Rana temporaria under normal conditions and after prolonged light and dark adaptations." Jour. Exp. Biol. 18:20.

DeLANNEY, L. E., 1941 - "The role of the ectoderm in pigment production, studied by transplantation and hybridization." Jour. Exp. Zool. 87:323.

DETWILER, S. R., 1937 - "Observations upon the migration of neural crest cells, and upon the development of the spinal ganglia and vertebral arches in Amblystoma." Am. Jour. Anat. 61:63.

DETWILER, S. R., & W. M. COPENHAVER, 1940 - "The growth and pigmentary responses of eyeless Amblystoma embryos reared in light and in darkness." Anat. Rec. 76:241.

DORRIS, Frances, 1940 - "Behavior of pigment cells from cultures of neural crest when grafted back into the embryo." Proc. Soc. Exp. Biol. & Med. 44:286.

DRAGER, G. A., & R. F. BLOUNT, 1941 - "The time of the appearance of melanophore expanding hormone in the development of Amblystoma maculatum." Anat. Rec. 81: suppl. 93.

DuSHANE, G. P., 1943 - "The embryology of vertebrate pigment cells. I. Amphibia." Quart. Rev. Biol. 18:109.

EASTLICK, H. L., 1940 - "The localization of pigment-forming areas in the chick blastoderm at the primitive streak stage." Physiol. Zool. 13:202.

ELIAS, H., 1943 - "Cause for blue, green, and red colour in Anura." Anat. Rec. 87:12.

ETKIN, W., 1941 - "On the control of growth and activity of the pars intermedia of the pituitary by the hypothalamus in the tadpole." Jour. Exp. Zool. 86:113.

FOSTREDT, G., 1939 - "Preliminary in vitro studies of melanophore-principle activity of the pituitary gland." Proc. Soc. Exp. & Med. 40:302.

HUMM, F. D., 1942 - "The growth and migration of cultured melanophores from the neural crest when grafted into the embryo." Jour. Exp. Zool. 90:101.

LEHMANN, F. E., 1929 - "Die Entwicklung des Änlagenmusters im Ektoderm der Tritongastrula." Arch. f. Ent. mech. 117.

LYNN, W. G. & Sr. A. de MARIE, 1946 - "The effect of thiouracil upon pigmentation in the tadpole." Science, 104:31.

MARSLAND, D. M., 1945 - "The mechanism of pigment displacement in unicellular chromatophores." Biol. Bull. 87:252.

NIU, M. C., 1947 - "The axial organization of the neural crest, studied with particular reference to its pigmentary component." Jour. Exp. Zool. 105:79. (See also 113:633, 1950)

NIU, M. C., 1954 - "Further studies on the origin of amphibian pigment cells." Jour. Exp. Zool. 125:199-220.

NIU, M. C. & V. C. TWITTY, 1953 - "The differentiation of gastrula ectoderm in medium conditioned by axial mesoderm." Proc. Nat. Acad. Sci. 39:985-989.

PARKER, G. H., 1943 - "Animal color changes and their neurohumors." Quart. Rev. Biol. 18:205.

RAVEN, Chr. P., 1936 - "Zur Entwicklung der Ganglienleiste. V. Uber die Differenzierung des Rumpfganglienleistenmaterials." Arch. f. Ent. Mech. 134:122.

ROSIN, S., 1943 - "Experimente zur Entwicklungsphysiologie der Pigmentierung bei Amphibien." Rev. suisse de Zool. 50:485.

SAWYER, C. H., 1947 - "Cholinergic stimulation of the release of melanophore hormone by the hypophysis in the salamander." Jour. Exp. Zool. 106.

SERRA, J. A., 1943 - "Sur la nature des melanines et la melanogenese." Genetica, 23·300.

STONE, L. S., 1932 - "Selective staining of the neural crest and its preservation for microscopic study." Anat. Rec. 51:267.

STONE, L. S., 1933 - "The development of the lateral-line sense organs in Amphibians in living and vital-stained preparations." Jour. Comp. Neur. 57:507.

SZEPSENWOL, J., 1945 - "The influence of the eyes on the melanophores in Amphibia." Anat. Rec. 93:185.

TWITTY, V. C., 1945 - "The developmental analysis of specific pigment pattern." Jour. Exp. Zool. 100:141.

TWITTY, V. C. & D. BODENSTEIN, 1944 - "The effect of temporal and regional differentials on the development of grafted chromatophores." Jour. Exp. Zool. 95:213.

TWITTY, V. C. & M. C. NIU, 1954 - "The motivation of cell migration studied by isolation of embryonic pigment cells singly and in small groups in vitro." Jour. Exp. Zool. 125:541-514.

WARING, H., 1941 - "The co-ordination of vertebrate melanophore responses." Biol. Rev. 17:120.

WATTERSON, R. L., 1942 - "The morphogenesis of down feathers with special reference to the developmental history of melanophores." Physiol. Zool. 15:234.

WEISS, P., 1941 - "Melanin formation by deplanted fragments of thalamus in Amphibian larvae." Proc. Soc. Exp. Biol. & Med. 48:343.

"Man is metaphysical and proud. He has gone so far as to think that the idealistic creations of his mind, which correspond to his feelings, also represent reality. Hence it follows that the experimental method is by no means natural to man, and that only after lengthy wanderings in theology and scholasticism has he recognized at last the sterility of such efforts . . . The human mind has at different periods of its evolution passed successively through feeling, reason, and experiment. First. feeling alone, imposing itself on reason, created the truths of faith or theology. Reason or philosophy, the mind's next mistress, brought to birth scholasticism. At last, experiment, or the study of natural phenomena, taught man the truths of the outer world are to be found ready-formulated neither in feeling nor in reason. These are indispensable merely as guides: but to attain external truths we must of necessity go down into the objective reality . . . . In the search for truth by the experimental method, feeling always takes the lead: it begets the a priori idea or intuition; reason or reasoning develops the idea and deduces its logical consequences. But if feeling must be clarified by the light of reason, reason in turn must be guided by experiment."

Claude Bernard

36. LIMB FIELD OPERATIONS

PURPOSE: By the application of experimental methods to the limb field (anlagé) of the Urodele embryo, to determine the
1. Powers of regeneration following partial and total extirpation of the anlagé.
2. The effect of rotating the limb field axis.
3. The effect of splitting the limb field.
4. The relative functions of the ectoderm and the mesoderm in limb formation.
5. The differentiating capacity of heterotopic transplants.
6. The relation of host and donor in xenoplastic transplants.
7. The genetic factors relating to limb formation, by means of
    a. Heterogenic transplants (i. e., between species with different rates of development.
    b. Heteroplastic transplants involving pigmentary differences.

MATERIALS:
Biological: Urodele larvae of stages #29 to #35.

Slow developing forms	Rapid developing forms
Amblystoma punctatum (maculatum)	Amblystoma tigrinum
Amblystoma texanum (microstomum)	Amblystoma mexicanum (axolotl)
Amblystoma jeffersonianum	
Amblystoma opacum	
Triturus rivularis	
Triturus simulans	
Triturus torosus	

Technical: Standard Operating Equipment.
Vital dyes and MS 222 freshly made up conc. 1/3, 000.

METHOD:
Precautions:
1. Use 0.1% sodium sulfadiazine if bacterial infection is encountered.
2. Be reluctant to examine the transplant. It should remain undisturbed for 30 minutes or more and any necessary transferring should be by wide-mouthed pipette.
3. Temperatures lower than that of the laboratory are best for Urodele recovery and survival. Some species do best at 10°C.
4. Operations are performed in Operating Medium; embryos are later transferred and raised in Growing Medium. Feeding should begin when the balancers disappear.
5. Muscular activity begins at about Stage #34. If operations are attempted at this stage it will be necessary to use freshly made MS 222 in operating medium 1/3, 000.

Control: The controls for each of the following experimental procedures will, of necessity, be different.

Procedure: Each of the following exercises deals with the limb field but since each illustrates a different principle, the procedures will naturally differ somewhat.

---

* The author acknowledges, with appreciation, the help of the late Dr. F. H. Swett in organizing this exercise.

REGENERATION FOLLOWING EXTIRPATION OF THE ANLAGÉ*

Secure embryos at stage #29 and remove all membranes. Place the embryos in a Petri dish with an agar base. Select those which are exactly at stage #29 and compare with the accompanying diagram on following page.

Place the embryo (stage #29) on its left side in a Permoplast or paraffin depression in an operating (Syracuse) dish. With a double-edged lancet or glass needles make cuts as indicated below and in the accompanying diagram. The circular cut can be made most easily by rotating the operating dish while cutting with iridectomy scissors in an immobile hand. The ectoderm is pigmented, the underlying mesoderm is white and the deeper endoderm is grayish-tan (having slight pigmentation). The purpose of the following procedures is to determine the areal extent and the depth of the limb field as of stage #29. The limb area is ventral to myotomes #3-#5, just posterior to the gill anlagen.

   a. Remove ectoderm alone from area marked "A" (see accompanying diagram).
   b. Remove ectoderm and all underlying mesoderm from area "A". Be certain to clean out all the white mesodermal cells beneath the excised ectoderm.
   c. Remove ectoderm from the larger area "B", leave the mesoderm undisturbed.
   d. Remove the ectoderm and mesoderm from the larger area "B". Again scoop out all of the white mesoderm cells by means of a hair loop.
   e. Make a semi-circular cut (as indicated by arrows) peripheral to the margin of area "B", deflect this flap of ectoderm anteriorly, and clean off and scoop out all mesoderm cells from beneath the flap of ectoderm. Should the excavation be so extensive that the flap of ectoderm does not cover, fill the cavity with yolk cells from another embryo of the same age. Apply a bridge (Brücke) for 30 minutes to hold the ectodermal flap in place until it heals.

The unoperated side of the embryo will function as the normal or control for comparison with the operated side in respect to limb development. Maintain in the same environment, however, some other unoperated embryos of the same age and stage as supplementary controls. The best controls would be operated embryos but with the tissue left in place, particularly since this is an attempt to determine the effect of extirpations.

HETEROTOPIC TRANSPLANTS

The orthotopic (homotopic) position is the normal position, the heterotopic one being a different or strange position for the anlagé. It is the purpose of this experiment to determine the differentiating capacity of the limb anlagé at other than the normal regions. If several donors are available, supernumerary limbs may be provided. Removing the ectoderm and/or the mesoderm from the donor, make the following transplantations:
   a. Ectoderm alone from the area "A" of donor to region "X" of host.
   b. Ectoderm and mesoderm from area "A" to region "X" of host.
   c. Ectoderm and mesoderm from area "B" to region "X" of host.
   d. Ectoderm and mesoderm from area "A" to region "Y" of host (on hand).

In all cases it is well to place the donor and the host side by side and to locate the regions concerned in both embryos before the operation is begun. Use MS 222 (1/3,000 conc.) if necessary, to quiet any muscular activity. The transplant must be made quickly and the transfer may be made on the point of a needle or on a small hair loop. With a ball tip gently pat the transplant into place and hold it there by means of a chipped coverslip (Brücke) for at least 30 minutes. If the glass cover tends to adhere to the ectoderm, try a small piece of lens paper whose ends may be fastened to the Permoplast base. In the case of the transplant to region "Y" on the host it will be necessary to place the host in a Permoplast depression with the head protruding. Provide an adequate wound area in the host, for healing is rapid.

---

*Limb extirpation is included in the exercise on "Extirpations" but the procedure here is considerably more detailed.

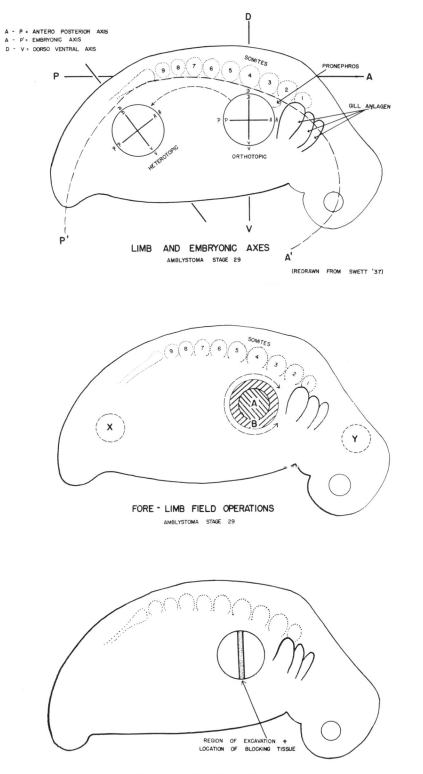

A - P = ANTERO POSTERIOR AXIS
A - P' = EMBRYONIC AXIS
D - V = DORSO VENTRAL AXIS

LIMB AND EMBRYONIC AXES
AMBLYSTOMA STAGE 29

(REDRAWN FROM SWETT '37)

FORE - LIMB FIELD OPERATIONS
AMBLYSTOMA STAGE 29

SPLITTING THE LIMB - FIELD
AMBLYSTOMA STAGE 29

ROTATION OF THE LIMB AXES

In these experiments it is necessary to mark the donor material in some way so that the axes may be identified when the transplant is oriented in the host site. Generally this may be accomplished in the normal course of excision where identifying marginal nicks may be used as identifying markers. Both anterior-posterior (A-P) and dorso-ventral (D-V) axes are concerned. Use Urodele embryos of stage #29 or younger.

    a. Carefully cut out the ectoderm and the mesoderm of area "B" so that the bulk of the limb area remains intact. Clean out the wound with a small hair loop, removing all loose (white) mesodermal cells, and replace the excised mass of tissue in the same wound area after making a 180° rotation of the graft, as indicated by arrows in the accompanying diagrams (Fig. F). Both axes will, in this instance, be reversed.

    b. Remove ectoderm and mesoderm of area "B" from the right side of the donor and orient it with the D-V axis still dorso-ventral but in the host wound area at the region of the left limb anlage. In this instance the A-P axis will be reversed. (Fig. A)

    c. Without disturbing the normal field of the host, transplant from other embryos both areas listed above, similarly rotated (i.e., as in "a" and "b") but to the locality of "X" on the hosts. In this manner a direct comparison may be made with the hosts normal limb field. (See diagrams for various other possible rotations of the two primary axes.)

    d. Repeat the above rotational transplantations with older embryos, using Urodele stages #35-#36, in order to determine whether there has been any further determination of axes within the limb field.

These transplantations should be followed as long as the larvae can be maintained so that the axial relations of the well developed limbs may be determined, and also to study the degree of innervation of the transplanted limb. The control for these experiments consists of excision and replacement without rotation of the limb field.

EFFECT OF SPLITTING THE LIMB FIELD

Surgical interference with the limb field will often result in duplication of limbs, the frequency varying with the species. Amblystoma punctatum is much more favorable than is A. tigrinum. Transplants often result in duplications, due to disturbances to the limb field.

Locate the limits of the limb field on Amblystoma stage #29 and then cut away a thin strip of ectoderm along the dorso-ventral axis of the field, splitting the field into two semicircles (see figure p. 275). With a small hair loop and needles, clean out the mesoderm lying in the exposed region (beneath the removed strip of ectoderm).

From another embryo of the same age or slightly older, remove a strip of mid-dorsal ectoderm with underlying neural tube material, trimming the strip down until it will fit into the excavated region of the limb field. See that all loose mesoderm is removed, and then place this strip of ectoderm (epithelial and neural) into the excavated region, holding it in place with a coverslip chip until it "takes" hold. Such a foreign strip of tissue will block the integration of the anterior and the posterior halves of the limb field.

Similarly split the limb field into dorsal and ventral halves. Notochord with overlying ectoderm provides an efficient block, but the notochord should be taken from later stages.

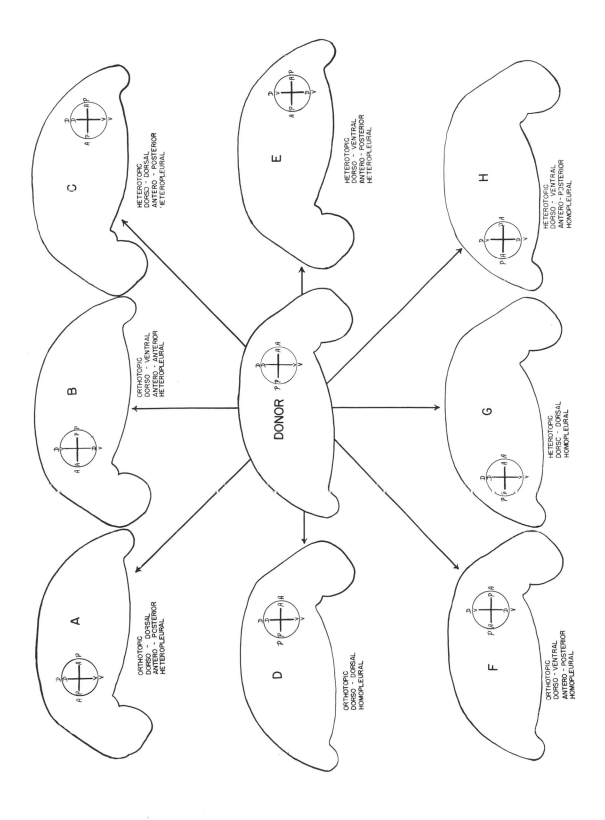

RELATION OF ECTODERM AND MESODERM IN LIMB FORMATION

The experiments on regeneration (above) throw some light on the relationship of limb bud ectoderm and mesoderm to normal limb development. Since mesoderm alone cannot be grafted, it is necessary first to transplant ectoderm to which the foreign mesoderm attaches, and then to make a second transplantation, carrying along together the normally unrelated ectoderm and mesoderm.

    a. Transplant the ectoderm alone from area "B" (see diagram) to the region "X" on a second embryo. The transplant should be exclusively ectoderm, i.e., all original mesoderm must be cleaned away with a hair loop. Within 24 hours the graft should be completely healed. Prepare another host by removing the entire limb anlagé, ecto- and mesoderm of area "X" of the previously operated embryo. This consists of original limb ectoderm plus flank mesoderm. Note carefully the exact stage of development of all embryos used; the size of the donor tissue; size of the host area; and the extent of the excision of mesoderm. Should this operation produce a perfectly normal limb it would indicate that the limb disc ectoderm is of prime and exclusive importance, in the development of the limb.

    b. Place flank ectoderm over limb-disc mesoderm, making certain that all flank mesoderm has been cleaned off of the transplant. Should a normal limb develop from this operation, it would suggest the importance of the limb disc mesoderm and the lability of the flank ectoderm.

    c. Transplant flank ectoderm only over limb disc mesoderm for 24 hours, until thoroughly healed. Then excise and transplant the entire disc material (ecto- and mesoderm) to the flank region of another host. In this case the limb disc mesoderm alone is being transplanted to a foreign region. Should a normal limb develop, this would confirm the importance of the mesoderm in limb development.

These heterotopic transplants are more graphic if they are made between A. punctatum and A. tigrinum (Harrison, 1933) and at stage #29 and #35.

GENETIC FACTORS RELATING TO LIMB FORMATION

RATES OF GROWTH - HETEROGONIC:

The following experiments are devised to demonstrate the growth rate differences inherent in transplants, especially when made between fast and slow growing species. Up to the beginning of the larval period, when the yolk has been absorbed, the more slowly developing Amblystoma punctatum has a considerable forearm with two digits while at the corresponding stage of development of Amblystoma tigrinum (fast developer) and A. mexicanum larvae have only mesenchymatous nodules. Shortly after this stage, however, the A. tigrinum limbs reach and surpass the size of those found in A. punctatum. To demonstrate that the transplanted limb generally maintains its inherent (genetic) rate of growth (Harrison, 1924) the following experiments are designed:

    a. Amblystoma tigrinum limb-bud is completely replaced by A. punctatum limb bud at stage #35.

    b. A. punctatum limb bud completely replaced by A. tigrinum limb bud at stage #35.

    c. Heterotopic transplants made between A. tigrinum and A. punctatum, with host limb fields untouched. This gives an excellent basis for comparisons.

Such transplantations as these, involving mesoderm alone, would demonstrate most conclusively the relative functions of ectoderm and mesoderm in limb formation, outlined in the previous set of experiments. The mesoderm of the limb bud seems to control the form, the rate of growth, and the ultimate size of the urodele limb. And in turn, the limb affects the number of ganglion cells in the adult spinal ganglia (Schwind, 1932).

DORSAL VIEW   VENTRAL VIEW

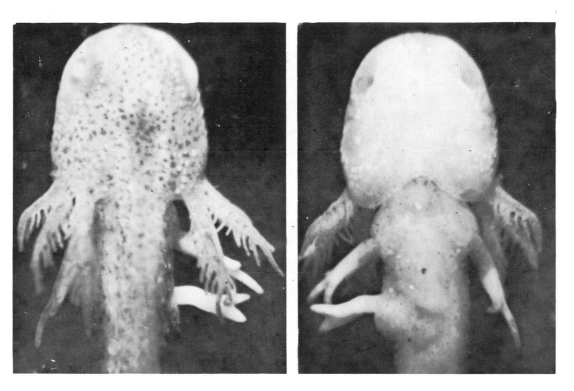

HETEROPLASTIC TRANSPLANTATION OF LIMB FROM A. TIGRINUM
TO RIGHT SIDE OF A. PUNCTATUM

PIGMENTARY DIFFERENCES:

This experiment is best demonstrated with the white axolotl, A. mexicanum, in limb transplantations with the highly pigmented A. tigrinum. There are three main types of pigment cells; Melanophores, with darker granular pigment; Xanthophores, with yellow pigment; and Guanophores, with the metallic, gold or silver, guanin. The pigmentation of a transplanted limb always resembles that of the host, except in transplants involving the white axolotl (Harrison, 1933). There are microscopic differences not only in color of pigment cells, as suggested above, but in their size and shape. Incidental to part "A" of this experiment, the effect of the host on the pigment of the donor limb can be determined in the A. tigrinum and A. punctatum transplants. If the rare white axolotl embryos are available, this experiment would be most graphic and significant.

The pigment cells are derived from the ganglion crest cells which migrate toward the limbs in the earliest motile stage of the embryos (DuShane, 1934). A few xanthophores and melanophores are developed when ectoderm from a normally pigmented embryo is grafted to the limb bud of a white form. This suggests that the white axolotl has the melanophores but that the ectoderm of the white axolotl lacks some of the activating principle which is found in the ectoderm of the pigmented species. DuShane suggests that the ganglion crest gives rise to cells which normally develop pigment and that a second factor (ecto- or mesodermal) is necessary to activate the process. Periclinal and sectorial chimeras often appear. (See section on "Neural Crest Origin of Pigment", page 265.)

XENOPLASTIC LIMB TRANSPLANTATIONS

These are transplantations between different genera and even more distantly related
(or separated) species. Using Amblystoma donors, such transplants may be attempted
to Bufo, Hyla, and Rana. In using Triturus donors, the student should first consult the
work of Twitty (1937), and others, which indicates that Triturus embryos produce a toxin
(from yolk) that paralyzes embryos of other genera. Depending upon the availability of
material, the following are suggested:
  a. Anuran belly ectoderm transplanted over the limb-field of a Urodele.
  b. Urodele limb-field (ecto- and mesoderm) transplanted to the post-gill region an
     Anuran embryo in the tail-bud stage.
  c. Anuran belly ectoderm (stage #16-#17) transplanted for 24 hours over Urodele
     limb-field mesoderm; then re-transplanted along with the urodele mesoderm, to
     the flank region of Urodele embryos. This would clearly demonstrate the rela-
     tion of foreign (xenoplastic) ectoderm and limb mesoderm in the formation of an
     heterotopic limb.

REGENERATION OF THE URODELE LIMB

Newly developing limbs of Urodele larvae have remarkable powers of regeneration.
Amblystoma or Triturus larvae with limbs (stage #38 or older) should be anesthetized in
1/3,000 MS 222 and the digits and limbs cut at various levels and angles, and be allowed
to regenerate. The following factors should be considered:
  a. Whether regenerative potencies can be eliminated by repeated extirpations.
  b. Whether the regenerated portion is structurally identical with that extirpated.
  c. Whether the level of the cut is the controlling factor in degree or perfection of
     regeneration.
  d. Whether regeneration is achieved equally in limbs previously transplanted to
     orthotopic or heterotopic positions.
  e. Whether limb regeneration is controlled by the associated girdle or nerve ele-
     ments.

In order to answer some of the above questions, it will be necessary to acquaint yourself
with the normal development and morphology of the limb and digits of the salamander.
Spalteholtz preparations of limbs and entire larvae should be made. Then, make the
following cuts on appropriate larvae and study the regeneration potencies.
  a. Cut off the right forelimb at the level of the wrist.
  b. Cut off the right forelimb halfway between the wrist and girdle, above the bend
     of the elbow.
  c. Repeat "a" and "b" but make the cuts at the greatest possible angles.
  d. Make transverse cuts at the levels of "a" and "b" but extend the cut only halfway
     through the limb (or wrist), leaving all parts attached.

In each case, make a sketch of the limb and the extent of the cut. When regeneration is
complete, dissect out the parts to demonstrate the details of regeneration or clear the
larva by the Spalteholtz method. This method will show cartilage and bone development
but little information relative to nerve and muscle regeneration.

OBSERVATIONS AND TABULATION OF DATA:

Drawings, photographs, and preserved specimens constitute the record of the above experiments on the limb field. It is most important that detailed records be kept, particularly regarding the age and stage of the donor and of the host, the extent (areal and depth)
of transplants, the angles of cuts, etc. Confirmatory histological analysis is excellent
but is not always necessary. It is more important that the student carries out thoroughly
one of the above procedures rather than to attempt parts of the entire exercise.

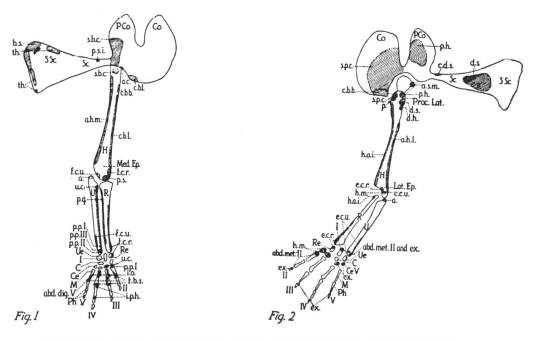

ANTERIOR LIMB AND GIRDLE OF AMBLYSTOMA PUNCTATUM

Fig. 1.   Medial view of the skeleton of the left anterior limb and girdle of Amblystoma punctatum, showing the areas of attachment of the muscles (length 44 mm.).

Fig. 2.   Lateral view of the skeleton of the left anterior limb and girdle of A. punctatum, showing the areas of attachment of the muscles (length 44 mm.).

ABBREVIATIONS USED IN FIGURES 1 AND 2

C, centrale	Ph, phalanges
Ce, carpale	Proc. Lat., lateral process
Co, coracoid	R, radius
H, humerus	Re, radiale
I, intermedium	Sc, scapula
Lat. Ep., lateral epicondyle	SSc, suprascapula
M, metacarpale	U, ulna
Med. Ep., medial Epicondyle	Ue, ulnare
PCo, procoracoid	

From I. W. H. Blount 1935: Jour. Exp. Zool. 69:407

DISCUSSION:

The time at which the antero-posterior axis of the limb field has been irreversibly po-larized has pushed back to the slit blastopore stage (Detwiler, 1933). The dorso-ventral axis undergoes permanent polarization during stages #33 and #34. The relationship of the ectoderm and the mesoderm in partial transplants suggests that the specific form of the limb is probably contained within the mesodermal portion of the limb-field while the ectodermal covering maintains a passive relation to the growth pattern of the underlying mesoderm. The fusion of transplants, splitting and twinning of limbs, altering of axes, and the relation of the girdles all indicate that the fundamental limb forming material is primarily mesodermal.

REFERENCES

ALLEN, B. M. & L. M. EWELL, 1959 - "Resistance to x-irradiation by embryonic cells of the limb buds of tadpoles." Jour. Exp. Zool. 142;309.

ALLEN, B. M. & L. M. EWELL, 1959 - "Resistance to x-irradiation by embryonic cells of the limb buds of tadpoles." UCLA- Gen. 12, 4-44.

BALINSKY, B. I., 1927 - "Xenoplastische Ohrblaschentransplantation zur Frage der Induktion einer Extremitatenanlage." Arch. f. Ent. Mech. 116:63.

BLOUNT, I. W. H., 1935 - "The anatomy of normal and reduplicated limbs in amphibia, with special reference to musculature and vascularization." Jour. Exp. Zool. 69:407.

BRANDT, W., 1940 - "Experimental production of functioning reduplications - a triple and functioning quintuple hindlimb in the frog." Jour. Exp. Biol. 17:396.

BREEDIS, C. 1952 - "Induction of accessory limbs and of sarcoma in the newt (Triturus viridescens) with carcinogenic substances". Cancer Res. 12:861.

BUTLER, E. G. & O. E. SCHOTTE, 1941 - "Histological alterations in denervated nonregenerating limbs of urodele larvae." Jour. Exp. Zool. 88:307.

DETWILER, S. R., 1917 - "On the use of Nile Blue Sulphate in embryonic tissue transplantation." Anat. Rec. 14:493.

DETWILER, S. R., 1933 - "On the time of determination of the anterior-posterior axis of the forelimb of Amblystoma." Jour. Exp. Zool. 54:405.

DETWILER, S. R. & B. L. MacLEAN, 1940 - "Substitution of limbs for brachial somites." Jour. Exp. Zool. 83:445.

FILATOW, D., 1932 - "Entwicklungsbeschleunigung in Abhangigkeit von einer Kunstlichen Vergrosserung der Anlage. Versuche an Amphibienaugen und extremitaten." Zool. Jahrb. 51:589.

FIMIAN, W. J., Jr., 1959 - "Leucocyte infiltration in localized regions of x-rayed amphibian limb tissue." Exp. Cell Res. 16:418.

GLICK, B., 1931 - "The induction of supernumerary limbs in Amblystoma." Anat. Rec. 48:407.

GRAPER, L., 1927 - "Entwicklungsmechanik der Wirbeltierextremitaten." Argebn. d. Anat. u. Entwicklungsgesch. 27:639.

HARRISON, R. G., 1933 - "Heteroplastic grafting in embryology." Harvey Lectures, p. 116.

HOLLINSHEAD, W. H., 1935 - "Determination of the dorso-ventral axis of the forelimb in Amblystoma tigrinum." Jour. Exp. Zool. 73:183.

KIORTSIS, V. & A. DROIN, 1961 - "La Gegeneration caudale des Urodiles". J. Emb. Exp. Morph. 9:77-96.

KORSCHELT, E., 1927 - "Regeneration und Transplantation." Berlin.

KRACZMAR, A. G., 1946 - "The role of amputation and nerve resection in the regressing limbs of Urodele larvae." Jour. Exp. Zool. 103:401.

NICHOLAS, J. S., 1933 - "The correlation of movement and nerve supply in transplanted limbs of Amblystoma." Jour. Comp. Neur. 57:253.

PIATT, J., 1942 - "Transplantation of aneurogenic forelimbs in Amblystoma punctatum." Jour. Exp. Zool. 91:79.

PUCKETT, W. O., 1936 - "The effects of x-irradiation on limb development and regeneration in Amblystoma." Jour. Morph. 59:173.

RAHMANI, T. & V. KIORTSIS, 1961 - "Le role de la peau et des tissus profundsdaus la regeneration de la patte". Rev. Suisse de Zool. 68:91-102.

ROBB, R. C., 1929 - "On the nature of hereditary size limitation. II. The growth of parts in relation to the whole." Brit. Jour. Exp. Biol. 6:311.

SCHOTTE, O. E. & E. G. BUTLER, 1941 - "Morphological effects of denervation and amputation of limbs in urodele larvae." Jour. Exp. Zool. 87:279.

SCHWIND, J. L., 1932 - "Further experiments on limbs containing tissue of two species." Jour. Exp. Zool. 63:365.

STINSON, B. D., 1958 - "Chemical enhancement of radioresistance in regenerating and developing limbs of urodele larvae." Jour. Morph. 103:382-434.

STONE, L. S., 1926 - "Further experiments on the extirpation and transplantation of mesoectoderm in Amblystoma punctatum." Jour. Exp. Zool. 44:95.

STULTZ, W. A., 1936 - "Relations of symmetry in the hind limb of Amblystoma punctatum." Jour. Exp. Zool. 72:317.

SWETT, F. H., 1937 - "Determination of limb-axes." Quart. Rev. Biol. 12:322.

SWETT, F. H., 1945 - "The role of the peribrachial area in the control of reduplication in Amblystoma." Jour. Exp. Zool. 100:67.

TAYLOR, A. C., 1943 - "Development of the innervation pattern in the limb bud of the frog." Anat. Rec. 87:379.

THORNTON, C. S., 1938 - "The histogenesis of the regenerating forelimb of larval Amblystoma after exarticulation of the humerus." Jour. Morph. 62:219.

TRAMPUSCH, H. A. L., 1958 - "The action of x-rays on the morphogenetic field." Koninkl. Nederl. Akad. von Wetenschaften C. 61:417-430.

TWITTY, V. C., 1937 - "Experiments on the phenomenon of paralysis produced by a toxin occurring in Triturus embryos." Jour. Exp. Zool. 76:67.

TWITTY, V. C. & J. L. SCHWIND, 1931 - "The growth of eyes and limbs transplanted heteroplastically between two species of Amblystoma." Jour. Exp. Zool. 59:61.

WADDINGTON, C. H., 1933 - "Heterogony and the chemical ground-plan of animal growth." Nature. 131:134.

WEISS, P., 1935 - "Homologous function of supernumerary limbs after elimination of sensory control." Proc. Soc. Exp. Biol. & Med. 33:30.

WEISS, P. & R. LITWILLER, 1937 - "Quantitative studies on nerve regeneration in Amphibia. II. Innervation of regenerated limbs." Proc. Soc. Exp. Biol. & Med.

WEISS, P., 1939 - "The epigenetic factors in limb regeneration of Amphibia." Current Science, August 1939.

(See also section on "Regeneration")

37. EYE FIELD OPERATIONS

PURPOSE: To determine the anlage for the optico-ocular apparatus; the limits of regeneration of parts of the eye field; the time and extent of self-differentiation; the inductive relations; and the extent of experimentally induced cyclopia.

MATERIALS:
    <u>Biological</u>:   Anuran embryos stages #7 to #17; Urodele embryos stages #11 to #30.
                 For heteroplastic transplantations, use:
                     Rana: catesbiana, palustris, pipiens, and sylvatica.
                     Amblystoma: punctatum and tigrinum.

    <u>Technical</u>:   Standard operating equipment.

METHOD:
    <u>Precautions</u>:
        1. It is important that the student become thoroughly acquainted with the normal development of the eye. This may be accomplished by dissecting living and preserved embryos at the stages listed above.
        2. The usual precautions must be observed for operations (see section on "Wound Healing").
        3. The optimum temperature at which to rear the operated embryos differs for the Anura and Urodela. For the Anura the range is 18°C. to 23°C. and for the Urodela it is about 12°C. to 18°C., depending upon the species.

    <u>Control</u>: For the excision, cauterizing, transplantation, and regeneration experiments the controls will be different. In many instances the untouched (bilateral) side may be considered as the control.

    <u>Procedure</u>:

PRELIMINARY STUDIES ON THE EYE FIELD

It is necessary to give here a brief description of the topography of the eye-forming materials. This is made possible largely by the work of Vogt (1929) in his classical paper on vital staining and mapping of anlagen, from Woerdeman (1929), Manchot (1929), Petersen (1923) and Fischel (1921).

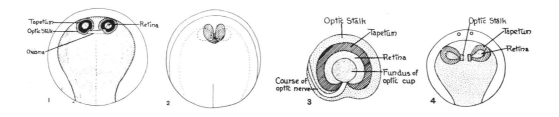

Fig. 1.   Schema of the topographical relations of the eye anlagen ('Augenplatten') in the early neural plate of an axolotl egg. (Copied from Woerdeman, 1929.)

Fig. 2.   Schema of a young urodelan neurula: the cross-hatched territory represents the material for the optic vesicles, optic stalks, and the recessus opticus, the broken line outlines the territory which the same material will occupy in the stage when the neural folds have elevated. (Copied from Manchot, 1929.)

Fig. 3.   Schema of the topography of the optic anlage, according to Peterson, 1923.

Fig. 4.   Schema of the topography of the optic anlagen, according to Fischel, 1921.

From Adelmann 1930: Jour. Exp. Zool. 57:223.

In the Anura the eye forming materials have been localised in the late blastula as lying about 40° to 50° above the equator (see section on "Vital Staining and Morphogenetic Movements"). In the early neurula when the boundaries of the medullary plate are barely discernible, the eye anlagé occupies a circular region with a diameter of about 1/3 the greatest breadth of the neural plate, at its antero-lateral boundary (see diagrams). During the elevation of the neural folds there is a ventro-lateral evagin-ation of the newly formed brain cavity to form the optic ves-icles. A narrow strip of median material separates the two eye anlagé. This median strip forms the chiasma and a por-tion of the lamina terminalis. Actually, therefore, the two eye anlagen are not completely separated.

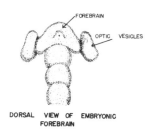

DORSAL VIEW OF EMBRYONIC FOREBRAIN

(Redrawn from Spemann, 1938)

Mangold (1928) found that when the presumptive eye field had been underlain with archenteric roof, as early as the medium sized yolk-plug stage (Anura stage #11 or Urodele stage #15), the field had eye forming potencies when introduced into a younger blastocoele. Mangold (1931) discussed the possible relation of the whole organism, the anlagé itself, and the immediate environment of the anlagé in the segregation of the eye forming potencies. It is one of the purposes of this exercise that the student determine the exact time and ex-tent of the determination and segregation of the eye-forming potencies. There are, how-ever, species differences. (See Glossary for definitions of "double assurance" in rela-tion to Rana esculenta and dependent differentiation.)

Exploratory dissections:
1. Using Anura stages #16 to #18 (or Urodela stages #20 to #30), dissect away the ectoderm of the head region to expose the optic vesicles and the central nervous system. This may be done with living material, or with formalin-hardened specimens.
2. Anesthetize Anuran stages #21 and older (or corresponding Urodele embryos) in 1/3,000 MS 222 (or 0.04% chloretone) and dissect out the entire optico-ocular apparatus. Note the po-sition and state of development of the lens. The larger tadpoles should be pinned down to a Per-moplast base and covered with lens paper (except for the head).
3. Remove the lens of later stages as follows. Pierce the skin in front of and ventral to the eye with a sharp glass needle, push the nee-dle backward or upward between the eye and the cornea parallel to the cornea. Pierce again at the posterior or upper margin of the eye. Cut the cornea by inserting the needle beneath it and rubbing a scalpel against it. Take two small but unequal sized hair loops and pass them over the lens, from opposite sides, and then pull them apart. In this manner the lens will be cleanly removed (as with scissors) with minimum of damage to the other parts of the eye.

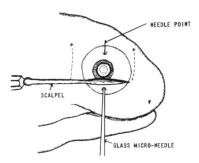

METHOD OF CUTTING THE CORNEA TO RE-MOVE THE LENS FROM THE AMPHIBIAN EYE TO TEST FOR WOLFFIAN (LENS) REGENERATION

(Needle is inserted through cornea on one side of the iris, passed between the cornea and the side of the iris. The needle is lifted against the cornea, and a sharp scalpel is then scraped against the needle, pro-viding a cutting edge to cut a slit in the cornea.)

4. In a somewhat similar manner, but with scissors, remove the entire eye
    ball of adult frogs or salamanders. Such hemorrhage as occurs is generally
    not of any serious consequence (see diagram of adult eye).

RANA PIPIENS

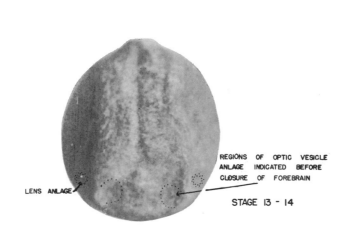

REGIONS OF OPTIC VESICLE
ANLAGE INDICATED BEFORE
CLOSURE OF FOREBRAIN

LENS ANLAGE

STAGE 13 - 14

OPTIC PROTUBERANCE

STAGE 17
(34 HRS. LATER)

DEFECT EXPERIMENTS

A. Excisions:* (See papers by Adelmann)
    1. Anura (stage #14) or Urodela (stage #15)
        a. Study the schematized diagram on the following page of a neurula showing
            the limits of the eye field. Remove the ectoderm only from either area
            "A" or area "B".
        b. Remove ectoderm and substrate (mesentoderm) from the same area
            ("A" or "B") of another neurula.
        c. Remove ectoderm only from area "C".

* See section on "Wound Healing" for details of post-operative care.

    d.   Remove ectoderm and substrate (mesentoderm) from area "C".
    e.   Remove the entire area "A - C - B", ectoderm only.
    f.   Remove the entire area "A - C - B", ectoderm and substrate (mesento-
        derm).

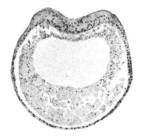

Camera-lucida drawing of a section through the prechordal region of an Amblystoma neurula (Harrison stage #15). The mesoderm has just begun to separate from the lateral portion of the roof of the archenteron. This gives an idea as to the distribution of the (mesentoderm) substrate referred to in the excision experiments.

Drawing from Adelmann 1930: Jour. Exp. Zool. 57:223.

2.   <u>Anura</u>* (stage #16 or #17) or Urodela (stage #21 to #25)
    a.   Remove the ectoderm only from over the right optic vesicle.
    b.   Remove the ectoderm and the optic vesicle from the right side.

Diagram, showing in stipple the area which it is necessary to remove in order to prevent completely the formation of an eye on the operated side.

From Adelmann 1929: Jour. Exp. Zool. 54:249

    c.   Insert a sharp operating (glass) needle, beneath the ectoderm and, with
        an up-lifting movement, cut the ectoderm along the dorsal, posterior,
        and ventral margins of a rectangular area which includes the entire eye
        field. This will provide a flap of ectoderm, with an anterior hinge. De-
        flect this flap forward, and with a stiff hair loop, scoop out the entire
        optic vesicle from beneath. Replace the ectodermal flap and allow it to
        heal in place. If the excavation is so extensive that there is no base upon
        which the ectoderm can lie, fill in the hole with yolk from another embryo.

B. <u>Cauterization</u>:
    Using a heated and slightly bent needle, attempt to cauterize the entire optic-
    ocular primordia on one side, as indicated in the accompanying diagrams. It
    may be necessary to dip the needle into glycerine to prevent the hot needle from
    drawing out some of the cellular contents of the neurula. The entire anlagé may
    be found both within and without the medullary plate area. This is a delicate
    operation and there will be high mortality, but the results (if the operation is
    properly executed) will be very significant.

When the embryos have reached the external gill stage, fix them in 10% formaldehyde and dissect out the optico-ocular apparatus to compare it with the controls. During the healing and early development of the excised areas, macroscopic examinations and records should be made. (See Glossary on "Double Assurance". This does not hold for Rana sylvatica, Rana palustris, Rana catesbiana or Amblystoma maculatum.)

---

* Rana sylvatica or Rana palustris are better for this than is Rana pipiens.

EYE FIELD OPERATIONS

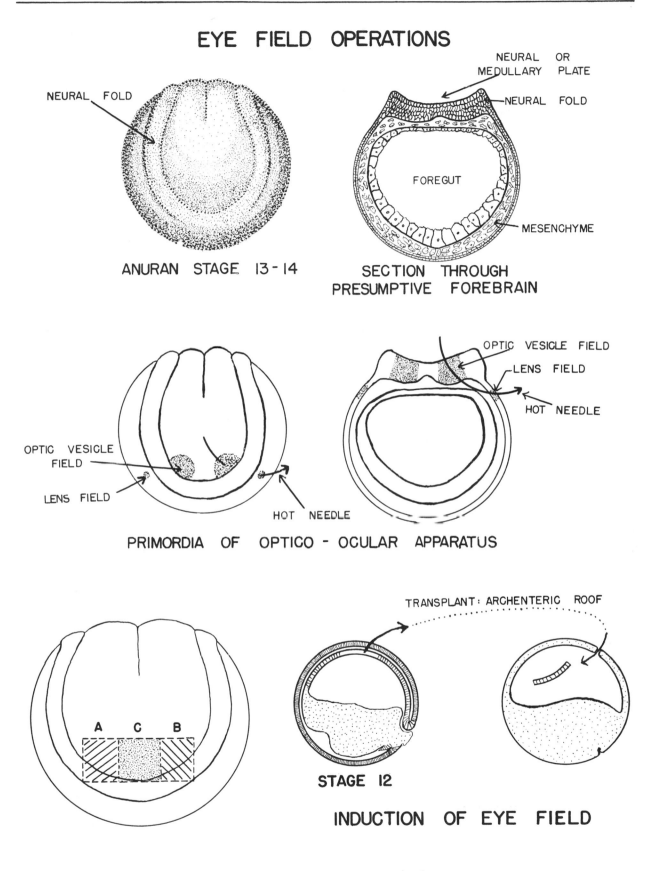

NEURAL OR
MEDULLARY PLATE

NEURAL FOLD

NEURAL FOLD

FOREGUT

MESENCHYME

ANURAN STAGE 13-14

SECTION THROUGH
PRESUMPTIVE FOREBRAIN

OPTIC VESICLE FIELD

LENS FIELD

HOT NEEDLE

OPTIC VESICLE
FIELD

LENS FIELD

HOT NEEDLE

PRIMORDIA OF OPTICO - OCULAR APPARATUS

TRANSPLANT: ARCHENTERIC ROOF

A   C   B

STAGE 12

INDUCTION OF EYE FIELD

(REDRAWN FROM SPEMANN '38)

SELF-DIFFERENTIATION OF THE EYE ANLAGE

Consult the exercise on "The Culturing of Isolated Amphibian Anlagé" for the description of the basic procedure necessary for this part of the exercise.

Isolate and attempt to culture the same areas used in the "Defect Experiments" (above).

The degree of self-differentiation is indicated by the degree of independent development in isolation culture. This part of the exercise should inform the student as to just when the lens and the vesicle (retina, etc.) are "self-differentiated".

EYE INDUCTIONS

This is an extremely delicate operation (Mangold, 1931) and should be attempted by only those students who have proven their skill in operative procedures.

Gastrulae (Anura stages #10 and #12) are decapsulated. The donor (stage #12) is dissected so as to expose the most anterior portion of the archenteric roof. This material is excised in one piece and is quickly inserted through the blastocoelic roof of the younger (stage #10) gastrula (see diagrams). If the normal "inductive" (see Glossary) influences are exerted on the overlying ectoderm of the blastocoelic roof, accessory optic structures will be formed. (See exercise on "The Organizer" for procedures.)

TRANSPLANTATIONS

Under this heading will be included the simpler transplantations of optic cup and/or lens primordium in order to determine their interrelationship in the normal development of the eye as a whole. There will also be included the homoplastic, heteroplastic, and xenoplastic transplantations of larval eyes.

LENS INDUCTION: (See Stone & Dinnean 1940 and Liedke 1942)
1. Remove the presumptive lens ectoderm from over the optic vesicle or cup of Anuran stage #16 or #17, (Urodela stages #21 to #26)* without injuring the underlying structures. Quickly excise a slightly larger piece of belly ectoderm from another embryo, of the same stage previously stained with Nile Blue Sulphate. Place it over the exposed optic vesicle. Gently pat it into place and, if necessary, hold it in place with a Brücke, lens paper, or piece of coverslip. It should heal within 20 to 30 minutes. (See section on "Wound Healing".)
2. Remove the ectoderm from over the optic vesicle of Anuran stage #17 (Urodela stages #21 to #26)*. Prepare a host embryo (of the same stage) by making a deep pit ventral to the somites at about the mid-body region, leaving the flap of ectoderm over the pit intact. (See A-2-c under "Defect Experiments" on the preceding page.) Quickly cut out the optic vesicle of the donor and transfer it to the excavated pit of the host. Orient the vesicle in the same position as in the donor, i.e., with the bulbous part of the vesicle facing outward. Replace the ectodermal flap over the transplanted optic vesicle, and hold it in place with Brücke until healed.

These two experiments are reciprocally related. Part 1 will indicate whether foreign (non-presumptive) ectoderm will respond to inductive influences from the intact optic vesicle and Part 2 will indicate whether the optic vesicle, transplanted to a foreign site, can there induce a lens in the overlying (foreign) ectoderm. All such embryos should be allowed to progress to the external gill stage before dissection analysis.

* After Urodele stage #26 (Anura stage #17) the potential lens forming ectoderm becomes adherent to the underlying optic cup, and cannot be completely removed. The older embryos can be anesthetized in MS 222.

TRANSPLANTATIONS:

TRANSPLANTING THE ANLAGÉ

When the anlagé is transplanted to a slightly older host, the conditions for the expression of any self-differentiation are somewhat different from those of an isolation culture. However, the nutritive factors are generally the more favorable, and axial relations can be determined. These operations are best on Urodele embryos. *

1. Decapsulate some Urodele embryos in stage #14, and locate the eye field at the anterior limit of the medullary plate (see figure on following page). Stain the entire donor in 1/500, 000 Nile Blue Sulphate.
2. Prepare host larvae by excising the ectoderm, mesoderm and some of the underlying yolk on the lateral belly region of stage #24 or #25 (see figures below). The prepared wound should be slightly larger than the prospective graft.
3. On the point of a needle transfer from the stained donor
    a. The right optic anlagé
    b. The median transverse neural fold and medullary plate
    c. The entire (anterior) optic anlagé (A-C-B in figure above)
    on the prepared host sites. Hold in place with Brücke, or by hand, for a few minutes until the graft becomes adherent. The vital dye will indicate the limits of the graft.

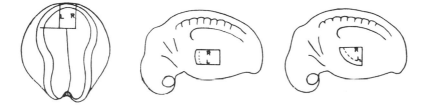

Schema of a typical experiment, showing the relations of
the transplanted median and left lateral strips of neural
plate and their orientation in the hosts. R, right; L, left.

From Adelmann 1930: Jour. Exp. Zool. 57:223.

By recording the exact shape of the graft at the time of excision, it will be possible to record the axial relations of the graft in the host site.

TRANSPLANTING THE OPTIC VESICLE AND LENS ECTODERM

The most complete study of heteroplastic eye transplantations has been made by Harrison (1929) and recently Eakin and Harris (1945) have determined the degree and onset of tissue incompatibility in xenoplastic transplants using the eye as the test object. As with other organ anlagen, eye transplants between the various species of Amblystoma are most successful and instructive. Since there are intrinsic differences in growth rate, these become exaggerated in such heteroplastic transplants.

Harrison (1929) pointed out that homotopic transplantations (in order to produce functional eyes) will succeed best at stages #27 to #29 at which time the vesicle is well marked off from the stalk and mortality is consequently lower. If, however, it is desired that the mesodermal and mesectodermal tissues be eliminated from the study, he suggests using stage #21, just after the closure of the neural folds. In any case, after making a circular

* Follow the standard operative procedures described elsewhere. See Schwind (1937) for results with the Anura.

incision around the eye region the optic vesicle at stage #21 (or cup at stage #28) is readily separated from its surroundings and the optic stalk may be cut close to its origin from the brain. The whole may then be removed without disturbing any of the adjacent mesodermal (mandibular arch) or mesectodermal (ganglion crest) structures. When reciprocal transplants are made it must be remembered that the eye vesicle of the A. punctatum

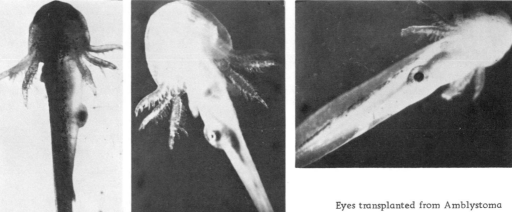

Eyes transplanted from Amblystoma
tigrinum to the belly region of
Amblystoma punctatum at stage #29.

(From Detwiler 1945: Jour.
Comp. Neur. 82:145)

Amblystoma eye transplanted
to the region of the ear.

embryo, at comparable early stages, is much larger than that of A. tigrinum. In consequence it is more difficult to place the punctatum graft in the A. tigrinum host than vice versa. The A. tigrinum optic vesicle, at a comparable stage, is smaller than that of A. punctatum, but it grows more rapidly and soon surpasses the A. punctatum eye in size (see illustrations from Harrison's paper).

    <u>Procedure:</u>* (Transplants between A. punctatum and A. tigrinum embryos or from
        A. mexicanum to A. punctatum stages #27 to #29.)
        1. First attempt to transplant the entire optic vesicle with overlying ectoderm
            from one species (Amblystoma) to another into an heterotopic region, i.e.,
            to the lateral belly region. (See photographs.)
        2. When "1" has been accomplished, transplant the entire optic vesicle and overlying ectoderm of another donor to the excavated optic region of another host
            (homotopic and heteroplastic transplant). It would be best to make the first
            attempts from A. tigrinum to A. punctatum.

---

* Follow the usual operative procedures described elsewhere.

3. Make the reciprocal transplant indicated in "2", i.e., from A. punctatum to
    A. tigrinum, including the entire optic vesicle and overlying lens ectoderm.
4. Make a large "U" shaped incision through the ectoderm covering the optic
    vesicle of A. punctatum at stage #27, with the open end of the "U" (uncut
    margin) toward the anterior, remaining as a hinge. Deflect this flap of ecto-
    derm forward, and scoop out the optic vesicle, cutting it at the origin from
    the brain. Quickly remove the overlying ectoderm from a donor embryo op-
    tic vesicle (same stage but either A. tigrinum or A. mexicanum) and cut it
    out without damage. Place it in the previously prepared host region, beneath
    the flap of host ectoderm. So far as possible attempt to orient the donor
    optic vesicle in the same position as the original host vesicle.

WOLFFIAN REGENERATION

This term is derived from the work of Wolff who, in 1895, found that when he removed
the lens from the eye of the European Triton that a new lens would regenerate. Such regeneration is presumed to occur from the dorsal rim of the iris by a budding process and
has been demonstrated for a large group of Urodeles, with but few exceptions. Its occurrence among the Anura is questioned. Among the Urodeles it has been described for
Triturus taeniatus, T. cristatus, Salamandra and the Axolotl (Wachs, 1914); for Triturus
viridescens (Stone and Chace, 1941); for Triturus torosus (Dinnean, 1942); for Amblystoma tigrinum up to stage #43 (Ballard, 1936). It has also been seen in Amblystoma
jeffersonianum, A. microstomum, and A. opacum as well as in the Japanese fire salamander, Triturus pyrrhogaster. In fact, Triturus (of all species) seems the most reliable, Amblystoma undependable, and the Anura generally negative.

1. Select larvae of A. tigrinum (up to stage #43), A. opacum, or any species of
    Triturus. The operation should be performed on a minimum of 10 specimens,
    all of the same age and stage.
2. Anesthetize the larva in 1/3,000 MS 222 (or 0.04% chloretone) and place it in a
    Permoplast depression made to fit so that the larva lies on its side.
3. Fasten the larval body into position with strips of lens paper held to the Permo-
    plast with insect pins.
4. To remove the lens from the right eye use a sharply-tapered glass needle (strong
    and pointed) and pierce the cornea at one side and run the needle beneath the cor-
    nea, across the lens, and out through the far side of the cornea. Avoid injury to
    the underlying lens. Gently scrape a sharp scalpel against the cornea, over the
    needle, thereby using the two instruments to cut through the cornea.
5. The lens is generally glass-clear. After separating the lens from the iris, with
    the glass needle, pick the lens out with #5 watchmaker's forceps. If this proves
    difficult, it may be possible to reach under the lens with the glass needle and lift
    it out. There should be no hemorrhage. Specimens in which the retina is injured
    should be discarded. The slit in the cornea will close and heal by itself. Healing
    is most rapid in bicarbonate-free Standard or Growing Medium. Examine the re-
    moved lens under the microscope. Keep the operated larvae in separate, prop-
    erly marked, finger bowls at controlled temperatures.
6. At weekly intervals anesthetize the operated larvae and examine the eye for signs
    of regeneration. Note changes in the pupil immediately after the operation and
    at regular intervals of 3 to 4 days thereafter. These changes are indicative of
    changes in respect to the lens within.
7. After one month, during which the larvae are maximally fed, they should be fixed
    in 10% formaldehyde and the eyes dissected. The unoperated eye may be consid-
    ered as the control. Estimate the ratio of the diameter of the lens against the
    diameter of the eye, for both the control and the operated sides, to determine the
    degree of regeneration.
8. If there are abundant larvae, the progress of Wolffian regeneration can be best
    studied by sectioning the eyes at 4 to 5 day intervals after the operation.

There has been considerable discussion, in recent years, about the possibility and the method of lens regeneration in later larval stages (Schotté and Hummel, 1939 and Stone and Sapir, 1940). The latter authors investigated Urodeles, Anura, and Fish, all of which were at least 25 and many as much as 80 mm. in length, and they came to the conclusion that at these advanced stages the rim of the iris does not possess the power to regenerate a new lens. In fact, there is evidence of species variation at the earlier larval stages for Stone and Dinnean (1940) found no Wolffian regeneration in A. punctatum at any time. Stone and Sapir (1940) state: "Among the Triturus this unique phenomenon has been proved beyond all doubt. It opens up an interesting field of study to determine more clearly what factors inhibit and release the regeneration of a lens from the rim of the iris in this group of salamanders."

ENUCLEATION AND PIGMENTARY RESPONSES

Scharrer (1932) in reference to salamander larvae, stated that ". . . . in addition to sight and smell, the lateral line sense organs may play a role in obtaining food" and Nicholas (1922) claimed that in the absence of the eyes, the sense of smell became paramount in the feeding reaction as evidenced by the animal's positive response to substances diffusing in the water. Detwiler and Copenhaver (1940) state: "We wish to emphasize the fact that in the absence of both the eyes and the nasal placodes the larvae feed as well as do the normal animals." Utilizing these facts, it is possible to enucleate (i. e., remove the eyes) Amblystoma larvae (stages #25 to #27) and rear them on Enchytrea (white worms) in light, darkness, and even under various concentrations of monochromatic lighting, to determine the relation of the eyes to both growth and pigmentary responses of the skin.

1. Enucleate Amblystoma larvae (stages #25 to #27) and keep them in adequate aquaria for 3 to 4 days in order to select those individuals which survived the operation most satisfactorily. If necessary, anesthetize them, before enucleation, in 1/3,000 MS 222.

2. Prepare a completely darkened environment (e. g., photographic dark room) but one in which the temperature does not vary from that of the light environment. This may require the circulation of air with a fan, for any dark cover will absorb radiant energy more rapidly than a light colored cover. The temperature must be checked at least once daily. Another and most satisfactory method is to coat the outside (sides and bottom) of finger bowls with flat black paint, and provide an overlapping black-painted cover. These darkened finger bowls, along with the controls (unpainted finger bowls), can then be kept together in a constant-temperature water bath. Daylight (but not sunlight) should be provided. If this is not possible, controlled artificial light (without heat) should be provided.

3. Place in each of 10 blackened finger bowls a single enucleated Amblystoma with 50 cc. of growing medium. Place in each of 10 more blackened finger bowls a single normal (unoperated) Amblystoma.

4. In a similar manner prepare 10 unpainted finger bowls, placing in each a single enucleated Amblystoma and in each of 10 more unpainted finger bowls, place a single normal (unoperated) Amblystoma.

5. All 40 finger bowls should be kept at the same temperature. The water should be changed on alternate days. The young larvae may be fed first on small Daphnia and, as they grow, on small and finally on large Enchytreid worms. The feeding should be identical for all larvae, experimentals and controls, in dark and in light.

6. The darkened animals may be changed and fed in a photographic darkroom, with a very dim red (photographic) light, in minimum time. The quickest procedure is to pour the larva and medium through a coarse sieve, to eliminate faecal material.

6. Keep the larvae to the time of metamorphosis (50 to 60 days), using this change as one criterion of growth rate. Measurements of all larvae should be taken at

bi-weekly intervals, and notations made on general coloration. Measurements can be made rapidly by pasting millimeter graph paper on the underside of a flat-bottomed finger bowl (or Petri dish) into which the larva is placed for a quick total length measurement.

If facilities and time allow, there are other variables to this experiment:

1. Instead of using a black-painted cover for the darkened finger bowls, cover them with glass (of Wratten celluloid) color filters which allows various monochromatic radiations through to the larvae to determine the relative value of parts of the spectrum in pigmentary response.
2. The eyes may be removed and transplanted to heterotopic positions, where they do not acquire nerve connections with the central nervous system, to determine whether they then function in pigmentary response.
3. The dark and light-adjusted enucleated (and normal) larvae may be transferred to the opposite environment (dark to light and vice versa) to determine the degree of adaptability (adjustment) in respect to a definite time interval. (Detwiler & Copenhaver in 1942 state that dark-adapted eyeless larvae are pale but darken in moderate lighting, while dark-adapted normal larvae tend to become lighter colored in moderate lighting.)

The conclusions from this set of observations should relate both the growth rate and to the pigmentary responses of eyeless larvae.

THE EXPERIMENTAL PRODUCTION OF CYCLOPIA

Adelmann (1936) states: "The hope of one day attaining an adequate understanding of cyclopia is considerably strengthened by two important considerations, first, the fact that the anomaly may be experimentally produced with considerable ease, and secondly, the fact that experimentally produced cyclopean monsters exhibit essentially the same features as those spontaneously arising." Stockard (1907 to 1910) produced cyclopean fish with various concentrations of $NaCl$, $LiCl$, $NaOH$, and amyl alcohol. Others have used acetone, and butyric alcohol and even physical variables. Amphibian cyclopean monsters have been produced by treating the eggs with lithium chloride, ethyl alcohol, chloralhydrate (LePlat, 1919, Cotronei, 1922, Guareschi, 1934, and Adelmann, 1934) phenol and chloretone (Lehmann, 1933).

Cyclopia can also be produced by surgical interference with early cleavage stages up to gastrulation, by constriction (Spemann, 1904), and by excision of parts of the archenteric roof (Mangold, 1931).

The experimental procedure is in general to expose the early blastula of any Amphibian to from 0.2% to 1.0% LiCl for periods up to 24 hours, then returning them to normal medium whereupon many of the surviving embryos will develop cyclopia. The effect is essentially one of vegetalization. Since the procedure is described in detail under "The Chemical Separation of Growth and Development" it will not be further discussed here.

DISCUSSION:

The embryonic eye is made up of two major parts, each of which originates from the ectoderm. The optical vesicle is the first to develop, being an evagination from the diencephalon. When this brain ectoderm makes contact with the overlying head ectoderm it "induces" the thickening of this ectoderm to form the lens placode. (See exception under the term "double assurance" in the Glossary.) This placode then invaginates to form a lens vesicle which becomes incorporated into the developing optic cup. The head ectoderm (from which the lens was derived) then closes over the lens to form the ectodermal portion of the (transparent) cornea. In the meantime mesenchyme (mesoderm) invades the whole eye structure, to give rise to the blood vessels, connective tissue, and finally the muscles of the eye.

That the mesentodermal substrate has something to do with the development of the eye field has been demonstrated (Adelmann, 1937). This eye-field is determined prior to the closure of the neural folds, as proven by excision and transplantation experiments.

In the heteroplastic and homotopic eye transplantations involving A. punctatum, A. tigrinum, and A. mexicanum (the axolotl) Harrison (1929) has demonstrated that the velocity of growth and, to a certain extent, the ultimate size of the eyes are due to intrinsic (genetic) factors of the donor tissues. The tigrinum eyes in punctatum hosts often exceeded the donor control eyes, and the punctatum eyes in tigrinum hosts often were smaller than the control eyes, explained by Harrison as due to factors in the circulating medium of the host which affected the growth rate of the graft. The form and function of the grafted eyes appeared to be quite normal. Even the intrinsic tendencies of the lens and/or the optic vesicles were maintained when in grafts, when they were from different genetic sources. In all cases where the optic nerve failed to connect, there was marked hypoplasia of the wall of the midbrain on the opposite side.

Schwind (1937) has shown that heteroplastic eye grafts between three species of Rana invariably failed to develop. Eakin and Harris (1945) used the optic vesicle as a test object in some xenoplastic transplantations between Urodele donors and Anuran hosts. Grafts from Triturus or Amblystoma donors to Hyla hosts never survived for very long, and were eventually destroyed, generally within a week. They state that "Incompatability between host and xenoplastic transplant is regarded as a humoral and cellular antagonism of the host in response to alien substances which diffuse out of the graft into the body of the host."

That the eyes have not lost their power of adjustment has been demonstrated recently by Stone and his co-workers (Stone & Ellison, 1945) by the exchanging of eyes between adult salamanders of different species. There is apparently a regression of the morphology and physiology of the eye and a recovery of both the normal structure and function, even in the adult eyes.

REFERENCES

ADELMANN, H. B., 1936 - "The problem of cyclopia." Quart. Rev. Biol. 11:161 & 284.

ADELMANN, H. B., 1937 - "Experimental studies on the development of the eye. IV. The effect of the partial and complete excision of the prechordal substrate on the development of eyes of Amblystoma punctatum." Jour. Exp. Zool. 75:199.

ALDERMAN, A. L., 1938 - "A factor influencing the bilaterality of the eye rudiment in Hyla regilla." Anat. Rec. 72:297.

BALLARD, W. W., 1939 - "Mutual size regulation between eyeball and lens in Amblystoma, studied by means of heteroplastic transplantation." Jour. Exp. Zool. 81:261.

DETWILER, S. R., 1944 - "Behavior of Amblystoma larvae lacking in forebrain, eyes, and nasal placodes." Proc. Soc. Exp. Biol. & Med. 56:195.

DETWILER, S. R. & W. M. COPENHAVER, 1942 - "Further experiments dealing with embryonic enucleation in Amblystoma." Proc. Soc. Exp. Biol. & Med. 51:334.

DINNEAN, F. L., 1942 - "Lens regeneration from iris and its inhibition by lens reimplantation in Triturus torosus larvae." Jour. Exp. Zool. 90:461.

DRAGOMIROV, W., 1935 - "Determination des Augenkeimes bei Amphibien." Acad. Sci. d. Ukraine, Trav. Inst. Zool. et Biol. 8:25 (see also 1933 Arch. f. Ent. Mech. 129:522).

FILATOW, D., 1937 - "Uber die Linseninudzierung nach Entfernung des Chorda-mesoderms bei Rana temporaria." Zool. Jarb. Abt. allg. Zool. u. Physiol. 58:1.

GREENE, W. F. & H. LAURENS, 1923 - "The effect of extirpation of the embryonic ear and eye on equilibration in Amblystoma punctatum." Am. Jour. Physiol. 64:120.

HALL, T. S., 1942 - "The mode of action of lithium salts in amphibian development." Jour. Exp. Zool. 89:1.

HANDFORD, S. W., 1945 - "The relation of age and temperature to the relative growth of the eyes of Amblystoma." Jour. Exp. Zool. 98:127.

HARRISON, R. G., 1929 - "Correlations in the development and growth of the eye studied by means of heteroplastic transplantation." Arch. f. Ent. Mech. 120:1.

HARRISON, R. G., 1933 - "Some difficulties of the determination problem." Am. Nat. 68:306.

HEWITT, D. C., 1934 - "Xenoplastic transplantation of amphibian eye rudiments." Jour. Exp. Zool. 69:235.

HOLTFRETER, J., 1935 - "Uber das Verhalten von Anurenektoderm in Urodelenkeimes." Arch. f. Ent. Mech. 133:427.

JACOBSON, A. G., 1958 - "The roles of neural and non-neural Tissues in lens induction." Jour. Exp. Zool. 139:525.

KOLLROS, J. J., 1943 - "Experimental studies on the development of the corneal reflex in amphibia. III. The influence of the periphery upon the reflex center." Jour. Exp. Zool. 92:121.

LEHMANN, F. E., 1934 - "Die Linsenbildung von Rana fusca in ihrer Abhangigkeit von chemischen Einflussen." Arch. f. Ent. Mech. 131:333.

LEPLAT, G., 1919 - "Action du milieu sur le developpement des larves d'amphibiens. Localisation et differentiation des premiers ebauches oculaires chez les vertebres. Cyclopie et Anophthalmie." Arch. de Biol. 30:231.

LIEDKE, K. B., 1942 - "Lens competence in Rana pipiens." Jour. Exp. Zool. 90:331.

LOPASCHOV, G. V., 1936 - "Eye-inducing substances." Biol. Zhurn. 5.

MANCHOT, E., 1929 - "Abgrenzung des Augenmaterials und anderer Teilbezirhe in der Medullarplatte." Arch. f. Ent. Mech. 116:689.

MANGOLD, O., 1931 - "Das Determinationsporblem. 3. Teil. Das Wirbeltierauge in der Entwicklung und Regeneration." Ergebnisse des Biol. 7:193.

MANUILOWA, N. A. & M. N. KISLOW, 1934 - "Uber die Einwirkung des Augenbechers auf das ventrale und determinierte Epithel bei Amphibien bei Hom- und Heterotransplantationen." Zool. Jarhb. Abt. f. Allgem. Zool. 53:521.

MIKAMI, Y., 1938 - "Experiments on the formation of free lenses in Triturus pyrrhogaster with special reference to Harrison's experimental results in Amblystoma." Proc. Imp. Acad. Tokyo. 14:195.

NICHOLAS, J. S., 1930 - "Movements in transplanted limbs innervated by eye muscle nerves." Anat. Rec. 45:234.

OKADA, Y. K. & Y. MIKAMI, 1937 - "Inductive effects of tissues other than retina on the presumptive lens epithelium." Proc. Imp. Acad. Tokyo. 13:283.

PATCH, E. M., 1941 - "Cataracts in Amblystoma tigrinum larvae fed experimental diets." Proc. Soc. Exp. Biol. & Med. 46:205.

PERRI, E., 1934 - "Ricerche sul compartamento dell'abbozzo oculare di Anfibi in conicioni di espianto." Arch. f. Ent. mech. 131:113.

PIATT, J., 1941 - "Grafting of limbs in place of the eye in Amblystoma." Jour. Exp. Zool. 86:77.

POPOFF, W. M., 1937 - "Uber den morphogenen Einfluss des Augenbechers auf verschiedene emnryonale Gewebe und auf die Anlage einiger Organe." Zool. Jahrb. 58.

REYER, R. W., 1948 - "An experimental study of lens regeneration in Triturus viridescens." Jour. Exp. Zool. 107. (See also Quart. Rev. Biol. 29:1-41, 1954)

SATO, T., 1940 - "Vergleichende Studien uber die Geschwindigkeit der Wilff'schen Linsenregeneration bei Triton taeniatus und bei Diemyctylus pyrrhogaster." Arch. f. Ent. Mech. 140:570.

SCHOTTE, O. E. & K. P. HUMMEL, 1939 - "Lens induction at the expense of regenerating tissues of amphibians." Jour. Exp. Zool. 80:131.

SCHWIND, J. L., 1937 - "Tissue reactions after homoplastic and heteroplastic transplantation of eyes in the anuran amphibia." Jour. Exp. Zool. 77:87.

SPERLING, F., 1943 - "Extra-epidermal and supernumerary lenses in association with cyclopean eyes in Amblystoma embryos." Anat. Rec. 85:413.

STONE, L. S., 1945 - "Heteroplastic lens grafts related to factors inhibiting lens regeneration in Triturus." Proc. Soc. Exp. Biol. & Med. 60:10.

STONE, L. S. & F. L. DINNEAN, 1940 - "Experimental studies on the relation of the optic vesicle and cup to lens formation in Amblystoma punctatum." Jour. Exp. Zool. 83:95.

STONE, L. S. & P. SAPIR, 1940 - "Experimental studies on the regeneration of the lens in the eyes of anurans, urodeles, and fishes." Jour. Exp. Zool. 85:71.

STONE, L. S., 1959 - "Regeneration of the retina, iris, and lens." in "Regeneration in Vertebrates" Thornton (ed.), Univ. Ch Chicago Press.

TEN CATE, C., 1956 - "The intrinsic embryonic development." Verh. Konerigl. Nederl. Akad. Wetensch. 51:1.

TWITTY, V. C. & H. A. ELLIOTT, 1934 - "The relative growth of the amphibian eye, studied by means of transplantation." Jour. Exp. Zool. 68:247.

WADDINGTON, C. H., 1936 - "The origin of competence for lens formation in the amphibia." Jour. Exp. Biol. 13.

WARREN, A. E., 1939 - "Observations on limb development in Rana sylvatica following unilateral eye extirpation." Arch. f. Ent. Mech. 139:50.

WOLFF, G., 1895 - "Entwicklungsphysiologische Studien. I. Die Regeneration der Urodelenlinse." Arch. f. Ent. Mech. 1:380.

WOERDEMANN, M. W., 1929 - "Experimentelle Untersuchungen über Lage und Bau der augenbildenden Bezirke in der Medullarplatte beim Axolotl." Arch. f. Ent. Mech. 116:220.

ZALOKAR, M., 1944 - "Contribution à l'etude de la régénération du cristallin chez le Triton." Rev. Suisse de Zool. 51:443.

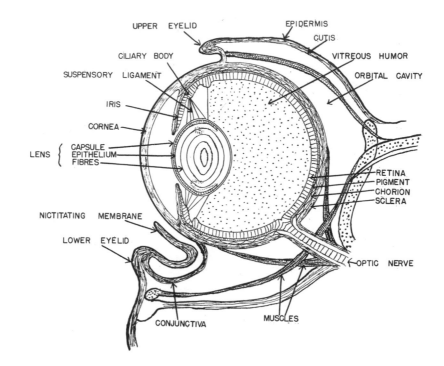

UPPER EYELID
EPIDERMIS
CUTIS
CILIARY BODY
VITREOUS HUMOR
SUSPENSORY LIGAMENT
ORBITAL CAVITY
IRIS
CORNEA
LENS { CAPSULE
EPITHELIUM
FIBRES
RETINA
PIGMENT
CHORION
SCLERA
NICTITATING MEMBRANE
LOWER EYELID
OPTIC NERVE
CONJUNCTIVA
MUSCLES

SCHEMATIC DIAGRAM THROUGH FROG'S EYE
(Redrawn from Mangold 1931)

"It might be wise to review Spemann's 1938 Silliman Lectures and ponder on some of his statements of fact before proceeding to the chaotic condition through which the successive experiments have led. Certainly to Spemann there was a continuity in development which he rejoiced to describe in oversimplified anthropomorphic terms. To him development was a continuum which had to be described in stepwise fashion. This was for convenience only and not because he considered the embryo to be developing and differentiating through active and inactive periods of response. His whole research career was founded on asking the embryo simple questions which are experimentally and intellectually possible of solution."

J. S. Nicholas 1960

38. HEART FIELD OPERATIONS

PURPOSE: By excising, transplanting, and blocking the fusion of the bilateral primordia, to determine the mode of heart formation.

MATERIALS:

Biological: Anura stages #15-#17: Urodela stages #22-#25, and #34-#38.

Technical: Standard Equipment

METHOD:

Precautions:

1. Carry out several exploratory dissections of embryos to determine the color and the extent of heart mesenchyme concerned in the later operations.
2. Alcohol sterilization of operating instruments will lessen mortality which is generally high in heart field operations.
3. Operations on Anura should be in full strength Standard Solution and on Urodela in Operating Medium. Following recovery from the operation, return the embryos to appropriate culture media.
4. The post-operated embryos should be kept at constant and low temperatures, Anura from 15°C. to 18°C., and Urodela from 10°C. to 15°C.

Control:

1. For the excision experiments, excision of mesoderm from any other region.
2. For production of double hearts by heart block, the same operation should be performed but no mesenchyme is removed and no block is introduced.
3. For heteroplastic transplantations, similar transplantations of somite mesoderm constitute the control condition.
4. For isolation culture, the isolation of somite mesoderm would constitute the control.

Procedure:

EXCISION OF PART OF THE HEART FIELD

At Anuran stage #16 and Urodele stage #23 the lateral mesoderm is converging from the two sides around the pharynx to form the single ventral heart (see diagrams). If the material of one of the lateral plates is excised, the formation of a normal, single tubular heart by the bilateral rudiments is prevented.

Outline and peel back the ectoderm over the heart field derived from the right side after placing the embryo in a shallow depression in Permoplast, in Operating Medium (Urodele) or in full strength Standard Solution (Anura). Leave a hinge of ectoderm for attachment so that it can be replaced over the wound. With a hair loop and micro-pipette scoop out all visible mesoderm from the one side. The mesoderm is clear white and granular. Replace the ectodermal flap. If the ectoderm is insufficient, graft some indifferent ectoderm from the lateral body wall and from a posterior position of another embryo. Lay a piece of moist lens paper over the wound for 20 to 30 minutes and, after complete healing, return the embryo to the normal culture medium either in a #2 Stender or a finger bowl. If the excavated space is extensive, it may be partially filled with yolk from another embryo of the same species and stage although this should be avoided if possible.

---

* The author acknowledges, with appreciation, the help of Dr. W. M. Copenhaver in organizing this exercise.

THE PRODUCTION OF DOUBLE HEARTS

This operation may be performed on the Anura (stage #16) or on the Urodela (stages #22-#25) although the latter are preferred because the development of the heart can be followed through the transparent skin of the ventral side without exploratory incisions.

Place the embryo in a Permoplast depression in such a position that the ventral heart forming areas faces upward. Locate the exact position of the future heart and with sharp glass needles make an incision posterior to the region of the thyroid anlagé and deep enough to reach the grayish endoderm of the pharyngeal floor. Carry this incision posteriorly to the position of the liver anlagé. With a fine hair loop clean out the loose cells in the mid-ventral line, forming a channel. Leave the lateral mesenchyme intact.

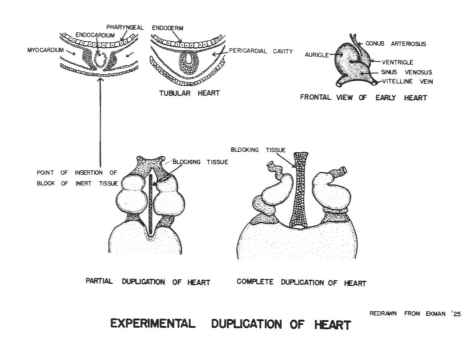

NORMAL DEVELOPMENT OF HEART

EXPERIMENTAL DUPLICATION OF HEART

REDRAWN FROM EKMAN '25

From a second embryo of the same species but of a later stage of development, remove a strip of notochord long enough to fill the excavated channel. Insert it into the operated embryo between the lateral heart rudiments, replace the ventral ectoderm, and hold the flap of ectoderm in position for 20 to 30 minutes by means of a Brücke or lens paper bridge. Alternative procedures may include flank ectoderm with underlying somite mesoderm instead of notochord. Return the embryo to the normal culture medium after the wound has healed over.

Should the above procedure fail to produce a double-hearted embryo, proceed with a more extensive operation on an embryo one stage younger. Remove the ecto-mesoderm by making a longitudinal slit from a position between the suckers posteriorly about 1/3 of the length of the embryo. Carry the cut dorsally on one side of the embryo to the ventral limits of the closed medullary fold, then forward, to complete a trapezoid. Avoid as much of the head ectoderm as possible. After outlining this area, carry the incision deeper until all mesoderm on the side of the operation is circumscribed. Remove this

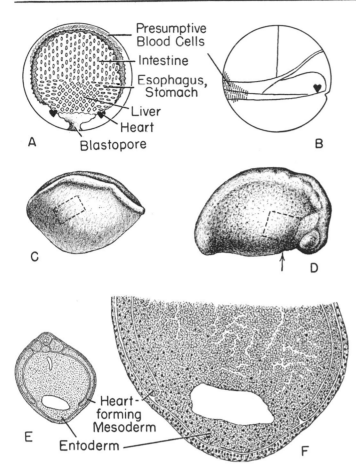

Location of presumptive heart material in Amblystoma. A, Organ-forming areas mapped on the
ventral portion of an opened gastrula, dorsal view;
B, gastrula, lateral view; C, neurula, stage 15,
right lateral view; D, stage 22. Heart-forming
areas on C and D are outlined by broken line;
E, transverse section at level of arrow in D;
F, enlargement of ventral portion of same section.
(A and B, redrawn after Holtfreter, '38: C, redrawn after Bacon, '45.)

(Courtesy W. M. Copenhaver and
W. B. Saunders Pub. Co. from
Willier, Weiss, and Hamburger
"Analysis of Development".
1955.)

large mass of ecto-mesoderm. From a slightly older embryo outline and remove an
area of similar shape, and including ecto- and mesoderm, but from the presumptive
hind-limb region. Transplant this mass to the operated (host) embryo wound area, hold
it in place for 30 minutes or more, and when healed, return the embryo to normal culture medium. (See Ekman, 1925.)

TRANSPLANTATION OF HEART FORMING AREAS

Early stages: In Anuran stage #17 or Urodele stage #25, the heart forming mesenchyme
from the bilateral sides have fused ventrally. Remove a rectangular piece of ventral
ectoderm along with all available adherent and underlying mesoderm, and transplant it
as one piece to the flank region of a second embryo, previously prepared. The second
(host) embryo should be slightly younger than the donor. Such a transplanted heart anlage
should give rise to a tubular heart of four typical parts, with its own pulsations but without any circulatory elements.

Late stages: Use Anura stage #19 or Urodela stage #34 to #38 where the heart is well
formed. Anesthetize the embryo in freshly made MS 222 (1/3,000 in operating medium)
and graft (transplant) the entire heart mass, plus liver and foregut, to the flank region of
an embryo of the same age or one stage younger. While this operation will not demonstrate self-differentiation (as above), it will show clearly the persistence of function in
the absence of innervation.

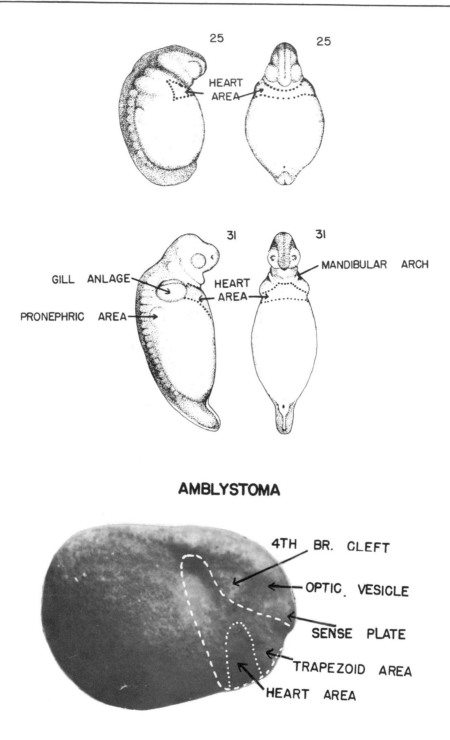

AMBLYSTOMA

RANA PIPIENS · STAGE 15

CULTURE OF HEART TISSUE IN ISOLATION

After the bilateral heart rudiments have fused ventrally it is possible to remove the mesodermal mass and the overlying ectoderm, and to have it differentiate in isolation in the appropriate medium. In general (see "Isolation Culture" exercise) the culture medium should consist of the normal culture medium which contains some (coelomic) body fluids from adults of the same species. In addition, it is now known that 0. 5% sodium sulfadiazine will retard the development of bacteria and hence prolong the life of the isolate.

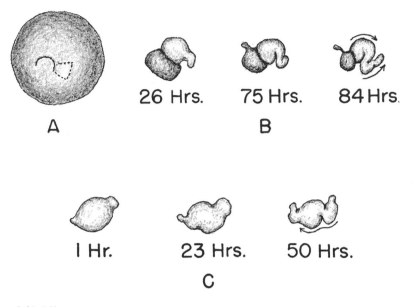

Self-differentiation of presumptive heart material cultured in modified Holt-freter's solution. A, Amblystoma punctatum, stage 11. Explant of gastrula wall from outlined area lateral to the blastopore differentiates as shown in B. Arrows show direction of contraction wave at 84 hours after explantation. C, differentiation of presumptive mesoderm explanted from an embryo of stage 15, late medullary plate stage. (Redrawn after Bacon, '45.)

(Courtesy of W. M. Copenhaver and W. B. Saunders Pub. Co., from Willier, Weiss, Hamburger "Analysis of Development" 1955.)

The explanted heart may be cultured in a hanging drop of medium, on the underside of a coverslip sealed over a depression slide; in Standard Solution in a depression slide; or over an agar-embryonic fluid base. If the medium is changed every 3 to 4 days, the explant may be carried to quite an advanced stage of differentiation.

HETEROPLASTIC TRANSPLANTATION OF HEART RUDIMENTS

Copenhaver (1930 to 1939) has successfully transplanted Amblystoma punctatum, Amblystoma tigrinum, Amblystoma mexicanum and Triton taeniatus hearts and heart parts reciprocally. In such transplants it is important to realize that there are intrinsic differences in growth rate and in final pulse rate, in consequence of which the chimeric heart attains functional interest. Specific parts of the heart, such as the ventricle, the sinus venosus, etc. may be interposed between the other parts of the host heart. These are, of course, orthotopic transplants.

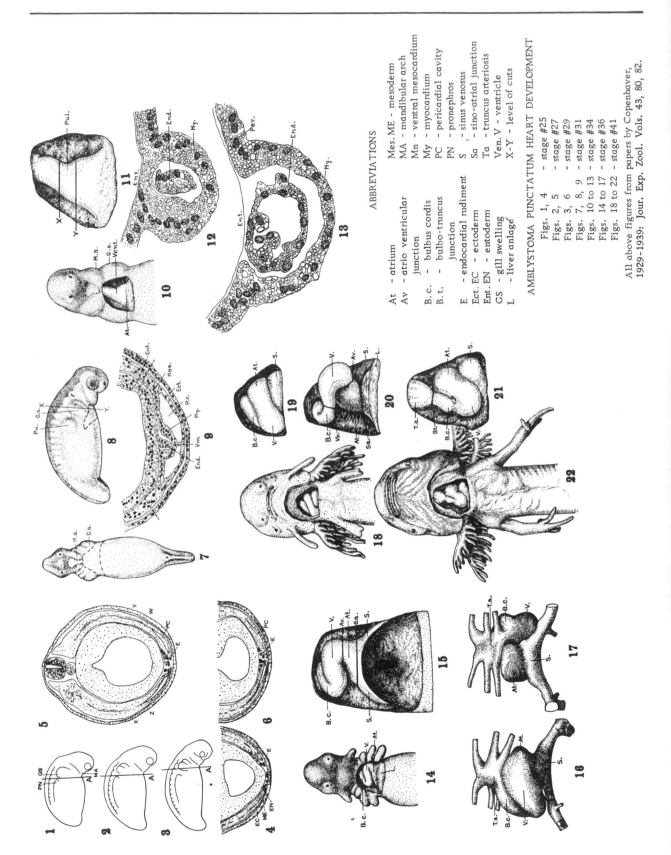

ABBREVIATIONS

At - atrium
Av - atrio ventricular
      junction
B. c. - bulbus cordis
B. t. - bulbo-truncus
         junction
E - endocardial rudiment
Ect. EC - ectoderm
Ent. EN - entoderm
GS - gill swelling
L - liver anlage

Mes. ME - mesoderm
MA - mandibular arch
Mn - ventral mesocardium
My - myocardium
PC - pericardial cavity
PN - pronephros
S ♀ - sinus venosus
Sa - sino-atrial junction
Ta - truncus arteriosis
Ven. V - ventricle
X-Y - level of cuts

AMBLYSTOMA PUNCTATUM HEART DEVELOPMENT

Figs. 1, 4   - stage #25
Figs. 2, 5   - stage #27
Figs. 3, 6   - stage #29
Figs. 7, 8, 9 - stage #31
Figs. 10 to 13 - stage #34
Figs. 14 to 17 - stage #36
Figs. 18 to 22 - stage #41

All above figures from papers by Copenhaver, 1929-1939: Jour. Exp. Zool. Vols. 43, 80, 82.

Variations in this procedure include:

    a. Reversing of the axis of the transplant but placing it in the otherwise orthotopic position, in order to determine the direction of pulsation in the transplant, and the control of the transplant over the host organ.

    b. Transplantation heteroplastically to an heterotopic position, such as in place of somites #7 to #10.

OBSERVATIONS AND TABULATION OF DATA:

In all instances comparable stage embryos should be carried along simultaneously with the experimentals in order to allow direct comparison of the results of heart field experiments. Most of the experiments can be terminated about 8 days after the operation, and the host may be anesthetized in 1/3,000 MS 222 and be dissected (along with the controls) to determine the degree of development. In heteroplastic transplants the pulse rates of controls, experimentals, and parts of experimental transplants should be determined. Photographs and drawings will constitute the record of these operations, and histological analysis is generally very instructive, providing comparable controls are available.

DISCUSSION:

Typical vertebrates have hearts of bilateral origin. In both the Urodeles and the Anura the prospective heart forming material is derived from the two lateral mesenchymal plates. By the time these mesenchymal anlagen have migrated to the ventral position, they have acquired self-differentiating capacities of heart so that if transplanted to an heterotopic position or explanted into a culture medium they will each give rise to a chambered, primitive heart, often with sinus, auricle, ventricle, and arterial bulb, all of which may exhibit typical rhythmic pulsations.

Heart anlagen may be split to give multiple hearts or an extra heart anlagé may be superimposed on the host heart material to produce a larger but normal heart, providing the axes of the host and the donor heart anlagen are the same.

The heart area of the amphibian is considered as an equi-potential system in that as little as half of the area possesses the requirements for the development of an entire and normal heart. Anterior and posterior portions of the heart area, transplanted to a foreign species (Copenhaver, 1930) will give rise to corresponding specific portions of the ultimate heart. The posterior transplant combines with the anterior portion from the host and generally acts as a pacemaker, giving the host the rhythmical control similar to that normally found in the donor species.

REFERENCES

BACON, R. L., 1945 - "Self-differentiation and induction in the heart of Amblystoma". Jour. Exp. Zool 98:87.

COPENHAVER, W. M., 1955 - "Heart, Blood Vessels, Blood and Entodermal Derivatives". Chap. in Willier, Weiss, Hamburger "Analysis of Development". Saunders, Philadelphia.

COPENHAVER, W. M., 1958 - "Distribution of radioactive sulfate in the heart of fetal, newborn, and adult rabbits". Anat. Rec. 131:669-680.

COPENHAVER, W. M., R. van DYKE, R. RUGH, 1960 - "Effects of x-irradiation on embryos at critical stages of heart development." Yale Jour. Biol. & Med. 32:421-430.

EKMAN, G., 1925 - "Experimentelle Beitrage zur Hertzenwicklung der Amphibien." Arch. f. Ent. Mech. 106:320.

EKMAN, G., 1929 - "Experimentelle Untersuchungen uber die fruheste Herzentwicklung bei Rana fusca". Arch. f. Ent. Mech. 116:327.

FALES, D. E., 1946 - "A study of double hearts produced experimentally in embryos of Amblystoma punctatum". Jour. Exp. Zool. 101:281.

GIRGIS, A., 1930 - "The development of the heart in the rabbit." Proc. Zool. Soc. London 3:755-782.

GOERTTLER, K., 1928 - "Die Bedeutung der ventrolateralen Mesodermbezirke fur die Herzenlagé der Amphibienkeim." Anat. Anz. Erg. Heft. 66:132.

GRAPER, L., 1907 - "Untersuchungen uber die Herzbildung der Vogel". Arch. f. Ent. Mech. 24:375.

HEGRE, E. S., 1945 - "Intracardiac transplantation in the urodele." Science. 101:469.

HILTON, W. A., 1913 - "The development of the blood and transformation of some of the early vitelline vessels in Amphibia."
    Jour. Morph. 24:339.

KEMP, N. E., 1953 - "Morphogenesis and metabolism of amphibian larvae after excision of the heart." Anat. Rec. 117:405 & 773.

KNOWER, J. M., 1907 - "Effects of early removal of the heart and arrest of the circulation on the development of frog embryos."
    Anat. Rec. 1:161.

LEHMANN, F. E., 1929 - "Die Entwicklung des Anlagenmusters in Ektoderm der Tritongastrula." Arch. f. Ent. Mech. 117:317.

LILJESTRAND, A., J. E. EDWARDS, 1957 - "X-ray irradiation of pregnant rats: attempts to produce cardiac anomalies in off-
    spring." Proc. Soc. Exp. Biol. & Med. 94:111-112.

MANGOLD, O., 1921 - "Situs inversus bei Triton." Arch. f. Ent. Mech. 48:505.

PIATT, J., A. RAVENTOS, 1953 - "Transplantation of irradiated tissues of embryonic Amblystoma." Snat. Rec. 115:409.

REEMSTMA, K., W. M. COPENHAVER, 1958 - "Anatomic studies of the cardiac conduction system in congenital malformations
    of the heart." Circulation. 17:271-276.

SCHUBEL, K., J. P. STOHR, 1924 - "Ein Beitrage zur Pharmokologie Transplanttatierten Amphibienherzen." Arch. f. Exper.
    Path. u. Pharmac. 104:

SPEMANN, H., H. FALKENBERG, 1919 - "Uber asymmetrische Entwicklung und Situs inversus viscerum bei Zwillingen und Dop-
    pelbildungen". Arch. f. Ent. Mech. 45:371.

STOHR, J. P., 1929 - "Zur Embryonalen Herzentransplantation." Arch. f. Ent. Mech. 116:300.

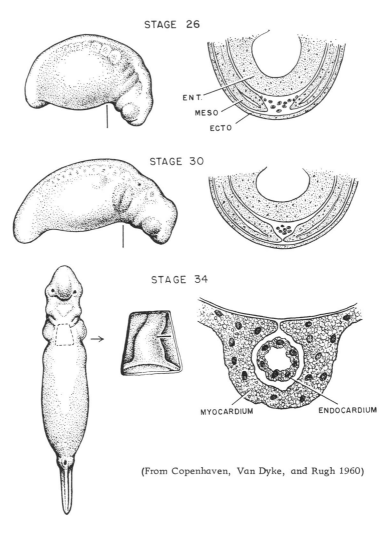

(From Copenhaven, Van Dyke, and Rugh 1960)

Cardiac differentiation in embryos of Amblystoma punctatum at Harrison's
developmental stages selected for x-irradiation. Vertical lines beneath the
stage 26 and stage 30 embryos indicate the plane of the cross sections shown
at the right.

39. REGENERATION

DEFINITION: The restitution of a lost organ in such a form that it is both structurally and functionally complete.

PURPOSE: To determine the ability of an embryo or larva to repair or replace a lost part.

MATERIALS:
<u>Biological</u>: Rana: stages #10 to #17 and 3.5 to 4.5 cm. tadpoles (may be used up to 8 cm.).
Amblystoma: stages #10 to #29 and larvae with limbs, before metamorphosis.
Triturus: stages #10 to #29 and late larvae.

<u>Technical</u>: Standard operating equipment.
Sodium sulfadiazine - 0.5% aqueous (to prevent post-operative infection).

METHOD:
<u>Precautions</u>:
1. Moderate precautions should be taken against bacterial contamination. Animals may be reared in 0.5% sodium sulfadiazine as protection.
2. Keep operated animals in separate containers. The Urodeles particularly tend to snap at any moving object and will bite off each others tails or appendages. Provide adequate volume of medium and space for each specimen.
3. After the wound is healed over all animals must be maximally fed (Enchytrea for the Urodela and spinach for the Anura).

<u>Controls</u>:
1. Tail-fin controls consist of unoperated embryos of the same age and stage.
2. Limb regeneration control consists of the limb of the opposite side.
3. Blastema control consists of the transplantation of some other and neutral area (unknown anlagé) into the blastema.

<u>Experimental procedure</u>:

TAIL-FIN REGENERATION

Using either anuran tadpoles (stage #25 or older) or urodele larvae (stage #45 or older) with distinct tail fins, select as many specimens as possible of the same age and at the same stage of development. If anuran tadpoles are used they may be placed in groups of 5 in single finger bowls containing a minimum of 25 cc. of medium. If Urodele larvae are used they must be kept in separate containers such as finger bowls, Lily cups, or #2 Stenders.

<u>The following directions are for Anuran tadpoles</u>:
1. Prepare 18 finger bowls, 6 each with the following solutions (50 cc. each).
   a. 10% Standard Solution (hypotonic)
   b. Standard Solution (isotonic)
   c. 200% Standard Solution (hypertonic)

---

* The author acknowledges, with appreciation, the critical suggestions of Dr. H. S. Emerson in organizing this exercise, particularly that part relating to inductions within the blastema, and acknowledgement of suggestions from Dr. E. G. Butler is made with pleasure.

2. Into each finger bowl place an equal number of tadpoles, a minimum of 5.
3. Mark the 6 finger bowls containing the same medium as follows:
    a. Vertical cut.
    b. Cut angled toward the dorsal body wall.
    c. Cut angled toward the belly.
    d. V-shaped cut, apex toward body.
    e. V-shaped cut, apex away from body.
    f. Control - no cut.
4. Consult the accompanying diagram of a frog tadpole (stage #25) to determine the
    angles of the various cuts prescribed. All but "a" and "f" (the control) are illus-
    trated.

FROG TADPOLE (STAGE #25) SHOWING LEVELS OF CUTS FOR TAIL—FIN REGENERATION STUDIES

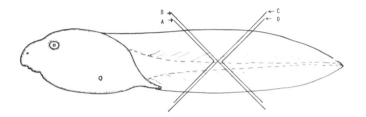

A - V-shaped cut with apex
    away from the body.
B - Transverse cut angled
    toward dorsal body.
C - Transverse cut angled
    toward belly.
D - V-shaped cut with apex
    toward the body.

5. Prepare an operating Syracuse dish with Permoplast base. Fill the dish with
    one of the above (3) solutions, beginning with the 10% Standard. Transfer all (5)
    tadpoles successively from each of the finger bowls containing the 10% Standard
    to the operating dish and cut the tail fin in the manner indicated on the previously-
    marked finger bowl. That is, there will be finally 18 finger bowls, containing
    six (6) different solutions, and representing five (5) different cuts, and a set of
    controls. The cuts should be made with a sharp scalpel while the tadpoles are
    immobilized with 1/10,000 MS 222 (made up in the same medium). If the cuts
    are made on the group from a single finger bowl, while in the same Syracuse
    dish, it will be somewhat easier to insure the cuts being similar.
6. Immediately return the tadpoles to the finger bowl with the appropriate medium,
    and properly marked. It is best to make the cut in the medium to be tested.
    (Do not save the tail tips unless for incidental chromosome counts - see "Tail
    Tip Technique".)
7. Place all 18 finger bowls under identical environmental conditions of light and
    temperature, and minimize evaporation by keeping them covered.

The tail fins should be examined under the dissection microscope daily for about ten days,
and the record consists of daily sketches beginning with a sketch immediately after cutting.
Note the color of the regenerating (blastema) tissue and the angle of the regenerate.

THE DEVELOPMENT OF ORGAN ANLAGEN IN REGENERATING BLASTEMAS

This experiment involves regeneration, transplantation, and possibly some induction. It
is based upon the assumption that the regenerating tissue (the blastema) is essentially
embryonic in nature and will either supplement an implanted organ anlagé or will, under
the influence of such an anlagé, be induced to form certain organs.

1. Select 20 to 30 frog tadpoles measuring at least 3.5 cm. in total length. They may measure as much as 8 cm. The younger ones are generally better, even though the blastema is, in consequence, smaller.

2. Anesthetize the tadpoles with 1/10,000 MS 222 and, with a sharp scalpel, cut off the tail fin at an angle toward the dorsal side of the body about 3 mm. from the body. The older tadpoles may exhibit some hemorrhage but this can be stopped, if necessary, by brief exposure to hypertonic medium. Record the exact date.

3. Allow these tadpoles (in any community crystallizing dish) to regenerate their tails. After about 3 days (and until about 8 days) there will appear a whitish growth bulging from the cut surface. This is the blastema.

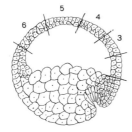

Regions of the early gastrula to be implanted into the blastema.

(From Emerson 1941: Jour. Exp. Zool. 87:403)

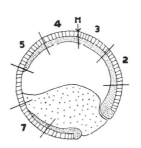

Regions of the late gastrula to be implanted into the blastema. M - the anterior limit of the presumptive neural plate.

(From Emerson 1942: Jour. Exp. Zool. 90:353)

4. Prepare donor material, consisting of various organ anlagen. Consult the Vogt map of organ fields of early gastrula. The eye and the sucker anlagen are generally the most satisfactory, and these may be taken from late tail-bud stages. A suggested list of satisfactory organ anlagen follows:

    Early and late gastrula ectoderm areas (see accompanying diagrams)
    Optic vesicle, with and without lens ectoderm
    Auditory (otic) vesicle
    Olfactory vesicle
    Sucker
    Gill bud
    Limb bud
    Forebrain vesicle
    Medullary plate or neural fold
    Hypophysis

5. Prepare the host as follows: Anesthetize a host (with pronounced blastema) in 1/10,000 MS 222 in Standard Solution or Spring Water. With a sharp-pointed lancet (or iridectomy scissors) gently cut between the blastema and the old tissue (of the tail) along the side of the tadpole. Then make two shallow cuts, one along the dorsal and the other along the ventral margins of the blastema. This will form a V-shaped cut with the apex of the "V" at the most posterior limit of the regenerating blastema. The operating area is small and this is a delicate operation.

6. Quickly excise the anlage to be transplanted and insert it beneath this flap of blastema tissue, orienting it so that its ectodermal layer is outermost. Replace the flap of blastema ectoderm and hold it down for 1 to 2 minutes with a ball tip. The sticky blastema cells will become attached to the transplant and will hold it in place. The transplant may be fixed any time from 18 hours to a month after the transplantation, sectioned and studied to determine the degree of differentiation and induction.

LIMB REGENERATION

The Urodeles show regenerative powers throughout life but the Anura exhibit them until metamorphosis and then only to a limited degree thereafter. It is instructive to study the regeneration of limbs and digits of Urodele larvae. It must be remembered, however, that the post-operative larvae must be treated normally with respect to food, oxygen, space, etc. If x-ray facilities are available, the effect of such irradiations upon regenerating limbs can be studied (see Butler, 1934 and Butler & Puckett, 1940, and illustrations on the following page).

Procedure:
1. Select Amblystoma or Triturus larvae beyond stage #38, when the limbs are developing or are already developed. It is essential that larvae of the same age and stage be used in order to determine the effect of cuts at various levels and angles.
2. Anesthetize the larvae in 1/10,000 MS 222 and make the following cuts with iridectomy scissors.
    a. Cut off the right forelimb at the level of the wrist.
    b. Cut off the right forelimb between the wrist and the pectoral girdle. One amputation above the elbow.
    c. Repeat the above two cuts but make them at the greatest possible angles.
    d. After cutting the larger skeletal elements (humerus, radius, and ulna) the skeleton within a few hours may begin to protrude distal to the original level of the amputation. In such an event, the larva should again be anesthetized and the protruding skeletal elements trimmed off, even with the soft tissues; otherwise healing may be faulty and the results of the experiment difficult to evaluate.

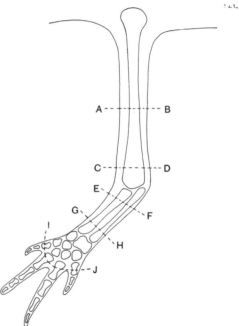

Left forelimb of advanced Amblystoma, indicating possible levels of amputation.

(from Schotté & Butler '41; Jour. Exp. Zool. 87:297)

Modified Wijhe method for regenerating cartilage (from V. R. Gregg and E. G. Butler, Princeton University).
1. Fix 24 hours or more in 5 cc of formalin and 95 cc of 70% alcohol.
2. Without washing, stain 10-60 minutes in 0.25% methylene blue to which 0.5% HCl has been added. The time depends upon the size of the limb.
3. Without washing, destain in 95% alcohol, changing as it becomes discolored, and until no more color comes from the tissue. Handle gently.
4. Dehydrate in absolute, 3 changes of 15 minutes each.
5. Clear in oil of wintergreen until clear. Can leave in this indefinitely.
6. Mount whole as follows:
    a. Wash off all excess salicylate with 60 min. in xylol.
    b. Place a drop of (Damar) balsam on slide, warm to almost drying in oven at 50°C. for 30+ minutes.
    c. Transfer stained specimen onto semi-dried balsam drop, add thick balsam drop, add thick balsam to cover at 2-4 hour intervals, and leave overnight.

d. Add more balsam, if necessary, and cover with coverglass over adequate glass chip supports to prevent compression. Allow to harden completely in a flat position. The cartilage will be blue and white distinct from the other tissues.

OBSERVATIONS AND RECORDING OF DATA:

There are three distinct parts to this exercise on Regeneration and for each specimen studied there must be a complete and separate record or case history. Such a record should consist of drawings or photographs taken at stated intervals (not more than 24 hours, in most cases) beginning immediately after the operation. The dates for all drawings, the temperature of the medium, the conditions of food, light, space, etc. , must all be recorded in the various places provided.

DISCUSSION:

Self-repair is a characteristic of all protoplasm, a necessary prerequisite in a competitive environment where natural selection plays such an important role. The exact method of this repair is not thoroughly understood. It is not established that such repair is the same for all animals, or at all stages within the life span of a single organism.

There are still two main concepts relative to the method of restitution. There are some who believe that there are reserve, mesenchyme-type cells in all organs, awaiting call for the specific function of regeneration. There is no doubt that an injury calls for the marshalling of active cells in the vicinity of the cut, but many of these calls are of vascular origin and may have nothing to do with regeneration. The second concept is that the injured cells at the cut surface, and nearby, undergo a period of de-differentiation, to be followed by an indifferent (embryonic) period, and then a re-differentiation, either into similar or dissimilar tissues. Some rigid adherents to this concept believe that re-differentiation can only be along the original lines of differentiation, implying incomplete de-differentiation. There is, of course, controverting evidence against this. In general the regenerated part does resemble in structure and in function the lost part. Buchanan (1940) says: "Perhaps the more widely held view, is that organismic control is established and maintained by reason of the diffusion of specific organizing substances arising as the result of specific metabolisms of organizing or inducing centers."

Regeneration is not limited to the structures or anlagen listed in this exercise, and minor experiments in regeneration are listed in other exercises which deal specifically with certain organ systems such as THE EYE, THE HEART, THE LIMB FIELDS, etc. However, this exercise will illustrate the principles involved and also the fact that Amphibian larvae do exhibit remarkable powers of regeneration.

Emerson (1941) has shown that parts of the early and late gastrula ectoderm can be implanted into a tail blastema and will differentiate into recognizable organs. This is therefore another method (in addition to isolation culturing) of determining the prospective potencies of various fields or areas of the early gastrula or, in fact, any early embryonic stage. Grafts into the larval tail blastema may survive as long as 100 days after transplantation (Emerson, 1944), and the differentiations may include eyes with lenses, brain parts, striated muscle and cartilage. This period of 100 days is long after the blastema has become an integral part of the tail. Differentiation is achieved with a week or two, and many of the grafts will disintegrate at this time. In most cases resorption of the graft is accomplished along with the resorption of the tail at the time of metamorphosis. Sometimes, however, a part of the graft may persist and will be found at the tip of the urostyle of the metamorphosed frog.

The tadpole tail regenerates rapidly. This may be due in part to the embryonic nature of the cells contiguous to the cut surface. The initial axis of regeneration is generally at right angles to the cut surface but this is rectified subsequently. Twitty and Delanney (1939) found that the tail of Amblystoma is capable of repeated regenerations after successive amputations even during long periods of continuous starvation. There is a gradual decrease in the rate (and degree) of regeneration as amputations are performed later in larval life (Goodwin, 1946); and newly hatched larvae respond the better possibly because they have incompletely differentiated tissue which can be more simply de-differentiated to form a blastema, and then re-differentiate as required.

Most Urodeles retain their powers of regeneration throughout life, but to a lesser degree after metamorphosis. The Anura, on the other hand, lose most of their regenerative powers after metamorphosis. However, there is recent evidence (Butler, Rose, Schotté, and Singer) that even the Anuran appendage will exhibit some powers of regeneration providing (Rose) the cut surface is continually irritated by hypertonicity with NaCl, or (Butler, Schotté, Harland and Singer) the connection of the appendage with the central nervous system is not interrupted. Schotté and Butler (1941) have demonstrated the regression of the humerus in a denervated limb of Amblystoma. In fact, these investigators make the statement that: "No blastema is ever established on a completely nerveless amputated limb."

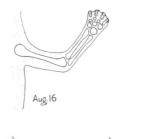
Aug.16

Aug.20

Regression of skeleton of forelimb
(Amblystoma) following denervation.
(Total time 52 days)

(From Schotté & Butler 1941:
Jour. Exp. Zool. 87:279)

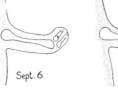
Sept.6   Sept.17   Oct.7

Regeneration of foot and digits of Rana
pipiens pre-metamorphic tadpole hind-
limb. Photo taken 24 days after transverse cut made at shank level.
(P. Bernstein)

In an early embryo when an embryonic field is extirpated, there is generally no regeneration. This means that at this stage regeneration as a property of the embryo is restricted to local fields, and is not related to "the organism as a whole".

There is still a great deal of room for further study of regeneration, particularly as it may be affected by mitotic inhibitors, colchicine, dinitrophenols, specific ions, pH, temperature, light (where pigment cells are involved).

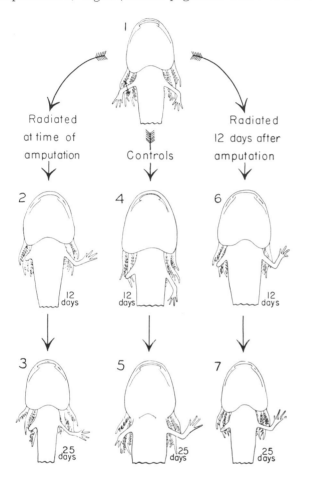

Fig. 1. A larva showing the stage in which the right fore limb was amputated. The double pointed arrow indicates the level of amputation.

Figs. 2 and 3. Larvae which were given a single exposure to x-rays immediately after limb amputation. Limb regeneration has been completely suppressed.

Figs. 4 and 5. Control larvae showing the progress of normal regeneration 12 and 25 days after limb amputation. Stippling on the limb stump in Figure 4 indicates the approximate extent of the normal regeneration blastema on the twelfth day.

Figs. 6 and 7. Larvae which were given a single exposure to x-rays on the twelfth day after limb amputation. A blastema was present at the time of radiation, as shown by stippling. Limb regeneration was completely suppressed.

(From Butler & Puckett 1940; Jour. Exp. Zool. 84:223)

Recent experiments have shown that the proximo-distal polarity of a Urodele limb can be reversed and the regeneration of distal structures obtained from the original proximal end of a limb. Such experiments, which are relatively easy to perform (Butler, 1955; Deck, 1955), involve amputation of a forelimb at the wrist level and insertion of the cut end into a pocket made in the body wall posterior to the shoulder region; later the limb is amputated above the elbow and the upper arm then becomes the free end of the transplanted limb. Such limbs regularly become innervated either by the brachial plexus or by spinal nerves posterior to the plexus. After innervation of the reversed limb has taken place, a blastema forms at the tip of the limb (its original proximal end) and develops into a wrist and digits. In this type of regenerative activity the interrelations between the blastema and the formed structures of the limb beneath it are of particular interest.

Fig. 1. Amblystoma opacum larva (RV-21).
Total length 29 mm at time of limb reversal. Photographed 64 days after reversal.
Tracing at lower right shows size and orientation of three-digit reversed limb. Normal
right limb has completely regenerated.
Portions of right gills were amputated so that
they would not obscure limbs. Photograph
has been slightly retouched in order better
to show details.

Fig. 2. Amblystoma opacum larva (RV-42).
Total length 28 mm at time of limb reversal. Photographed 58 days after reversal. Tracing at lower right shows size and
orientation of four-digit reversed limb.
Normal right limb has completely regenerated. Right gills were amputated so that
they would not obscure limbs. Photograph
has been slightly retouched in order better
to show details.

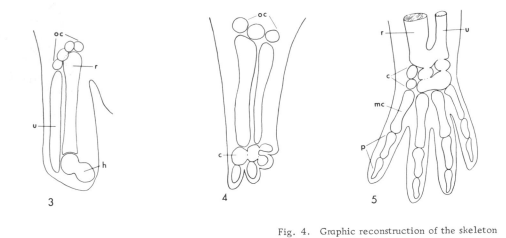

Fig. 4. Graphic reconstruction of the skeleton
of a reversed limb of Amblystoma opacum
larva (RV-59). Point of attachment of
limb to body wall is at the top; three of
the original carpals (oc) are present. At
the free end of the reversed limb has been
established a regenerate in which new car-
pels (c) and the skeletal components of 4
digits are being mapped out.

Fig. 3. Graphic reconstruction of the skeleton of
a reversed limb of Amblystoma opacum
larva (RV-51). Point of attachment of limb
to body wall is at the top; 4 of the original
carpals (oc) are present. Limb has undergone regression so that only a small portion
of humerus (h) remains, articulating with
radius (r) and ulna (u).

Fig. 5. Graphic reconstruction of the skeleton
of the hand and wrist of a reversed limb of
Amblystoma opacum larva (RV-62).
Original proximal ends of radius (r) and
ulna (u) have fused. New carpals (c),
metacarpals (mc) and phalanges (p) are
present.

(Courtesy of Dr. E. G. Butler, from
Jour. Morph. 96:265, 1955.)

REFERENCES

ABELOOS, M., 1932 - "La régénération et les problemes de la morphogénèse." Gauthier-Villars, Paris.

ALLEN, B. M., L. M. EWELL, 1959 - "Resistance to x-irradiation by embryonic cells of the limb-buds of tadpoles." Jour. Exp. Zool. 142:399-336.

BARBER, L. W., 1944 - "Correlations between wound healing and regeneration in fore-limbs and tails of lizards." Jour. Exp. Zool. 89:441.

BRACHET, J., 1946 - "Aspects biochimique de la Regeneration." Experientia II/2.

BRUNST, V. V. & E. A. SCHEREMETIJEWA, 1933 - "Untersuchung des Einflusses von Rontgenstrahlen auf die Regeneration der Extremitaten beim Triton." Arch. f. Ent. Mech. 128:181.

BUCHANAN, J. W., 1940 - "Regeneration." Am. Nat. 74:481.

BURR, H. S., M. TAFFEL & S. C. HARVEY, 1940 - "An electrometric study of the healing wound in man." Yale Jour. Biol. & Med. 12:483.

BUTLER, E. G. & J. O. O'BRIEN, 1942 - "Effects of localized x-radiation on regeneration of the Urodele limb." Anat. Rec. 84:407.

BUTLER, E. G. & O. E. SCHOTTÉ, 1941 - "Histological alterations in denervated non-regenerating limbs of urodele larvae." Jour. Exp. Zool. 88:307.

BUTLER, E. G., 1955 - "Regeneration of the urodele forelimb after reversal of its proximo-distal axis." Jour. Morph., 96: 265.

BUTLER, E. G. & H. F. BLUM, 1955 - "Regenerative growth in the urodele forelimb following ultraviolet radiation." Jour. Nat. Cancer Inst., 15:877.

CAMERON, J. A., 1937 - "The mitotic rate in tadpole skin after repeated injury." Biol. Bull. 72:37.

CHILD, C. M., 1941 - "Patterns and Problems in Development." Univ. Chicago Press.

CLEMENT-NOEL, H., 1944 - "Les acides pentosenucleiques et la regeneration." Ann. Soc. Roy. Zool. de Belg. 75:25.

DAVID, L., 1934 - "La contribution du materiel cartilagineux et osseux au blastem de regeneration des membres chez les Amphibiens urodeles." Arch. d'Anat. Microsc. 30:217.

DECK, J. D., 1955 - "The innervation of urodele limbs of reversed proximo-distal polarity." Jour. Morph., 96:301.

DETWILER, S. R., 1946 - "Midbrain regeneration in Amblystoma." Anat. Rec. 94:229.

EMERSON, H. S., 1944 - "Embryonic grafts in regenerating tissue. III. The development of dorsal and ventral plate ectoderm of Rana pipiens gastrulae." Jour. Exp. Zool. 97:1.

GIDGE, N. M. & S. M. ROSE, 1944 - "The role of larval skin in promoting limb regeneration in adult Anura." Jour. Exp. Zool. 97:71.

GODLEWSKI, E., 1928 - "Untersuchungen uber Auslosung und Hemung der Regeneration beim Axolotl." Arch. f. Ent. Mech. 114:108.

GOODWIN, R. A., 1946 - "A comparison of regeneration rates and metamorphosis in Triturus and Amblystoma." Growth. 10:75.

GUYENOT, E. & K. PONSE, 1930 - "Territoires de regeneration et transplantations." Bull. Biol. 64:252.

HARRISON, R. C., 1933 "Some difficulties of the determination problem." Am. Nat. 67:306.

HELFF, O. M., 1937 - "The relation of the dorsal nerve cord and notochord to tail regeneration in Anuran larvae." Anat. Rec. 70:(suppl.) 101.

HELLMICH, W., 1929 - "Untersuchungen uber Herkunft und Determination des regeneration Materials bei Amphibien." Arch. f. Ent. Mech. 121:135.

HERRELL, W. E., 1934 - "Growth and regeneration of tissue in frog tadpoles following the administration of an extract of the anterior pituitary gland." Anat. Rec. 59:47.

HERTWIG, G., 1927 - "Beitrage zum Determinations-und Regenerationsproblem mittels der Transplantation haploidkerniger Zellen." Arch. f. Ent. Mech. 111:292.

HOLTER, H. S., G. HOLTER, G. AVERY, 1955 - "An experimental analysis of the development of the spinal column." Jour. Morph. 96:145-172 (also 99:1-40)

HOLTFRETER, J., 1938 - "Differenzierungspotenzen isolierter Teile der Anurengastrula." Arch. f. Ent. Mech. 138:657.

HOOKER, D., 1930 - "Studies on regeneration in the spinal cord. IV. Rotation about its longitudinal axis of a portion of the cord in Amblystoma punctatum embryos." Jour. Exp. Zool. 55:23.

HORN, E. C., 1942 - "An analysis of neutron and x-ray effects on regeneration of the forelimb of larval Amblystoma." Jour. Morph. 71:185.

KORSCHELT, W., 1927 - "Regeneration und Transplantation." Borntraeger, Berlin.

LECAMP, M., 1942 - "Effect of amino-acids on regeneration." Comp. rendu. Soc. Biol. 214:330.

LIOSNER, L. D., 1938 - "Untersuchungen über die Eigenschaften der Regenerationsknospe des Amphibienschwanzes." Bull. de Biol. et. Med. Exper. 6:262.

LITWILLER, R., 1939 - "Mitotic index and size in regenerating amphibian limbs." Jour. Exp. Zool. 82:273.

LIVERSAGE, R. L., 1959 - "Relation of the central and autonomic nervous systems to the regeneration of limbs in adult urodeles." Jour. Exp. Zool., 141:75.

MILOJEVIC, B. D., 1924 - "Beiträge zur Frage uber die Determination der Regenerate." Arch. f. mikr. Anat. u. Entwmech. 103:80.

MORGAN, T. H., 1927 - "Experimental Embryology." Macmillan.

NAVILLE, A., 1924 - "Rècherches sur l'histogenèse et la régénération chez les Batraciens Anoures." Arch. de Biol. 34:235.

NEEDHAM, J., 1942 - "Biochemistry and Morphogenesis." Cambridge Univ. Press (p. 430ff.).

NICHOLAS, J. S., 1955 - "Regeneration", in "Analysis of Development." Willier, Weiss, Hambruger (eds.) Sarmders, Phila.

PEADON, A. M., 1953 - "The effects of thiourea on limb regeneration in the tadpole." Growth. 17:21.

POLEZHAYER, L. W., 1946 - "The loss and restoration of regenerative capacity in the limbs of tailless amphibia." Biol. Rev. 21:141.

PRUTSCHER, L., 1939 - "Histological mechanism of regeneration of striated muscle in Anura." Magyar Orv. Arch. 40:1.

PUCKETT, W. O., 1938 - "The effects of intra-peritoneal injections of pituitary substances on the rate of tail regeneration in frog tadpoles." Anat. Rec. 71:337.

RICHARDSON, D., 1945 - "Thyroid and pituitary hormones in relation to regeneration. II. Regeneration of the hind leg of the newt, Triturus viridescens, with different combinations of thyroid and pituitary hormones." Jour. Exp. Zool. 100:417.

ROSE, F. C., H. QUASTLER & S. M. ROSE, 1955 - "Regeneration of x-rayed salamander limbs provided with normal epidermis." Sc. 122:1018.

ROSE, S. M., 1945 - "The effect of NaCl in stimulating regeneration of limbs of frogs." Jour. Morph. 77:119.

SALTPETER, M. M. & M. SINGER, 1960 - "The fine structure of mecenchym atous cells in regenerating forelimb of the adult newt Triturus." Dev. Biol. 2:516-534.

SANDERS, F. K. & J. Z. YOUNG, 1946 - "The influence of peripheral connexion on the diameter of regenerating nerve fibers." Jour. Exp. Biol. 22:203.

SCHOTTÉ, O. E., 1940 - "The origin and morphogenetic potencies of regenerates." Growth Supplement. 59-76.

SCHOTTÉ, O. E. & E. G. BUTLER, 1944 - "Phases in regeneration of the urodele limb and their dependence upon the nervous system." Jour. Exp. Zool. 97:95.

SINGER, M., 1947 - "The nervous system and regeneration of the forelimb of adult Triturus. VII. The relation between number of nerve fibers and surface area of amputation." Jour. Exp. Zool. 104:251.

SINGER, M., 1952 - "The influence of the nerve in regeneration of the amphibian extremity." Quart. Rev. Biol. 27:169.

SINGER, M. M., M. H. DAVIS & M. R. SCHEUING, 1960 - "The influence of atropine and other neuropharmacological substances on regeneration of the forelimb in the adult urodele, Triturus". Jour. Exp. Zool. 143:33-46.

SPEIDEL, C. C., 1947 - "Correlated studies of sense organs and nerves of the lateral-line in living frog tadpoles. I. Regeneration of denervated organs." Jour. Com. Neur. 87.

SPEIDEL, C. C., 1957 - "Regenerative changes in the tail tissues of x-rayed tadpoles observed in vivo." Anat. Rec. 127:448.

STOLZ, R. & W. LUTHER, 1957 - "Uber die Regenerative rontgenbestrahlter Nerven bei Amphibienlarven." Strahlentherapie. 102:73-77.

SWETT, F. N. & M. WALLACE, 1941 - "Growth potencies and polarity relations in the cells which replace the extirpated embryonic limb rudiment." Jour. Exp. Zool. 86:51.

THORNTON, C. S., 1942 - "Studies on the origin of the regeneration blastema in Triturus viridescens." Jour. Exp. Zool. 89:375.

THORNTON, C. S., 1959 - "Regeneration in vertebrates". Univ. Chicago Press.

TWITTY, V. E. & E. DELANNEY, 1939 - "Size-regulation and regeneration in salamander larvae under complete starvation." Jour. Exp. Zool. 81:399.

VALLETTE, M., 1929 - "Regeneration du museau et territoires de regeneration chez les Urodeles." Bull. Biol. de la France et de la Belg.

WEISS, P., 1944 - "The technology of nerve regeneration. Sutureless tubulation and related methods of nerve repair." Jour. Neurosurgery. 1:400.

WORONZOWA, M. A., 1938 - "Die Regenerationspotenzen der Schultergurtelmuskulatur beim Axolotl." Bull. de Biol. et Med. Exper. 6:82.

WRIGHT, M. R., 1947 - "Regeneration and degeneration experiments on lateral line nerves and sense organs in anurans." Jour. Exp. Zool. 105.

(See also section on Limb Field Operations)

"I have no theory to propose to explain the origin of organic fitness and human purpose other than the endowment of living beings with the differential sensitivity and reactivity tropisms, organic memory, trial and error behaviour, leading in higher animals to intelligence and purpose. I do not doubt the reality of the mechanistic principles of physics and chemistry and natural selection in the evolution of organisms with all their adaptations. But with crude mechanism that finds everything the result of accident and chance I have no more sympathy than with transcendental vitalism. Those who say there are no ends, values, purposes in the living world may understand atoms, molecules, and even genes, but they do not understand organisms. They see the elements of which life is composed, but they fail to see the pattern and beauty of the entire tapestry of life."

E. G. Conklin 1944

F. Endocrine Factors in Development
40. EFFECT OF THYROID AND OF IODINE ON AMPHIBIAN METAMORPHOSIS

PURPOSE: To demonstrate the relationship of the thyroid hormone, or its major constituent (iodine), to metamorphic changes in the Amphibia.

MATERIALS:

    <u>Biological</u>:   Hatched tadpoles of Rana, Bufo, or Hyla

                      Neotonous Urodele larvae (Necturus, Axolotl, etc.)

    <u>Technical</u>:   Thyroid tablets (Armour & Company)

                      Thyroxin crystals (Hoffman-La Roche Company)

                      Freshly dissected thyroid glands (frog, rat, sheep, etc.)

                      Iodine crystals dissolved in 95% alcohol

                      Millimeter ruled graph paper on underside of Petri dish (for measuring)

METHOD:

    <u>Precautions</u>:

        1.   The number of tadpoles per unit of volume per finger bowl must be the same for all observations. The best ratio is 25 tadpoles per 50 cc. of medium in each finger bowl.

        2.   The medium for the experimental animals should be changed daily except where thyroxin is used. The thyroid tablets or glands provide an excellent medium for bacterial growth which, in itself, would eventually kill the tadpoles.

        3.   Avoid overdosing or overfeeding, particularly of iodine or thyroid material. The effect of thyroid is an acceleration of development which may be carried beyond the tolerable limit and the tadpoles will be literally "burned up".

    <u>Controls</u>: Since the treatment of the tadpoles involves feeding, a basic diet of boiled spinach (1 square inch per tadpole per day) should be provided for both the control and the experimental animals. The controls and the experimentals should be from the same batch of eggs, at exactly the same stage and size at the beginning of the experiment.

    <u>Procedure</u>:

PREPARATION OF EXPERIMENTAL MEDIA

<u>Thyroxin</u>: Dissolve 10 mgm. of crystalline thyroxin in 5 cc. of 1% NaOH (it is soluble only in alkaline media) and then add distilled water to make 1 liter. This will be a 1/100,000 concentration of thyroxin and may be kept in the refrigerator almost indefinitely and may be considered the stock solution from which lower concentrations of experimental media are made.

<u>Thyroid Tablets</u>: Dissolve five 2-grain tablets in about 5 cc. of distilled water, using a mortar and pestle. Add an equivalent amount (in weight) of whole wheat flour, and grind together thoroughly. With a spatula, spread the paste thinly onto clean lantern slide covers and allow it to dry. When dry, chip the mixture off of the glass, powder and store it in stoppered bottles in the refrigerator.

* The author acknowledges with appreciation, the help of Dr. S. A. D'Angelo in organizing this exercise.

Iodine Solutions: Dissolve 0.1 gram of pure crystalline iodine in 5 cc. of 95% alcohol, and then dilute to 1 liter with distilled water. This will provide a concentration of 1/10,000 as a stock solution, which can be further diluted when required for experimental uses.

Freshly Dissected Thyroid Glands: Three sources of fresh glands are recommended.

a. From the frog: Since the amphibian thyroid gland is difficult to locate, use the large bullfrog (Rana catesbiana) if available. Rana pipiens glands can be used, however.

Remove the lower jaw by cutting through the angles of the jaw and posteriorly to the xiphisternum. Deflect the ventral skin forward and expose the underlying muscles in the vicinity of the glottis. Clip off the anterior end of the xiphisternum, exposing the hypoglossal muscle which should be cut. With forceps, strip these muscles forward, locate the hyoid cartilage. The thyroids will be seen posterior to the lateral hyoid processes and close to the jugular veins. The preliminary dissections should be checked by microscopic examination of the removed gland, for there are other glands in the same general vicinity.

When the dissection technique has been perfected, add a known number of crushed glands to each of the experimental (finger) bowls each day. It is difficult to control the amount of thyroid tissue consumed by a tadpole, but if the glands are thoroughly crushed the distribution will be the more homogenous.

b. From the rat: Experimental rats are generally available in the laboratory and fresh rat thyroids can be excised, crushed (with clean sand, if necessary) and fed to tadpoles directly. Again it is important to reduce the size of the pieces of thyroid tissue to a minimum.

c. From the slaughter house: Fresh thyroids of large mammals (sheep, pig, cow) are generally available. Such thyroids may be weighed, macerated in 1% NaOH, and squeezed (broken up with mortar and pestle) and the mash made up to a known volume (e.g., 100 cc.) with Standard Solution. The maceration liberates the thyroid colloid into the surrounding medium and the fresh and homogenous thyroid mixture may be added in known quantities to the various experimental finger bowls. Such a freshly made thyroid mash will remain usable for several days if frozen quickly.

A second procedure is to dehydrate the fresh glands in acetone, freeze them quickly and solidly, later to chop the pieces into small bits which can be ingested by the tadpoles.

PREPARATION OF THE (NORMAL) CONTROL FOOD

Anuran tadpoles can be reared to and through metamorphosis on a variety of foods. The most consistently satisfactory diet is washed and par-boiled spinach or lettuce. Spinach must be washed to remove arsenic powder used to destroy insects and must be boiled to soften the tissues. Such spinach cannot be kept more than 24 hours at refrigerator temperatures as it becomes acidified and will kill the larvae. A rough estimate of the amount to provide is 1 square inch of spinach leaf per tadpole, until they are about a month old when they will require more, per day. The larger bullfrog tadpoles naturally require more food. The Urodele larvae (e.g., Necturus or Amblystoma) are fed small Daphnia, and later small white worms, Enchytrea. Other "normal" foods are rolled oats, oatmeal and dried shrimp, liverwurst, etc. Some investigators use a mixture of wheat flour with egg yolk or alfalfa. Since all foods are a source of bacterial infection and growth, the food and medium should be changed daily and the culture should be kept at a uniform and fairly low (18°C.) temperature.

EXPERIMENTAL PROCEDURE

1. Inseminate eggs of Rana pipiens and separate them into groups of 5 to 10 eggs, and
    place about 200 in a flat, white enamel pan measuring about 4 x 12 x 20 inches.
    Cover the pan with a glass plate and allow the eggs to develop at about 23-25°C. At
    the 11 mm. stage (about 14 days) begin to feed the tadpoles a uniform diet, prefer-
    ably of fresh, washed, and boiled spinach. Change the water and add fresh food three
    times per week. If available, separate the tadpoles so that there are no more than
    100 per enamel pan and they will grow faster.

2. When the hind limb buds have attained a length of about 1 mm., select as many as
    are available at exactly the same stage of development. Place 5 such tadpoles in
    each finger bowl containing 50 cc. of Standard Solution or Spring Water. (If avail-
    able, the 12 inch crystallizing dishes may be used with 25 such tadpoles.) In any
    case the stage of development, volume of medium, and size of container must be
    identical for all groups of tadpoles.

3. Treat the experimental animals as follows (the controls receiving the spinach diet
    only while the experimentals receive, in addition, the following).

    Thyroxin: Place tadpoles in various concentrations for 1 week. Do not suspend
    normal feeding.
       a. Concentration of 1/1,000,000
       b. Concentration of 1/10,000,000
       c. Concentration of 1/100,000,000

    Doses of 1/500,000,000 have been known to accelerate development.

    Thyroid Tablets: Add approximately 50 mgm. of thyroid-wheat mixture per day
    per tadpole, for a period of one week. Do not suspend normal feeding, and
    change the culture medium daily just before adding thyroid.

    Iodine: Add concentration and normal food but add no further iodine unless the
    medium is changed.
       a. Concentration of 1/500,000 for 7 and for 14 days.
       b. Concentration of 1/1,000,000 for 7 and for 14 days.

    Fresh Mammalian Thyroid: This experiment can have only qualitative significance
    because it is difficult to control the dose of the thyroid colloid expelled from the
    living (fresh) glands or the amount ingested by each of the tadpoles. It will be
    significant, however, if the student can demonstrate any acceleration of amphib-
    ian metamorphosis by the use of mammalian thyroid gland tissue or colloid. It
    is possible simply to squeeze fresh thyroid glands directly into the experimental
    dishes, thus liberating some of the colloid to be ingested.

    If bullfrog tadpoles are available, their thyroids may be used in the same manner.
    Such tadpoles can also be used as test animals, providing they are second-year
    tadpoles and have begun the development of their hind limbs.

4. Neotony is a condition of permanent larval state, during which the forms can repro-
    duce. Examples are Necturus and the Mexican Axolotl. Such forms can be caused
    to complete their arrested development, and metamorphose, by treating them with
    the thyroid hormone or iodine. If available, attempt to get rid of the otherwise
    permanent external gills of such forms by treating them with thyroxin. Even A.
    punctatum and A. tigrinum may be hastened through metamorphosis by thyroid
    treatment.

OBSERVATIONS AND TABULATION OF DATA:

There is high mortality in this type of an experiment.

Mount some millimeter graph paper on the underside of some flat-bottomed Petri dishes to use as a guide in determining the size changes in tadpoles. The important criteria are:
  a. Hind limb length
  b. Total length, i. e., from snout to tip of tail
  c. Body length, i. e., from snout to base of tail

Other items to note will be changes in the mouth, the shape and size of the head, the appearance of the forelimbs, resorption of the tail, first shedding of skin, formation of the tympanum, and finally relative dehydration, etc. By means of averages of these size changes, determine the body proportions that show maximum response to the thyroid.

While the tadpoles are exposed to the thyroid or iodine treatment for only a short time (1 to 2 weeks) the final data should not be collected for from 1 to 2 weeks (or more) after the cessation of the experimental conditions. Some of the tadpoles should be kept until they achieve metamorphosis and the time of emergence from the water of the experimentals and parallel controls should be noted. Normally Rana pipiens larvae will reach stages of metamorphosis in about 75 days after the eggs are fertilized, if kept at laboratory temperatures of $23^{\circ}-25^{\circ}C.$, fed well, and not crowded.

Arrange your data in tabular form and illustrate with drawings or photographs.

DISCUSSION:

It is not within the province of this Manual to carry an endocrine study beyond the macroscopic examination. The relation of the thyroid and/or the pituitary gland to metamorphosis has been the subject of long and thorough studies. There are, however, other embryological approaches to the problem which might bear investigation. These are suggested in the form of questions, as follows:

  1. Will thyroid or iodine affect stages of development prior to the limb-bud stages, or stages prior to the normal functioning of the host thyroid? Is there any effect on the blastula or gastrula or neurula, for instance?
  2. The pituitary is known to have thyreotropic function, but which of these glands is the ontogenetic precursor?
  3. What would be the effect on the embryos (larvae) following extirpation of either or both the thyroid and the pituitary anlagen?
  4. What is the effect on them of grafting thyroids (or pituitaries) of the same and of advanced ages into the tail blastemas of tadpoles.
  5. What is the effect of thyroid and of thyroidectomy upon the regenerative processes of the larva?

REFERENCES

ADAMS, A. E., 1941 - "Studies in experimental zoology." Edwards Bros. Ann Arbor, Mich.

ADOLPH, E. F., 1931 - "Body size as a factor in the metamorphosis of tadpoles." Biol. Bull. 61:376.

ALLEN, B. M., 1938 - "The endocrine control of amphibian metamorphosis." Biol. Rev. 13:1.

BOWER, C. M., 1938 - "Growth rates of the hind limbs of Rana sylvatica during normal and induced metamorphosis." Anat. Rec. 72: suppl. 99.

BOWERS, C. Y., A. SEGALOFF & B. BROWN, 1959 - "Factors affecting the thyroid gland uptake of I^{131} of the Rana catesbiana tadpole." Endocrin. 65:882-888.

CLEMENTS, D. I., 1932 - "Comparative histological studies of the thyroid and pituitaries in frog tadpoles in normal and accelerated metamorphosis." Jour. Roy. Micr. Soc. 52:138.

COPENHAVER, W. M., 1955 - "Growth of thyroid tissue in the gills of Amblystoma punctatum reared in propothyouraul". Jour. Exp. Zool. 129:291-308.

ETKIN, W., 1936 - "The phenomenon of amphibian metamorphosis. III. The development of the thyroid gland." Jour. Morph. 59:69. (See also Jour. Exp. Zool. 71:317)

ETKIN, W. M., 1955 - "Metamorphosis" in Willier, Weiss, Hamburger (eds.) "Analysis of Development." Saunders, Philadelphia.

GUDERNATSCH, J. F., 1912 - "Feeding experiments on tadpoles." Arch. f. Ent. Mech. 35:457.

GUNTHORP, H., 1932 - "Results of feeding thyroid glands of various vertebrates to tadpoles." Physiol. Zool. 5:397.

HUNT, E. & J. N. DENT, 1957 - "Iodine uptake and turnover in frog tadpoles." Physiol. Zool. 30:87-91.

INGRAM, W. R., 1929 - "Studies on amphibian neotony. I. The matamorphosis of the Colorado axolotl by injection of inorganic iodine." Physiol. Zool. 2:149.

LYNN, W. G. & H. WACHOWSKI, 1951 - "The thyroid gland and its functions in cold-blooded vertebrates." Quart. Rev. Biol. 26:123.

SCHNEIDER, R. A., 1939 - "Effects of feeding thyroid substance." Quart. Rev. Biol. 14:289.

SPAUL, E. A., 1925 - "Iodine and amphibian metamorphosis." Proc. Zool. Soc., London. 995.

SWINGLE, W. W., 1926 - "The effect on amphibian differentiation of feeding iodofibrin, iododestin, and iodogliadin." Anat. Rec. 34:130.

UHLENHUTH, E. & H. KARNS, 1928 - "The morphology and physiology of the salamander thyroid gland. III. The relation of the number of follicles to development and growth of the thyroid in Amblystoma maculatum." Biol. Bull. 54:128.

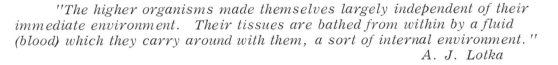

"The higher organisms made themselves largely independent of their immediate environment. Their tissues are bathed from within by a fluid (blood) which they carry around with them, a sort of internal environment."

A. J. Lotka

"It would appear, when the marine ancestors of terrestrial vertebrates emerged from the sea and adventured upon dry land, they packed, as it were, a portion of their saline environment in their baggage, and took along with them on their excursion as an essential part of their internal milieu . . . we ourselves carry about with us in our arteries and veins, if not a portion of the actual ocean, at least a roughly approximate replica of its brine . . . There are strong indications that the fluids of the highest animals are really descended from sea water."

L. J. Henderson

"Since the Stone Age the average size of man has increased by five centimeters (2 inches). When members of the Scottish nobility wanted to present a pageant for Queen Victoria during her wedding tour, they found that the historic suits of armour were too small. The descendants had outgrown the armour of their ancestors."

F. Kahn, 1944

"Countless human beings are being starved to death for the need of nitrogen (as protein) even though they are living in an atmosphere of 79% nitrogen, which they cannot use. This is probably the greatest paradox of terrestrial life, and at the same time the greatest tragedy of mankind."

F. Kahn, 1944

41. THYROIDECTOMY AND EARLY AMPHIBIAN DEVELOPMENT

PURPOSE: By means of surgical extirpation to determine the functional relationship of the thyroid anlagé in the early larva to metamorphic changes in the later tadpole.

MATERIALS:

Biological:　Anura (stage #17) or Urodele (stage #31) larvae.

Technical:　Standard Equipment.

METHOD:

Precautions:

1. Avoid injury or removal of heart anlagé which is just posterior to the thyroid anlagé.
2. Avoid post-operative bacterial infection. If necessary, use 0.1% sodium sulfadiazine in operating and in culture media.

Control: The control consists of embryos of similar age and stage in which similar surgical incisions are made but without the removal of any tissue. Such animals should be given identical treatment as the experimentals.

Procedure:

1. Remove the embryos from their jelly capsules and fertilization membranes. If there is any muscular activity, anesthetize them in 1/3,000 MS 222 (freshly made up). Ciliary movement cannot be reduced by narcosis.
2. Make a shallow depression in the Permoplast (or paraffin) of the operating dish. Use Urodele Operating Medium for Urodeles and 2X Standard Solution for Anura, adding 1% sodium sulfadiazine if there is difficulty with infection. Place the embryo on its left side, head away from the operator.
3. Insert the point of a double-edged lancet (or operating glass needle) between the position of the thyroid and the heart anlagé, (see diagrams) and make an outward cut through the throat ectoderm. Remove a wedge of tissue, the apex of which reaches the floor of the pharynx just at the point of the slightly pigmented thyroid evagination. Carefully excavate the cells with the hair loop, avoiding particularly the heart mesoderm. Part of the pharyngael floor will, of necessity, be removed with the thyroid. (If the student finds this operation difficult, refresh his memory of the position of the thyroid anlagé by studying both transverse and sagittal sections of tail-bud stages. A complete dissection study of the living tail-bud stage prior to thyroid extirpation is definitely recommended, for this is a delicate operation.)
4. Transfer the operated embryo to an agar-base in a #2 Stender filled with operating medium for about 30 minutes during which the wound will heal. Then transfer the embryo to Urodele Growing Medium or Standard Solution (depending upon the genus) for further development, preferably at a temperature slightly below that of the laboratory. Begin feeding at appropriate stage of development.

OBSERVATION AND TABULATION OF DATA:

Operated and control embryos must be given identical treatment with respect to volume, medium, light, food, etc.

1. Make sketches at 15 minute intervals of the wound healing of the operated animals.
2. At weekly intervals following the operation, make drawings (or photographs) of thyroidectomized and control embryos.

3. Select some embryos that show definite effect of thyroidectomy at a time when
    metamorphic changes are beginning to appear in the controls, and treat them
    with 1/1,000,000 thyroxin to determine whether it is possible to compensate for
    the loss of the thyroid gland in bringing the larvae through the critical stage of
    metamorphosis. (Consult exercise on "Thyroid and Amphibian Metamorphosis".)

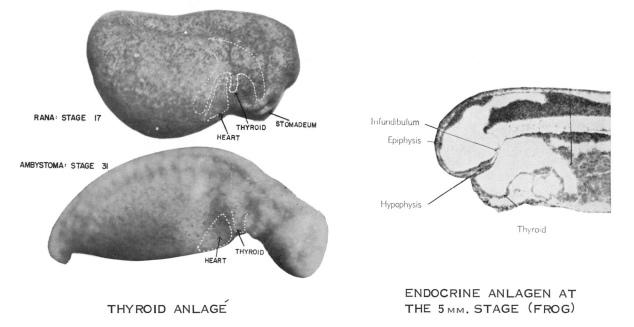

THYROID ANLAGÉ   **ENDOCRINE ANLAGEN AT
                                            THE 5 MM. STAGE (FROG)**

DISCUSSION:

Thyroidless tadples will not generally go through metamorphosis. This stage in Rana
pipiens controls should be attained at about 75 days at laboratory temperatures, providing the food, space, and other factors are adequate.   There is no doubt but that the
pituitary gland is closely related to the thyroid in function. The active element of the
thyroid gland is iodine, and this may be administered in different forms (e. g., crystalline iodine, KI, or in thyroxin). Thyroidless embryos stimulated by thyroxin may occasionally surpass the controls in metamorphic changes.

REFERENCES

ALLEN, B. M., 1938 - "The endocrine control of amphibian metamorphosis." Biol. Rev. 13:1.
BAUMAN, G., 1936 - "Modifications des premiers stades du developpement des oeufs de bactraciens anoures sans l'influence de
    la Thyroxine." C. R. Soc. de Biol. 121:1032.
BOWERS, C. Y., A. SEGALOFF & B. BROWN, 1959 - "Factors affecting the thyroid gland uptake of I-131 of the Rana catesbiana
    tadpole." Endocrin. 65:882-888.
HOSKINS, E. R. & M. M. HOSKINS, 1919 - "Growth and development of Amphibia as affected by thyroidectomy." Jour. Exp.
    Zool. 29:1.
HUNT, E. & J. N. DENT, 1957 - "Iodine uptake and turnover in the frog tadpole." Physiol Zool. 30:87-91.
LARSON, M. E., 1927 - "The extirpation of the thyroid gland and its effects upon the hypophysis in Bufo americanus and Rana
    pipiens." Sci. Bull. Univ. Kansas. 17:319.
STOKES, M., 1940 - "Early localization of the thyroid anlagé in Hyla regilla." Proc. Soc. Exp. Biol. & Med. 45:681.
TAYLOR, A., 1934 - "Athyroidism in the salamander, Triturus torosus." Jour. Exp. Zool. 273:153.

42. HYPOPHYSECTOMY AND EARLY AMPHIBIAN DEVELOPMENT

PURPOSE: By means of surgical extirpation to determine the relation of the epithelial hypophysis to early amphibian development.

MATERIALS:
    Biological: Early tail-bud stages of any amphibian (Anura stage #18, Urodela stage #29).

    Technical: Standard equipment.

METHOD:
    Precautions:
1. Use only embryos that are not injured during removal from their jelly capsules.
2. Avoid bacterial contamination following the operation. If this becomes a factor, operate in 0.1% sodium sulfadiazine in Standard Solution (or Operating Medium for Urodeles).
3. Endeavor to remove the hypophysis completely, but no other tissue. (The success of this operation can be tested only by subsequent histological examination.)

    Control: The control for this experiment consists of surgical cutting in the vicinity of the hypophysis, but without removal of any cells.

    Procedure:
1. Remove all coverings, including the vitelline (fertilization) membrane, from a group of embryos at the appropriate stage (see above). Place them in 2X Standard Solution or in Spring Water (Anura) or in Urodele Operating Medium (Urodeles) over a base of agar. The agar will prevent adhesion of the epidermis to the glass bottom of the dish.
2. Prepare an operating dish with base of soft paraffin or of Permoplast, and, with a ball tip, mould a depression so that the embryo can be held securely with its face looking upward toward the operator.
3. Locate the hypophyseal groove (from stomodeum to hypophysis) and its dorsal hypophyseal pit. This is the region of ingrowing of the pigmented, ectodermal cells which constitute the hypophysis. Use a double-edged lancet, or micro- (glass) needles to remove the wedge of pigmented hypophysis. This anlage grows inward between the roof of the pharynx and the floor of the brain (infundibulum) but neither of these other tissue areas should be disturbed, if possible. With small hair loop excavate all pigmented cells from the hypophyseal pit. *
4. Leave the embryo in operating medium until the wound heals, about 30 minutes, then return it to the normal culture medium (i.e., Standard for Anura and Growing Medium for Urodeles). Keep operated embryos separately in #2 Stenders, with agar bases, preferably at temperatures slightly below that of the laboratory.

OBSERVATIONS AND TABULATION OF DATA:

1. Make sketches immediately after the operation and at 15 minute intervals during the healing process of the hypophyseal area. Healing should be complete within 1 hour.

---

* See section on "Thyroidectomy and Early Development" for photograph of sagittal section of Anuran embryo showing hypophysis, page 321.

RANA PIPIENS

HYPOPHYSEAL INVAGINATION

STAGE 18

STAGE 17

GILL ANLAGE

STAGE 19

STOMODEAL CLEFT

HYPOPHYSEAL INVAGINATION

HYPOPHYSEAL ANLAGÉ

HYPOPHYSECTOMY   CONTROL

HYPOPHYSECTOMIZED
AT STAGE 18

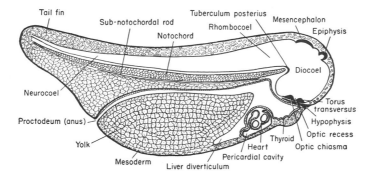

Tail fin   Sub-notochordal rod   Tuberculum posterius   Mesencephalon
                        Notochord   Rhombocoel   Epiphysis

                                                    Diocoel

Neurocoel

Proctodeum (anus)   Torus transversus

Yolk   Hypophysis
                                                    Optic recess
                          Thyroid   Optic chiasma
Mesoderm   Heart   Pericardial cavity
         Liver diverticulum

RECONSTRICTION OF THE 5 MM. TADPOLE
IN SAGITTAL SECTION

2. At weekly intervals after the operation make drawings (or take photographs) of the operated and control embryos, side-by-side, to show any
    a. Changes in pigmentation
    b. Differences in rate of development (i. e., size differences)
    Remember that these embryos must be fed after the stage #42.

3. Embryos which show pronounced effects of hypophysectomy (silvery appearance), stunting, etc.) should be sectioned (transversely and sagitally) to determine the extent or success of the hypophyseal extirpation. Control embryos of the same age should be sectioned for direct comparison. Note also any variations in the development of the thyroid glands.

DISCUSSION:

The hypophysis is the anlagé of the pars anterior, the pars intermedia, and the pars tuberalis of the adult pituitary gland. The gland is derived entirely from ectoderm, but these portions are derived from head rather than brain ectoderm. Removal of this ectoderm (epithelial hypophysis) after its ingrowth has begun seems to prevent regeneration of the same type of tissue so that the relationship of the pars intermedia to the pigmentary system is clearly indicated. Such embryos should survive for many weeks.

The method of transplantation might be super-imposed upon this procedure of extirpation. The host hypophysis might be transplanted in toto (if so removed) to the flank or tail-bud region of the same embryo, to determine whether it could support the pigmentary system although separated from the infundibular portion of the pituitary. This double-treatment of a single embryo is rather drastic, and it is not always possible to remove the hypophysis intact. The initial attempts might therefore be a direct transplantation of an hypophysis excised from another individual, after removal of the original host anlagé.

Atwell and Holley (1936) have shown that if the epithelial hypophysis of Rana sylvatica is removed at the tail-bud stage, some of those which became silvery would, nevertheless, metamorphose. The thyroids, gonads, and adrenals of such forms showed no effect of hypophysectomy. The silvery tadpoles which achieved metamorphosis lacked the pars intermedia but possessed sufficient of the anterior lobe to stimulate the normal thyroid to carry the animals through the critical period of metamorphosis.

REFERENCES

ALLEN, B. M., 1929 - "The influence of the thyroid gland and hypophysis upon growth and development of Amphibian larvae." Quart. Rev. Biol. 4:325.
ALLEN, B. M., 1957 - "The effects of heavy gamma irradiation upon pituitary glands transplanted into hypophysectomized tadpoles of Bufo boreas." Jour. Exp. Zool. 136:185-200.
ATWELL, W. J. & E. HOLLEY, 1936 -""Extirpation of the pars intermedia of the hypophysis in the young amphibian with subsequent silvery condition and metamorphosis." Jour. Exp. Zool. 73:23.
BLOUNT, R. F., 1933 - "Total growth and body proportions as influenced by pituitary rudiment implantation and extirpation in Urodele embryos." Anat. Rec. 5546.
GREENWOOD, A. W., 1924 - "The growth rate in hypophysectomized salamander larvae." Brit. Jour. Exp. Biol. 2:75.
HOGBEN, L. T., 1924 - "The Pigmentary Effector System." Oliver & Boyd, Edinburgh.
KLATT, B., 1933 - "Weitere Versuche (Hypophysesextirpation und Implantationen) an Tritonlarven." Arch. f. Ent. Mech. 130:79.
SAXEN, L., E. SAXEN, S. TOWONEN & K. SALIMAKI, 1957 - "The anterior pituitary and the thyroid function during normal and abnormal development of the frog." Ann. Zool. Soc. Vanomo. 18:1-44.
SCHOTTE, O. E., 1926 - "Hypophysectomie et Metamorphose des Batraciens Urodeles." C. R. Soc. Phys. et Nat. Hist., Geneve. 43:95.
SMITH, P. E., 1920 - "The Pigmentary, Growth, and Endocrine Disturbances Induced in the Anuran Tadpole by the Early Ablation of the Pars Buccalis of the Hypophysis." Am. Anat. Memoires, #11:1.
SWINGLE, W. W., 1921 - "The relation of the pars intermedia of the hypophysis to pigmentation changes in Anuran larvae." Jour. Exp. Zool. 34:119.

G. Chemical Embryology
43. CYTOCHEMICAL TESTS FOR GAMETES AND EMBRYOS OF AMPHIBIA

The following tests have all been tried and proven successful, and should be used on small and large ovarian eggs, isolated germinal vesicles, testes, the gastrula and neurula stages. The tests are largely for proteins, with emphasis on the amino acids and nucleo-proteins. Some tests for carbohydrates, lipids, and enzymes are included.

Specific suggestions are as follows:
1. Stain immature or post-ovulation ovary of Rana pipiens with
    a. Safranin and light green (note yolk nuclei).
    b. Iron haematoxylin (note chromosome and nucleolar structure)
    c. Toluidine blue - stains both nucleic acids.
    d. Unna's methyl green-pyronine (combine with enzymes). Thymonucleic acid green, ribonucleic acid red.
    e. Feulgen - specific for thymonucleic acid. Plasmal reaction.
2. Glycogen and lipid distribution in öogonia and early öocytes.
3. Protein tests:
    a. Nucleoprotein extraction - Mirsky & Pollister (Fred testes).
    b. Biuret - Xanthoproteic - Ninhydrin tests (Frog testes).
    c. Arginine - Tyrosine - Tryptophane tests (Frog testes smears; frog ovary).
    d. Test for - SH proteins, nitroprusside test (Frog testes smears, embryos).
4. Tests for enzymes: peroxidases - Indolphenoloxidases (Frog testes smears).
5. Miscellaneous: Test for Phosphorus and Oxygen.

PROTEIN TESTS

NUCLEOPROTEINS: (Mirsky & Pollister, 1942)

Grind up a large number of whole frog testes in neutral sodium chloride solutions of three concentrations, in two of which the nucleoproteins are soluble and in the third they are insoluble.

1. Extract with 1 M NaCl-volume about 10 X that of testes mash. Becomes viscous
2. Centrifuge at 10,000 r.p.m., providing a viscous, slightly opalescent supernatant fluid. Viscosity due to nucleoprotein dissolved therein.
3. Add 6 volumes of distilled water - nucleoprotein percipitates in a fibrous mass, settling rapidly so that the supernatant fluid can be siphoned off.
4. Wash percipitate in 0.14 M NaCl (in which it is insoluble).
5. Redissolve in 1 M NaCl.
6. Centrifuge again at high speed to remove the suspended material.
7. Re-percipitate by adding 6 volumes of distilled water.
8. Stir the mixture with a glass rod with a crook at its end, collecting a fibrous nucleoprotein which will wind around the glass rod.

(Further purification can be achieved by repeating the above process)

NUCLEIC ACIDS:*

A. Toluidine Blue:

1. Stain sections (ovary) for 20 minutes in saturated aqueous solution of Toluidine Blue.
2. Differentiate twice for 10 minutes in 95% alcohol.
3. Mount as usual.
    Toluidine blue is taken by both nucleic acids, an orthochromatic (blue) color is given only by nucleic acids, found in both the cytoplasm and nucleus.

B. The Plasmal Reaction:

The following procedure has been used successfully with the amphibian ovary, particularly the immature and post-ovulation ovary. It is based on Voss (1922 and 1931) and Lison (1936). The reaction is given by a special type of phospholipid in which an aldehyde group appears upon treatment with the sublimate. The procedure follows:
1. Fix the ovary in saturated corrosive sublimate - 5 minutes.
2. Wash in distilled water.
3. Dehydrate, clear, embed, section (10 μ), and then hydrate.
4. Place directly in Feulgen reagent for 15 minutes.
5. Wash with 3 changes of distilled water saturated with SO_2.
6. Rinse in distilled water.
7. Mount in pure glycerine and observe under the microscope.

Plasmalogen is a component of the cytoplasm which gives a positive Feulgen test. Being a phospholipid, the control for this test consists of fixing the ovary with Carnoy's fluid and washing twice with alcohol for 15 minutes each. This extracts most of the lipids.

C. The Nucleal Reaction:

This reaction depends upon the combination of the N-sulphinic acid in fuchsin-sulphurous acid with the aldehyde component released from a molecule by mild and partial hydrolysis. However, it must be remembered that the failure of any tested tissue to give this reaction may be due to any of four following causes (Gardiner, 1935).
1. The substance may not contain the aldehyde component.
2. The hydrolysis may be insufficient to release the aldehyde group from the molecule.
3. The hydrolysis may result not only in splitting off of the aldehyde group but also in its disintegration, so that it cannot react with the sulphinic acid to form the new compound.
4. The aldehyde-containing substance, and consequently the aldehyde set free on hydrolysis, may be so small in quantity that, although the reaction actually occurs, the compound is too minute in amount to be visible even with high magnification.

Gardiner (1935) says further: "Typically chromatin gives the reaction, but it does not invariably do so, nor is it the only cellular substance capable of it." Stowell (1946) says: "The preponderance of evidence indicates that with the proper precautions the Feulgen technic for thymonucleic acid is one of the most specific histochemical reactions."

---

* The cytoplasm of cells contains principally ribonucleic acid (also known as yeast or phytonucleic acid) while the nucleus contains largely desoxyribonucleic acid (also known as thymonucleic acid). The ribonucleic acid is transformed into thymonucleic acid during development.

THE PROCEDURE

The procedure given here is based on the paper by Rafalko (1946): Hydrochloric acid is necessary only to release the sulphur dioxide from the sulphites used in the formation of the leuco-basic fuchsin and in the sulphurous acid bath following staining. Both the acid and the sulphite were eliminated and direct charging of both the basic fuchsin and the bath water with sulphur dioxide gas was substituted.

Bubble sulphur dioxide gas from a small aperture in glass tubing into 100 cc. of 0.5% basic fuchsin, beneath a hood. Decolorization takes place in 1 hour and the reagent is ready for use. Distilled water is similarly saturated, and may be stored in tightly corked bottles for weeks. To get SO_2, use simple flask-and-funnel generator and sodium bisulphite and dilute sulphuric acid.

1. Fix tissues in Zenkers (or Bouin) for 2 - 20 minutes.
2. Wash not more than 20 minutes, embed and section in the usual manner.
3. Place in distilled water - 2 minutes.
4. Normal HCl at room temperature - 2 minutes.
5. Normal HCl at 60°C. for 8 to 10 minutes.
6. Normal HCl at room temperature, rinse only.
7. Distilled water - rinse.
8. Sulphurous acid - 2 minutes.
9. Leuco basic fuchsin - 1-1/2 to 2 hours.
10. Sulphurous acid bath for sufficient time to remove the free, unreacted leuco basic fuchsin; three 1 minute changes should be sufficient.
11. Tap water for 10 to 15 minutes.

It is possible, and even advisable, to counterstain with fast green in aqueous or alcoholic solutions. Dehydration is accomplished either through the alcohols or from water through triethyl phosphate (Nelsen, 1945: Stain Techn. 20:131) directly unto xylene. The latter is a shorter method and does not appreciably remove the aqueous counterstain.

The Feulgen reaction is essentially Schiff's aldehyde test applied to a tissue cell. The aldehyde is the carbohydrate released from the nucleic acid component of chromatin after hydrolysis with normal HCl; this carbohydrate, a d-ribodesose (Levene, 1931), combines with the active principle of fuchsin-sulphurous acid, an N-sulphinic acid with the formula

$$R \cdot H \big< \begin{matrix} H \\ SO_2H \end{matrix}$$ (Weiland and Scheuring, 1921)

to form, a blue-red color, often almost purple. The validity of the test rests upon the absence from the tissues of any aldehyde other than that tested, which might combine with sulphinic acid. If the fuchsin-sulphinic acid is oxidized, the color may be restored to act as a stain rather than as a reagent. Gardiner (1935) says: "It is impossible in the Bouin material to distinguish the chromatin from other cell constituents taking haematoxylin, but the Feulgen preparations show clearly that this perinuclear substance is not chromidial."

D. Unna's (1921) Methyl-Green Pyronine Stain for Nucleic Acids:

Methyl green stains thymonucleic acid green while pyronine stains the ribo-nucleic acid red. It is important that Gruebler's Pyronine be used and this procedure works best on late embryonic or adult tissues rather than the oocytes and early cleavage stages. The stain is as follows:

Gruebler's methyl green	0.15 gm.
Pyronine B	0.25 gm.
Alcohol........................	2.50 cc.
Glycerine......................	20.00 cc.
Carbolic acid (0.5% aqueous)........	77.50 cc.

Fix the tissues in 95% alcohol, embed and section in the usual manner, and stain in the above (Unna's) stain for 20 minutes.

The albumins and globulins are stained red by the pyronine, while the nucleo-proteins are stained blue-green with the methyl green. To separate the albumins and globulins one can take advantage of the differential solubility. The albumins and pseudo-globulins are soluble in water, the globulins are not soluble in water. Both are soluble in salt solutions. Failure to stain with methyl green would indicate the absence of nucleoproteins.

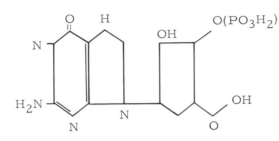

Guanin - d - ribose nucleotid   Guanin - 2-desoxy - d - ribose -
(Ribosnucleic acid)   nucleotid (Thymonucleic acid)

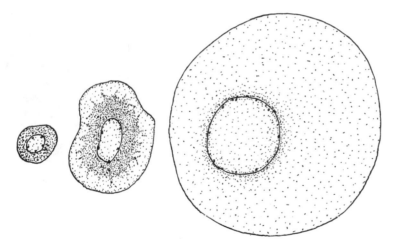

The distribution of ribonucleic acid at three stages in the oogenesis of the amphibian egg. (Redrawn from Brachet, 1944.)

E.   Azure A-Phthalate (Pollister)

Fix tissue in Carnoy's 10 min., wash once in 50% alcohol.
Immerse in Azure sol. (Pollister) - 2 hrs.
Flood slide with tertiary butyl alcohol in glycerine.
    Differentiates between nucleic acids.

F.   Methyl Green-Pyronin Y Method for Nucleic Acids*

1.   Paraffin Method
    a.   Fixation: Absolute methyl alcohol .... 24 hrs.
                        Change once soon after fixation, using small
                        pieces of tissue 2-3 mm thick.
    b.   Dehydration: Absolute n-Butyl alcohol .... 30 min.
                        Absolute n-Butyl alcohol change .... 30 min.
    c.   Embedding: Alcohol-paraffin mixture in oven at 56°C. ...... 1 hr.
                        Mixture: 50% n-Butyl alcohol + 50% melted paraffin.
                        Oven temp. must not exceed 56°C. at any time.
                        Pure paraffin, 4 changes during .... 2 hrs.
                        Embed.

*Courtesy Dr. M. E. Long, from Long & Taylor, 1956.

2. Tissue Smear Method:
   a. Making smears: Tease small piece of tissue on slide. Moisten tissue with physiological saline, distribute in thin film. Do not allow film of cells to dry.
   b. Fixation: Place slide face down carefully in shallow dish of absolute methyl alcohol, supporting ends of slide with glass rods. Immediately transfer to methyl alcohol in Coplin jar with screw top. Fix for several 24 hr. periods. Slide can remain in methyl alcohol indefinitely.

3. Ascites Fluid Smear Method:
   a. Shake bottle of fluid thoroughly so that sediment is well distributed throughout.
   b. Centrifuge samples of fluid at 3000 + rpm for 5 minutes.
   c. Decant supernatant fluid from centrifuge tube.
   d. With straight 6" tube dropping pipette transfer sediment from centrifuge tube to glass slide. Distribute in thin film.
   e. Fix fluid film as in tissue smear method. Do not allow to dry.

4. Preparation of Methyl-Green-Pyronin Y Staining Solution.
   a. Acetate Buffer Solution (0.2 M, pH 4.2)
      Using only analytical reagents:
          Glacial acetic acid   M.W. 60.05
          Sodium acetate   M.W. 165.09
      For 0.2M Acetic Acid, add 1.15 cc Acetic to 98.85 cc distilled water
      For 0.2 M Sodium Acetate, add 2.72 gr. Sodium Acetate to 100 cc distilled water.
      Mix 75 cc of 0.2 M Acetic Acid + 25 cc of 0.2 M sodium Acetate for pH 4.16.
      Adjust pH with either sodium Hydroxide or Acetic Acid.
   b. Purification of Methyl Green in Acetate Buffer:
      Wash 0.5% Methyl Green in Acetate Buffer with Chloroform in a separatory funnel (about 5 liters may be needed) until all violet color has been removed from the stain-buffer solution. Let solution stand in open flask until residual chloroform has evaporated (may be overnight).
      Use Commercial Certified Methyl Green. Different batches of this dye appear to present varying shades of blue-green in the final reaction result with D N A.
   c. Purified Methyl-Green Pyronin Y Staining Solution.
      100. cc Purified Methyl Green in pH 4.2 Acetate Buffer
         0.1 gr. Pyronin Y (Commerc. Cert.)
      Keep refrigerated in glass-stoppered bottle.
      Solution may be reused for months, but always bring to room temperature before using.

5. Methyl Green-Pyronin Y Staining Procedure:
   a. (1) Sections cut at 5μ.
         Decerate and hydrate from absolute ethyl alcohol in fresh alcohols to 2 quick rinses in distilled water. Let stand in 50% alcohol if necessary, not distilled water.
      (2) Tissue and Ascites fluid smears placed directly into absolute alcohol and proceed as in (1) above.
   b. Stain: Sections ....5 min.
            Smears....................1 hour
   c. Handle each slide individually.
   d. Quick plunge into distilled water. Use fresh water frequently.
   e. Quick blot with No. 1 filter paper (7 cm circles good).
   f. Immediately place in Tertiary Butyl-alcohol mixture - 30 sec. with continuous agitation.
      Alcohol mixture:
          Tertiary Butyl Alcohol ....3 parts
          Absolute Ethyl Alcohol...........1 part
   g. Quick rinse in xylene

      h. Xylene, 2 changes of 5 minutes each. Wipe forceps dry before carrying another slide through procedure from stain so that staining solution will not be contaminated.

      i. Mount slide in xylene-balsam medium.

  6. Ribonuclease test:

      a. Hydrate 2 (a + b) slides from same source to distilled water as in 5. a. above (1) and (2).

      b. (1) Enzyme reaction: 0.01% ribonuclease in distilled water, room temperature for 1 hour. Purified ribonuclease is obtained from Worthington Biochemical Corp., Freehold, N.J.

          (2) Solvent control: Distilled water, room temperature 1 hr.

      c. Stain slides a and b at same time as in section 5, b to i.

G. Identification of Nucleic Acid by the Use of Enzymes:*

  1. Ribonuclease (crystalline) can be used to digest away the ribonucleic acid, following which Toluidine Blue will give blue nuclei and cytoplasm colorless or following which Unna's stain would give green nuclei and colorless cytoplasm. See Kunitz (1940) for simple method of preparing crystalline ribo-nuclease.

      A concentration of 0.1 mgm./cc. of water, properly buffered (McIlvaines buffer to pH 7.0), of the crystalline ribonuclease should be used with the tissue, incubated at 50°C. for 3 hours. Wash with distilled water; stain with Toluidine Blue or Unna. The best fixatives for this test are Carnoy, or the alcohol-formol-acetic mixtures, Zenker's without formol but with acetic acid. Fixation no more than 1 hour for Amphibian eggs.

      A positive stain following this procedure identifies thymonucleic acid, and will be essentially nuclear.

  2. Thymonuclease (McCarty, 1946: Jour. Gen. Physiol. 29:123) acts in a few minutes at room temperature. If the tissues are rinsed and followed with Toluidine Blue or Unna, the positively staining elements will represent the ribonucleic acid which is essentially nucleolar and cytoplasmic. (It must be remembered, however, that the specificity of these enzymes has not been conclusively demonstrated, and certain variables are involved in their use.) Brachet (Private Com.) reports that Miss MacDougall at Cold Spring Harbor stated that she obtained ribonuclease completely free of proteolytic action and that it worked just the same on sections. Brachet was unable to find a decrease in the arginine and pyronine reaction after digesting tissues with ribonuclease.

NOTE: The student is advised to run controls for all of the preceding page procedures, and to gain a prior acquaintance with the standard procedures with safranin-light-green and the iron haematoxylin. It must be remembered that the chromosomes consist of more than thymonucleic acid; that both types of nucleic acids may be found in both the cytoplasm and the nucleus; that staining reactions which are essentially chemical reactions involving the use of enzymes rather than adherent staining, depend on fixation, pH, and temperature, and concentration of the enzymes (Stowell and Zorzoli, 1947); and that the technique of combining the use of enzymes with specific staining procedures has not yet been fully checked for reliability.

      Another approach which, if combined with the above, would give more reliable results, is the U.V. absorption photography (Caspersson, Lavin and others). Both nucleic acids absorb in the ultraviolet range, but the bands are sufficiently far apart so that if the tissues are pre-treated with enzymes, then the absorption is read, an analysis can be made.

---

* These enzymes are still very expensive.

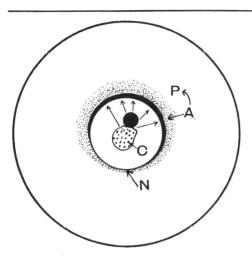

SCHEMATIC REPRESENTATION OF
THE PASSAGE OF (RIBOS-) NUCLEIC
ACID FROM THE NUCLEOLUS TO-
WARD AND THROUGH THE NUCLEAR
MEMBRANE, TO APPEAR AS CYTO-
PLASMIC NUCLEIC ACID WHICH IS
SYNTHESIZED INTO CYTOPLASMIC
PROTEINS. (P).

   (Redrawn from Brachet after
      Caspersson, Hyden)

A - cytoplasmic (ribos-) nucleic acid
C - chromatin
N - nuclear membrane
P - synthesized cytoplasmic proteins
      (from "A")

(Nucleolus - solid black)

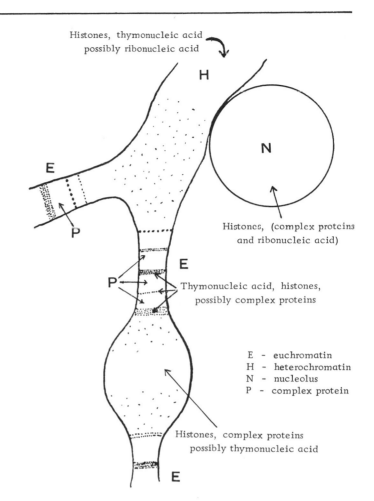

Histones, thymonucleic acid
possibly ribonucleic acid

Histones, (complex proteins
and ribonucleic acid)

Thymonucleic acid, histones,
possibly complex proteins

E - euchromatin
H - heterochromatin
N - nucleolus
P - complex protein

Histones, complex proteins
possibly thymonucleic acid

SCHEMATIC (CHEMICAL) STRUCTURE OF THE
CHROMOSOME (Redrawn from Brachet after
Caspersson)

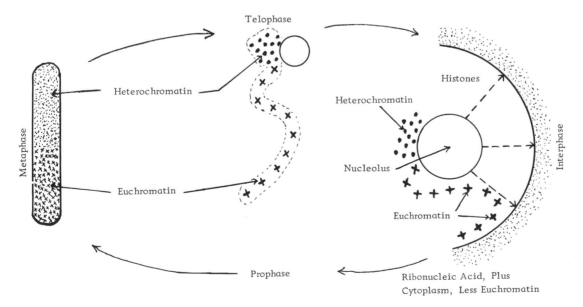

Telophase

Heterochromatin

Metaphase

Euchromatin

Prophase

Histones

Interphase

Heterochromatin

Nucleolus

Euchromatin

Ribonucleic Acid, Plus
Cytoplasm, Less Euchromatin

SCHEMATIC REPRESENTATION OF THE CHANGES IN
THE NUCLEOPROTEINS DURING MITOSIS
(Redrawn from Brachet after Caspersson)

H. General Protein Tests (Standard):

1. Biuret Test for Peptides - this is a crude and relatively insensitive test for peptides or proteins in general, but has the advantage of being rapid and rather simple. The procedure is as follows:

    a. Harden tissues in 10% formaldehyde for 24 hours if formalin is not included in the fixative. Wash thoroughly.

    b. If the material is to be sectioned, it should be cut thickly. The reactions must be carried on in an alkaline environment which tends to macerate the tissues. It is a more satisfactory test for the presence of these substances in relatively large pieces of tissue.

    c. Place the tissue in 1% NaOH or 1% KOH in a watchglass; add a few drops of 1% aqueous $CuSO_4$, and stir. A red color develops in the presence of simple peptides; a blue-violet color with the higher peptide and proteins.

2. Xanthoproteic Reaction - this is also a crude but simple test for proteins and is positive in the presence of tyrosine, phenylalanine, tryptophane, all phenolic compounds, and all the peptides except the protamines.

    a. Harden the tissues in 10% formaldehyde for 24 hours, if formalin is not included in the fixative. Strong fixation is necessary.

    b. Immerse the tissue in concentrated HNO_3 for some minutes, until it becomes intensely yellow.

    c. Wash in distilled water.

    d. Immerse in diluted ammonia, or expose the tissue to ammonia vapors. An orange color indicates a positive test.

    e. Mount directly and examine in pure glycerine.

3. Ninhydrin Reaction for Amino Acids and Lower Peptides - this test gives a blue or violet color in the presence of amino acids, free or bound peptides and proteins. The reaction is not highly specific, however, for it is negative to amino acids proline and hydroxyproline, and it is positive to certain amines, aldehydes, sugars with free aldehyde or keto groups and ammonia compounds. With these non-protein and non-amino acid compounds, the color reaction is much less intense and tends to be reddish instead of blue.

    Serra (1946) points out the importance of hard fixation to prevent the color moving about within the tissues and becoming adherent to unnatural cell structures. The reaction is as follows (Serra and Lopes, 1945):

    a. Sectioned material is immersed in equal volumes of 0.4% solution triketo-hydrinden-hydrate (ninhydrin) in distilled water and any phosphate buffer held to pH 6.98. The phosphate buffer may be made by adding 6 cc. of a M/15 secondary sodium phosphate to 4 cc. of M/15 primary potassium phosphate.

    b. Place the material in a watchglass and over a boiling water bath, among the vapors, for 1 to 2 minutes after the water boils.

    c. Mount in pure glycerine. If the tissues are thick, compress beneath a coverslip to separate the cells from each other. The color will fade within a few hours.

I. Tests for Various Common Amino Acids:

1. Arginine: The development of histo-chemical tests of great specificity has immeasurable significance in relation to an understanding of cell morphology and physiology, particularly in respect to the nuclear inclusions. Thomas (1946) and Serra (1946) following Sakaguchi (1925) have perfected the test for arginine.

The empirical formula for arginine is

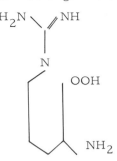

According to Thomas (1946) "when the Sakaguchi reaction is applied to a protein, a color is imparted to the protein molecule." By the methods of Thomas and of Serra, the red color of the following reactions may be regarded as proof-positive of the presence of arginine.

It is suggested that sections of the testes and of the ovary be tested for arginine. The red color generally develops in both the cytoplasm and the nucleus of most cells, but there is considerably more color in the chromosomes, nucleoli, and intermitotic chromatin than in the remainder of the cell. The spermatozoan heads, representing concentrated nuclear material, give a most intense reaction (see Thomas, 1946).

Thomas (1946) and Serra (1946) have independently modified the original Sakaguchi (1925) reaction as a specific test for arginine in biological materials. The Thomas procedure is negative for guanidine, urea, creatine, creatinine, and other amino acids that might be encountered in biological tissues. The presence of arginine is demonstrated by a strong red or red-orange color which is transient but can be prolonged for several hours by proper dehydration. The usual ethyl alcohol tends to extract some of the color, as do most of the other dehydrants, but Thomas (1946) has found that tertiary butyl alcohol will dehydrate the tissues without the removal of color and aniline oil is used to clear. The system must be kept alkaline because the color fades in either neutral or acid media.

Serra (1946) now advises the use of glycerine in which the color seems to be stabilized for many months.

a. The Method of Serra (1946)
    (1) Harden fixed tissues in 10% formaldehyde for 24 hours unless formalin was included in the original fixative.
    (2) Prepare an alkaline a-naphthol-urea mixture and bring it to 0° to 5°C., in a watchglass. The mixture is as follows:
        (a) 0.5 cc. diluted a-naphthol. Use stock solution 1% crystallized a-naphthol in 96% alcohol and, just before using, dilute to 1/10 with 40% alcohol.
        (b) 0.5 cc. normal NaOH.
        (c) 0.2 cc. of 40% aqueous urea solution.
    (3) After 12 to 15 minutes in the above mixture, add 0.2 cc. of 2% NaOBr, and stir well for 3 minutes. This solution should be freshly made up by pouring 0.7 cc. of liquid bromine into 100 cc. of 5% NaOH, agitating, and cooling.
    (4) Add 0.2 cc. of 40% urea, stir.
    (5) Add 0.2 cc. of 2% NaOBr and again stir well. The color will now develop if arginine is present and should attain its maximum intensity in about 3 to 5 minutes
    The color can be somewhat stabilized by passing the tissue through 4 changes of pure glycerine.

Serra claims that if the tissue is placed in pure NaOBr solution for 3 minutes after step "e" (above) the color becomes more intense and is stabilized in glycerine. He uses this test for basic proteins, for proteins in general which contain arginine, and for guanidine derivatives in which only one H-atom of one amino group is substituted by a radical of the alkyl or fatty acid type.

b.   The Method of Thomas (1946)
With this method the red color develops when a solution of arginine or a protein solution containing arginine is treated with a-naphthol, alkali and hypochlorite. Guanidine itself is negative but when one of the guanidine H-atoms is substituted by an alkyl, fatty acid, or cyano radical, then there is a positive color reaction. The color develops and fades rapidly but the addition of urea helps to hold the color for several minutes. Rapid dehydration is critically important, and is accomplished by tertiary butyl alcohol followed by aniline oil.

(1) Fix tissues in Bouin's fluid. Carnoy's or 10% formalin are equally good.
(2) Sectioned material must be firmly affixed to slides, with the usual paraffin albumin method. The slides may be left in 70% alcohol until ready for the tests.
(3) Hydrate the tissues down to distilled water, then place the slide in a-naphthol in 10% alcohol, by volume.
(4) Transfer to sodium hypochlorite solution for 20 seconds. This is a 0.15 normal solution of sodium hypochlorite in 0.05 normal sodium hydroxide. This solution can be made from commercial "Clorox" (see Albanese & Frankston, 1945) or by the method of Van Slyke & Hiller (1933).
(5) Transfer to urea for 5 seconds. This is an alkaline urea made up by adding 20% urea to 0.05 normal sodium hydroxide.
(6) Dehydration: 80% tertiary butyl alcohol for 30 seconds. To the 80 cc. of tertiary butyl alcohol add 1 cc. of 5 normal sodium hydroxide and 19 cc. of distilled water. Transfer to 100% tertiary butyl alcohol for 2 minutes.

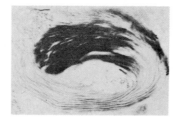 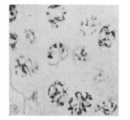

Amblystoma testes, Bouin fixation showing positive Arginine reaction.

(Courtesy L. E. Thomas 1946: Jour. Cell. & Comp. Physiol. 28:145)

(7) Clearing: 100% aniline oil for 2 minutes.
                  100% toluene for 5 seconds.
(8) Mounting: Clarite.

2. Tyrosine: According to Serra (1946) "Tyrosine seems to be present in almost all natural proteins in amounts which are not very different for the various classes, excepting principally silk fibroin, pepsin and insulin." The formula for tyrosine is

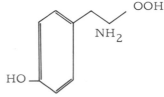

A modified Millon's reaction, devised by Serra and Lopes (1945) has been used to detect the presence of tyrosine, in the protein molecule, but the color is also produced by other phenolic compounds. Millons is mercuric or mercurous nitrate in nitric acid and nitrous acid. The control consists of egg albumen, gelatin and phenol. A transient color is produced by tryptophane but the tyrosine color attains its maximum intensity in about 3 minutes and lasts for some months, fading gradually with time. Their procedure follows:

a. Immerse tissues in mercuric solution for 30 minutes. This is made up of 7.5 gms. $HgSO_4$; 5.5 gms. $HgCl_2$; and 7.0 gms. Na_2SO_4 dissolved in 85 cc. of distilled water to which 12.5 gms. of conc. H_2SO_4 had been added, the whole being made up to 100 cc. volume with distilled water. The reaction should take place in a glass stoppered bottle in water bath at $60^{\circ}C$.

b. Cool the bottle in running water for 10 minutes.

c. Add to the mercuric solution in the bottle an equal volume of distilled water.

d. Develop the color by adding a few drops of 1 M $NaNO_2$ (6.9% aqueous), freshly prepared. The color may last for months if the tissues are mounted in glycerine. Compress cells apart beneath coverslip.

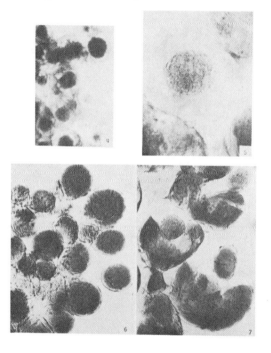

OOCYTES OF RANA RIDIBUNDA

Fig. 4. Tyrosine reaction, photographed without filter.

Fig. 5. Tyrosine reaction, photographed at higher magnification than Fig. 4 and without filter.

*Fig. 6. Arginine reaction, photographed with green filter. Slight differential between cytoplasm and nucleus.

*Fig. 7. Same as Fig. 6 except that the nuclei have been separated from the cytoplasm by compression after the arginine reaction.

Photographs by courtesy J. A. Serra
*Figures unpublished.

A second procedure may be used and is known as the diazo reaction for histidine and tyrosine. This test gives an orange or yellow color in the presence of histidine and tyrosine of the proteins. It is the histidine which imparts the reddish tinge.   Lison (1936) follows a different procedure to demonstrate the presence of phenolic compounds and axoproteids.   Serra's (1946) procedure follows:

a.   Treat tissues for 2 to 3 minutes with saturated aqueous solution of sodium carbonate.

b.   Add a few drops of diazo reagent, stir well, and observe in pure glycerine.

The diazo-reagent (prepare just before using, keep cool)

Place 1.5 cc. of sulphanilic acid in a 50 cc. flask in an ice bath.
This is made by dissolving 0.9 gms. pure sulphanilic acid in 9 cc.
of concentrated HCl, and adding water to make 100 cc.

Add 1.5 cc. of a 5% aqueous solution of $NaNO_3$, shaking well.

Add 6 cc. of $NaNO_2$ after 5 minutes, constantly shaking mixture.

Add cooled distilled water to make 50 cc. total volume.

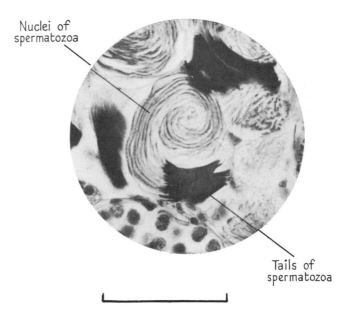

Modification of the Sakaguchi test
for Guanidine derivatives.   Triturus
vulgaris testis.

Courtesy J. R. Baker, 1947: Quart.
Jour. Microsc. Science. 88:115.

3.   Tryptophane: Tryptophane comprises from 1 to 3% of the great majority of proteins.   Its formula follows:

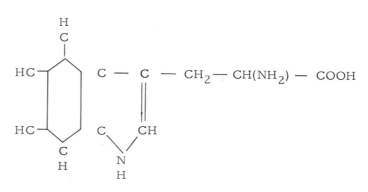

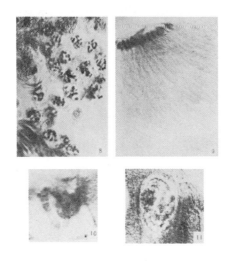

Fig. 8. Testis of Rana ridibunda perezi. Arginine reaction (green filter).
Fig. 9. Spermatozoa of Helix aspersa, heads to upper left. Arginine reaction.
Fig. 10. Salivary gland chromosomes of Chironomus larvae. Tyrosine reaction.
Fig. 11. Salivary gland chromosomes of Chironomus larvae. Tryptophane reaction.

Photographs by courtesy of J. A. Serra

Since this amino acid results from the hydrolysis of many proteins and the test is sensitive, a satisfactory procedure is available for animal tissues.
a. Harden the tissues in 10% formaldehyde, if they were not previously fixed in a formalin fixative, for 5 hours; wash well.
b. Immerse for 3 to 5 seconds in an aqueous solution of sodium silicate.
c. Immediately immerse the pieces in Voisenet reagent for 10 to 15 minutes, in a small glass-stoppered bottle. This reagent is made by adding 1 drop of 2% aqueous formol and 1 drop of 0.15% aqueous $NaNO_2$, with stirring, to 10 cc. of concentrated HCl. Solution is freshly made before using.
d. Mount in glycerine and observe directly. Tissues may be compressed apart between coverslip and slide. The color fades hence the tissue must be examined within a few hours.

J. Test for the -SH Groups:

The following test gives a stable red coloration in the presence of the tripeptide glutathione. According to Serra (1946): "it is possible not only to demonstrate the existing -SH groups but also to reduce SS groups to SH groups by means of a pre-treatment of the materials with a solution of 10% KCN for 10 minutes." Of course, the arginine test is also positive for the -SH group proteins. An intense reaction for protein -SH presumably demonstrates the existence of active metabolic and synthetic changes in the proteins (Brachet, 1940). Protein denaturation involves an unfolding of polypeptide chains and an increase in -SH reacting groups. Hence, a positive -SH reaction might indicate either an active synthesis or a breakdown of proteins. The procedure follows:
1. Fix tissues for no more than 4 hours at room temperature in 10% formaldehyde. Rinse in distilled water.
2. Immerse tissues or sections in 5% aqueous zinc acetate - 30 seconds. Rinse in distilled water.
3. Treat with 10% aqueous solution sodium nitroprusside containing 2% concentrated ammonia. Brilliant red color develops within 5 minutes. Wash in distilled water and mount in glycerine.

The glutathione is partially soluble, hence the reaction will vary with fixation and other preliminary treatments. Fresh material, without fixation, gives even more reliable results.

Fix oöcytes in trichloracetic acid for 10 minutes, wash in distilled water, place in 5% zinc acetate for a few seconds, and wash again in distilled water. Treat with 10% aqueous sodium nitroprusside plus a few drops of NH₄OH, and mount in glycerine under a coverslip.

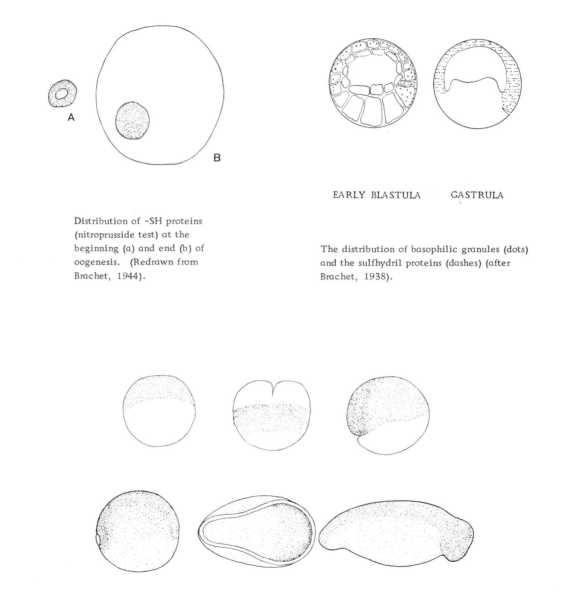

EARLY BLASTULA   GASTRULA

Distribution of -SH proteins (nitroprusside test) at the beginning (a) and end (b) of oogenesis. (Redrawn from Brachet, 1944).

The distribution of basophilic granules (dots) and the sulfhydril proteins (dashes) (after Brachet, 1938).

Location of the -SH proteins by the nitroprusside test during various stages in the early development of the amphibian embryo. (Redrawn from Brachet, 1944)

THE GLYCOGEN TESTS

The plasmal reaction is generally used for plasmalogen (a phospholipin) in the cytoplasm and consists of the Feulgen reaction. But this can also be used for glycogen if the proper preliminary treatment is given to the tissues, as follows:

1. Fix pieces (small) of ovary (amphibian) for 1 hour in 4% chromic acid.
2. Wash 5 minutes in running water.
3. Immerse for 15 minutes in Feulgen reagent.
4. Wash 3 times in water saturated with SO_2.
5. Rinse in water and mount in glycerine.

Glycogen makes its first appearance soon after the first fat globules of the vitellus appear, with a concentration in a ring about the nucleus. There is none in the germinal vesicle.

Bevelander and Johnson (1946) give a simple method of histochemical localization of glycogen, as follows:

1. Fix tissue in Carnoys for 24 hours.
2. Mount sections on albumen smeared slides, flooded with Lugol's solution at $40^{\circ}C$.
3. Remove the paraffin with xylol.
4. Flood the sections with a saturated solution of Iodine in 100% alcohol.
5. Mount in clarite to study.

Bensley (1939) describes a stain for glycogen as follows:

1. Boil the following gently until the color darkens, then cool.
   Carmine . . . . 2 gms.
   Potassium carbonate . . . . 1 gm.
   Potassium chloride . . . . 5 gms.
   Distilled water . . . . 60.0 cc.
2. Add 20 cc. of concentrated ammonia.
3. Allow to ripen for 24 hours. This becomes the stock solution.

THE LIPID TESTS

Identification of the various lipid substances in the cell is very difficult (Lison, 1936). Solubility tests are unreliable, and formalin fixation alters normal solubility of some fatty substances. Cytochemical and macrochemical tests may vary, even with the identical lipids. Glycerides and fatty acids are never birefringent in the dissolved condition when examined in vivo, but after treating with formalin or freezing they may become crystalline and birefringent. Tests with Osmic Acid, Sudan III, when coupled with other (physical) tests will give substantially reliable analytical results.

Serra and Lopes (1945) in studying the cytophysiology of the nucleolus give the following procedure:

1. Fix for 16 hours in 10% formol.
2. Wash tissues well in running water.
3. Stain with Sudan III in alcohol:
   At 70° stain for 25 to 75 minutes.
   At 40° stain for 22 hours.
The tests for lipids is not quantitatively reliable.

ENZYMES*

1. Histochemical Test for Peroxidase: This test should be applied to immature or post-ovulation amphibian ovaries containing oöcytes of various sizes.
   a. Fix the ovary in 10% formol for 10 minutes. This destroys the catalase.

---

* See Sumner and Somers 1947.

b.   Wash thoroughly in distilled water.

c.   Immerse the tissue in saturated aqueous solution of benzidine containing a few drops of acetic acid per 10 cc.

d.   Immerse in 1% hydrogen peroxide (perhydrol diluted to 1%).   Note the oxygen bubbles and the blue followed by brown coloration.   The reaction will appear most intense in the ovarian capillaries.

2.   Histochemical Test for Indophenoloxidase: This test should be applied to the immature or post-ovulation ovary of any amphibian.   The method is essentially that of Voss (1924).

a.   Make up Solution A by dissolving 0.5 gm. of alpha-naphthol in 100 cc. of boiling distilled water; boil for 5 minutes; cool and filter.

b.   Make up Solution B by dissolving 0.5 gm. dimethylparaphenylenediamine* in 100 cc. of cold distilled water and allow it to stand for 24 hours.   Filter.

c.   When ready to make the test, mix equal parts of "A" and "B"; add an equal volume of 0.64% NaCl and mix thoroughly.

d.   Pour some of the mixture in a Stender and add the tissue to be tested.   The mixture can be further diluted with physiological saline solution to prevent too intense a reaction.

This procedure has been modified by Child by diluting the reagent as follows:

a.   To 10 cc. of distilled water add 1 drop of dimethylparaphenylenediamine. *

b.   To 10 cc. of distilled water add 1 mgm. of alpha-naphthol.

c.   Place the fresh tissue to be tested in physiological saline and to each 1 cc. of this solution add 1 drop of each of the solutions "a" and "b".

Note which of these methods stains the yolk nucleus of the small oöcytes.

When tissue is placed in an alkaline solution of sodium glycerophosphate, enzymatic activity liberates phosphate which, as it is formed, is precipitated by the calcium ions.   This calcium phosphate is then made visible by conversion to cobalt sulfide which gives the black coloration, indicating the presence of the enzyme.

THE TEST FOR PHOSPHORUS

Phosphorus is found in the nucleolus, the chromosomes, and the protoplasm generally. It is in the thymo- and ribonucleic acids, in conjugated phosphoproteins and in the nucleoproteins.   Serra and Lopes (1945) say: "It seems that we can safely conclude that the phosphorus reaction, the coloration with basic and acidic stains and the nuclease reaction, show the existence of nucleotides of the ribose type in the nucleolus."   The nucleolar inclusions probably have a greater concentration of these nucleotides than does the remaining part of the nucleolus.   The nucleoli are richer in nucleotides, as determined by this phosphorus test, when they are young.

The method of Angeli, A., (1933 Riv. di Biol. 10:702)

1.   Sections treated for 20 minutes with solution made up of
        3 gms. ammonium molybdate
       20 cc. distilled water
       20 cc. of 30% aqueous hydrochloric acid

2.   Reduced in N/50 stannous chloride.

3.   Rinsed quickly in distilled water.

4.   Washed in 2.5% aqueous ammonia.   If phosphorus is present in any form there will develop a blue-green color

---

* If the reagent is in solid form, it should be heated on a water bath until it melts.

The method of Serra and Lopes (1945)

1. Fix small pieces of tissue in a mixture of 2 volumes of 95% alcohol, 1 volume of formol, and a few drops of glacial acetic acid per 10 cc. of total volume. Carnoy's fixative is also satisfactory.
2. Wash in running water, then in distilled water.
3. Hydrolyze for 3 days or more at 10° to 12°C. and in darkness, if possible. Use 3 cc. of the following reagent: to 20 cc. of distilled water add 0.5 gms. ammonium molybdate and 10 cc. of 30% HCl, dilute the mixture to a total of 50 cc. with distilled water.
4. Transfer to temperature of 20° to 25° for several days.
5. Add 1 drop of acetic benzedine. (Dissolve 25 mgms. of benzedine in 5 cc. of pure glacial acetic acid. Dilute to 50 cc. with distilled water. Stir or agitate for 3 minutes.)
6. Add 2 drops of pure saturated sodium acetate. The tissue, if phosphorus is present, will rapidly develop an intense blue color. The color is durable.
7. Mount in glycerine to which has been added a few crystals of sodium acetate.

THE WINKLER METHOD OF MEASURING OXYGEN CONSUMPTION*

This is a titrimetric method of measuring dissolved oxygen, first used in 1908 by Warburg in a study of the change in rate of oxygen consumption of the Arbacia egg following fertilization. It has been used recently by Barth (1942) in a study of the oxygen consumption of fragments of the amphibian gastrula.

STOCK SOLUTIONS: (For Class Use)

1. Manganese chloride (40%, iron-free) .... 500.0 cc.

2. Potassium iodide (15%) in NaOH (36%) kept in dark ...... 500.0 cc.
   Dissolve 180 grams of NaOH in distilled water, cool, add 75 grams of KI, make up to 500. cc and keep in cool dark place.

3. Hydrochloric acid (C. P. conc., no free Cl_2) .... 500.0 cc.

4. Sodium thiosulphate (N/100) .... 5000.0 cc.
   For each liter dissolve 2.482 grams of C. P. grade $Na_2S_2O_3 \cdot 5H_2O$ in distilled water. If solution is to be kept several days, add 4 cc. of 1n-NaOH per liter.

5. Starch solution (0.5%) .... 300.0 cc.
   Emulsify 1 gram of potato starch with 25 cc. of water and pour slowly into 175 cc. of boiling water, boil a few minutes, allow to settle, decant off the clear supernatant fluid. If it is to be kept for several days add a few drops of chloroform.

OXYGEN CONSUMPTION DURING THE FIRST CLEAVAGE OF THE FROG'S EGG

1. Prepare an ovulating female (Rana pipiens) and secure several mature males.
2. Prepare 3 respiration bottles consisting of 125 cc. glass-stoppered bottles. Mark them A, B, and C.
3. Prepare 3 Erlenmeyer flasks, 250 cc. capacity, and into each introduce an equivalent number of glass beads or small marbles. Mark them A, B, and C, and cork them.

---

* This is a modification of the method used by Dr. A. Tyler in the course in Marine Embryology given at the Marine Biological Laboratory, Woods Hole, Mass.

4. Prepare 3 finger bowls, mark them A, B, and C, and into each introduce exactly 10 cc. of Spring Water (Standard Solution) or any medium in which frog's eggs are normally inseminated. Into finger bowl "C" only, introduce and macerate one pair of adult frog testes. Allow these bowls to stand for 10 minutes.

5. By stripping, remove a few eggs from an ovulating female and discard them. Then strip about 200 eggs into finger bowl "B" (no sperm) and "C" (sperm suspension), and see that the eggs are completely covered with the medium. Avoid transfer of any sperm from bowl "C" to bowl "B". Allow them to stand for 2 minutes, then add to each of the three finger bowls exactly 250 cc. of the same medium (i.e., Spring Water). This will provide a total volume in each bowl of 260 cc., plus eggs in two of the bowls.

6. Using a clean section lifter, gently separate the eggs from the bottom of bowl "B" and then bowl "C" after 5 minutes. (Avoid possible insemination of eggs in bowl "B" by washing off and drying the section lifter each time it is used.) Allow the jelly on the eggs to expand another 5 minutes.

7. Fill Erlenmeyer flask "A" with the medium from finger bowl "A" to overflowing, and add the cork stopper without introducing any air. Fill flask "B" with the supernatant fluid from finger bowl "B", then carefully count out 100 eggs from bowl "B" and add them to the flask, then cork without introducing any air. Similarly fill Erlenmeyer flask "C" with the supernatant fluid from finger bowl "C", count out 100 eggs from finger bowl "C" and add them to this flask, insert the cork without introducing any air. Retain finger bowls "B" and "C" for the duration of the experiment to determine the developmental changes in the eggs. During the subsequent 3 hour period there should be variable oxygen consumption in "B" and "C" as compared with "A" in which there should be no oxygen change.

8. Make the stoppers in the Erlenmeyer flasks secure by placing a heavy rubber band lengthwise around the entire flask and stopper. Note the time and temperature and place the three flasks on a standard shaker, agitating about 5 to 25 round trips per minute at 2 to 10 inches amplitude. This will facilitate oxygen consumption. Agitate for 3 hours, or until after the control eggs (in finger bowl "C" have completed the first cleavage).

9. Determination of the oxygen consumption:
   a. Transfer with minimum agitation and exposure to air, supernatant medium from each of the flasks to 50 cc. calibrated bottles, marked A. B. and C.
   b. Using 1 cc. measured pipettes, transfer 0.2 cc. of the Manganese chloride solution (listed above) and 0.2 cc. of the KI-NaOH solution into each of the calibration bottles, inserting the tip of the pipette about halfway down the bottle. Avoid air bubbles in replacing the glass stopper.
   c. Agitate the bottles for several minutes, then allow the precipitate to settle so that there is some clear fluid at the top.
   d. Carefully remove the stopper and introduce 0.4 cc. of HCl just below the surface of fluid in each of the calibrated bottles. Stopper (without air) and shake until the precipitate is dissolved.
   e. Transfer the fluid from each of the bottles to similarly marked (clean) 125 cc. capacity Erlenmeyer flasks for titration. Solution "C" at least contains some free iodine which must be titrated soon in order to avoid loss due to volatility.
   f. Titration procedure for each sample (A, B, and C):
      (1) Add sufficient sodium thiosulphate to cause most of the yellow (iodine) color to disappear.
      (2) Add 4 or 5 drops of the starch solution to give a distinct blue color. Continue the titration until the blue color just disappears. Each cc. of N/100 sodium thiosulphate corresponds to 0.0025 millimoles of O_2. The relative values of solutions A, B, and C should be determined, and since the number of eggs in B and C is known, the oxygen consumption per fertilized and unfertilized egg can be determined.

This procedure seems at first a bit crude and yet very accurate results can be obtained. The reactions in the procedure are as follows:

$$MnCl_2 + aNaOH = Mn(OH)_2 + 2NaCl$$

$$4MN(OH)_2 + O_2 = 2Mn_2O_3 + 4H_2O$$

$$Mn_2O_3 + 6HCl = 2MnCl_2 + 3H_2O + Cl_2$$

$$Cl_2 + 2KI = 2KCl + I_2$$

Therefore, for each molecule of O_2 present, two molecules of I_2 are liberated. In titrating, the free iodine reacts with the sodium thiosulphate to form tetrathionate and sodium iodide as follows: $2Na_2S_2O_3 + I_2 = Na_2S_4O_6 + 2NaI$, which are both colorless, allowing the end point to be determined by the disappearance of the blue color that forms when iodine reacts with the starch indicator.

Once this procedure is stabilized, and the student has achieved reproducible results, it is suggested that the following additional tests be made:

1. Oxygen consumption at various stages of development, particularly during a series of early cleavages and at gastrulation.
2. Effect of cyanide, dinitrophenol, iodoacetate, colchicine.
3. Effect of low and of high pH.
4. Effect of temperature over definite time interval.
5. Oxygen consumption of artificially activated eggs (parthenogenetic) and of androgenetic eggs.

REFERENCES

ASTBURY, W. T., 1941 - "Proteins." Chemical Industry. 60:491.

BARTH, L. G. & L. JAEGER, 1947 - "Phosphorylation in the frog's egg." Physiol. Zool. 20:133.

BEHRENS, M., 1938 - "Uber die Verteilung der Lipase und Arginase zwischen zellkern und protoplasma der Leber." Zeit. f. Physiol. Chemie. 258:27.

BENSLEY, R. R., 1943 - "Chemical nature of cytoplasm." Biol. Symposium. 10:323.

BEVELANDER, G. & P. L. JOHNSON, 1946 - "The histochemical localization of glycogen in the developing tooth." Jour. Cell. & Comp. Physiol. 28:129.

BOYD, E. M., 1938 - "Lipoid substances of the ovary during ova production in Rana pipiens." Jour. Physiol. 91:394.

BRACHET, J., 1960 - "The Biochemistry of Development." Pergamon Press, N.Y.

BRAGG, A. N., 1939 - "Observations upon Amphibian deutoplasm and its relation to embryonic and early larval development." Biol. Bull. 77:268.

CASPERSSON, T. & J. SCHULTZ, 1940 - "Ribonucleuc acids in both nucleus and cytoplasm and the function of the nucleolus." Proc. Nat. Acad. Sci. 26:507.

CHANTRENNE, H., 1943 - "Recherches sur des particules cytoplasmiques de dimensions macromoleculaires riches en acide pentosenucleique." Enzymologie. 11:14.

DAVIDSON, J. N. & C. WAYMOUTH, 1946 - "Establishment of cytochemical techniques." Nature. 157:755.

DUSPIVA, F., 1942 - "Die Verteilung der Peptidase auf kern und plasma bei Froschoozyten im Verlauf der Zweiten Wachstumsteroide." Biol. Zentrlbl. 62:403.

FERNANDES, A. & J. A. SERRA, 1944 - "Euchromatine et heterochromatine dans leurs rapports avec le noyau et le nucleole." Bol. Soc. Brot. 19:67.

FEULGEN, R., 1926 - "Die Nuclealfarbung." Abderhalden Handb. der biol. Arbeit. 5:1055.

GARDINER, M. S., 1935 - "The origin and nature of the nucleolus." Quart. Rev. Mikr. Sci. 77:523.

GREGG, J. R. & R. BALLANTINE, 1946 - "Nitrogen metabolism of Rana pipiens during embryonic development." Jour. Exp. Zool. 103:143.

GREGG, J. R. & C. M. POMERAT - "The glycogen content of the embryo of Rana pipiens during development." Growth. 6:231.

GUDERNATSCH, F. & O. HOFFMAN, 1936 - "A study of the physiological value of a-amino acids during the early periods of growth and differentiation." Arch. f. Ent. mech. 135:136.

HARRIS, D. L., 1944 - "Phosphoprotein phosphatase, a new enzyme from the frog egg." Biol. Bull. 87:164.

HEATLY, N. G., C. H. WADDINGTON & J. NEEDHAM, 1937 - "Studies on the nature of the amphibian organization center, VI." Proc. Roy. Soc., London B. 122:403.

HOTCHKISS, R. D., 1948 - "A Microchemical Reaction Resulting in the Staining of Polysaccharide Structures in Fixed Tissue Preparations." Arch. of Biochemistry. 16:131.

JEENER, R., 1946 - "Sur quelques proprieties physique des proteines du noyau cellulaire." Comp. rendu. Soc. de Biol. 140:1101 (See ibid. 140:1103).

KUNITZ, M., 1940 - "Crystalline ribonuclease." Jour. Gen. Physiol. 24:15.

LISON, L., 1936 - "Histochimie animale Methods et problemes." Gauthier-Villars, Paris.

LONG, M. E. & H. C. TAYLOR, 1956 - "Nuclear variability in human neoplastic cells." Ann. N.Y. Acad. Sci. 63:1095-1105.

McCARTY, I., 1946 - "Purification and properties of desoxy-ribonucleic acid isolated from beef pancreas." Jour. Gen. Physiol. 29:123.

MIRSKY, A. E. & A. W. POLLISTER, 1943 - "Studies on the chemistry of chromatin." Trans. N.Y. Acad. Sci. 5:190. (See also 1943: Biol. Symposia, 10:249)

NEEDHAM, J., 1942 - "Biochemistry and Morphogenesis." Macmillan.

NOWINSKI, W. W., 1939 - "Intermediary carbohydrate metabolism in amphibia. I. Carbohydrate breakdown before metamorphosis." Bioch. Jour. 33:978.

PAINTER, T. S. & A. N. TAYLOR, 1942 - "Nucleic acid storage in the toad's egg." Proc. Nat. Acad. Sci. 28:311.

POLLISTER, A. W. & H. RIIS, 1948 - "Nucleoprotein determination in cytological preparations." Cold Spring Harbor Symp. Biol. 12:147.

RAFALKO, J. S., 1946 - "A modified Feulgen technique for small and diffuse chromatin elements." Stain Techn. 21:91.

SAKAGUCHI, S., 1925 - "Uber eine neue Farbenreaktion von protein und arginine." Jour. Biochem. (Japan). 5:25.

SAWYER, C. H., 1942 - "Cholinesterase in developing Amblystoma." Proc. Soc. Exp. Biol. & Med. 49:37.

SCHMITT, F. O., 1939 - "The ultrastructure of protoplasmic constituents." Physiol. Rev. 19:270.

SCHULTZ, J., 1941 - "The function of heterochromatin." Proc. 7th Int. Gen. Cong. 257-262.

SERRA, J. A., 1946 - "Histochemical tests for proteins and amino acids; the characterisation of basic proteins." Stain. Techn. 21:5.

SERRA, J. A. & A. Queroz LOPES, 1945 - "Chemical constitution of the nuclear inclusions in growing oöcyte cells." Nature. 155:792.

SPIEGELMAN, D. & M. D. KAMIN, 1946 - "Genes and nucleoproteins in the synthesis of enzymes." Science. 104:581.

STACEY, M., R. E. DERIAZ, E. G. TEECE & L. T. WIGGINS, 1946 - "Chemistry of the Feulgen and Dische nucleal reactions." Nature. 157:740.

STOWELL, R. E., 1946 - "The specificity of the Feulgen reaction for thymonucleic acid." Stain Techn. 21:137.

STOWELL, R. E. & A. ZORZOLI, 1947 - "The action of ribonuclease on fixed tissues." Stain Techn. 22:51.

SZE, L. C., 1953 - "Changes in the amount of desoxyribonucleic acid in the development of Rana pipiens." Jour. Exp. Zool. 122:577-601.

THOMAS, L. E., 1946 - "A histochemical test for arginine-rich proteins." Jour. Cell. & Comp. Physiol. 28:145.

UNNA, P. G., 1921 - "Chromolyse." Abderhalden Handb. der Biol. Arbeit. 5:1.

VOSS, H., 1931 - "Untersuchungen mit der Plasmalfarbung am Axolotei." Zeitschr. Anat. Entw. Gesch. 94:712.

WRINCH, D., 1942 - "Native proteins, flexible frameworks and cytoplasm organizations." Nature. 150:270.

ZIELINSKI, M. A., 1937 - "Phosphagen and creatine in frog's eggs." Jour. Exp. Biol. 14:48.

"Anyone considering the human body is repeatedly tempted to exclaim: This is the most wonderful of all organs. However, one soon recalls that what was previously learned concerning other organs: the fantastic structure of the bones with the bone marrow, which produces several hundred million cells every second; the beating heart, which for seventy years sucks in and expels one sixth of a quart of blood every second; the liver, which within a thimbleful of its substance carries on as many chemical processes as a six-story factory; the brain with its millions of telephone connections and mysterious functions of consciousness - truly it is impossible to give preference to any region of the body."

F. Kahn, 1944

III. EXPERIMENTAL FISH EMBRYOLOGY
44. THE CARE AND FEEDING OF LABORATORY FISH*

SIZE OF TANK:

This depends upon whether the fish are to be raised in colonies; whether they are large or small, active or sluggish; whether they are sociable; and whether the adults eat their eggs or their young. In general the shape should be rectangular, with the depth and breadth the same and the length twice as great. The most satisfactory size is $8\frac{1}{2}$ x $8\frac{1}{2}$ x 16 inches (supplied in quantity by Wil-Nes Co., 220 E. 134 St., New York City.) Such a tank may be used for colonies of Oryzias, Paradise, or Platys, which represent egg-layers, bubble-nest builders, and live-bearers. This size tank may also be partitioned off for a Betta breeding tank. Larger tanks will be necessary for Hemichromus or the large mouth-breeders. The fast-moving Zebras do well in a long and narrow tank, measuring 4 x 4 x 24 inches.

STRUCTURE OF THE TANK:

Except for the frame, the tank should have walls of glass and bottom of slate or glass. None of the frame should come in contact with the contained water. A glass cover should be provided, which will keep out all dust and reduce evaporation. A corner of this glass plate may be removed in order to facilitate the introduction of the daily food ration. The edge of the glass plate may be protected by adhesive tape, or ground lightly with a metal file.

REPAIR OF THE TANK: (Generally not recommended for modern tanks)

When a leak occurs it will be necessary to remove the glass plate on that side, at least. Occasionally all the glass plates should be removed and the entire frame cleaned. This is a tedious performance but a little extra care will reduce the necessity for repetitions. Never move a tank containing water.

Remove the glass plates in the proper order. When the bottom is glass, it is the first to be removed since it was the last to be put in place. Soften the cement which holds the glass in place by means of a cup of cleaning fluid (Dri-Kleen), and remove the cement and wedge out the glass with a putty knife. Remember that the glass is brittle. Thoroughly clean the frame and glass before replacing the parts, and cement with regular aquarium cement.

It is virtually impossible to cover a leak with aquarium cement and to have it hold. Even the slightest leak should be remedied by complete removal of the faulty plate. After a repair job, run water through the tank for several days.

CLEANING THE TANK:

Even a new tank should be treated with dilute $KMNO_4$ solution for at least 24 hours before use, and an old tank may occasionally require a complete cleaning (Brine and "elbow-grease" are the best). In such cases a thorough washing with soap and water, a soaking with dilute $KMNO_4$, and a 24-hour rinsing are in order.

* The author expresses profound appreciation for help in organizing this section, particularly from Drs. I. R. Aronson and W. Atz of the American Museum of Natural History, and also their co-workers Drs. Evelyn Shaw, and Phyllis Cahn.

Some fish are naturally dirtier than others (e. g. , Hemichromus, Tulapia) and it will be necessary to siphon off the faecal material and uningested food almost daily. If aerators are used, they must be shut off and the debris allowed to settle for a time before siphoning. If the aerators themselves become clogged with debris and vegetation they should be removed and cleaned by dipping them in acetic acid or vinegar, and rinsing.

Some vegetation is good for the tank, but when an aquarium is so green that the fish cannot be seen, it is a sign of contamination resulting from too much light. The so-called scavengers such as snails, fresh water flounders, catfish, loaches, and tadpoles, will help to keep the vegetation down but the best method is to reduce the light ration. Plants that supply abundant oxygen help materially to keep the tank clean.

The best scavengers are the moss-back snails. Small, live-bearing snails are better than the larger and often more colorful snails. It should be stated, however, that while no snails eat living fish or fish fry, some snails will damage fish eggs. There are fungus spores in all aquaria but these will never attack healthy fish. Scavengers are not really necessary in a perfectly balanced tank, where there is no overfeeding.

AQUARIUM WATER:

Never use distilled or rain water as these do not contain the necessary minerals. Conditioned tap water is best. Fill the tank 2/3 full of warm tap water (the warming helps to drive out any chlorine or other toxic gases) and let it stand until the water is cool. Place sterilized sand or gravel in the back corners of the tank, plant such vegetation as is suitable (see below) and slowly siphon in additional tap water. In a 5-gallon tank the water should have a depth of about 5-6 inches. Let this tank stand in sunlight for 1 day, or aerate for a similar period. Metal frame tanks of 3-gallons or more should not be moved after filling because the weight of the water plus the strain on the frame will cause leaks. See that all tanks are evenly and adequately supported before adding the water. Evaporation is balanced by adding distilled water to the original level at least once each week.

The pH of the water should be near the neutral point (6. 8-7. 2). Some fish breed better when the water is slightly acid (6. 8) and others when it is slightly alkaline (7. 2). The addition of chalk, plaster of Paris, or other so-called neutralizers is ill-advised. If the pH must be very accurately controlled this should be done with harmless phosphate buffers and the water tested by colorimetric or electrical pH determinations.

The temperature of the water needs to be regulated for the tropical fish and for those whose breeding reactions depend somewhat on temperatures. Regulation is best by thermostat and electric heater. These are the only metal structures that ever come in contact with aquarium water, and they are protected since even the slightest amount of copper or selenium is toxic to fish. Glass heaters with thermostats are readily available. The temperature range for fish is 70° - 85°F., the breeding temperatures being the higher ones. In fact, one of the methods of regulating breeding (of the tropicals particularly) is to keep the fish for a period at the lower level of the tolerance range and then elevate the temperature to 80° - 82°F. when they will generally breed. It is most important to regulate the temperature during the period from October to April when the laboratory temperatures are generally below the tolerance range or are somewhat variable.

Aeration of water when the fish are in it is generally accomplished by appropriate vegetation. Two functions of plants are to add oxygen and to release toxic gases. Artificial aeration is not necessary in a properly balanced aquarium unless it is overcrowded but should be provided where colonies of fish are likely to deplete the normal supply of

oxygen or where the light is insufficient to maintain the plants.   Artificial aeration is
particularly harmful to fish fry which are extremely delicate and are damaged by the air
bubbles and excess currents of water. (See Downing and Truesdale 1956)

AQUARIUM LIGHTING:

The most uniform lighting is that from the northern skies, without direct sunlight.
Aquaria may be exposed to direct sunlight but for not more than 1 hour each day.   Continuous artificial lighting may upset the normal fish cycles since many fish actually sleep
and some seem to carry on maturational processes during the night and oviposition during the day, e.g., Oryzias.   The best conditions are attained if the background behind
the tank is light (white cardboard) and a 50-75 watt bulb is placed above and toward the
front of the tank with reflector throwing the light toward the back of the tank away from
the observor.   The bulb should be at least 8-12 inches away from a 5-gallon tank and the
light should be on for an 8-hour day.   For fluorescent light use only warm, yellowish or
white tubes, not daylight tubes.   If the aquarium becomes discolored with an abundant
growth of algae, reduce the light ration.

AQUARIUM VEGETATION:

The plants that are used in fish aquaria have three functions, to provide a means of
achieving chemical balance, to aerate, and to add beauty.   Unfortunately the last function
is generally the only one considered.

The plants should not be dropped into the tank but should be spaced appropriately.   In general, the two back corners should have abundant gravel (or sand) and the taller (Sagittar-
ias) plants carefully placed.   See that the roots are completely covered in the non-floating
plants.   The smaller plants may be placed in the back center, leaving the front of the tank
free.   This will facilitate cleaning (with siphon), will space the plants properly so that
they will be exposed to light and give off oxygen, and will also provide an artistic background for the fish.

The type of plants to use depends upon a number of factors such as the size of the tank,
the amount of oxygen needed, and whether the plants are to be used for hiding of female
(Betta) or fish fry.   A list of plants is given below but it must be remembered that all
plants should be sterilized before placing them in an aquarium.   This sterilization is
accomplished by washing them in a dilute solution of potassium permanganate for 10 minutes and then rinsing them in clear water for an equivalent period. (See Atz 1950)

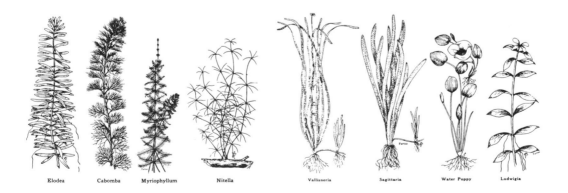

Elodea   Cabomba   Myriophyllum   Nitella   Vallisneria   Sagittaria   Water Poppy   Ludwigia

Courtesy General Biological Supply House, Inc.
Chicago   Illinois

PLANTS SUITABLE FOR FISH AQUARIA

*Anachris; dark green foliage with heavy stems.
Australian under water clover.
Bladderwort; do not use with fry since it is carnivorous.
Cabomba; red or green; somewhat floating, glossy green, fan-like leaves.
Cellophane plant from Honduras; excellent for oxygenation.
Duckweed; floating, small plant sometimes used as accessory food by fish.
Elodea; survival value not good unless abundant light.
Ludwigia; colorful, foliage green above and pink below.
*Myriophyllum; feathery and therefore excellent for female Bettas or fry to hide in.
*Nitella gracilis; excellent, grows well in aquarium.
Riccia salvinia; floating, excellent surface plant.
*Sagittaria; species natans, pusilla or microfolia. Excellent both as decorative and
    oxygen producing. Strong growing plants.
Salvinia; floating plant excellent as cover for fry.
Spatterdock; broad light green leaves, quite ornamental, excellent plant.
Vallisineria; long ribbon-like leaves, plant in back of aquarium.
*Utricularia; species vulgaris or minor: good for fry to hide in, highly decorative.
Water lettuce, floating.
Water hyacinth, floating.
Also inside or outside filters using charcoal or plastic wool (Superfleece, West-
    chester Aquarium Supply, White Plains, N.Y.)

THE FEEDING OF FISH:

"Overfeeding kills fish more frequently than underfeeding." It should be remembered
that fish are cold-blooded animals (even the tropicals!) and that most of them can survive for considerable periods without any food whatsoever. There are several simple
rules that should be stated:

1. See that there is variety in the food. Alternate between living and dry food, or
   between different mixtures of dry food.
2. The food particles must be small enough for the fish to digest. Uningested food
   simply leads to contamination of the tank, and should be removed daily.
3. Feed frequently rather than too much. Tropicals should be fed more often than
   other fish, some fanciers feeding small amounts 3 times each day.
4. The amount of food varies with the
   a. Species
   b. Season (temperature and activity). Feed less in winter than in summer.
   c. Breeding or non-breeding.
   d. Stage of development (fry to adult).
   The oft-stated rules that you should "feed what they can eat in 5 minutes" or
   "feed only as much as they can catch before it hits the bottom of the tank" are
   too general to be of value. One should study different species, under various
   conditions, and observe the amount ingested prior to apparent, even though temporary, satisfaction. An adult Oryzias or Platy will do well on two worms (Tubifex or Enchytrea) per day, alternated with a small pinch of dry food.

There are many specific foods recommended, each fancier devising his own formula.
This should indicate the wide latitude of fish tolerance of foods. The most common foods
will be listed below.

Living Foods:
1. Plant material - fish need their "salads" too. Algae, Duckweed, and Water
   lettuce are occasionally eaten by fish.

* The most satisfactory plants for laboratory aquaria.

2.   Animal material -

   Artemia - the brine shrimp eggs can be purchased (Brine Shrimp Sales Co.,
      1655 West Winton Ave., Haywood, Calif.) in large numbers and raised in salt
      solutions. Day old brine shrimp are excellent food for fish fry. (See Demp-
      ster 1953)
   Daphnia - and other small crustacea are very good. Can be sifted out so that
      smaller specimens are given to fry of 3 weeks or older. Carapace of older
      specimens may be harmful to young fish. (See U. S. Fish & Wildlife Serv.
      FL #331)
   Drosophila - the common fruit fly used in Genetics courses, a natural food
      which can be raised easily in the laboratory. Vestigial mutant is preferred.
   Earthworms - generally too large but may be cut or chopped up.
   Euchytrea - white worms, excellent, even good for fry when finely chopped.
      These may be cultured in damp humus, in a cool and dark environment by
      feeding them on milk-soaked bread once each week. Cover the humus with a
      glass plate to reduce evaporation and, if possible, pass cold running water
      through glass tubing submerged in the humus, to keep the culture moist and
      cool. Allow one month for the culture to get started after inoculation.
   Infusoria - (Protozoa) inadequate for adult fish but excellent for carrying fry
      through critical first 3 weeks after hatching. Raise on hay infusions and add
      in small amounts to fry tank.
   Mealworms - particularly good for fish when chopped fine.
   Mosquito larvae - a natural food, excellent.
   Tubifex - the red worm used most commonly. This is a sewage worm and can
      be handled by adult fish but should not be a steady diet. Should be kept in
      running cold water to reduce incidence of transmitting parasites to fish.
(See "Culture Methods for Invertebrate animals." Dover Pub., 180 Varick, N. Y. C.)

Prepared Foods:
   Ant eggs
   Baby fish food, powdered for fry
   Beef, shredded
   Cereals - fine grained varieties
   Clams, chopped finely
   Daphnia, dried
   Dried flies
   Egg, hard boiled yolk
   Lacto-Peop (see Tricker)
   Lettuce, wilted
   Lobster; canned and shredded
   Oysters, chopped finely
   Potato, boiled or baked white
   Salmon, dried and dried eggs
   Shrimp; canned, shredded or dried
   Spinach, partially cooked
   Oatmeal, cooked with or without dried shrimp
     (And a large variety of powdered foods in any 10 cent store or pet shop).

It is even possible to make up a home-made mixture which contains all of the necessary
ingredients. Take one can each of dog food, shrimp, and salmon; add a can of meat
scraps and grind all together with 1 lb. of partially cooked spinach through a fine meat
chopper. Spread the mixture out thinly on heavy brown paper and place in the direct sunlight until thoroughly dry. Regrind when dried, through finest coffee grinder. The sun
will kill any parasites and may add some vitamin value, or a small amount of cod liver
meal may be added to the above for vitamins. This mixture should be stored in stoppered
bottles in the refrigerator. It should be made fresh every two weeks.

FORMULAE FOR BALANCED FISH FOODS

The prepared foods readily available are satisfactory in emergencies but they generally lack some nutritional requisite, particularly vitamins. Two formulae are given below which are currently used at the American Museum of Natural History.

1. <u>Aronson's formula</u>: (See Zoologia 34:136, 1949)
   a. $\frac{1}{2}$ finger bowl of chopped spinach.
      $\frac{1}{2}$ finger bowl of chopped lettuce.
      Add a little water to the above and bring to a boil, then stop.
      Separate the fluid from the solid by straining through a fish net.
   b. Take $\frac{1}{2}$ lb. liver, chop fine, add spinach water and grind.
   c. Take finger bowl of dried shrimp, add $1\frac{1}{2}$ finger bowl of pablum.
   d. Add all the above mixtures together, with a pinch of salt. Mix thoroughly.
   e. Spread out thin on hard wood board, place in sunlight to dry. If too wet, add more pablum to take up the moisture.
   f. When almost dry, put through fine meat grinder twice. For small fish, put through grinder a third time. Will keep in refrigerator for a long time.

2. <u>Gordon's formula</u>: (The Aquarium 1943, Vol. 12:87)
   a. Get $\frac{1}{2}$ lb. beef liver, 10 tablespoons of Pablum (or Seravim), 1 teaspoon of salt.
   b. Remove the connective tissue covering the liver, and the larger blood vessels. Cut the liver into $\frac{1}{2}$ inch pieces and chop until it is a liquid mash. If available, use a Waring Blender (i.e., liquidizer), which is rapid and thorough. If the liquidizer is used, an equivalent weight of water must be added to the liver, and the subsequent mash is strained through an ordinary sieve.
   c. Add the Pablum (or Seravim) to form a thick paste. Mix well.
   d. Place the mixture in small glass jars, and cover but do not screw the cover on. Set the jar (containing liver-Pablum mash) in water, and bring the water to a boil. Turn the fire off and let the jar stand in the boiling water about one-half hour. This serves to coagulate the blood and other liver proteins without destroying the valuable vitamins. It also pasteurizes it to some extent. Screw top on tightly. Keep in cool place (refrigerator) where it will last a month, if not opened.

The fishes are fed once each day, generally early in the morning, so that they have the entire day to clean up all the food that is given to them. The uneaten food should be removed at the end of the day, if possible. No further feeding should be made when there is food left in the tank. The food may be added to the tank from the end of a scalpel, the amount being about the size of one rice grain per fish (unless they are very large fish). The fish will soon learn to come for the food, tear it apart, and eat it all.

The approximate numbers of named species are:
              Plants - 200,000
              Insects - 250,000
              Primitive vertebrates - 27
              Fishes - 7,400
              Amphibia - 925
              Reptiles - 3,500
              Birds - 10,000
              Mammals - 2,700

45. FISH DISEASES

It is almost safe to say that there is no reliable remedy for a sick fish, no matter what the cause. Prevention is all important for really there is no cure! However, there are several simple rules to keep in mind:

1. Never add new fish to an old aquarium until they have been sterilized and have been quarantined for a few days. All new fish should be given a salt treatment, regardless of their source.
2. Provide separate aquaria for sick fish and isolate them as soon as there is any indication of trouble.
3. When shipping large numbers of fish it is said that mortality will be reduced if a small amount of aspirin is added to the water (reasons unknown). (See McFarland '60)
4. When sick fish are found in a regular aquarium, this aquarium should be put through a thorough process of cleaning and sterilization. Fish diseases are generally very contagious (for the fish!).
5. Overcrowding and overfeeding are probably the second and third most frequent causes of illness, the first being parasitization.
6. The chlorine in drinking (tap) water is a good bactericidal for human beings but harmful to the fish. Chlorine will naturally evaporate from standing water if there is sufficient exposed surface, but warming or agitating the water will hasten the process. (See Cole and Lewis 1958)

Some fanciers recommend a tonic salt bath for all fish once each month. Such a bath is made by adding 3/4 teaspoonful of NaCl and 1/4 teaspoonful of Epsom Salts (Mg_2SO_4) to a gallon of boiled and cooled tap water. The fish may be left in this for 24 hours. If the fish are definitely sick, the dose should be increased by using only one quart of water and expose them for 1/2 hour, or less if they indicate intolerance of the treatment.

Nigrelli (1961) has made a thorough analysis of the diseases (and other causes of death) of marine, temperate, and tropical fish. Some of the parasitic, and infectious diseases and other causes of death he lists are:

Parasitic and infectious diseases.
    Diseases of the skin and gills:
        Saprolegnia (fungus)
        Tuberculosis
        Ichthyophthirius (a Ciliate) commonly called "Ich".
        Gyrodactylids (a Trematode)
    Diseases of the circulatory organs:
        Ruptured sinus venosus (due to Gordiid worms).
    Diseases of (general) internal organs:
        Mechanical destruction (by Gordiid worms).

Non-parasitic and non-infectious diseases.
    Diseases of the digestive system:
        Liver degeneration
        Biliary cirrhosis
    Diseases of the reproductive organs:
        Egg bound
        Ovarian degeneration

Diseases of the skeleton and organs of locomotion:
    Swim bladder trouble
    Lordosis
Diseases due to nutrition:
    Malnutrition

Diseases of the circulatory system: Diseases of age:
   Ruptured myocardium   Senility
   Splenomegaly   Unknown and accidental causes:
   Gas embolism   Edema
   Internal hemorrhage   Fighting
Diseases of the organs of vision: Jumping out of tank
   Blindness   Changes in water temperature and
                           chemistry

Fortunately most of these ailments will not be encountered in the laboratory. However, there are some rather common ailments generally known under the names of Finrot, Fungus, Bladder disease (which causes the fish to constantly spiral about because of poor equilibration), the "Ich" parasites, mouth diseases, and "fluke" parasites of the liver or intestine. Mouth fungus can sometimes be cured by brushing the mouth of the infected fish with 10% neo-silvol or 2% mercurochrome, 2 to 4 times daily, or by giving them an intense salt treatment of 2-1/2 tablespoons of iodized salt* per gallon of water, decreasing the salt concentration by adding fresh water after 24 to 48 hours exposure. "Ich can be treated by brief immersion of the infected fish in dilute potassium permanganate, Acriflavin, or salt.** Also a 1% NaCl solution used at high temperatures (83° F. or more) will tend to eliminate the protozoan parasite cysts (white spots) which reproduce as cysts at the lower temperatures. (See U.S. Fish & Wildlife Serv. F.L. #70)

Nigrelli (1943) described a total of 10 major factors which contribute to the loss of fish in captivity, listing them as follows:

1. Crowding: There is an optimum population density for each species, and when fish are crowded beyond this density they tend to kill each other off to re-establish the optimum density (Breder & Coates, 1931). There is also the greater opportunity for the spreading of an infectious disease.

2. Temperature: The range of tolerance is great providing the change is made gradually. Rapid changes in temperature render many fish the more susceptible to parasitic infection. Possibly a rapid increase in temperature brings the encysted parasites out into activity while a decrease in temperature may cause them to encyst.

3. Light: Many larval trematodes are positively phototropic, and fish behavior may be affected by a constant source of strong light. There is an optimum concentration for plant and fish, in relation to light.

4. H-ion concentration: This varies with the species, the optimum for marine fish being around 8 and for fresh-water forms near the neutral (pH 7.0) level. Most fish aid in controlling the pH of their medium, and few, if any, can tolerate an acid environment.

5. Specific gravity: An increase in the density of the medium increases the respiratory and metabolic rates. Since fishes can tolerate a greater density range than can parasites, this fact is often used in prophylactic and therapeutic measures.

6. Flow and aeration of water: Chlorine and nitrogen are toxic in certain concentrations, and even oxygen may be too concentrated and cause gas embolisms. There is an optimum level, different for different fish (e.g., very low for the Betta) which must be maintained.

---

* Rock salt or Turks Island Sea Salt are very good.

** One heaping teaspoonful per gallon of water is a good concentration to be used for several hours per day over several weeks, if necessary. Sea salt, rock salt, Kosher salt, are all better than iodized table salt.

7. Metabolic waste products: Water in which fish have lived for a time is known as "conditioned water" and presumably such water is better for that particular species than for others, due, it is thought, to the concentration of certain species specific beneficial metabolites.

8. Diet: Many fish diseases are due to vitamin deficiency, particularly when fish are kept in captivity and fed artificial diets. Liver and renal damage are probably the major ailments encountered.

9. Handling: Directly or indirectly handling may be the cause of the majority of deaths. Abrasions are sites for infections. Even with the greatest care, moving established pairs or colonies from one tank to another usually means the loss of some specimens. New fish, regardless of size, are often attacked by the permanent residents of a particular aquarium.

10. Parasitism: Many ecto-parasites show no host specificity, hence there is great virulence (see Nigrelli & Atz, 1943: Zoologica 27:1).

REFERENCES

"The Aquarium Journal" - San Francisco Aquarium Society. Golden Gate Park, San Francisco 13, Calif. ($3.00 per year).
"The Aquarium" - Aquarium Publishing Co. P. O. Box 832, Norristown, J.J. ($3.00 per year).
"Tropical Fish Hobbyist" - 245 Cornelison Ave. Jersey City, N. J. ($3.25 per year).

"During the past several years the investigations in this field (Developmental Physiology) have centered to a tremendous degree upon the cellular complex arising during development with a many-faceted study of the individual cell parts. While in many ways the attacks on this single element have been more definitely focused than previously, the degree of complexity of the major problems of differentiation has not lessened for in many cases we have moved only in descriptive vocabulary, changing from the physiomorphological to the chemical and sometimes to physical terminology. It is true that in realizing the relative complexity of specific cell components as functional entities we have advanced considerably in this half century. We need a consolidation of our present position combined with a more vigorous attack on the physical principles involved before we can really synthesize the facts and factors which we, at present, intuitively place in a perspective of greater prominence than the future may show to be warranted."

J. S. Nicholas 1960: Ann. Rev. Physio. 22:95

46. FISH SUITABLE FOR LABORATORY EXPERIMENTATION

There is an ever increasing number of fish species which are being adapted to laboratory conditions so that they will breed normally and thereby provide suitable material for embryological studies. The following list consists of good breeders, providing large numbers of eggs or live bearers with many young at a time.

a. Egg-layers

Eggs dropped or attached to vegetation.
1. Oryzias latipes, the Japanese Medaka. Hardy fish which provides eggs almost daily, each female giving 1-80 fertilized eggs each morning. Development slower than that of tropicals, described elsewhere.
2. Brachydanio rerio, the zebra fish, provides eggs daily but eats them almost immediately if they are not removed. Eggs can be collected by allowing them to drop through a nylon net or a glass rod trap.
3. Tanichthys albonlubes, the White Cloud Mountain Fish. Dependable breeders.
4. Anoptichthys jordanii, The Blind Cave Tetra which breeds easily under aquarium conditions and produces large quantities of eggs. Eggs hatch in 24 hours.
5. Astyanax mexicanus, eyed ancestor of Anoptichthys.
6. Barbus conchonius, the Rosy Barb. Other species are the Clown (Breveretti), Gold dwarf (B. gelius), and Pygmy (B. phutunis) Barbs are from India. Breeding directions for Barbs similar to those for Danio.
7. Chriopeops goodei, the Blue Dace. Excellent breeder.
8. Hemichromis bimaculatus, the Jewel Fish. Will produce about 400 eggs every 3-4 weeks if congenial pairs are kept together. Attaches eggs to bottom of container, or to pieces of crockery which may be removed with eggs for study. Large fish, voracious eater, viability of embryos high.
9. Eggs supplied for experimental purposes by Commissioner of Fisheries, U. S. Department of Interior, Washington, D. C.
    Salmon, Trout, and Whitefish.
10. Pterophyllum eimekei, the freshwater angel fish deposits eggs on Sagittaria, Spatterdock, or Cryptocoryne. Fry hatch in 48 hours.
11. Ambassis lala, the glassfish deposits eggs on Myriophyllum or Riccia. Fry hatch in 48 hours.
12. Hippocampus hudsonius, the sea horse. Incubation period 6 to 7 weeks. (Floating Nitella provides an excellent protection for adhesive eggs)

Bubble nest builders.
In general these fish are isolated from each other until males and females show tendency to build surface nests of bubbles. Pairs of such fish are then brought together and observed for several hours to determine whether they will mate or fight. After oviposition, the females are removed from the tank and the males care for the eggs and young through hatching. Females will be destroyed by the males if they are not removed.
1. Betta splendens, the Siamese Fighting fish. Suggest getting pure colors, such as red, white, and blue (representing varieties). Mortality of eggs and embryos is very high, but the egg is excellent for study and the courtship and fertilization procedures allow the investigator to secure eggs at the moment of insemination. Very rapid embryonic development.
2. Gourami, various species such as Dwarf, Blue, Mosaic, and Kissing Gouramis all of which breed rather frequently and eggs develop rapidly.

3. Paradise: Brown and Albino. These need not be kept in isolation until they show signs of bubble-nest building, and breeding. Early embryos develop rapidly with high viability, but mortality great after about 2 weeks when there is a change of diet. Many will go through to sexual maturity.

Strippers: (See Fundulus below)

b. Live Bearers

With these fish the eggs are fertilized within the female where they develop in a chamber, without any maternal connections, sometimes beyond a stage comparable to the hatching stage of egg laying fish embryos. The young lie folded head to tail and are born singly. Females may be induced to drop their young prematurely by excessive handling such as transferring to new tanks, etc.

The gestation period is irregular since it depends upon the temperature of the environ-ment of these cold blooded forms. Psychological factors may also enter into the picture, females dropping their young so early in their development that they cannot survive, or retaining them too long. For most live bearers the best temperature is about 75° F., although some species can stand as much as 10° C. lower or higher.

The young must be caught in traps, or provided with hiding places in vegetation, or the adults must be removed because there is a tendency for them to eat their young almost immediately. Since the young are born at an advanced stage, these fish are the easiest to raise in large numbers. Infusorian food is too small for them and they must be put on a diet of chopped white worms (Enchytrae) or small Daphnia. The adults are good eaters, accepting almost anything whether at the surface, dropping, or on the bottom. Species should be segregated because there is frequent interbreeding among live bearers, par-ticularly between the Swordtails and Platys. Live bearers are generally omnivorous.

From the standpoint of early embryology these fish are not so satisfactory, but there are numerous experimental approaches that are yet to be made on these forms.

1. Lebistes reticulatus, the common Guppy. The Gold Guppy and the Black Tail Guppy are very good.
2. Gambusia affinis, breed at 5-10 week intervals, called Mosquito fish from southern U.S. Is pugnacious and cannibalistic.
3. Xiphophorus, the Swordtails. Red or Green Swordtails very good. These may be hybridized with the Platys. (Species helleri most common.)
4. Xiphophorus maculatus, the multicolored "Platy" brought to the U.S. from Mex-ico by Dr. Myron Gordon and distributed widely by him. The mutants Red, Blue, and Gold Crescent are all excellent. Female may drop as many as 60 young at a time, at monthly intervals. P. variatus is found in at least 20 patterns.
5. Xiphophorus hellerii, the Mexican Swordtail.
6. Mollienesia latipinna, the Sailfin Molly. The Perma Black Molly is very com-mon and entirely satisfactory. Breeds at 5-10 week intervals. Predominantly herbivorous. Require large aquarium and heavy aquatic greens in which the young can hide during growth.

c. Breeding of the Betta

These are bubble nest builders which should be raised in isolation except for the breed-ing periods. Originally these fish were found in extremely stagnant pools and they seem to survive best when there is no vegetation and they are confined in small covered con-tainers. Pint sized mayonnaise jars or many kinds of plastic containers two-thirds filled with conditioned tap water and covered (but cover not screwed on) seem to be entirely satisfactory for the adults over long periods. When the fish shows tendency to build a bubble nest it may be transferred to a breeding tank. In order to have Betta eggs, it is necessary to have on hand many specimens (in jars) and half a dozen breeding tanks, since the investigator must await the indications of sexual activity of individual fish. The adults should be fed daily, alternating between living food such as Enchytrea or Tubifex, and mixed dry food. One or two worms per day are adequate, and only enough dry food for the fish to eat before it hits the bottom of the container.

The breeding tank should have a 5-gallon capacity and contain about 5 inch depth of conditioned water. A glass partition, held in place by split rubber tubing, should be used to divide this tank into equally sized sections. In the back corners of the tank plant some Vallicineria or Sagittaria and add some Nitella or Utricularia, the latter two plants providing a hiding place for the female if she is attacked. After the breeding tank has stood for 2 days, place a pair of bubble-blowing Bettas on the two sides of the glass partition and await developments. Frequently one can anticipate the desire to breed in females with bulging abdomens or active males, and when such fish are placed in a single tank on either side of a glass partition, they show interest in each other and begin to build a bubble nest. Breeding temperature 78° F.

When satisfied that there is breeding interest on the part of the fish, carefully transfer the female (in dip net) to the male's side of the tank or pull out the glass partition. Observe these fish at frequent intervals for several hours. If the male chases the female and nips at her the pair is not ready to breed and should be separated. If, however, the female helps to build the bubble nest or the male continues to build the nest, showing only casual interest in the female, it is quite likely that they will produce fertile eggs during the next 48 hours. During this period the fish should not be disturbed in any way.

The Bettas have an elaborate courting procedure, with the male displaying all of his colorful assets to their best advantage. Copulation is generally at the surface where the male wraps his body, as best he can, around that of the female, approximating their genital pores. There is a rapid vibration of the male's body during a period of about 5 seconds when the bodies are clamped close together whereupon the male, exhausted, drops away and appears to be lifeless for another 5-10 seconds. The female is likewise rather inert for a few seconds, but shortly eggs will be seen to drop away from her and immediately both male and female become very active in collecting the newly fertilized eggs in their mouths. Copulations will occur at frequent intervals over a period of 6-48 hours and after each copulation a variable number of eggs (0-120) may be dropped. Many of the eggs that reach the bottom of the tank will not be found by the fish if the bottom is covered with sand or gravel. It is therefore better to omit the sand and gravel from the breeding tanks. With their mouths full, the fish rise to the surface and place the eggs on the surface between supporting air bubbles. The eggs appear opaque at this time, becoming translucent within 10-20 minutes if they are not dead or unfertilized. (While this is generally true, occasionally perfectly normal eggs will appear to be opaque.) In rare instances the female will be seen to eat the eggs rather than carry them to the nest, in which case only those eggs saved by the male will survive. Females should be removed as soon as possible after the completion of egg laying because the males will kill them.

The eggs are fertilized at the moment of copulation so that the investigator can quite easily time insemination and watch the earliest stages of development. It is important, however, not to disturb the nest any more than necessary to pipette out (large-mouthed pipette) a few eggs as needed. Such eggs can be cultured in Syracuse dishes. In 48 hours after the last eggs are dropped, the male should also be removed because by this time the young fry have hatched (36 hours) and can take care of themselves. The male may eat them when the fry become active.

Betta fry are extremely difficult to carry through the first three weeks of development. This may be in part due to injuries sustained when the male parent rescues them and returns them to the bubble nest after they hatch. The food for such fry should be Protozoa (Infusoria) cultured in a separate tank and added to the fry tank along with a pitch of the smallest grain fish fry food. This food will allow the Protozoa to propagate within the fry tank, so that it will not be necessary to add fresh Protozoa more than twice a week. The fry tank temperature should be 80° F. There should be adequate light (75 watt bulb within 6-8 inches of the top of the tank) but no direct sunlight. The best light is north skylight.

After about 2 weeks, add to the previous diet the smallest pieces of chopped white worms (Enchytrea), but do not overfeed because the subsequent contamination would be fatal to the fish. Breeding activity will first be seen in fish about 6 months of age.

d. The Zebra Fish, Brachydanio Rerio

THE EARLY DEVELOPMENT OF BRACHYDANIO RERIO, THE ZEBRA FISH

Brachydania rerio is a Cyprinid fish from India which can be raised in fresh water in the laboratory. The young will spawn at from 5-7 months, the most fertile period being 9-18 months. A general description of the conditions necessary for continuous production of eggs will be given (see papers by Roosen-Runge, Hisoaka & Legault).

The zebra fish tank should be long and narrow to allow the fish ample room to dart back and forth since they are very active. A tank measuring 24 x 4 x 4 inches will prove satisfactory. Place about 12 specimens in such a tank, 7 or 8 of which are males. Larger tanks measuring 24 x 18 x 10 inches may be used for 10-12 pairs of fish. The temperature of the water should be regulated at 27° C. although the eggs will develop normally even at 25° C. The bottom of the tank should be covered with marbles, or with smooth stones, or even a matting of plant material among which the eggs will drop and be protected from the fish which normally hunt out and eat their own eggs. Eggs can be collected by using a porous nylon net for the bottom so that the eggs can drop through. Aeration should be provided if possible.

When the fish are kept in schools there will be continuous spawning so that from 10-50 eggs may be found daily. It is best to catch the eggs as they are laid, using a dip-tube, for the eggs develop very rapidly. The eggs should be transferred to Stenders or to Syracuse dishes which may be covered with cheese cloth and returned to the normal environment of the aquarium for further development. However, since the eggs develop very rapidly it is generally best to observe them in separate dishes as described below.

Place a thin film of beeswax, paraffin or permoplast on the bottom of a #2 Stender, to the thickness of about 2 mm. In the center of this film excavate a depression about the diameter of the zebra fish egg. This opening will allow the reflected microscope light to pass through the egg but will block out all extraneous light, and will at the same time tend to keep the egg oriented. Avoid any heat from the microscope lamp by intercepting it with a flask of water.

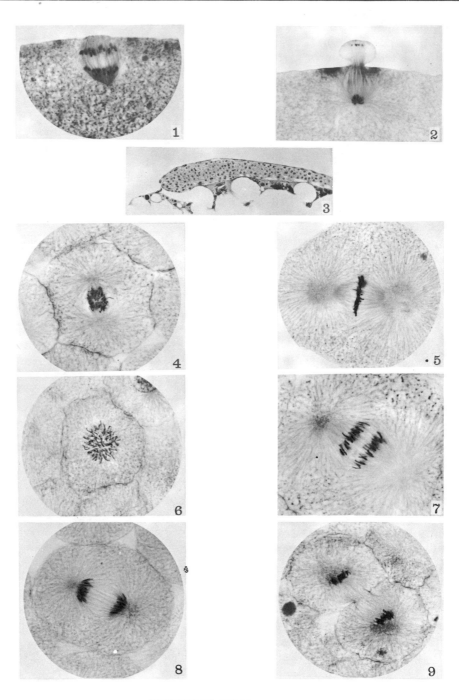

WHITEFISH DEVELOPMENT *

Fig. 1 - First polar body formation in anaphase
Fig. 2 - First polar body formation in telophase
The polar body about to be pinched off
Fig. 3 - Blastula formation. Note distinct cells above yolk
Fig. 4-9: Mitosis in whitefish blastula cells

Fig. 4 - Late prophase
Fig. 5 - Metaphase, lateral view
Fig. 6 - Metaphase, polar view

Fig. 7 - Anaphase, lateral view
Fig. 8 - Late anaphase, lateral view
Fig. 9 - Telophase, lateral view

* These photographs reproduced by kind permission of The General Biological Supply House, Inc., Chicago.

THE ZEBRA FISH EGG*

The egg is fertilized as it is laid. It is white, nearly opaque, and homogeneously filled with granules. Its original diameter is 0.625 mm. and increases within a minute to 0.750 mm. and then shrinks to about 0.590 mm. after 2 minutes. This swelling of the membrane and shrinking of the egg is associated with the formation of the perivitelline space. The membrane is soft and extensible.

The protoplasm at oviposition is slightly concentrated, the egg as a whole becomes oval and acquires a polar axis. The cell nuclei are visible after the first cleavage even in the living egg. The schedule of early development at 27° C. follows:

            15 minutes - movement inside yolk.
            35 minutes - 1st. cleavage depression.
            40 minutes - 1st. cleavage completed.
            60 minutes - 2nd. cleavage depression, right angles to the first.
            67 minutes - 2nd. cleavage completed.
            92 minutes - 3rd. cleavage depression, parallel to the first.
           104 minutes - 4th. cleavage depression, parallel to the second.
           117 minutes - 5th. cleavage depression, parallel to the first.
      136-146 minutes - 6th. cleavage depression, horizontal.

These time intervals are approximate, and at 25° C. the cleavage intervals are from 17-20 minutes after the first cleavage which is slightly delayed. The 10th cleavage is attained in 3 hours at 27° C.

Fixation is in Bouin or Bouin-Dioxan mixtures, with dehydration in Dioxan plus benzol. The membrane and yolk may be removed after fixation. The best stains are the haemotoxylins.

e. The Jewel Fish, Hemichromus

These fish are somewhat temperamental and random pairs will not necessarily be congenial. Combinations must be tested and when a congenial pair has been brought together they should be left together permanently.

The Jewel Fish is rather large and should be provided with a 15 gallon tank for each pair. They are voracious eaters, consuming large numbers of Tubifex and much oatmeal-shrimp mixture. The latter food is made by cooking oatmeal and adding to it dry shrimp commonly used alone as fish food. The tank must be cleaned frequently.

---

* This description is based largely on the work of Dr. Roosen-Runge. He has worked with the zebra fish, Brachydanio rerio, more than any other investigator, believes that there is no fish to compare with it for embryological studies. The eggs can be obtained at all times and in great quantities if the following conditions are met: The fish are kept in schools of 12 to 18 specimens, of which two thirds are males, and at a temperature of 26° to 29° C. The tanks should be from 8 to 15 gallon capacity. The fish are fed once daily with mixed dry food, and occasionally with small pieces of (rat) liver. Spawning occurs almost daily, the fertilized eggs sinking to the bottom where there should be marbles or coarse gravel to hide the eggs from the fish. Eggs are removed immediately with large pipette to finger bowls where they will develop very rapidly (cleavage on an average of 18 minutes, gastrulation in 12 hours). The water in the finger bowl should be changed daily. The eggs do not tolerate well the lower temperatures.

The egg is not sticky, is nearly transparent, develops pigment late, has no disturbing oil drops in the yolk, and develops so rapidly that the germ ring and the closure of the blastopore can be observed during the course of a single laboratory period. A 10x objective (total magnification 100x) shows the fine cellular detail and permits observation of the living nuclei. The egg lies naturally on its side, so that a profile view of the blastodisc and yolk is inevitable when viewed through the microscope. Its use in operational procedures has not yet been adequately tested. (See Roosen-Runge, 1936: Anat. Anz. 81:297; 1938, Biol. Bull. 74:119; 1939, Biol. Bull. 77:79; 1939, Anat. Rec. 74:439 for details. A motion picture of the development of this egg is available through The Wistar Institute.)

The female turns a brilliant pink in color when about to breed, which may be as frequently as every 7 to 10 days at 80°-84° F. The fish generally attach their eggs to the bottom of the tank, first excavating a clear circular area in the sand or gravel. Taking advantage of this tendency it is well to place, on the bottom of such a tank, broken pieces of a flower pot or crockery, onto which the fish will attach their eggs. These pieces of crockery may then be removed and the early development studied. The fish develop very rapidly (See Noble, Kumpf, and Billings, 1938).

f. The Sea-horse, Hippocampus Hudsonius

Since it is now known that the brine shrimp, whose eggs can be kept in a dry condition for a long period, can be cultured in salt water and then fed to sea horses, these curious fish can now be maintained in the fresh-water laboratory and the unique method of rearing the young studied.

Sea water may be obtained by direct shipment from the seashore, or Turks Island Salt may be added to distilled water to simulate sea water. Sand is placed in the bottom of the 4 to 6 gallon all-glass aquarium, adequate for one pair of fish. The original salt water line must be indicated on the aquarium and this line maintained by the semi-weekly addition of distilled water to replace that lost by evaporation. Direct and intense (sun) light should be avoided. (See references by Breder, MacGinitie and Chin)

Sea horses may be fed entirely on small Guppyi, Mosquito Larvae, Enchytrea (white worms) Tubifex (red worms), and brine shrimp. Fresh water food cannot survive for long in a salt water aquarium, hence there must be no overfeeding. Brine shrimp live naturally in the same environment as the sea horses, and are excellent food for the fish. Brine shrimp do better at higher temperatures (up to 100° F.) and in slightly hypotonic sea water. The occasional addition of some wilted lettuce is advised. The success of a Sea Horse colony depends largely upon the success of a Brine Shrimp culture as food.

The female sea horse deposits her fertilized eggs in the brood pouch of the male where they are incubated for from 6 to 7 weeks. The breeding period is March through June. The young fry are fed on Protozoön infusions or on the smallest of the brine shrimp.

Little is known of the normal development of these eggs and embryos, but since the adults can now be reared in the inland laboratory, it is expected that they will provide new fruitful material for investigation.

g. The Japanese Medaka, Oryzias Latipes

These fish may be kept in groups of 50 in ten gallon tanks, and in such a colony egg layers will be found almost daily throughout the year. The ratio of males to females should be about 2/1. Breeding females may be isolated with (2) males in small half-gallon fish bowls, covered with wire screen to keep them from jumping out. Vegetation should be reduced so that the eggs will not be covered with algae. (See section on Reproductive Physiology and Embryology of Oryzias for further details, and see papers by various authors such as Goodrich, Robinson, Solberg, and Waterman.)

CHARACTERISTICS OF THE ADULT FISH: ORYZIAS LATIPES

Oryzias latipes has a wide distribution in China and Japan except in the mountains. It is found in ponds, stagnant pools, running streams and rice fields. The adults measure from 20 to 40 mm. in length with an average of about 30 mm. The wild species is

* Available through Beldt's Aquarium, 2141 Crescent Avenue, St. Louis, Missouri.

blackish-brown while the cultivated species is orange or white, with or without black spots. There are no color changes with breeding activity. The embryos begin to show coloration about one week after hatching. (See references to Briggs, Egami).

The sexes may be distinguished by the following characters:

	MALE	FEMALE
Copulatory organ	Sometimes anal fin	None
Anal fin	Parallelogram	Triangular
Anal fin rays	Rarely branching: 17-21	All bifurcated terminally: 19-21.
Ventral fin	Barely reaches anterior margin	Large; reaches past anus to anal fin.
Dorsal fin	Long; reaches base of caudal fin; notch at posterior margin.	Short; lobular; rounded at posterior; no notch.
Anal opening	Small and circular	Large and elliptical; nipple-like U.G. papilla as skin fold posterior to the anus.
Breeding season (April-October)	Body slender; stream-lined	Abdomen swollen with eggs.

REPRODUCTIVE PHYSIOLOGY

The ovary of Oryzias is single and enormous, making the female easily distinguishable from the male. In the mature fish it contains hundreds of follicles, each with an egg in some maturation stage. The ovary itself is saucer-shaped with a membrane across its dorsal surface, the various sized follicles projecting into the lumen beneath this membrane.

The mature eggs rupture their follicular walls, without hemorrhage, and emerge into the ovarian lumen. This process requires from 20-60 minutes (see Robinson and Rugh, 1941) and generally takes place shortly before daylight. There is slight constriction of the egg as it emerges, with evidence of muscular aid from the follicular wall or the ovarian stroma.

The maturational processes are apparently at their peak during the quiescent period of sleeping and coincidental with revived activity at dawn, the eggs are ruptured and oviposition occurs. There is no doubt that the light cycle in some way regulates the egg-laying periods, although other factors such as food, pH, and temperature cannot be ignored.

The eggs are held in the ovarian lumen until all the matured ones have ovulated and oviposition of all of the eggs occurs during a very brief period. A single female may produce from 1-80 eggs per day, the average being between 20-30. During a single season 500-800 eggs may issue from a single female, more being laid on sunny than on rainy days.

The oviduct is a single, muscular, and non-glandular tube about 1 mm. in length extending from the posterior ventral margin of the ovary to the exterior just posterior to the urino-genital papilla. A ventral aspect of the female shows this opening partially obscured by the papilla. The connection of the ovary with the oviduct is like a thin-walled, broad, flat funnel which is no doubt made up largely of smooth muscle fibres and is therefore very elastic. The tissues of the oviduct are continuous with those of the ovary, its very much reduced lumen continuous with that of the ovarian lumen. The sole function of the oviduct is egg transport, or rather it is a muscular organ for extruding the matured eggs.

Fertilization of the egg occurs during or immediately after oviposition. Copulation takes 20-90 seconds, is preceded by a brief courtship and is accomplished by the male holding the female with its dorsal and anal fins while spreading the milt over the eggs with its pectoral fin. Since Oryzias is polygamous, best results are obtained in tanks of 30-50 fish in which there is an excess of males. The eggs remain attached to the female for 4-5 hours or until they are brushed off by the vegetation or other objects.

THE ORYZIAS EGG

The egg of Oryzias is small (1.27 mm. in diameter), transparent, and possesses a thick (0.032 mm.) membrane between which is a perivitelline space filled with a fluid. The membrane is traversed by 8 striations parallel to the surface, and also by numerous radial canaliculi. The outer surface of the membrane is wavy, the inner surface smooth. There are scattered threads (0.025 mm. long) each possessing 3 segments, found everywhere but at the vegetal pole. At this pole there are many longer (0.95 mm.) delicate and sticky filaments, each with two less obvious segments. These filaments entangle the eggs with other eggs, causing them to cluster. Both the chorion and the filaments are derived from the follicle while the egg is still in the ovary.

The egg possesses a thin protoplasmic layer around a yolk sphere, uniform except at the poles and definitely thicker at the animal pole where the germ disc will form. Liquid yolk fills the bulk of the egg, and is white or yellowish. In the ovary this yolk appears to be opaque but becomes translucent shortly after fertilization. At oviposition many oil globules may be seen between the yolk and the periblast. During early development these decrease in number by confluence and merge into a single large globule at the vegetal pole. This oil globule is gradually used up as nutritive substance and disappears simultaneously with the disappearance of the yolk sac.

THE BREEDING AND EARLY DEVELOPMENT
OF ORYZIAS LATIPES*

DEFINITION: A study of the normal reproductive processes and early development of the oviparous fresh-water Cyprinodont, Oryzias (Aplocheilus) latipes, called the "Medaka" in Japan where it is found.

PURPOSE: To acquaint the student with reproductive processes and a type of early development not customarily studied in embryology courses, material suitable for laboratory experimentation.

MATERIALS:

Biological: Pairs of mature Medakas (Oryzias latipes).
Plant material for aeration: Nitella, Utricularia, Elodea, Cabomba.
Food: Living Tubifex or Enchytrae.
Dried shrimp, dried Daphnia, small-grained mixed dry fish food.

Technical: Aquaria: 1, 5, 10 gallon capacities.
Fish bowls: Ten cent store variety for pairs of fishes, Wire covers.
Celluloid cups for feeding living worms to fish.
Feeding ring for dried food.
Aeration: Stream of air bubbles (not necessary if plants are abundant).
Artificial lighting: Gooseneck lamps with 25 watt bulbs if daylight is inadequate or irregular.

---

* The author acknowledges, with appreciation, the help of Dr. A. N. Solberg, Dr. A. J. Waterman, Mr. L. Roth and Mr. E. G. Robinson in organizing this exercise. (See new references by Briggs and by Egami)

METHOD:

Precautions:
1. See general precautions in introduction to Fish studies.
2. Keep aquaria covered, the fish may jump out.
3. Do not use chlorinated tap water until it has been properly conditioned.
4. Avoid crowding: A pair of fish in a single aquarium, a dozen in a 5-gallon aquarium, or 30-50 in a 10-gallon tank is a good proportion.
5. Optimum temperature about 25°C. to 27°C.
6. Northern daylight best, but artificial lighting is satisfactory, avoid over-heating with lamp.
7. Remove eggs from the aquarium, or pick eggs off of the female, since the Medaka will eat its own eggs, larvae, or even the fry.
8. Light, food, temperature and pH are controlling factors in breeding, important in that order.

Controls: This exercise is one of observation rather than experimentation hence there is no need for a control. It must be remembered, however, that laboratory conditions may not represent conditions of the normal environment of the fish. If, however, fish can be raised to sexual maturity under a certain set of laboratory conditions, it may be assumed that these conditions closely simulate those in nature.

OVULATION, AND FERTILIZATION:

Oryzias latipes should be secured fresh from the dealer and kept for 2-3 weeks under uniform conditions and close observation in order to select and have available females that may be depended upon to provide fertile eggs almost daily.

Since Oryzias eggs are ovulated shortly before being laid, determine the approximate time of oviposition of several females (see Discussion below). On the morning following several days of regular oviposition, anesthetize a female in 1/3000 MS 222 in aquarium water from 1-2 hours prior to the time of anticipated oviposition. (The lighting conditions will regulate this quite satisfactorily.) Pin the female, belly down, in a Permoplast operating dish filled with aquarium water, and remove the dorsal and lateral body wall. This will expose the dorsal side of the ovary through which ripe eggs may be seen. Observe the eggs in situ, or excise the entire ovary and place in normal aquarium water and observe under binocular magnification. Only completely mature eggs will be liberated from their follicles, a process which takes from 20-60 minutes. (Compare the process with that previously observed in the other cold-blooded form, e.g., the frog.)

The fertilization of the egg occurs at the time of or shortly after oviposition, and is accomplished by the male using his anal and dorsal fins to hold the female while spreading milt over the eggs with his vibrating pectoral fins. This occurs after a characteristic courtship on the bottom of the tank. It may be possible to delay oviposition by keeping the male away from the egg-laying female until arrival at the laboratory in the morning.

EARLY DEVELOPMENT OF ORYZIAS LATIPES:

In an aquarium containing several dozen fish you will find eggs (1-80 per female) every morning. Since the eggs are laid shortly after daylight these observations must be made very early in the day.

Using a dip-net, catch a female which has a cluster of eggs attached and transfer it to a finger bowl of aquarium water. Pick off the eggs either with a wide-mouthed pipette or a pair of forceps. Eggs which appear to be opaque within 10 minutes after removal are very likely to be dead. Separate the eggs so that there are about 10-20 per finger bowl. Keep no vegetation with the eggs.

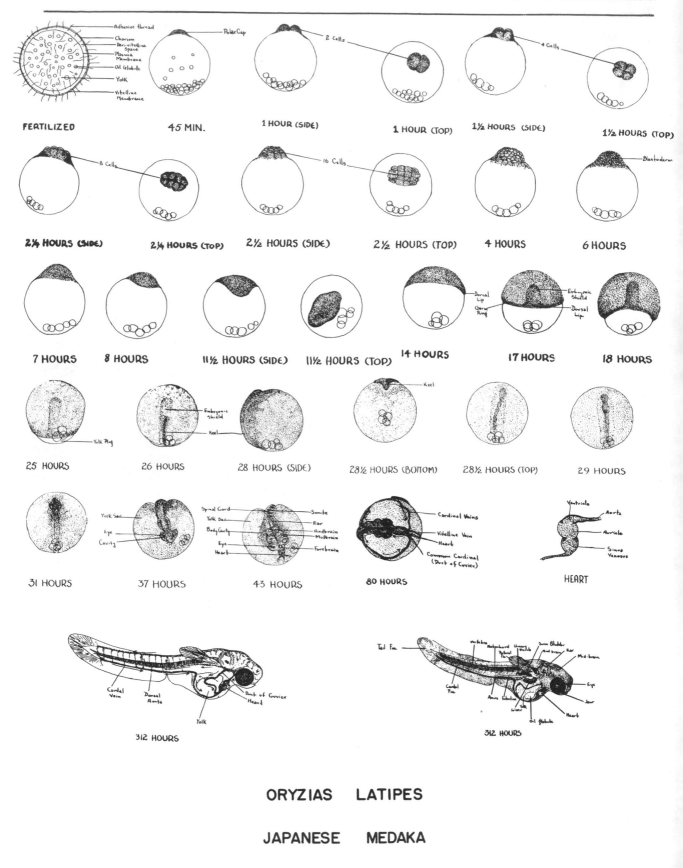

ORYZIAS   LATIPES

JAPANESE   MEDAKA

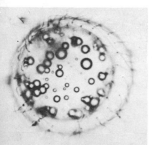

JUST FERTILIZED

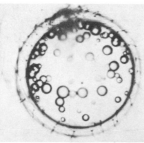

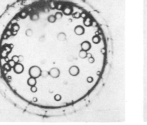

CONCENTRATION OF PROTOPLASM AT POLAR CAP

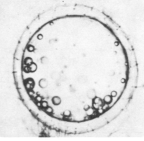

2 CELL — 1 HOUR

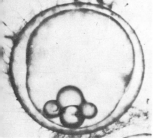

BLASTULA — 3 HOURS

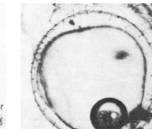

3 HOURS — H. P.

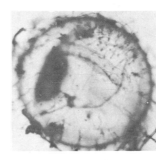

10 HOURS

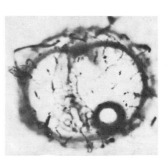

12 HOURS

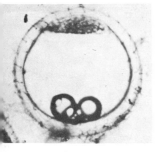

15 HOURS

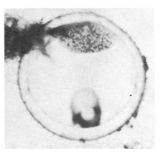

18 HOURS

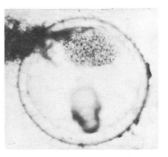

35 HOURS

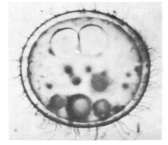

40 HOURS

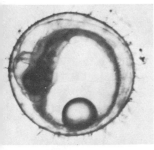

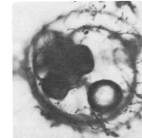

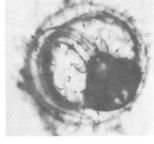

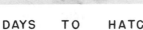
— TWO DAYS TO HATCHING —

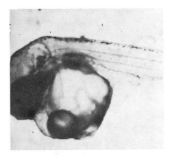

YOLK SAC - HATCHED

EARLY DEVELOPMENT
OF
ORYZIAS LATIPES
—
THE JAPANESE MEDAKA

Photographs by L. Roth

OPTIC VESICLES

TAIL SOMITES

Observations should be made under dissecting microscope (mag. x 17 or more) with both direct and transmitted lighting. Since the development is rapid (see diagrams and photographs by Roth) and hatching generally occurs within 6 days, it will be necessary to make rather constant observations or to supplement any series with observations on other eggs. The schedule of development follows:

TIME SCHEDULE OF DEVELOPMENT:

1. Egg becomes translucent, perivitelling space widens, germinal disc becomes lens-shaped: 10 minutes after fertilization.
2. First cleavage: 1 hour after oviposition; cleavage meridional, nuclei visible.
3. Second cleavage: $1\frac{1}{2}$ hours, meridional, right angles to first; blastomeres equal.
4. Third cleavage: 2 hours, plane parallel to first cleavage; blastodisc appears rectangular in outline with no space beneath.
5. Fourth cleavage: 3 hours, parallel to the second; central blastomeres smaller than peripheral ones. Note margins of boundary cells. Is there any incorporation of yolk?
6. Fifth cleavage: $3\frac{1}{2}$ hours, unlike most teleost eggs, this cleavage does not give rise to layers of cells.
7. Sixth cleavage: 4 hours, after which the cleavages are no longer synchronous but give rise to a many-layered blastodisc.
8. Blastula: By 6-8 hours the sub-germinal cavity first appears. The blastodisc is elevated and a thickened marginal periblast of syncital nature may be seen. Observe in optical section if possible. Compare the periblast nuclei with those in the center of the blastodisc in regard to shape and color. By 24 hours there is nucleation of these periblast cells and the marginal thickening is accentuated to become the germ ring. This germ ring will grow down over the yolk in much the same manner as a bathing cap is pulled down over the head.
9. Gastrula: It is difficult to designate a specific time when gastrulation begins but it is accomplished by invagination, accompanied by delamination and overgrowth at the time the germ ring has grown around about a third of the yolk mass. The blastopore is represented as the uncovered portion of the yolk mass and embryonic structures first appear with the closure of this blastopore.
10. Embryonic development:
    First day: The embryonic shield appears as a result of the thickening of the cells along a region which represents the axis of the future embryo. This appears during gastrulation as a result of migration of cells and will extend toward the center of the blastodisc from a point along its margin. This embryonic shield should be observed from all aspects. If possible, determine the regions of most active growth and the source of cells that go into the various parts of the embryonic shield. During the first 24 hours the embryo will encircle 3/8 of the yolk mass, the optic vesicles will appear and there will be fewer than 10 somites.
    Second day: The embryo extends 5/8 around the yolk; the heart beats about 50-60 times per minute; the blood is colorless; Kupfer's vesicle is seen at the caudal end; and there may be 18 somites.
    Third day: The embryo extends 3/4 around the yolk; the heart is beating as in the adult, about 150-170 per minute; the blood is slightly pink in color; pigment appears in the optic cup; and there are 20-28 somites.
    Fourth day: Embryonic movements begin; the blood is red; somites number 30-38.
    Sixth day: Numerous chromatophores appear, hatching may occur on the 6th day, depending upon temperature. In the hatching process the tail moves violently to break the membrane, and the tail region emerges first. The size schedule is as follows:

             Just hatched: 4.5 - 5.0 mm. in length.
             One month: 11.5 - 13.0 mm. in length.

Oryzias latipes reaches maturity in $1-1\frac{1}{2}$ months, and the life span is 1-2 years. Generally a fish hatched in one summer dies after it breeds during the following summer. The life span of laboratory fed fish has not been determined.

Care of Material: Avoid crowding, and observe eggs without undue handling. They may be left in Stenders or finger bowls throughout development. When the fry hatch they should be fed #0 (finest grain) baby fish food and protozoa. While the range of temperature tolerance is $7^{\circ}-39^{\circ}C$. the optimum for all stages is between $20^{\circ}-25^{\circ}C$. In studying the normal series, use a constant and recorded temperature and compare with the accompanying drawings and photographs.

Fixation of any fish embryonic material may be in Bouin-Dioxan or in Stockard's solution (5 pints formalin, 4 pints glacial acetic, 6 pints glycerine, and 85 pints water) and after 3 days may be transferred permanently to 10% formalin. Sectioning is difficult but can be accomplished if the chorion is removed after fixation.

Note: A synthetic medium of balanced chemicals may be used for Oryzias if conditioned tap water proves to be deleterious. This solution will also inhibit the growth of molds and bacteria.

NaCl	1.0 gram
KCl	0.03 grams
$CaCl_2$	0.03 grams
$MgSO_4$	0.08 grams
Distilled Water	to 1 liter

OBSERVATION AND TABULATION OF DATA:

It is important that the student become thoroughly acquainted with the reproductive physiology of the fish particularly since there are very few fish with which this can be done (see Robinson and Rugh, 1943). Compare any observations with those on the frog.

The observations on early embryonic development are to be made under low magnification almost continuously during the first 2-3 hours, then several times daily thereafter until the embryo hatches (6th day). Note particularly the following:

1. Somites: number as criterion of age; manner of formation; positional relation to future parts of the central nervous system.
2. Development of the central nervous system: neuromeres; fore, mid, and hindbrain; cerebrum, cerebellum, medulla and cord; optic vesicle, lobe and lens; olfactory pit and otocyst.
3. Circulatory system: appearance and shape of the heart; the initial heart beat; development of blood vessels including sketches of the circulation on the 4th and 6th days; changes in blood color from day to day.
4. Numerous wandering mesenchyme cells found toward the posterior end in 2-3 day old embryos; observe movement and mitosis.
5. Chromatophores: appearance, behavior, function; color and shape, contractility; response to light.
6. Movement: blastodisc; body; and finally the fins.
7. Fry: behavior in response to various types of stimuli.

DISCUSSION:

Oryzias (Aplocheilus) latipes, the Japanese Medaka (also known as the Geisha Girl fish) has been adapted so satisfactorily to laboratory conditions that it promises to contribute much to the field of experimental embryology. For this reason a rather thorough description of the adult fish, the reproductive physiology, and the egg will be given here.

DEVELOPMENT OF THE PLATYFISH, XIPHOPHORUS (PLATYPOECILUS) MACULATUS

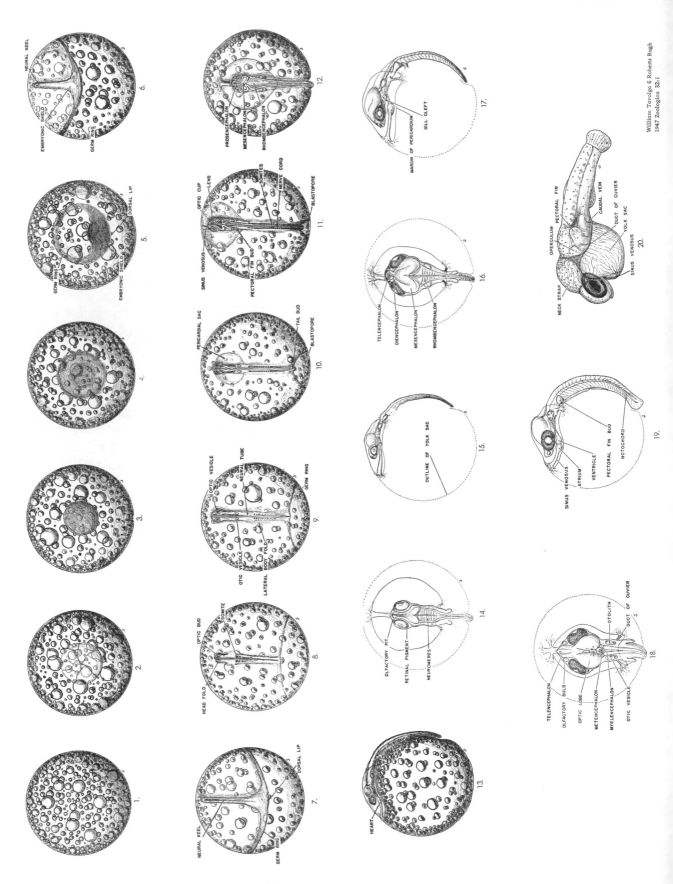

William Tavolga & Roberts Rugh
1947 Zoologica 32.1

h. The Platy, Platypoecilus Maculatus

THE MULTI-COLORED PLATY; (XIPHOPHORUS)

These live bearing Poeciliid fish are found in Mexico in the vicinity of the Rio Papoloapan and Rio Panuco where the waters are slightly alkaline (pH tolerance of the fish is 6.4 - 8.0) and the temperature variable (temperature tolerance 65°F. to 90°F. with optimum at 75°F.). Dr. Myron Gordon of the N. Y. Aquarium has collected many specimens on expeditions to Mexico and has distributed them freely for research purposes.

These fish breed frequently and may drop as many as 80 young at a time. They are less apt to devour their young than are the Guppies, but should be separated from their young shortly after birth. The best aquarium temperature for breeding is 75°F. and the water should be very slightly alkaline. Food is alternated between Tubifex or Enchytrea and mixed dry granular food. The fish may be kept in colonies but gravid females should be isolated just before dropping their young.

The two species, P. maculatus and P. variatus, are rather common now, the former being so variable in color that there are hardly two fish with similar markings. The major types are (1) Greyish blue with crescent markings; (2) Redish brown with speckles; (3) Dark fish with black stripes and some black scales. The Gold Platy is a mutation in which the black pigment has been lost and the yellow xanthine base has been exposed. The colors are no bar to crosses, the varieties and species interbreeding freely. In fact the Platy may be crossed with the Swordtails. There is now on the market a Platy-Swordtail hybrid known as the Montezuma Swordtail and another, the Black Swordtail, which is a hybrid between the Mexican Swordtail and the Black Platy. Dr. Gordon has worked out the genetic story in considerable detail, linking it with the inheritance of a type of fish (melanotic) cancer. The embryology of these fish has been worked out (See Tavolga & Rugh, 1947). Combined with the known genetic make-up, embryological studies would be highly instructive. (See particularly papers by Gordon.)

DEVELOPMENT OF THE PLATYFISH, XIPHOPHORUS (PLATYPOECILUS) MACULATUS

DESCRIPTION OF NORMAL DEVELOPMENT STAGES

Stage 1. Mature Ovum (Fig. 1)

The mature infertile ova, after the yolk has been deposited, average 1.5 mm. in diameter. They are of a clear yellow color with peripherally arranged fat globules of various sizes. These globules vary somewhat in size and number depending on the individual ovary. However, the eggs in any one ovary are all very similar in this character. When the egg is damaged, the globules are found to be adherent to the peripheral membrane; they are composed of a colorless fluid somewhat less viscous than the yellow colored matrix.

The germinal vesicle cannot be seen in the living egg, but it has been demonstrated by Hopper (1943) to be peripheral in position in sectioned material.

The vitelline membrane is probably present since a fertilization membrane is subsequently demonstrated. No tertiary membrane, such as is found in oviparous species, is present around the egg.

Immature eggs appear to be more opaque than mature fertilized ones. It may be that this change takes place at fertilization as it does in Fundulus (Oppenheimer, 1937), but in this viviparous species it is difficult to substantiate.

Stage 2.   Cleavage (Fig. 2)

Cleavages may be seen only occasionally, and only in eggs preserved in formalin. The cleavage cells are very thin, broad and flat, and since they are not raised above the yolk surface to any visible extent, this stage is poorly distinguished from the previous one. Fig. 2 shows the cleavage stage more distinctly than it actually appears. Using a glass needle and a pair of sharpened watchmaker's forceps, the fertilization membrane can be removed from such eggs while in the saline solution, and the contents left in place. Such a membrane cannot be demonstrated around infertile ova. This fertilization membrane persists throughout the gestation period and is ruptured together with the follicle just prior to parturition.

Stage 3.   Compact Blastula (Fig. 3)

This is the earliest stage which can be identified readily by gross study. The cells are small and tightly packed into a small grayish protoplasmic disc, which is slightly raised above the yolk surface. A segmentation cavity has been described beneath the disc (Hopper, 1943).

Stage 4.   Diffuse Blastula (Fig. 4)

Gastrulation begins at this stage with the blastodisc flattening out into a thin membrane of cells. The periphery of the blastodisc is uniformly thickened, indicating the region of proliferation and probable involution.

Stage 5.   Early Germ Ring Gastrula (Fig. 5)

Gastrulation continues during stage 5 with a peripheral spreading of the blastodisc in all directions. The embryonic shield is visible as a widening and thickening of a sector of the rim of the blastodisc.

Stage 6.   Late Gastrula - Early Neurula (Fig. 6)

The embryonic shield takes on an elongate form and becomes raised from the yolk surface, indicating the antero-posterior axis of the developing embryo. The notochord is present, and the anterior end of the neural keel can be seen. The nerve cord is formed from a solid core of invaginating tissue; the neurocoele appearing after invagination is completed, as seen in sectioned material. This type of neurulation is typical of teleosts.

Stage 7.   Late Neurula (Fig. 7)

The germ ring at this stage is somewhat below the equator and the embryo has become further elongated. Since elongation takes place principally in the posterior portion, a region roughly corresponding to the dorsal blastopore lip of amphibian gastrulae, the anterior end of the embryo lies in much the same position as did the original embryonic shield of stage 5.

The neural keel has invaginated throughout the greater length of the embryo, and a neurocoele is present in the anterior one-fourth.

Stage 8.   Head Fold (Fig. 8)

A prominent head fold is present by stage 8. The neurocoele is open for about the anterior half of the length of the embryo. The optic buds are present and attached to the short, thin stalks, and they are, at this stage, without a cavity. Two pairs of rather diffuse somites are evident, but there is considerable variation in the time of their first appearance. Somites sometimes appear as early as stage 7.

Stage 9. Optic and Otic Vesicles; 1.1 mm. (Fig. 9)

The head fold has now begun to elongate anteriorly. The blastopore is still a wide open structure and the caudal end has not progressed back much farther than its position in stage 8. The optic primordia now possess cavities, and are usually still attached to the prosencephalon by thin optic stalks. The brain is divided into three general regions: a narrow prosencephalon, a slightly wider mesencephalon, and a short rhombencephalon. Otic vesicles have invaginated at the level of the rhombencephalon, but are still connected to the exterior by the endolymphatic ducts. Usually, 7 pairs of somites are visible at this stage.

The pericardial sac, which develops very early, closely enfolds most of the head fold at this stage.

Stage 10. Tail Bud; 1.5 mm. (Fig. 10)

The optic vesicles are detached from the brain and are slightly flattened around the in-vaginating lens primordia. The mesencephalon and rhombencephalon have become widened and more thin walled. The otic vesicles are slightly ellipsoid and are completely cut off from the superficial ectoderm. There are ten pairs of compact somites visible. The tail bud has begun to form and extends slightly over the region of the dorsal lip of the open blastopore.

The region of the pericardial sac that is extra-embryonic is easily distinguishable, and, upon dissection, the heart can be found as a straight tube on the floor of the pericardial sac. The vascular system is apparently complete at this time, but the blood islands are never visible under gross examination. The heart exhibits no regular beat, only an occasional twitch.

Stage 11. Pectoral Fin Buds (Fig. 11)

The optic vesicles partially envelop the lens primordia. The prosencephalon shows little differentiation, but the mesencephalon has widened out considerably. Indications of neuromeres can be seen in the rhombencephalon. The entire brain possesses a thin roof, and this is especially true at the hind-brain level. In later stages, the roof of the mesencephalon becomes thickened, but that of the myelencephalon remains thin as the posterior tela chorioidea. The otic vesicles show little or no change, aside from a general growth, in this and several of the following stages. Fig. 11 shows the presence of the anterior fin buds.

Posteriorly, 18 to 20 small, compact somite pairs blend into a poorly differentiated region in the now prominent tail bud. It is noteworthy that, although a sizeable tail bud is present at this stage, the blastopore is open in majority of the embryos. This is in contrast to the case in most teleosts, and even in the closely related Fundulus.

In the heart, the ventricular and atrial portions are distinct, and at the anterior end, the sinus venosus projects in front of the head. The heart exhibits a fairly rhythmical beat at this time. The color of the blood is light pink, but barely perceptible.

Stage 12. Regular Heart Beat; 1.8 mm. (Figs. 12, 13)

The optic cups envelop the lenses closely. Olfactory placodes are visible. The brain has undergone further development; the telencephalic region is slightly expanded; the mesencephalon has a thicker roof; the rhombencephalon is greatly widened.

The somites are more closely packed and less distinct. The vascularization of the peri-cardial membrane is in the form of small capillary-size vessels. The extra-embryonic circulation can be followed at this stage. The blood leaves the embryo through the ducts of Cuvier at the posterior ventral margin of the pericardial membrane, drains into the yolk portal system and the vascularized pericardial membrane, and collects at the elongated sinus venosus.

The mid-gut is broad and extends under about one-third of the embryo. The hind-gut is short, and the fore-gut, upon dissection, is shown to possess a distinct first pharyngeal pouch and a corresponding visceral furrow.

Stage 13.   Early Retinal Pigment; 2.1 mm. (Figs. 14, 15)

Olfactory pits are distinct. Pigment can be seen in the retina as a thin gray band. The brain and the head are further enlarged. The pericardial sac has increased to its maximal size. In the future stages the head enlarges to fill the serosa-like cavity and sinks down into the yolk mass. In side view, the stomodaeum, five gill clefts and the sixth furrow can be seen.

Stage 14.   Early Motility; 2.8 mm. (Figs. 16, 17)

The head is expanded to almost 0.5 mm. across the mesencephalon. The eyes exhibit more pigment and are pushed forward by the expanding mesencephalon. The latter possesses a thickened roof where the optic lobes are developing. The telencephalon has a somewhat rhomboidal-shaped cavity and the diencephalon is small and hardly distinct; this is typical of the teleosts. Both the metencephalon, which is poorly defined, and the myelencephalon have thin roofs. The neuromeres are still visible in the latter.

The heart possesses a long sinus venosus and a narrow atrium that has been twisted to the left of the thick-walled ventricle. The blood vessels of the pericardial membrane are enlarged to a size equal to almost one-half the diameter of the ducts of Cuvier.

The anterior fin-buds are club-shaped and rounded. The somites have taken the form of myotomes, and, when the living embryo is removed from its membranes, the posterior portion exhibits a slow twitching motion. The tail is conical and acuminate.

All six gill slits are distinct and open at this stage. The mid-gut is narrowed toward the posterior portion of the embryo, and fore-gut is an undifferentiated tube.

Stage 15.   Otoliths in Ear Vesicles; First Extra-ocular
Melanophores; 3.2 mm. (Figs. 18, 19)

In this stage the telencephalic vesicles are beginning to show as lateral bulges. The diencephalon is shorter than the telencephalon and less distinct. The optic lobes possess a solid roof. The metencephalon is more distinct and thickened, and the myelencephalon is somewhat narrowed.

The eye pigment has become considerably darker and some iridiophores are present. The pupil is ellipsoidal. The olfactory bulbs have completely invaginated. The otic vesicles are enlarged and three crystal-like otoliths are present in each.

The fin buds are laterally flattened. The caudal tip of the notochord is slightly upturned and the tail tip is laterally compressed, exhibiting a rudimentary sign of a heterocercal type of tail structure.

A few stellate melanophores are usually found in the connective tissue above the mid-dorsal, posterior region of the mesencephalon. This is the first indication of extra-ocular melanophores.

The gut is completely separate from the yolk and the anterior intestinal portion is twisted into two coils. The posterior portion is straight and ends in a somewhat long post-anal region. The gill slits, except the first, are beginning to sink into a common cervical sinus, the forerunner of the opercular cavity.

Stage 16.   Fin Rays; 3.2 mm.

First indications of fin rays in the caudal and pectoral fins are present. Melanophores are spreading to the myelencephalon region.

Stage 17. Anal and Ventral Fins; 3.4 mm.

Anal fin and the skeletal elements of the ventral fins are beginning to appear. Smaller, dot-like, melanophores appear on the lateral body folds. Head is further enlarged and fills the entire pericardial membrane tightly. The operculum is formed at this time.

Stage 18. Dorsal Fin; 3.7 mm.

Primordium of dorsal fin becomes visible, but there are no skeletal elements within it. Melanophores have spread over the entire mid- and hind-brain regions. Embryos at this stage are capable of swimming about, although the yolk sac prevents them from rising from the substrate.

Stage 19. Eyes and Mouth Mobile; 3.9 mm.

Through the enveloping pericardial membranes, the eyes may be seen to move and the mouth to open. The operculum is functional here. Fascial and peritoneal melanophores appear as small black dots.

Stage 20. Pericardial Sac Splitting; 4.2 mm.

The pericardial extra-embryonic membrane begins to split down the dorsal midline, starting at the anterior margin just above the sinus venosus. (This is the first step in the formation of the "neck strap," described by Turner (1940a) in many viviparous cyprinodonts.)

Stage 21. Mouth Protruding; 4.6 mm.

The pericardial sac has split open as far as the anterior margin of the eye, allowing the mouth to protrude. The peritoneal melanophores are more numerous and small fascial melanophores are concentrated around the notochord. Stellate cutaneous melanophores are very sparsely scattered over the entire embryo, and many are concentrated in the mid- and hind-brain regions.

Stage 22. Broad "Neck Strap"; 5.1 mm. (Fig. 20)

The pericardial membrane has split as far back as the posterior third of the eye, exhibiting a broad, vascularized "neck strap". The appearance of sclerotomes is here accentuated by concentrations of small melanophores in the fascial tissue around them. Cutaneous melanophores are more numerous, sometimes present in the caudal fin rays.

Stage 23. Fin Rays in Dorsal Fin; 6.1 mm.

The "neck strap" (pericardial membrane) has been reduced to about one-half the width of the eye, and is situated back of the posterior margin of the eye. Fin rays begin to appear in the dorsal fin. Large cutaneous melanophores are thickly scattered over the entire embryo. The yolk sac begins to show a rapid reduction in size, measuring 1 mm. in diameter. It is noteworthy that the yolk sac begins to involute at about the same time that the pericardial membranes are in the process of accelerated regression.

Embryos at this stage, if removed from their mothers, will feed readily on small Daphnia.

Stage 24. "Neck Strap" Breaking Down; 6.5 mm.

The "neck strap" may be completely broken down at this stage, but it is sometimes present as a narrow band of tissue. The general shape of the embryo is determined by the condition of the "neck strap," the cephalic flexure straightening as the head lifts up into the main body axis. The melanophores in the dorsal head region are stellate and more closely packed.

Stage 25.   Pre-Parturition; 6.9 mm.

The extra-embryonic membranes and the yolk flanges are absent.   The yolk has been reduced to a mean diameter of .8 mm.   No trace of the adult color pattern is yet visible,
there being only a general increase in the number of melanophores on the peripheral
areas.   This is true even in embryos of Culture Nos. 187 and 195, where the adult pattern (induced by the gene Sp for spotting and St for stippling) is composed of large masses
of macromelanophores and micromelanopores.   Nor can these two types of melanophores
be distinguished.

Stage 26.   One Hour after Birth; 7.9 mm.

Birth activity begins with a rupture of the fertilization and follicle membranes by the
violent movements of the embryos.   The embryos break into the ovarian sac and then
one by one they are extruded through the oviduct into the water.

In earlier stages, the heart extends forward from the conus, and the sinus venosus lies
directly beneath the tip of the head.   As the yolk mass becomes reduced, the heart pivots
on the conus and the yolk sac portal system shrinks until the ducts of Cuvier drain
directly into the sinus venosus, which eventually moves into place posterior to the conus.

Growth proceeds rapidly and within 24 hours after birth the young fry reach an average
length of 8.7 mm.

Rate of Development

In order to obtain some estimation of the developmental rate in Platypoecilus maculatus,
records were kept on the number of embryos and their stages found in each timed gravid
female.   The morphological age of the embryos was determined by comparing each with
the twenty-five established graded stages.

The following terms are used in this section: Theoretical age is the value determined
for the entire embryonic brood from the date of the previous brood, less the seven day
interval (as determined by Hopper, 1943).   Morphological age for each embryo is established by comparison with the graded series of stages.   Chronological age represents
the actual developmental rate for each stage.

The theoretical age of all the members of a brood was determined by recording the date
of birth of a previous brood.   This is based upon the fact that fertilization of a successive
complement of eggs within a gravid female takes place on about the seventh day after the
birth of its previous brood (Hopper, 1943).   Theoretically then, the embryos carried by
a gravid female, which had dropped a brood eight days previously, are 24 hours old.

This theoretical age value, it must be noted, is only an approximation, since maturation
and fertilization of a complement of eggs is spread apparently over a period of two or
three days.   The seven day interval, as determined by Hopper (1943), has been found to
be only an average time lapse.   The estimation of the true chronological age may be determined by comparing the theoretical and the morphological age values.

A reliable estimation of the theoretical age was obtained by study of those broods from
fully matured females which contained 25 or more embryos, and which had given birth
to at least two previous broods at an interval of approximately 28 days.   Only 21 out of
55 females examined had these qualifications.   Data on many young females were found
to be unreliable since many of them had run highly irregular reproductive cycles, varying from 35 to 90 days between broods; and a large percentage of their embryos were
dead or abnormal.   For these purposes, too, data on exceptionally small embryonic
broods (those containing less than 10 embryos) were not considered.

The chart (Fig. 21 on page 383) summarizes the data on 21 embryonic broods plotted in the following manner: Each vertical bar represents all the members of one entire brood carried by a single gravid female platyfish. The length of each vertical bar, projected on the ordinate, shows the range of morphological ages found in each embryonic brood. In some cases, especially during the later portion of the gestation period, the embryos are all of a single morphological age; these are represented by plus (+) signs.

The embryos are divided into theoretical age groups according to the number of days that have elapsed since the birth of the previous brood (less the seven day interval) and are arranged along the abscissa. Usually there is more than one brood in each age group.

The mean morphological ages for all the embryos of each theoretical age group are also plotted on the chart, and these values are connected by the dotted line.

From the chart, it may be seen that there are two kinds of variations. First, there is the wide range of morphological stages among the embryos found within any one gravid female; and second, the variations of the average morphological age of a brood with respect to its theoretical age.

The greater apparent spread of morphological stages in the earlier broods may be attributed to the unequal time lapse between stages distinguished on the basis of morphology alone.

Using the information described previously on the reproductive cycle of the platyfish, it was thought that not only a graded series of morphological stages but also a chronological series could be obtained. On the basis of these data, some estimations of the time of development of each stage could have been made. However, the variation, as demonstrated by the chart, proved to be so great that an estimation of the true chronological age was impossible.

i. The Normal Telecost: Fundulus Heteroclitus

Within the last decade a considerable volume of research has been published on the brook-trout (Salmo fario) and the rainbow-trout (Salmo iridaeus) in Europe; on Oryzias latipes in Japan and the United States; and finally, on Fundulus in this country. Before proceeding to experimental techniques it is in order that we describe, in summary form, some of the characteristic features in the development of the Teleost egg.

The egg consists of a large mass of fluid yolk surmounted by a disc of protoplasm, both contained within a plasma membrane and protected by a heavy chorion. The embryo is derived from the blastodisc which alone divides, ultimately to form a sheet of cells which will encompass the yolk (epiboly). The semi-gel medium which contains the blastoderm cells is bound to the yolk by an encircling gel layer (Lewis, 1943).

With expansion of the blastoderm there is a thinning of its center and a thickening of the "Randring" or germ ring around its periphery. From a specific point on this germ ring the thickened embryonic-shield extends toward the center of the blastodermic area. With continued epiboly of the circumferential germ ring, there is an interruption at a point near the origin of the embryonic-shield, and an infolding (involution) of cells to form the endodermal roof of the archenteron. Differentiation of the embryonic-shield into brain, optic and otic vesicles, and somites then occurs.

Oppenheimer (1936) has confirmed the earlier statement by Morgan (1893) that the (Fundulus) embryo could survive without its yolk, by explanting the blastoderm alone into Holtfreter's solution to find that if the excision is made prior to the 32-cell stage hyperblastulae developed but after that stage, embryonic structures and frequently embryos were differentiated. Devillers (1947) cultured the small pike egg in 3 times Holtfreter's solution beginning at the blastula stage to secure definitive embryonic structures. The trout egg (Salmo fario) did not give comparable results, indicating ontogenetic stage and differentiation may not be the same in different species. Oppenheimer (1947) believes that the yolk has a physical relationship to the early morphogenetic movements which must not be minimized.

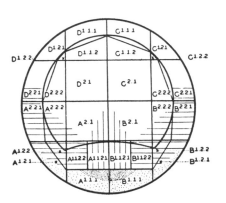

Representation in the cleaving blastoderm of the embryonic areas mapped out in the gastrula. The long axis is here represented by the second plane of cleavage.

The nervous system is indicated by vertical hatching, notochord by heavy stipple, endoderm by light stipple, and mesoderm by horizontal hatching.

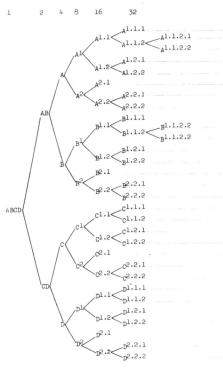

	Notochord and endoderm
A1.1.1	Nervous system posterior to midbrain
A1.1.2	Mesoderm, midbrain to 2d somite
A1.2.1	Endoderm, mesoderm
A1.2.2	Mesoderm posterior to 2d somite
A2.1	Nervous system and mesoderm, forebrain
A2.2.1	Posterior mesoderm
A2.2.2	Mesoderm and extra-embryonic membrane
	Notochord and endoderm
B1.1.1	Nervous system posterior to midbrain
B1.1.2	Mesoderm, midbrain to 2d somite
B1.2.1	Endoderm, mesoderm
B1.2.2	Mesoderm posterior to 2d somite
B2.1	Nervous system and mesoderm, forebrain
B2.2.1	Posterior mesoderm
B2.2.2	Mesoderm and extra-embryonic membrane
C1.1.1	Germ-ring -- tail-bud blastema
C1.1.2	Extra-embryonic membrane
C1.2.1	Germ-ring
C1.2.2	Extra-embryonic membrane
C2.1	Extra-embryonic membrane
C2.2.1	Germ-ring
C2.2.2	Extra-embryonic membrane
D1.1.1	Germ-ring -- tail-bud blastema
D1.1.2	Extra-embryonic membrane
D1.2.1	Germ-ring
D1.2.2	Extra-embryonic membrane
D2.1	Extra-embryonic membrane
D2.2.1	Germ-ring
D2.2.2	Extra-embryonic membrane

CELL LINEAGE OF FUNDULUS. SCHEME FOR THE LOCATION OF MATERIALS IN THE BLASTODERM WHEN THE FIRST CLEAVAGE IS TRANSVERSE

(From Oppenheimer 1936: Jour. Exp. Zool. 73:405)

The axis of the second cleavage plane tends to coincide with the longitudinal axis of the embryo. Cleavage, in general, tends to be geometric and so predictable that early cell lineage studies are possible. Teleost cleavage is essentially the non-determinate type. There are variations in the qualitative distribution of parts of the blastodisc so that Oppenheimer (1936) says: "This lack of constancy of relationship between particular cells of the cleaving blastoderm and specific parts of the embryo is, of course, strictly compatible with the fact that the development of the teleost is of the inductive type."

Pasteels (1936) and Oppenheimer (1936) have shown, by means of vital staining, that the fate map of Salmo and Fundulus are not unlike those for the Amphibia; that the periphery of the blastoderm furnishes the mesoderm for the embryo; that the prospective endoderm is found in the cellular blastoderm rather than in the yolky portion of the egg; that the prospective chorda lies in a crescentic area (Fundulus) just anterior to the prospective endoderm; and that the prospective nervous system lies just anterior to the chorda-mesoderm. Gastrulation does not involve differential mitosis but rather (as in the Amphibia) a re-arrangement of the cells, the types of movement being described as involution, extension, and convergence. The initial expansion of the blastoderm is considered as epibolic movement.

FUNDULUS HETEROCLITUS

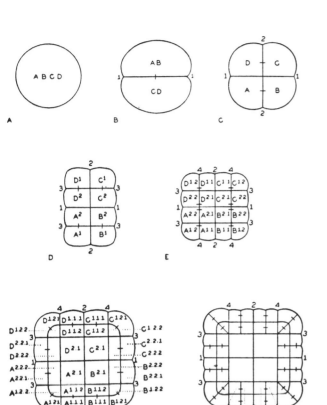

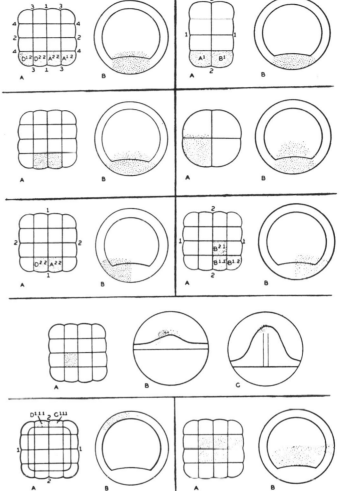

The typical cleavage pattern of the egg of
Fundulus heteroclitus. Schematic. A represents the uncleaved blastoderm, B the two-
cell stage, C the four-cell stage, D the
eight-cell stage and E the sixteen-stage.
F and G show the direction of the fifth and
sixth planes of cleavage in the marginal
cells of the sixteen-cell stage; these planes
are not represented in the central cells of
the sixteen-cell stage because they are here
horizontal and difficult to follow.

A, B, C, D and E are drawn at approximately the same scale; the magnification
is greater for F and G. The position of
the first four planes of cleavage is indicated
by numerals; see text for explanation of the
designation of cells by letter and number.

Diagrams illustrating the results of experiments
in which stained blastomeres were followed
through to gastrulation. The figures marked
"A" in each case represent the blastoderms
immediately after staining those marked "B"
and "C" are the later stages of the same
embryos.

The relation of the first or second cleavage
plane to the embryonic axis may be determined. Occasionally the embryonic axis is
oblique to the early cleavage planes.

Usually two of the 8-cell stage blastomeres or
four of the marginal cells of the 160-cell stage
blastoderm give rise to the early embryonic
shield, and (in one instance) two of the 16-cell
stage blastomeres formed the entire shield.
The germ ring is formed by peripheral cells of
the 32-cell stage and the material for the forebrain comes from the central cells of the 16-
cell stage.

(From Oppenheimer 1936: Jour. Exp. Zool. 73:405)

NORMAL DEVELOPMENT OF FUNDULUS HETEROCLITUS AT 25°C.

Age in hours	Oppenheimer stage	Developmental stage
0	1	Unfertilized egg.
1	2	1 cell.
1½	3	2 cell.
2	4	4 cell.
2½	5	8 cell.
3	6	16 cell.
3½	7	32 cell.
4	8	64 cell.
4½		128 cell.
5		256 cell.
5½-6		Early high blastula.
7-9	9	Late high blastula.
10-12	10	Flat blastula.
13-15	11	Expanding blastula. Blastula enlarges.
16	12	Gastrulation begins. Early gastrula.
18		Blastoderm about one-third over surface of yolk.
19½	13	Blastoderm about one-half over surface of yolk. Middle gastrula.
21		Blastoderm about two-thirds over surface of yolk.
22		Blastoderm about three-fourths over surface of yolk.
23		Embryonic shield condenses to form keel.
24	14	Optic vesicle first visible as an expansion of the forebrain. Large yolk plug.
25	15	Small yolk plug.
26	16	Blastopore closes.
27		First somites formed.
28		Four somites.
31	17	Optocoele develops.
33	18	Auditory placode forms. Optocoele connects across brain.
34	19	Optic cup forms, and lens develops. Neurocoele develops. About 10 somites.
38	20	Expansion of the mid-brain to form the optic lobes.
40		Melanophores first appear on yolk.
42		Melanophores appear on embryo.
44	21	Heart pulsates. No circulation. Hind-brain enlarges.
46	22	Circulation begins, through dorsal aorta and vitelline vessels.
48		Circulation through ducts of Cuvier.
60	23	Otoliths develop.
72		35 somites developed.
78	24	Pectoral fin bud appears.
84	25	Retinal pigmentation begins. Urinary vesicle formed. Caudal fin begins to develop.
90	26	Liver develops. Cartilage begins to differentiate.
102	27	Pectoral fin round.
108		Lens of eye just obscured by retinal pigmentation.
114	28	Pigmentation of peritoneal wall.
120	29	Circulation in pectoral fin.
126	30	Fin rays in caudal fin visible.
144	31	Air bladder develops.
168		Neural and hemal arches in vertebrae in tail are developed.
192		Head flexure begins to straighten out.
216		Head flexure nearly straightened out.
240		Mouth opens.
264	32	Hatching.
	33	Pigmentation of air bladder.

(From Solberg 1938: Jour. Exp. Zool. 78:445)

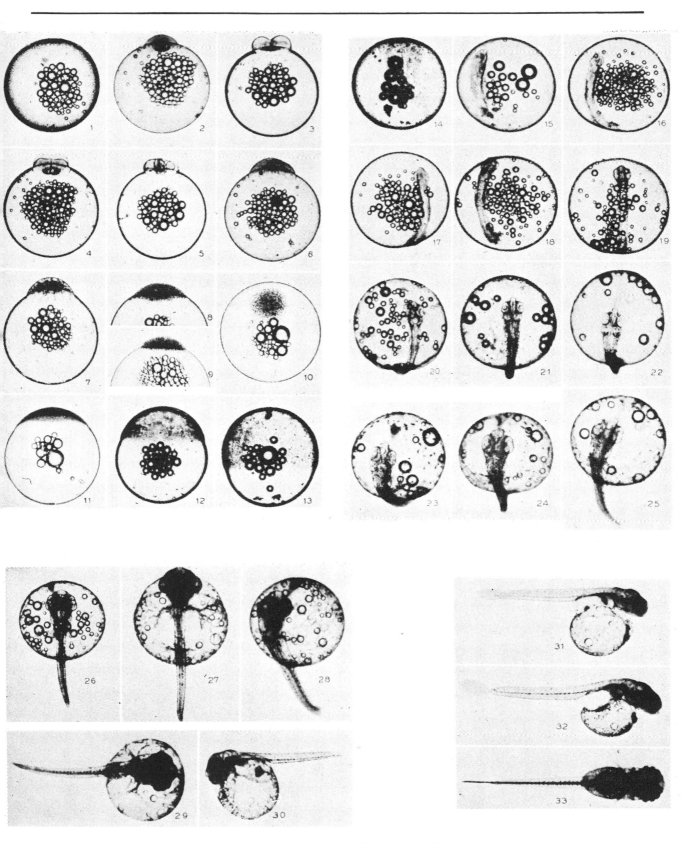

NORMAL STAGES OF FUNDULUS

Photographs by Jane M. Oppenheimer

It seems apparent from the work of Morgan (1895), Lewis (1912), Hoadley (1928), Nicholas and Oppenheimer (1942) and Tung (1943) that the early blastodisc can adjust to the removal of single or groups of blastomeres, and still give rise to normal embryos. This suggests that there is no qualitative division in the early stages of Fundulus, and that all regions are totipotent. It now appears that all parts of the trout blastula are equipotent (Luther, 1937) and, when the blastoderm of the blastula stage is quartered, each gives rise to tissues and organs (in tissue culture or transplantations) representing all parts of the embryo.

Gastrulation is the time when there is qualitative segregation of areas, and Oppenheimer (1936) and Luther (1935) have shown that the dorsal lip of the blastopore functions in teleosts much as it does in the amphibia. Secondary embryos can be induced by heterotopic transplantations of pieces of the dorsal lip. Oppenheimer (1947) believes that the Fundulus dorsal lip shows regional determination, supported by the studies of Eakin (1939) in Salmo.

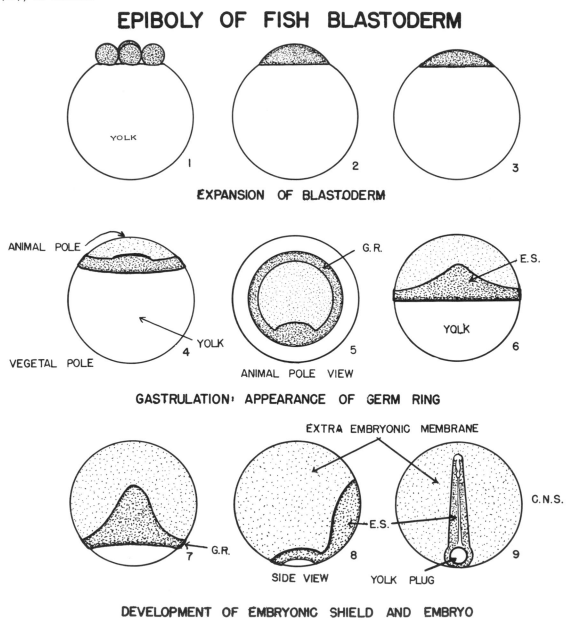

EPIBOLY OF FISH BLASTODERM

EXPANSION OF BLASTODERM

GASTRULATION: APPEARANCE OF GERM RING

DEVELOPMENT OF EMBRYONIC SHIELD AND EMBRYO

(Redrawn from Oppenheimer 1936)

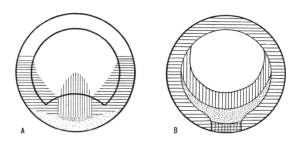

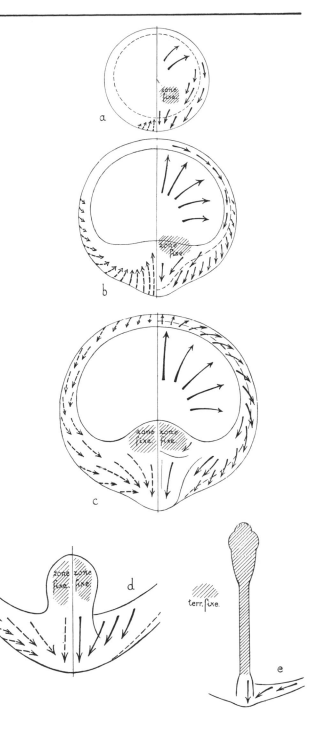

Fig. A and B. Maps showing position of areas for prospective tissues in the early gastrulae of Fundulus (A) and Salmo (B).

Endoderm, light stipple; notochord, heavy stipple; prechordal plate, cross-hatching; nervous system, vertical shading; mesoderm, horizontal shading. Fig. A after Oppenheimer, 1936; Fig. B. simplified after Pasteels, 1936. Drawn by Rosemary Gilmartin.

(From Oppenheimer 1947: Quart. Rev. Biol. 22:105)

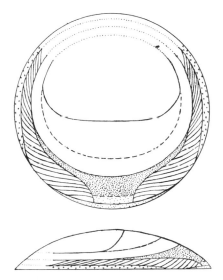

Repartition des territoires de la blastula vue de haut et de profil. Pointillé dense, chorde; pointillé espacé, plaque pré-chordale et entoderme; croix, lames latérales. Système nerveux et ectoderme en blanc. Une ligne interrompue sépare le matériel neural céphalique du troncal.

Mouvements morphogénétiques à divers stades de la formation de l'embryon. A gauche, feuillet profond (flèches brisées). A droite, feuillet superficiel (flèches pleines). Le fin trait continu représente les formes extérieures de l'embryon; le trait interrompu, la limite d'invagination.

MORPHOGENETIC MOVEMENTS IN THE BLASTULA AND EARLY GASTRULA OF THE TROUT AS DETERMINED BY VITAL DYES

(From Pasteels 1934: Comp. rendu. l'Assoc. des Anat., Bruxelles)

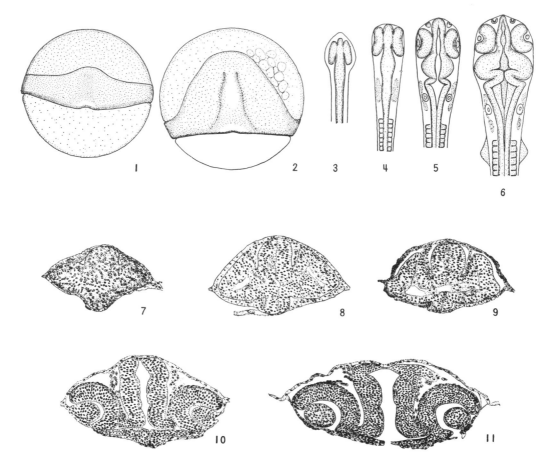

Semi-diagrammatic sketches of preserved Fundulus embryos to show the comparative stages of organ formation. Made with the assistance of a camera-lucida.

1. Twenty-eight-hour-old embryo in which the embryonic shield is differentiating and invagination has begun.
2. Thirty-six-hour-old embryo in which the embryonic axis has begun to be recognizable.
3. Forty-eight-hour-old embryo, just before the formation of the somites.
4. Ten-somite embryo. Note the beginning of the optic cups and auditory structures.
5. Fifteen-somite embryo. Considerable change has occurred in the organization of the brain and sense organs.
6. Twenty-five somite embryo, eighty hours of age. Note the increase in size as well as the degree of differentiation.

Camera-lucida drawings of sections through the optic vesicles of Fundulus embryos.

7. Embryo in one-somite stage.
8. Embryo in seven-somite stage.
9. Embryo in ten-somite stage. Note the flattened optic vesicles and lens anlagen.
10. Embryo in fifteen-somite stage. The optic cups are nearly complete and the lenses are developing.
11. Embryo in twenty-five-somite stage. The lenses are completely separated from the ectoderm.

(From Jones 1939: Trans. Am. Microscopical Soc. 58!1)

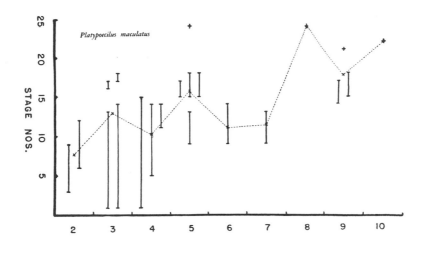

THEORETICAL AGE IN DAYS

Fig. 21. Chart showing age variations in 21 embryonic broods. Each vertical bar represents an entire brood removed from a female. Dotted line connects the mean morphological ages for each theoretical age group. (See detailed description in text.)

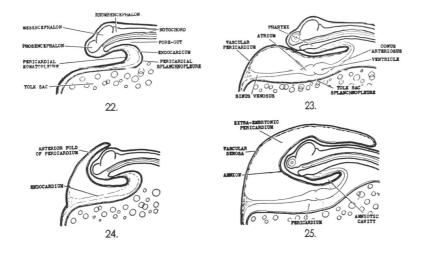

Fig. 22. Diagrammatic sagittal section of Fundulus embryo before development of pericardial sac.

Fig. 23. Diagrammatic sagittal section of Fundulus embryo at maximum development of pericardial sac.

Fig. 24. Diagrammatic sagittal section of Platypoecilus embryo at beginning of formation of extra-embryonic pericardium.

Fig. 25. Diagrammatic sagittal section of Platypoecilus embryo at maximum development of the pericardial amnion and pericardial serosa.

47. EXPERIMENTAL PROCEDURES WITH FISH EGGS AND EMBRYOS

Fish material has been generally considered too difficult for experimental (operative) procedures by graduate students of embryology. However, Nicholas, Oppenheimer, Luther, Eakin and others have demonstrated that the fish egg and embryo can be studied much in the manner of the classical experiments with amphibian eggs and embryos. Through the very generous help of Dr. Oppenheimer, the following procedures are outlined: (1) Vital staining of presumptive areas, (2) Excision and reconstitution, (3) Explantation and culturing in vitro, and (4) Transplantation.

In all of this work there are three very important considerations.

1. Preparation of the egg or embryo: The fish egg is provided with a tough chorion, or outer shell. This must be removed for most experiments, or a window must be provided through which the vital dye or a graft may be inserted. The method is described by Nicholas (1927) as follows:

    a. Mortality is greatest during the cleavage stages. Shell removal after the embryo has formed a distinct cap on the upper surface of the yolk will be the more successful, and should be attempted first.

    b. It may help to hold the egg in a Permoplast or other soft depression. Use very sharp-pointed scissors (iridectomy) and insert one blade between the egg and its shell so that its point is at a tangent to the egg. Enter the shell to the right of the embryo above the omphalomesenteric vein, but forward. If one point of the scissors is longer than the other, this may be used for the puncture and invasion of the shell. If the invasion is properly made, the embryo should not be injured. A small amount of fluid will escape from around the embryo.

    c. Avoid any pressure against the egg or yolk sac, either of which will rupture with the slightest pressure. The chorion is relatively so tough that it will hold the egg to the scissors, so that the latter may now be rotated into such a position that a cut may be made. Assist in the rotation of the egg with a hair loop or spear-point needle. When properly oriented on the scissors, cut through the chorion and continue the cut around the egg (or embryo) dividing the shell, as nearly as possible, into equal halves.

    d. Discard those eggs or embryos which have been ruptured or are in any way damaged. (If prepared, some parts of such damaged embryos may be used for in vitro experiments described below.)

    e. The removed eggs and embryos of Fundulus will develop in distilled, fresh, or sea water providing the yolk membrane is intact. It is probably best to use filtered water of the normal environment for eggs of the various species used.

2. Operating medium: It has just been stated that the Fundulus embryo can survive a wide range of osmotic conditions. (See Kao et al 1954). This may not be equally true of freshwater forms. In general, for marine forms, Holtfreter's (Standard) Solution is used but in concentrations twice or three times the normal and in normal or double concentration for freshwater forms. In general, therefore, the slightly hypertonic media are advised. Trinkaus ('56) uses double-strength bicarbonate-free Holtfreter' solution with phosphate buffer to which egg yolk from Fundulus eggs is added.

3. Asepsis: Prior to decapsulating the egg (or embryo) wash it in 8 to 10 changes of large volumes of sterile water, in a sterile finger bowl. After decapsulating,

transfer the embryo (gently) with wide-mouthed and sterile pipette through several changes of sterile medium. All glassware and solutions should be autoclaved, instruments and pipette should be flamed before use. Steel instruments
are used exclusively. (Oppenheimer has reduced mortality from the usual 50%
to almost 0% by using aseptic precautions - private communication.) Sulfadiazine
(0.002%) is safe to use in any of the culture media.

POTENTIALLY SIMPLE METHOD FOR REARING GERM-FREE FISH*

Aquatic animals, particularly fish that can be deprived of all detectable adherent organisms are highly useful in experiments involving nutrition, infection, and immunity.
Shaw and Aronson ('54) have been successful in dipping fish eggs of Tilapia macrocephala
into 0.04% formaldehyde-aquarium water for 10 minutes, and then transferring them to
sterile water aseptically. Such eggs developed into germ-free fry, and survived for
several weeks after hatching, deriving their food from the large store of yolk. The fry
that died did not disintegrate, but were starved to death and gave rise to no bacteria. No
microorganisms could be cultured from the dead fry even in various nutrient broths or
thioglycollate medium. No mold or fungus growths were found. Thus, this treatment
appeared to be effective in decontamination. Since Tilapia are normally raised on dried
food, which can be sterilized, the abundant eggs of this form may be cultured in a germ-
free environment for experimental purposes.

a. Vital Staining of Fish Embryos

Procedure:
1. Prepare vital-dye stained cellophane. Grübler's Nile Blue Sulphate and
   Neutral Red are to be used separately, and together. The cellophane (thinnest available) should be soaked in 1% aqueous solutions for a day or more,
   then dried on clean white paper. The cellophane is preferable to the agar
   because it remains in one piece and can be removed. Store the red, blue,
   and the combination-stained cellophane in clean marked envelopes until used.
   These vital dyes are not considered to be toxic.
2. Pass the eggs (in their shells) through sterile media. Marine forms are to
   be treated in double strength Holtfreter's and freshwater forms in normal
   Holtfreter's (Standard) Solution. When tap or fresh water are used the stain
   penetrates too rapidly and may even damage some of the cells.
3. Following the (Nicholas, 1927) technique described above, cut a minute window through the chorion of the egg to be studied.
4. With watchmaker's forceps insert a small piece of stained cellophane through
   the window and maneuver it into the described position with a fine hair loop.
   The chorion will generally hold the cellophane in position, where it should
   be left for from 15 to 45 minutes. The penetration and diffusion of the dye
   can be observed directly. The dye penetration is best in hypertonic media.
5. After adequate staining has occurred, carefully remove the stained cellophane
   with watchmaker's forceps, wash the egg with chorion in one change of sterile medium and place it in a covered #2 Stender, containing the normal medium, and at appropriate temperatures for that embryo.
6. Observe during the next 36 to 48 hours, keeping the embryo at the lower
   limit of viable temperatures if it is desired to prolong the early stages. The
   record consists of a series of drawings of the changing position of the stained
   areas, beginning immediately after applying the dye. (See Brummett 1954
   for carbon marking procedure.)

* Courtesy of Dr. E. Shaw, Science 1957. 125:987-988.

VITAL—STAINING OF THE AREAS OF THE PRESUMPTIVE MESODERM OF FUNDULUS

Drawings A to D represent stages in the development of a single embryo, reading from left to right.

Note that the mesoderm is derived from the lateral wings of the embryonic shield, from the germ ring, from the germ ring 180° distant from the embryonic axis, and from the extra-embryonic membrane.

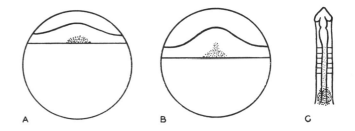

Successive stages in the development of embryos in which the presumptive endoderm has been vitally stained. When stain has been applied to the posterior lip of the early embryonic shield (A), the invagination of stained cells may be watched as gastrulation proceeds (B). Occasionally the stain still remains localized in the region of Kupffer's vesicle after the blastopore is closed (C).

VITAL—STAINING OF THE AREAS OF THE PRESUMPTIVE NERVOUS SYSTEM OF FUNDULUS

A, B, C, represent stages in the early development of a single embryo.
First embryo - entire nervous area.
Second embryo - spinal cord area.
Third embryo - mid- and hind-brain areas.
Fourth embryo - nervous contributions from either side of the embryonic axis.
Fifth embryo - fore-brain and eyes from material anterior to the shield.

(From Oppenheimer 1936: Jour. Exp. Zool. 73:405)

b. Injury, Ablation and Recovery of Fish Embryos

Nicholas and Oppenheimer (1942) have found that up to the 16-cell stage the Fundulus blastomeres are totipotent, and that removal of as much as 50% of the embryonic proto-plasm can be survived by the embryo. On the basis of their work, the following proce-dures are given.

The early stages may be operated on through the chorion, (either by direct pricking with a steel needle or through a window), or after the removal of the chorion. The first pro-cedure is not so easily controlled and pressure factors may be involved, and yet it has the advantage of protection of the embryo against bacteria infection. The second method (i. e., decapsulating the embryo) involves the possible hazard of infection but removes the tension factor and allows more accurate operational technique. (See previous section for method of decapsulation.) Both should be attempted. Use any fish egg available, such as Oryzias, Betta, Paradise or Hemichromis.

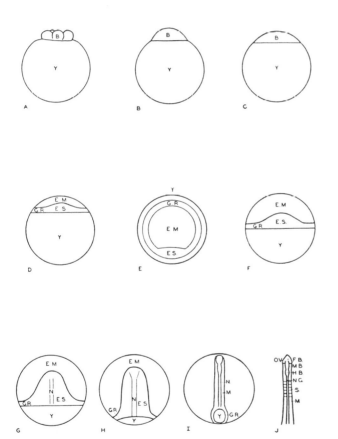

Schematic representation of successive stages in the transformation of the blasto-derm to the embryo. The blastoderm (B) slowly expands over the yolk (Y), as is shown in Figs. A, B and C. As gastrula-tion commences (Figs. D and E) the cells are piled up at the periphery of the blasto-derm to form the germ ring (G. R.) and the embryonic shield (E. S.); the central por-tion of the blastoderm becomes the extra-embryonic membrane (E. M.). During the course of gastrulation the blastoderm gradually covers the yolk (diagrams F, G, H and I); late in gastrulation a refractile streak (N) visible in the shield represents the keel of the central nervous system. Fig. J shows the extent of embryonic differentiation a few hours after the yolk is completely covered; O. V., optic vesicle; F B., forebrain; M.B., mid-brain; H.B., hind-brain; N.C., nerve cord; S. somite; M. unsegmented meso-derm.

The egg is drawn in profile in all figures except figure E, which represents the stage shown in Fig. D seen from the animal pole.

(From Oppenheimer 1936: Jour. Exp. Zool. 73:405)

A. Removal or Destruction of a Blastomere: Two to 4-cell stage embryo.

1. With sharp-pointed steel needle invade the chorion directly over one of the blasto-meres of a 2 or 4-cell stage, and rupture it. Avoid damage to the yolk and con-tiguous blastomeres.

2. Make a small window in the chorion, directly over the blastomeres. Prepare a micro-pipette with terminal bore slightly smaller than the diameter of a single blastomere. If the edges of the pipette opening are rough, so much the better

Pass this pipette through the small aperture, and gently suck up a single blasto-mere. This may require first the loosening of the blastomere with a slight cir-cular movement of the pipette. If the pipette is attached by a small-bore rubber tube held in the mouth the suction can be the better controlled. By this oral suc-tion method 1 and then 2 blastomeres of the 4-cell stages should be removed.

Fig. 1.   Embryo after spinal cord transection anterior and posterior to the fin at stage 23; conduction restored across anterior lesion. Note localized kyphosis of tail.

Fig. 2.   Embryo resulting after cord transection in trunk region at stage 23. This embryo showed no functional restitution.

Fig. 3.   Cord transection between somites 6 and 7; operation at stage 26.

Fig. 4.   The medulla was separated from spinal cord by transection at stage 26. This embryo showed functional and anatomical regeneration. Note both lordotic and kyphotic curvatures.

(From Nicholas & Oppenheimer 1942:
Jour. Exp. Zool. 90:127)

B.   Removal of Parts of the Germ Ring: Stages #10 to #15.

The germ ring is so adherent to the underlying yolk that the suction procedure must be used cautiously or the yolk will exude whereupon death follows.

1.   Use the window or decapsulation method, and suck out the ectoderm (only) of the germ ring up to not more than 20% of the ring. Concentrate on those parts of the germ ring distant from the early shield.

2.   Suck out parts of the early neural keel (stage #15), with and without the adjacent germ ring. (Nicholas and Oppenheimer found that if 25% of the keel is removed, development ceases.)

C.   Ablation Experiments on Later Stages: (Stages #20 to #23 all decapsulated.)

1.   Remove the pectoral fin as it appears as an anlagé posterior and ventral to the ear vesicle (stage #20).

2.   Remove the eye from one side only. This may be accomplished by drawing the eye into a small-bore pipette and then cutting it off at the base with a fine needle knife.

3.   Remove the otic vesicle (stage #20). With controlled oral suction the ear vesicle can be removed without injury to the adjacent medulla, but there is generally no regeneration and the embryo later shows circus movements in consequence.

4. Remove small parts of the nerve cord (stages #17 to #20). This may also be done by suction, but it is difficult to limit the amount removed. Not more than the equivalent of 2 somite lengths should be removed, and a minimum of the adjacent notochord and lateral mesoderm.

5. Remove parts of the brain, also by the suction method. This operation seems to be less drastic for the embryo than some of the others, but it is somewhat more difficult to localize the ablation. No two embryos will be identically treated, hence individual records are required.

There is a quantitative decrease in regenerative or regulative capacity during early development as revealed by the preceding operations. Nicholas and Oppenheimer, using Fundulus, found no permanent damage up to the 16-cell stage of many of the operated forms. "Up to this point the blastomeres may be regarded as totipotent so long as one-half of the original content of the egg is left untouched." (Nicholas & Oppenheimer, 1942.) Following this stage there is rapid reduction in regulation, with progressive differentiation. (See Enami 1958, Proc. Jap. Acad. 34:44 & 50 for ablation experiments on caudal neurosecretory organs of fish larvae such as Fundulus)

D. Transections of the Spinal Cord of Motile Stages: (stage #23)

The nerve cord is transected (without removal of any tissue) with a sharp steel needle or iridectomy scissors, avoiding injury to the notochord if possible. The transections should be at different levels and records should include description of the type of movement upon development to stage #26. Histological analysis will determine the degree of damage and reconstitution.

DISCUSSION:

With the increasing physiological complexity of the embryo there is a decrease in the regulative capacity, noted first at the 16-cell stage. When as much as 50% of the protoplasmic material of the 16-cell stage is removed in Fundulus (Nicholas & Oppenheimer, 1942.) defects appear and few of the fish gastrulate, but the same proportion of protoplasmic material can be removed at the previous (8-cell) stage and this will be followed by complete regulation. Following the 16-cell stage there is a rapid drop in regulation, so that at the blastula stage the embryo can tolerate a loss of not more than about 20% of the protoplasmic mass.

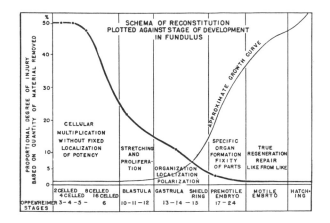

(From Nicholas & Oppenheimer 1942: Jour. Exp. Zool. 90:127)

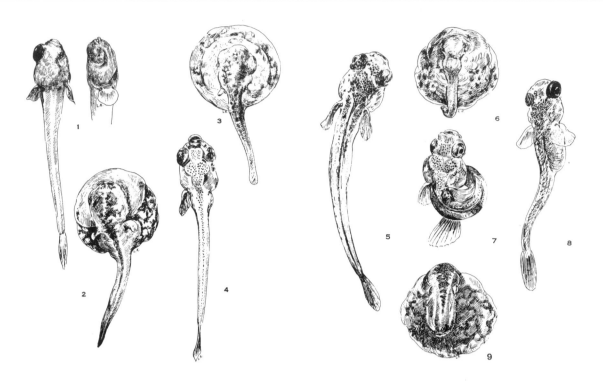

Fig. 1.   Dorsal and lateral views of a Fundulus after hatching revealing the shortening of the head with orbital formation following ablation of the eye at stages 21-23.

Fig. 2.   Stage 27 embryo showing the recovery and healing of an embryo after the removal of the eye in Stage 22.   Indications of the future mouth and head asymmetry are already evident.

Fig. 3.   The healing after operation at Stage 22 shows a puckering of the opercular region following the removal of fin tissue.   The embryo is slightly bent toward the side of operation.

Fig. 4.   The removal of the fin in Stages 20-22 gives rise always to the type of animal here shown at the time of hatching.

Fig. 5.   The ear was removed in its early vesicle stage, Stage 20.   At the time of operation slight damage was done to the right half of the brain which is reduced in size.   The C curvature is characteristic of the posture of the earless forms.

Fig. 6.   The operation performed at Stage 17 involved a slight injury to the mid-brain and the constrictions made by the pipette are still evident at Stage 25 anterior and posterior to the original site of injury.

Fig. 7.   The result obtained by an injury to the anterior part of the medulla; the circular region shows a deficit extending to the notochord which was slightly enlarged.   There is no reconstitution. Operation performed at Stage 18.

Fig. 8.   Development without repair after injury to the left side of the brain.   Operation performed at Stage 18.

Fig. 9.   The free portion of the tail bud of a stage 20-embryo was removed.   The wound healed and was covered with epidermis.   The rounded eminence is a notochordal projection covered with epithelium.   Embryo Stage 25.

(From Nicholas & Oppenheimer 1942: Jour. Exp. Zool. 90:127)

Injury or ablations of the embryonic shield and neural keel generally show localized effects, particularly when they occur in the midline of the embryonic axis.   After organ differentiation, the damage tolerated must be only a small fraction (less than 10%) of the available tissue.   This applies particularly to the formed brain, sense organs, fin, tail, etc.

In all of this type of work it must be remembered that some of the results may be due to incidental handling of the embryo, as in decapsulating.   Also, it is somewhat more difficult to excise a specific region, and only that region, in fish than in the amphibian (or even chick) embryos.   Collateral injuries may be the primary cause of failure in reconstitution.   Operational skill with fish material is achieved only with great patience, persistence, and repetition.

c. The Culturing of Fish Explants in Vitro

This type of investigation, so readily achieved with amphibian and even with chick material, proves satisfactory but to a lesser degree with fish embryonic parts. Oppenheimer (1938) cultured parts of Epiplatys fasciolatus in a modified Ringer's for from 4 to 7 days and secured tail-like differentiation without histogenesis. (See also Trinkhaus and Drake 1956)

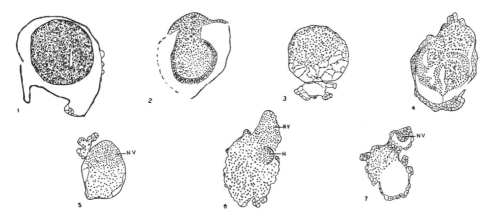

Figs. 1 to 7. The types of differentiation attained in isolation blastoderms which have not gastrulated. These are hyperblastulae, masses of cells generally differentiating only a hollow vesicle whose wall represents the ectodermal portion of the yolk-sac epithelium. The stage at which the blastoderms were removed from the yolk, and the number of days they survived before preservation, are indicated in parentheses. Cell walls are represented only in Fig. 1.

Fig. 1. Hyperblastula in which the non-differentiated embryonic cells form a compact mass in the center of the vesicle. (16-celled; 4 days.)

Fig. 2. Hyperblastula in which the non-differentiated mass of cells is continuous with the vesicle epithelium at one region only and surrounded elsewhere by a columnar epithelium. (32-celled; 3 days.)

Fig. 3. Explant whose differentiated cells are joined to the vesicle epithelium by a mesenchymatous network. (8-celled; 4 days.)

Fig. 4. Explant in which the cellular arrangement suggests the occurrence of irregular cell movements. Except for the formation of columnar epithelium no histogenic changes have taken place. The cell movements were not those of gastrulation. (16-celled; 3-3/4 days.)

Fig. 5. Hyperblastula containing two different types of cells, one non-differentiated, the other with denser nuclei and more heavily staining cytoplasm (NV). These probably present cells which have commenced self-differentiation of nervous tissue without the inductive stimuli of gastrulation. (64- to 128-celled; 3-3/4 days.)

Fig. 6. Hyperblastula in which one group of cells has the dense nuclei characteristic of nervous tissue (NV), while another group (N) is surrounded by a heavy sheath similar to that normally surrounding the notochord. These cell groups are large spherical masses, surrounded by homogeneously arranged non-differentiated cells; their differentiation has been independent. (2-celled; 3 days.)

Fig. 7. Hyperblastula in which a small group of cells, probably epidermal in origin, have begun to self-differentiate nervous tissue (NV). (8-celled; 6 days.)

(From Oppenheimer 1939: Jour. Exp. Zool. 72:245)

Procedure:

   1. Insure complete asepsis, autoclaving the media and sterilizing all instruments and glassware. Culturing can be in deep depression slides, or in covered and sealed #1 Stenders.

2. Culture medium: For marine forms the filtered and sterilized sea water can be used. For fresh-water forms, Standard (Holtfreter's) Solution should be used, in normal and in double strength. To vary the medium, it is suggested that 0.1% glucose or 1% glucose plus 0.1% peptone be added prior to autoclaving. (See various media used with chick explants.)

3. Pass the egg to be studied through 7 to 10 changes of sterile medium isotonic for that egg, to free it of most of the bacteria.

4. Decapsulate the egg in the manner described above (Nicholas, 1927) at stages #2 to #7.

5. Using sharp, sterile, steel knives dissect away the blastodermic disc of any stage from 1 to 32-cells. Clean away all adherent yolk granules and culture in hanging drop (see chick exercise), in sterile medium. (These will generally form hyperblastulae.)

6. From later stages (stages #7 to #12) explant the entire embryonic mass (exclusive of the yolk) into culture dishes with hypertonic and sterile media and observe for 48 hours or more for differentiations. Histological analyses will be necessary to determine the degree of differentiation.

7. Bisect the entire egg of stage #13 in the manner indicated in the diagram below, using a sharp and sterile steel needle. As the needle is pressed through the egg and into the underlying Permoplast base of the operating dish, the cut surfaces of the two halves are pinched apart in such a manner that the cut surfaces are usually closed together and the yolk is contained within the half-sized vesicles. When this occurs, the entire halves may be cultured. When there is rupture, parts of the germ ring and embryonic shield should be further dissected away and cultured in isolation.

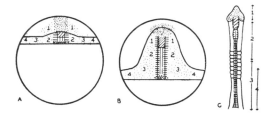

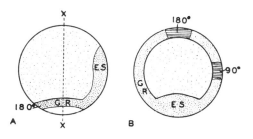

The localization of presumptive nervous system, mesoderm and endoderm in the early gastrula (A) and the middle gastrula (B), and the position of these tissues in the seven-somite embryo (C).

The position of the nervous tissue is indicated by heavy stipple (forebrain and optic vesicles), diagonal hatching (mid-brain and anterior hind-brain) and vertical hatching (posterior hind-brain and spinal cord). The cells whose position is indicated by horizontal hatching aid in the formation of mid-brain, hind-brain and spinal cord.

The mesoderm is indicated by the lightly stippled areas. The areas marked by the numbers 1, 2, 3 and 4 ultimately lie in the regions of the embryo indicated by the arrows accompanying diagram C.

The endoderm is represented by open circles. The endodermal cells that have invaginated are not shown.

(From Oppenheimer 1936:
Jour. Exp. Zool. 73:405)

Scheme of operations. In order to isolate the germ ring of late gastrulae originally located 180° away from the dorsal lip of the blastopore, the eggs are divided into two parts by cutting along the plane X-X shown in Fig. 1A. Fig. 1B shows a dorsal aspect of the blastoderm. The cross-hatched regions represent the material involved in the grafts of germ ring originally 90° or 180° from the embryonic axis. The heavy stippling indicates germ ring (GR) and embryonic shield (ES), the light stippling extra-embryonic membrane.

(From Oppenheimer 1938:
Jour. Exp. Zool. 79:185)

8. Parts to be cultured at stages #12 or #13:
    a. Portion of the germ ring 180° from the embryonic shield.
    b. Embryonic shield and related germ ring in half embryo.
    c. Dorsal lip material only, i.e., margin of the embryonic shield.
9. Parts to be cultured at later stages, #15 to #24:
    a. Embryonic shield alone at stage #15.
    b. Optic vesicle of stage #17.
    c. Melanophores of extra-embryonic membrane, stage #20.
    d. Heart anlage' of stage #20.
    e. Somites and related nerve and notochord of stage #20.
    f. Pectoral fin of stage #24.

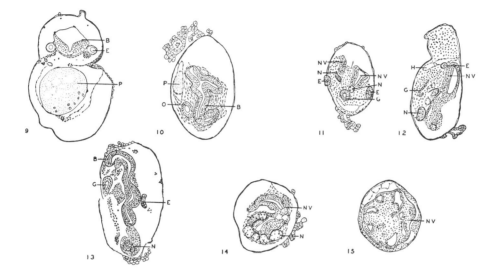

Figs. 9 to 15. Sections through isolated blastoderms which have undergone gastrula-
        tion and have formed embryonic structures.
Fig. 9.   The ear region of the embryo shown in Fig. 8. The organs are in their
        topographically normal relationships. B, hind-brain; E, ear; P, periblast.
Figs. 10 and 11. Two sections through an embryo whose structures are in topograph-
        ically normal relationships although periblast (P) is found only in the eye
        region. The embryonic axis was curved, therefore the eye region, shown
        in Fig. 10, was cut frontally, and the ear region, shown in Fig. 11, trans-
        versely. In Fig. 10, optic vesicles (O), forebrain and optic lobes (B), and
        periblast are seen, and in Fig. 11 medulla (NV), notochord (N), gut (G)
        and ears (E). Posteriorly in the head the embryonic axis is double, and
        the secondary nervous system is imperfect. (64- to 128-celled; 4 days.)
Fig. 12.   Sagittal section through an embryo in which gut (G), notochord (N),
        medulla (NV) and heart (H) show in general typical relationships to each
        other. One ear is ventral (E) rather than lateral, however, due to twist-
        ing of the embryonic axis; the notochord is somewhat contorted, and
        posteriorly grades off into a dense group of cells continuous with the
        nervous system. (256-celled; 4 days.)
Fig. 13.   Sagittal section through an embryo in which grain (B), gut (G) and ear
        (E) are in their normal positions, but the notochord (N) is greatly con-
        voluted and forms a mass without association with the nervous system.
        (64-celled; 4 days.)
Figs. 14 and 15. Two sections through a blastoderm in which irregularities of the
        nervous system have resulted from the distortion of the substrate after
        gastrulation. A floor plate has been formed only in regions where the
        notochord (N) and nervous tissue (NV) are in contact. (32-celled; 4 days.)

(From Oppenheimer 1936: Jour. Exp. Zool. 72:247)

If the period of isolation can be extended to more than 4 days it will be necessary to renew the culture medium at that time. Generally the limit of differentiation will be
achieved before that time, usually within 48 hours. If the culture is made in a hanging
drop (see chick exercises) the complete process of development can be observed under
the dissecting microscope without disturbing the explant, and if it is bacteria-free, it
should survive.

Yamamoto (1939 Fac. Sci. Tokyo Univ. 15:269) gives a formula for a synthetic medium
which is isotonic to the Oryzias egg.

$$M/7.5 \text{ NaCl}............100 \text{ cc.}$$
$$M/7.5 \text{ KCl}.............2.0 \text{ cc.}$$
$$M/11 \text{ CaCl}_2............2.1 \text{ cc.}$$
$$pH \text{ to } 7.3$$

To such a medium 0.1% glucose may be added for nutrition for the explants of Oryzias.

Hayes, Darcy and Sullivan (1946: Jour. Biol. Chem. 163:621) have analyzed the ovarian
or coelomic fluid of the salmon, which fluid appears suddenly just at the time of hatching. They find it to be a clear, limpid, and slightly translucent medium with the following constituents:

Ions per 1,000 liter of water:
Sodium .... 151 milliequivalents
Potassium .... 3.2   "
Calcium .... 7.1   "
Magnesium .... 2.6   "
Chlorine................ 116.0   "
HPO_4 .... 4.0   "
HCO_3 .... 13.4   "

Since the ripe eggs of the Salmon lie freely within the body cavity, and hence within this
fluid medium, this medium may be considered as isotonic to the eggs at this stage. This
fluid is, however, hypertonic to blood. Sodium chloride is the dominant salt, with other
ions in the approximate ratio that they are found in sea water. In the eggs the potassium
dominates, and the calcium and magnesium are not osmotically active. At fertilization,
in water, the egg loses osmotic pressure by about 3%. During development the egg and
embryo take up calcium and sodium from the environment so that the final amounts are
4 and 3 times the initial amounts respectively. Phosphorous intake is markedly increased, probably in connection with skeleton formation. (See references by Trinkhaus
& Drake 1956: Devillers 1957)

d. Induction of Secondary Embryo by Grafting of Dorsal Lip

The fish egg can be used as a host for successful transplantations without the necessity
of a Brücke or bridge to hold the graft in place. Healing and development are so rapid
that the whole experiment can be concluded within several days.

Procedure:
1. Pass the egg and its chorion through 7 to 10 changes of sterile medium.
   This should be hypertonic, such as double or triple Standard (Holtfreter's)
   Solution.
2. Decapsulate the egg, using the technique of Nicholas (1927) described above.
   The steel needles or watchmaker's forceps must be sterile. Use stage #13
   when the germ ring has passed over about 3/4 of the yolk. Similarly prepare the donor, of the same age and stage.

3. Dissect out of the donor the region comparable to the amphibian dorsal lips, i. e., the margin of the germ ring from which arises the embryonic shield. Clear it of all adherent yolk. Use sharp and sterile steel needles. It will help to follow the graft if the entire donor is previously stained in 1/10,000 Nile Blue Sulphate.

4. Prepare the host for the graft, using two different sites in as many hosts. Operate in double Standard (Holtfreter's) Solution, or stronger.
    a. Loosen the embryonic shield on one side, using sharp, steel needles. The cells will tend to grow together rapidly, and will hold any graft in place. Insert the excised dorsal lip material, pushing it beneath the margin of the embryonic shield.
    b. Loosen some superficial cells of the extra-embryonic blastoderm at some distance from the embryonic shield, and quickly insert the excised dorsal lip material.

5. After the wound has healed and the graft seems to be held intact, transfer the embryo (by wide-mouthed pipette) to a covered #2 Stender containing sterile, normal (isotonic) medium for that egg. Culture it for a few hours to as many as 7 days, depending upon the success of the take and health of the embryo.

Localization in the nerve keel of the late gastrula. Cells removed from the region A differentiate when grafted on extra-embryonic membrane to form optic lobe, cells from the region C to form spinal cord. A defect in the region B resulted in a deficiency in the region of Mauthner's cell.

(From Oppenheimer 1936: Jour. Exp. Zool. 73:405)

An embryo in which 180° germ ring from an early gastrula has formed caudal fin dorsal to the brain of the host. Fixed 8 days after operation.

(From Oppenheimer 1938: Jour. Exp. Zool. 79:185)

TRANSPLANTATION EXPERIMENTS BY DR. JANE OPPENHEIMER

Fig. 1. An early stage in induction in Fundulus, drawn 6-1/2 hours after operation. The first visible effect of dorsal lip implantation in Fundulus is concentration of cells in the vicinity of the graft; here host cells (H) stained with Nile blue sulphate aggregate in the region of the graft (G) stained with neutral red. P, primary embryo.

Fig. 2 and 3. Two perch embryos (I) induced by dorsal lip grafts implanted into the edge of the blastoderm 180° away from the primary dorsal lip; drawn 2 and 5 days after operation, respectively. P, primary embryo. Fig. 3 drawn by Miss L. Krause.

(From Oppenheimer 1936: Jour. Exp. Zool. 72:409)

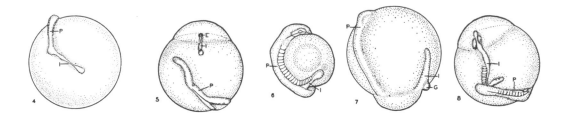

Fig. 4.   Axial structures (I) induced from the extra-embryonic epithelium of a Fundulus egg by implanta-
           tion of young dorsal lip into the edge of the blastoderm; drawn 21-1/2 hours after operation.
Fig. 5.   Embryonic structures (I) induced in Fundulus by implantation of a dorsal lip material into extra-
           embryonic epithelium; drawn 2-3/4 days after operation. E, ear.
Fig. 6.   Perch embryo (I) induced by dorsal lip implanted into extra-embryonic epithelium; drawn 1-1/2
           days after operation. This embryo was probably a lateral hemi-embryo; somites were formed
           on one side only.
Figs. 7 and 8. Two stages in the development of a Fundulus embryo induced by the implantation of very
           young dorsal lip into a very young gastrula; drawn at 18 hours and 3-1/4 days after operation.
           The right part of the graft, which had been stained with Nile blue sulphate, failed to invaginate
           and formed a knob (G) at the right side of the developing induced embryo; as a result the in-
           duced embryo (I), although two ears were formed, was a lateral hemi-embryo with somites
           present only on the left side.

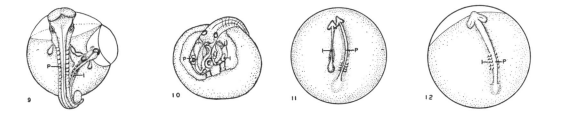

Fig. 9.   Fundulus embryo (I) induced by a dorsal lip graft implanted into the edge of the blastoderm;
           drawn 3 days after operation. The ears and right fin of the induced embryo are formed posterior
           to the corresponding structures in the primary embryo (P).
Fig. 10.   Head structures of Fundulus (I) induced by a dorsal lip graft which was originally implanted into
           extra-embryonic epithelium but which shortly after implantation became incorporated into the
           primary embryonic shield; drawn 3 days after operation.
Fig. 11.   Fundulus embryo (I) induced by the implantation of very young dorsal lip; the graft was incor-
           porated into the primary embryonic shield. Drawn 22 hours after operation.
Fig. 12.   Somites (I) induced by a dorsal lip graft implanted into the primary embryonic shield; 1 day
           after operation. The accessory somites persisted for 2 days and subsequently were absorbed into
           the host; compare embryo shown in Fig. 6, where somites induced in an extra-embryonic region
           exhibited a different segmentation from the host's.

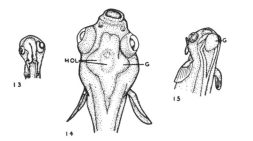

Fig. 13.   A dorsal lip graft implanted anteriorly in
           the embryonic shield was partially absorbed
           into the forebrain, with the result that this
           structure has wider walls than normal.
Fig. 14.   A graft of cells removed from a lateral part
           of the shield formed brain (G) in the mesen-
           cephalic region of the host. HOL, optic
           lobes of host.
Fig. 15.   A perch embryo in which dorsal lip implanted
           into the embryonic region was transformed to
           brain; drawn 6 days after operation.

(From Oppenheimer 1936: Jour. Exp. Zool. 72:409)

48. THE GENETICS OF FISH*

Through an intensive series of researches Gordon (1927-1948) has demonstrated that the mechanism of inheritance is essentially Mendelian for fishes, as it has been proven to be for all other groups studied. There are wild types (gray) of the Platy (Platypoecilus maculatus) and domesticated albino and golden types which can be interbred readily. In all, there are some 150 varieties of patterns in this one species, relatively few of which have, as yet, been thoroughly analysed from a genetic point of view. Recently (1944-1948) Dr. Gordon has concentrated on the inheritance of melanomas, which study is closely akin to cancer studies on higher forms.

The Platy is readily available at any Aquarium Supply House, and the three major varieties (wild, albino, and golden) may be procured for simple genetic crosses. The golden mutant arose from a wild stock in 1921 and the albino appeared first, also from a wild stock, in 1934. When these mutants are interbred, the wild variety re-appears.

Following are a series of genetic crosses that have been made by Dr. Gordon, indicating clear-cut dominance and recessiveness of various pigment patterns. These are offered here as suggestive of the type of study in the field of developmental heredity that is now possible. (See pages 368-375 and also papers by Goodrich et al.)

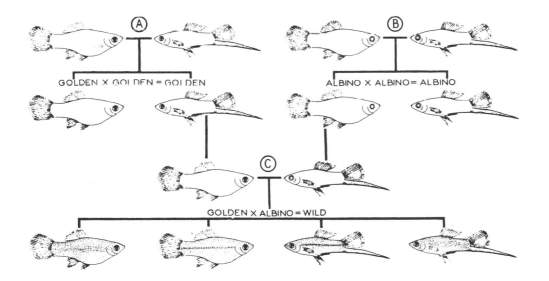

BACK TO THEIR ANCESTRAL COLORS

When the golden swordtails are inbred, they produce nothing but golden; when the albino swordtails are inbred, they produce nothing but albinos. When the golden swordtail is mated with the albino, they produce young all of which have the coloring of the wild swordtail.

---

* These figures are kindly loaned by Dr. Myron Gordon of the New York Zoological Society. See Gordon's "The Physiology of Fishes", Academic Press 1957.

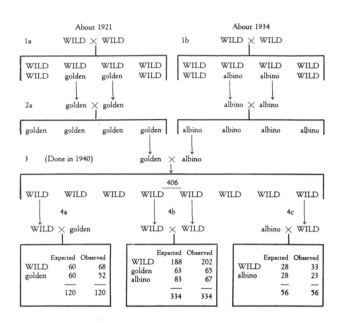

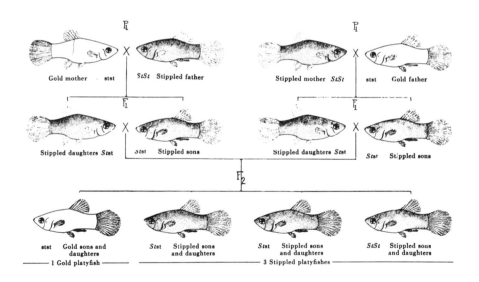

HISTORY OF SEPARATION AND REUNION OF COLOR GENES IN THE SWORDTAIL

This chart shows the independent origin of the golden and the albino. and the results obtained when these mutations were crossed. The backcrosses of the "synthetic" wilds to golden and albinos show the genetic structure of these differences. Some of the discrepancies in the ratios in the backcross and F_2 results may be accounted for by the differential viability of the three types of swordtails. The albino is the weakest, and the golden is definitely weaker than the wild type. The total of 334 F_2 offspring is made up of the progeny of several females. Some F_1 matings produced F_2 young in the ratio of 9:3:4 so closely as to be remarkable.

This diagram illustrates the way in which the gray or stipple pattern of the platyfish is inherited. In the pair on the left, the father carries the dominant factor (StSt) for stippling while the mother is non-stippled (stst). The parents are designated as P_1. The first filial generation (F_1), obtained from this mating, are all stippled (Stst) like their father. Similar results are obtained when the mother (see pair on right) is the stippled parent (StSt) and the father is non-stippled. The offspring of this mating are also all stippled, this time like their mother (Stst). When the individuals of the first generation (F_1) are bred together from either series, and the second generation (F_2) is produced, the following results are obtained: there are three stippled fishes (StSt) or (Stst) to every non-stippled one (stst). There are male and female representatives in each group. This is an example of simple mendelian inheritance of a single heritable character. The stippling is actually due to the presence in the skin of very small black cells, technically known as micromelanophores.

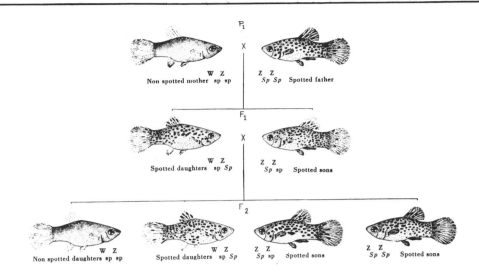

This diagram illustrates the peculiar way in which the spotted (Sp) pattern is inherited. The female is represented by the formula W Z while the male is Z Z. The spotted factor is associated with sex. When the spotted platy is the male parent (Zsp Zsp) and a non-spotted platy is the female parent (Wsp Zsp), all the offspring of the mating, both the sons and daughters, are spotted like their father. When the spotted individuals of the first generation (F_1) are mated together, brother to sister, the ratio of three spotted platyfishes to one non-spotted is obtained in the second generation (F_2). Up to this point the results of this mating resemble the inheritance of the stippling factor, but note the following significant fact: all the non-spotted fishes obtained in the second generation are females. And the spotted platyfishes contain both males and females, but there are two spotted sons to every non-spotted daughter. This is an example of the inheritance of a sex-linked heritable factor. A similar type of inheritance is found in birds and moths for certain characters.

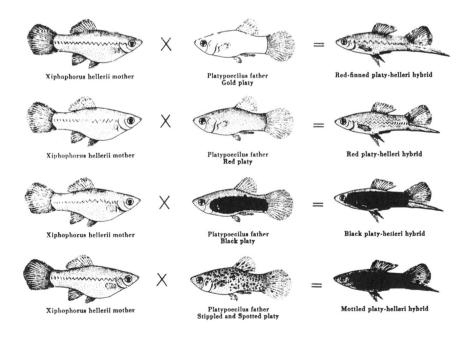

The platyfishes and the Mexican swordtail will readily hybridize. The hybrids are classified according to the original varieties of the species used in the cross. The gold platy and the swordtail produce the red finned platy-helleri hybrid. The red platy and the swordtail produce the red platy-helleri hybrid. The black platy and the swordtail produce the black platy-helleri hybrid. The stippled and spotted platy and the swordtail produce the mottled platy-helleri hybrid. These hybrids frequently develop the neoplastic disease known as melanosis.

Mexican platyfish, Platypoecilus maculatus. The fish on the
left is a female spotted (and stippled) platy. On the right, the
fish is the gold platy. When these two fishes are mated, the
inheritances of the spotted character may be traced through the
succeeding generations. For results of a cross of this type, see
the accompanying diagram. Photograph by Myron Gordon.
(From Fraser and Gordon.)

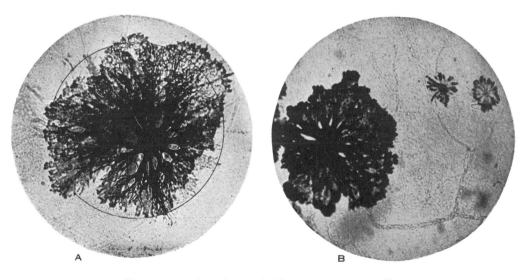

A. Photomicrograph made by a double exposure. A partially
contracted large black pigment cell (macromelanophore) is
superimposed upon a partially expanded one. The limits of the
first are contained within the circle. In the contracted state,
note the narrow black processes formed by the pigment particles.
In the expanded condition the pigment particles are arranged in
sheets. It is by a process of pigment cell expansion and contraction that color changes in fishes take place. B. This picture is
a photomicrograph of the black pigment cells of the spotted and
stippled platyfish. The spots of the platy are due to large black
cells called macromelanophores. The gray ground color of the
platy is due to the smaller pigment cells, micromelanophores.
Note the blood vessel which reaches each pigment cell, both the
large and the small. Photographs by Myron Gordon.

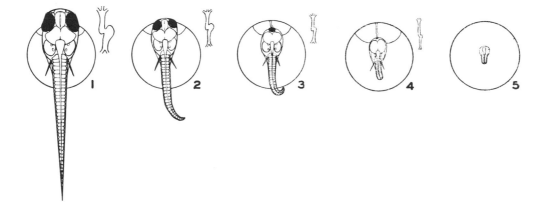

The teratological forms of fish embryos produced by irradiating germ cells. No. 1 represents a control
embryo 4 days after fertilization. No. 2 shows slight reductions in the anterior and posterior regions.
The succeeding stages (3, 4 and 5) show greater reductions of head and tail. Other parts are entirely
lacking in these embryos. Deformities of the heart are shown in drawings to the right of each embryo.
Embryos deformed as much as No. 5 often do not develop a heart. The heart deformities consist
chiefly of an elongation, and improper formation of the chambers, usually associated with an edema
of the pericardial cavity.

(From Solberg 1938: Jour. Exp. Zool. 28:417)

DISCUSSION:

The foregoing sections on Fish indicate that this Class of Vertebrates is coming into its
own in the field of Experimental Embryology. Most of the procedures outlined are of an
operational nature.

There are also the studies on hybridization; on environmentally induced teratologies
(Stockard, 1921); on the effect of x-irradiation of one of the gametes (Solberg, 1938); on
the physiological response of the embryo to changes in the environment (Waterman, 1940
and the various Japanese workers with Oryzias). There is an ever increasing amount of
work of a cytological and cytochemical nature, all of which should be included in an exhaustive treatise on experimental embryology of fish.

The fish are rapidly becoming a contestant for attention along with the amphibia. Possibly the work of Oppenheimer (1939) can be cited as a bridge between these two classes
of vertebrates, for she found that a large variety of fish anlagen differentiated quite normally when grafted into the amphibian hosts and that "Fish epidermis and cartilage have
been found morphologically continuous with comparable structures formed by amphibian
cells in grafts," and "the fish grafts are occasionally seemingly innervated by nerves
originating from the amphibian cranial ganglia; it is not known whether the apparent innervation is a functional one." (Jour. Exp. Zool. 80:392)

REFERENCES

ADELMANN, H. B., 1936 - "The problem of cyclopia." Quart. Rev. Biol. 11:61.

ALEXANDER, L. E., 1942 - "The capacity of the eye cup of Fundulus heteroclitus for induction and regeneration of lenses as studied in lenseless eyes." Jour. Exp. Zool. 91:111.

ALLEE, W. C., A. J. KINEL & W. H. HOSKINS, 1940 - "The growth of goldfish in homotypically conditioned water; a population study in mass physiology." Jour. Exp. Zool. 84:417.

ALLEN, A. L., 1958 - "The effects of x-irradiation upon embryonic development in the paradise fish." Government Contract AT (1-1)-349.

ARMSTRONG, P. B., 1936 - "Mechanism of hatching in Fundulus heteroclitus." Physiol. Zool. 71:407.

ARONSON, L. R., 1945 - "Influence of the stimuli provided by the male cichlid fish, Tulapia macrocephala, on the spawning frequency of the female." Physiol. Zool. 18:403.

ARONSON, L. R., A. M. HOLZ-TUCKER, 1949 - "Ovulation in the mouthbreeding cichlid fish, Filapia Macrocephala." Anat. Rec. 105:88-89 (See also Physiol. Zool. 18:403 and Zoologica. 34:133-158)

ATZ, J. W., 1950 - "The functions of plants in Aquaria." Aq. Jour. 21:40-56.

BELL, G. M. & W. S. HOAR, 1950 - "Some effect of U - V radiation of sockeye salmon eggs A. alevins."

BIRNIE, J. H., 1934 - "Regeneration of the tail fin of Fundulus embryos." Biol. Bull. 66:316.

BONDIE, von Cecil, 1945 - "Stages in the development of the picked or spiny dogfish, Squalis acanthis." Biol. Bull. 88:220.

BONNET, D. D., 1939 - "Mortality of the Cod egg in relation to temperature." Biol. Bull. 76:428.

BREDER, C. M., Jr., 1957 - "Minature circulating systems for small laboratory Zoologica (N.Y.) 42:1-10.

BRIGGS, J. C. & N. EGAMI, 1959 - "The medaka (Oryzias latipes)" Jour. Fish Res. Bd. Canada. 16:363-380.

BRIGGS, J. C. & J. S. WILSON, 1959 - "Comparison of the teratogenic effects of trypon blue and low temperature in the medaka fish (Oryziaslatipes)" Quart. J. Florida Acad. Sci. 22:54-68.

BRUMMETT, A. R., 1954 - "The relationship of the germ ring to the formation of the tail bud in Fundulus as demonstrated by carbon marking technique." Jour. Exp. Zool. 125:447-486.

BROWN, M. E., 1957 - "The physiology of fishes." 2 vols., 947 Academic Press, New York.

BURGER, J. W., 1939 - "Some experiments on the relation of the external environment to the spermatogenetic cycle of Fundulus heteroclitus." Biol. Bull. 77:96 (see ibid. 80:31)

CAHN, P. H., 1952 - "Spectral effects on the growth rate and endocrine histology of the teleost, Astyanax mexicanis". Zoologica 37:(1)33.

CHILD, C. M., 1945 - "A further study of oxidation-reduction pattern in teleost development." Jour. Exp. Zool. 100:577.

CHIN, E., 1959 - "An inexpensive re-circulating sea-water system." Progressive Fish Culturist. 21:91-93.

CLARK, E. L., R. ARONSON, 1951 - "Sexual behaviour in the guppy, Lebistes reticulatus." Zoologica. 36:49-66.

COATES, C. W., 1950 - "Tropical fishes as pets." 258 pp. Liveright Pub. Co., New York.

COLE, V. W. & W. M. LEWIS, 1958 - "The removal of residual chlorine from tap water that is to be used in aquaria." Turtox News. 36:204-206.

DEMPSTER, P. P., 1953 - "The use of larval and adult brine shrimp in aquarium fish culture." Calif. Fish & Game. 39:355-364.

DEVILLERS, C., 1947 - "Explantations 'in vitro' de blastoderms de poissons (salmo esox)." Experienta. 3:71.

DEVILLERS, C., J. COLAS & L. RICHARD, 1957 - "Différenciation in vitro de blastoderme de Truite déprouves de couche enveloppante." J. Emb. Exp. Morph. 5:264-273.

DILDINE, G. C., 1936 - "The effect of light and temperature on gonads of Lebistes." Anat. Rec. 67:suppl. 61.

DOUDOROFF, P., 1945 - "The resistance and acclimatization of marine fishes to temperature changes. II. Experiments with Fundulus and Atherinops." Biol. Bull. 88:194.

DOWNING, A. L. & S. A. TRUESDALE, 1956 - "Aeration in aquaria." Zoologica (N.Y.) 44:129-143.

EAKIN, R. M., 1939 - "Regional determination in the development of the trout." Arch. f. Ent. Mech. 139:274.

EGAMI, N., 1954 - "Effect of artificial photoperiodicity on time of oviposition in the fish Oryzias latipes." Annot. Zool. Japan 27(2): 57-62.

EGAMI, N., 1958 - "Studies in Neurosecretion". Proc. Jap. Acad. 34:44-50, 164-168.

EGAMI, N., 1959 - "Record of the number of eggs obtained from a single pair of latipes kept in laboratory aquarium". Jour. Fac. Sci. Un. Tokyo. 8:521-538.

EISLER, R., 1957 - "Some effects of artificial light on salmon eggs and larvae." Trans. Amer. Fish. Soc. 81.

EISLER, R., 1957 - "The influence of light on early growth of chinook salmon." Growth 21(525):197.

EVANS, G., 1936 - "The relation between vitamins and the growth and survival of goldfishes in homotypically conditioned water." Jour. Exp. Zool. 74:449.

FARRIS, E. J., 1950 - "The care and breeding of laboratory animals." N.Y. Zool. Soc.

GOLTSOFF, P.S. & E. GOLTSOFF, 1959 - "Homoplastic implantations of toadfish embryos in the peritoneal cavity of the adult fish." N.Y. Acad. Sci. 80:44-53.

GOODRICH, H. B., R. L. HINE & H. M. LESHNER, 1947 - "The interaction of genes in Lebistes reticulatus." Genetics. 32:535.

GORDON, M., 1943 - "Feeding Platyfishes and Swordtails." Aquarium 12:86.

GORDON, M., 1943 - "Genetic studies of speciation in the Swordtail-Platyfish group and of the experimentally produced hybrids." Trans. N.Y. Acad. Sci. 5:63.

GORDON, M., 1948 - "The biology of Melanomas." N.Y. Acad. Sci. Publ. 4:216.

GORDON, M.   - "Inheritance in the guppy." Aquarium Journal. 24:105-133.

GRODZINSKI, M. Z. 1948-49 - "The influence of temperature upon the rate of the heart in the embryos of teleost fishes." Bull. Inter. Acad. Polonaise. Sci. et Last. Ser. B. N. 7-10 B11.

GRODZINSKI, Z., 1949 - "The influence of alternating temperatures upon the heart rate of the embryos of the sea trout, Salmo trutta." Bull. Inter. Acad. Polonaise Sci. et Lettr. Cl. Sci. Math et Nat. Ser. B. Sci. Nat. (2) Zool. (4/6)

GRODZINSKI, Z., 1952 - "Influence of some internal factors upon the heart rate in sea trout embryo. Salmo trutta." Bull. Inst. l'Acad. Polonaise des Sci. and des Lettres 4-6 BII 165-178.

HASLER, A. D. & W. M. FABER, 1941 - "A tagging method for small fish." Copeia 3:162.

HAYES, F. R., D. PELLUET & E. Gorham, 1953 - "Some effects of temperature on the embryonic development of the salmon (Salmo salor)." Can. Jour. Zool. 31:42-57.

HEROLD, E. S. & M. ROBONWICZ, 1951 - "Stable requirements for raising sea horses." Aquar. Jour. 22:234-242.

HERVEY, S. F. & J. HEMS - "The goldfish". Batchworth Press, London.

HISAOKA, K. K. & H. I. BATTLE, 1958 - "The normal developmental stages of the zebrafish, Brochydanio rerio." Jour. Morph. 102:311-328.

HISAOAKA, C. K., 1960 - "Further studies on the embryonic development of zebrafish, Brachydanio rerio." Jour. Morph. 107:205-226.

HUMM, D. G. & R. S. YOUNG, 1956 - "The embryological origin of pigment cells in platyfish-swordtail hybrids." Zoologica. 41(1):1-10.

INNES, W. T., 1956 - "Exotic aquarium fishes." 533 pp. Aquarium Publ. Co. P. O. Box 832, Morristown, Pa.

KALLMAN, K. D., 1960 - "Dosage and additive effects of histocorruptability genes in the teleost Xiphophorus maculatus." Am. N.Y. Acad. Sci. 87:10-43.

KONNO, Ketal, 1955 - "On the influence of gamma-ray radiation on the aquatic animals. 1. On the influence in the early development of goldfish (Carassius auratus L.)." J. Tokyo Univ. Fisheries. 41(2):163-168.

KAO, C.Y., 1954 - "Internal hydrostatic pressure of the Fundulus egg." Jour. Cell Comp. Phys. 44:447-462.

KESSEL, R. G., 1960 - "The role of cell division in gastrulation of Fundulus heteroclitus." Exp. Cell. Res. 20:277-282.

LEGAULT, R., 1958 - "A technique for controlling the time of daily spawning and collecting of eggs of the zebra fish, Brochydanio." Copeia. 4:328-330.

MacGINITIE, S. E., 1947 - "Sea water systems at marine laboratories." Science 106:171-173.

MATSUI, K., 1940, 1941, 1943 - "Temperature and heart beat in a fish embryo, Oryzias latipes." Sci. Rep. Tokyo Bunrika Daigaku. 5(81-88): 39-51, 129-138, 159-178, 313-346.

McFARLAND, W. N. & K. S. NORRIS, 1958 - "The control of pH buffers in fish transport." Calif. Fish & Game. 44:291-310.

McFARLAND, W. N., 1960 - "The use of anesthetics for the handling and the transport of fishes." Calif. Fish and Game. 44:407-431.

NACHSTEDT, J. & H. TUSCHE - "Breeding aquarium fishes." Aquarium Stock Co., N.Y. 7, N.Y.

NICHOLAS, J. S., 1927 - "Application of experimental methods to the study of developing Fundulus embryos." Proc. Nat. Acad. Sci. 13:695.

NICHOLAS, J. S. & J. M. OPPENHEIMER, 1942 - "Regulation and reconstitution in Fundulus." Jour. Exp. Zool. 90:127.

NIGRELLI, R. F., 1961 - "Fish Diseases." Merch. Vet. Manual.

NORTHCOTE, T. G., 1958 - "Effect of photoperiodism on response of juvenile trout to water currents." Nature. 181:1293-4.

OPPENHEIMER, J. M., 1953 - "The development of transplanted fragments of Fundulus gastrulae." Proc. Nat. Acad. Sci. 39:1149.

PADMANABHAN, K. G., 1955 - "Breeding habits and early embryology of Macropodus cupanus (C and V)." Bull. Cent. Rev. Inst. Univ. Travamore Ser. C. 4(1):1-46.

PHILIPS, F. S., 1940 - "Oxygen consumption and its inhibition in the development of Fundulus and various pelagic fish eggs." Biol. Bull. 78:256.

PICKFORD, S. E. & J. W. ATZ, 1957 - "The physiology of the pituitary gland of fishes." 637 pp. N.Y. Zool. Soc.

PRICE, John W., 1943 - "A device for observing living fish embryos at controlled temperatures. Ohio Jour. Sci. 43(2):83-85.

RICHARDS, A., 1935 - "Analysis of early development of fish embryos by means of the mitotic index. I. The use of the mitotic Index." Am. Jour. Anat. 56:355.

ROBINSON, E. J. & R. RUGH, 1943 - "The reproductive processes of the fish, Oryzias latipes." Biol. Bull. 84:115.

ROOSEN-RUNGE, E. C., 1939 - "Karyokinese during cleavage of the zebra fish, Brachydanio rerio." Biol. Bull. 77:79 (see ibid. 75:119).

ROSE, S. M., 1959 - "Population control in guppies." An. Midland Nat. 62:474-481 (see also Ecology 41:188-199, 1960).

ROTHSCHILD, Lance, 1958 - "Fertilization in fishes and lampreys". Biol. Rev. Camb. Phil. Soc. 33:372-392.

RUBINOFF, I., 1958 - "Raising the atherinid fish, Menidia menidia, in the laboratory." Copeia 2:146-147.

SCRIMSHAW, N. S., 1945 - "Embryonic development in Poeciliid fishes." Biol. Bull. 88:233.

SCHAPERDANS, W., 1954 - "Fischkrankheiten" 708 pp., Akademie Verlag, Berlin.

SCHNEIDER, E. - "All about breeding tropical fishes." Garden City, N.Y.

SHAW, E. S. & L. R. ARONSON, 1954 - "Oral incubation in Tilapia macrocephala". Bull. Am. Mus. Nat'l Hist. 103:381-415.

SMITH, S., 1957 - "Physiology of fishes." Chapter on Early Development and Hatching." Acad. Press. N.Y. pages 323-360.

SOLBERG, A. N., 1938 - "The development of a bony fish." Progressive Fish Culture #40.

SPEK, J., 1933 - "Die bipolare Differenzierug des Protoplasmus des teleostei eies und inre Enstelung." Protoplasma. 18:32.

STOCKARD, C. R., 1921 - "Developmental rate and structure expression: an experimental study of twins, double monsters, and single deformities, and the interaction among embryonic organs during their origin and development." Am. Jour. Anat. 28:115.

STONE, L. S. & P. SAPIR, 1940 - "Experimental studies on the regeneration of the lens in the eye of anurans, urodeles, and fishes." Jour. Exp. Zool. 85:71.

STRAUGHAN, R. P. L., 1956 - "Keeping the dwarf seahorse". 24 pp. All-Pets Books, Inc., Fond Du Lac, Wisc.

STRAWN, K., 1954 - "Keeping and breeding the dwarf seahorse". Aquarium Journal. 25:215-219.

SUZUKI, R., 1957 - "Development of goldfish eggs inseminated with some foreign sperms. Dob. Zasshi 66:(1):34-

TAVOLGA, W. & R. RUGH, 1947 - "Development of the platyfish, Platypoecilus maculatus." Zoologica. 32:1.

TCHOU-SU, M. & C. H. CHEN, 1936 - "Recherches sur 1-activabilite de la fecondabilite de l'ouef du poisson osseux caraccius auratus." Chinese Jour. Exp. Biol. 1.

TRINKHAUS, J. P. & J. W. DRAKE, 1956 - "Exogenous control of morphogenesis in isolated Fundulus blastoderms by nutrient chemical factors." Jour. Exp. Zool. 132:311-348.

TUNG, T. C., C. Y. CHANG & F. Y. TUNG, 1945 - "Experiments on the developmental potencies of blastoderms and fragments of teleostan eggs separated latitudinally." Proc. Zool. Soc. London. 115:175.

WALLBUMN, H. M., 1958 - "Genetics of the siamese fighting fish." Beta Splendins." Genetics. 43:289-298.

WELANDER, A. D., 1954 - "Some effects of x-irradiations of different embryonic stages of the trout." Growth. 18:227-255.

WINGE, O. & E. DETLERSEN, 1948 - "Colour inheritance and sex determination in Lebistes reticulatus." Compt. rendu. Labor. Carlsberg, Ser. Physio. 24:227.

WOLF, L. E., 1931 - "The history of the germ cells in the viviparous teleost, Platypoecilus maculatus." Jour. Morph. & Physiol. 52:115.

WOODHEAD, P. M. J., 1957 - "Reactions of salmonid larvae to light." J. Exp. Biol. 34(3):402-416.

YAMAMOTO, T., 1940 - "The change in the volume of the fish egg at Fertilization." Proc. Imp. Acad. Tokyo Univ. 16:482.

YAMAMOTO, T., 1954 - "Physiological studies on fertilization and activiation of fish eggs. V. The role of Caions in activation of Oryzias eggs." Exp. Coll. Res. 6(1)256-68.

YANAGIMACHI, R., 1953 - "Effect of environmental salt concentration on fertilizability of herring gametes." J. Fac. Sci. Hokkaido Univ. VI Zool. XI(3):481.

YANAGIMACHI, R., 1957 - Dobutsugaku Zasshi. Zoological Magazine 66:218, 222, 226.

"*Aquiculture is as susceptible to scientific treatment as agriculture; and the fisherman, who has been in the past the hunter, if not the devastating raider, must become in the future the settled farmer of the sea, if his harvest is to be less precarious.*"

W. A. Herdman

"*The saltness of the sea is due to numerous springs of water, which in penetrating the earth, find salt mines, and dissolving parts of these, carry away with them to the ocean, and to the other seas, from whence they are never lifted by the clouds that produce the rivers.*"

Leonardo de Vinci

"*I have two small embryos, preserved in alcohol, that I forgot to label. At present I am unable to determine the genus to which they belong. They may be lizards, small birds, or even young mammals.*"

Karl Ernst von Baer 1928

"*Beast and fowl, reptile and fish, mollusc, worm, and polyp, are all composed of structural units of the same character, namely, masses of protoplasm with a nucleus. There are sundry very low animals, each of which, structurally, is a mere colourless blood-corpuscle, leading an independent life. But at the very bottom of the animal scale, even this simplicity becomes simplified, and all the phenomena of life are manifested by a particle of protoplasm without a nucleus. Nor are such organisms insignificant by reason of their want of complexity. It is a fair question whether the protoplasm of those simplest forms of life, which people an immense extent of the bottom of the sea, would not outweigh that of all the higher living beings which inhabit the land put together. And in ancient times, no less than at the present day, such living beings as these have been the greatest of rock builders.*"

T. H. Huxley 1960

IV. EXPERIMENTAL CHICK EMBRYOLOGY

No attempt will be made here to describe the most delicate of the transplantation operations (e.g., those by Willier and by Hamburger and their students) that have been performed on the chick embryo. The student is, however, directed to the work of these investigators, particularly to inter-specific transplantations.

Recent work of Spratt (1947, 1948) has demonstrated that the extreme precautions of a dust-free operating room, ultra-violet lighting, masking, etc., are not necessary so long as reasonable precautions are taken to avoid the actual introduction of bacteria into the hen's egg. It is therefore safe to predict that the chick embryo will be used increasingly in courses in Experimental Embryology, and that it will supplement the work on the amphibia admirably well. The hen's egg is available during the months when amphibian material is scarce.

Aside from the general procedures for handling the hen's egg in the laboratory, the experimental procedures to be described will include (1) Determination of morphogenetic movements by means of vital dyes and charcoal particles, (2) Explantations or the culturing of isolates on artificial media (3) Chorio-allantoic grafting and (4) Transplantations.

This exercise has the single experimental object, the hen's egg. It involves four different procedures and in this respect this exercise cannot be weighed with the others of this Manual. It is recommended that the material on the hen's egg be assigned to the second half of the second (Spring) semester, when the amphibian material is no longer available and after the student has had the benefit of some months of experimental and operational experience with amphibian material.

49. PROCURING AND CARE OF LIVING MATERIAL

Procuring of eggs: One must establish a reliable source of highly fertile eggs, which prove to be perfectly normal in development. There are the usual seasonal variations in fertility with the low point during late Summer and Fall, and the high point just after the peak of the Winter. With optimum conditions fertility may reach as high as 90% but the low point may go to 25% or even less. There is no evidence that any particular breed lends itself better than others to operational procedures. However, certain flocks of hens give more viable eggs, particularly when they are provided with adequate sunlight.

Storing of eggs: If possible, eggs should be used shortly after being layed. However, eggs may be stored at cool temperatures (10° C.) for as long as a week. The percentage of development will drop rapidly thereafter.

Incubators: The small (Oakes) incubators will hold several dozen eggs and are quite satisfactory although they are not provided with as sensitive temperature and humidity controls, and forced-air draft for ventilation, as are other and larger models. The large (Buffalo) incubators are excellent for the incubation of larger numbers of eggs, and the physical factors are well controlled. Place the incubator away from drafts and sunlight.

Temperature control: Most incubators are provided with temperature control devices regulated close to the optimum range of 102° - 103° F. (about 38.2-39.0° C.). If the incubator is not provided with forced draft, the temperature should be regulated at about 100° F. (37.5° C.). Since the heated air tends to rise, the hanging thermometer should have its mercury bulb at the level of the eggs. Each inch above the eggs the temperature may register at least a degree higher than at the egg level. Once controlled incubation has begun it should not be interrupted if normal development is desired.

Humidity control: A relative humidity of 60% is best, although higher humidity is not deleterious. In the smaller incubators several finger bowls of water should be placed among the eggs. In the larger incubators there are generally large pans beneath the eggs which pans should be filled with sand and kept constantly moist. Dehydration is one of the commonest contributors to lethality.

Rotation of the eggs: The hen generally turns the eggs frequently. This is not necessary for the first day or two but thereafter all eggs should be turned at least twice daily in order to prevent adhesion of the membranes. Rotation of operated eggs will, of course, be limited.

The candling of eggs: Incubation time is not an accurate criterion of ontogenetic age so that it is necessary to provide a device for sending light through the blastoderm so that its age can be approximated by direct observation. The mail order houses offer inexpensive candling equipment but it is very simple to make one. Fasten a light socket to a board; place around the socket a large tin funnel cut to fit, which acts as a reflector; invert over the 100 watt bulb a small waste basket through the bottom of which is cut a circular hole; fasten beneath the hole a piece of coarse wire gauze, somewhat depressed, to cup an egg; cover the hole (outside of basket) with a heavy felt cloth (to cut out extraneous light) and cut a slit in its center slightly shorter than the length of the average egg. A switch may be provided for the light, fastened to the base board. The entire cost should be about 50 cents. The egg is placed over the slit in the black cloth, and will be caught by the wire screen, and a strong light will come up through the egg so that the blastoderm can be seen directly. It must be remembered that the 100 watt bulb gives off a great deal of heat so that the examination should not be extended for long. A dark room for the candling is best.

The blastoderm can be seen by 48 hours and the yolk-sac circulation by 60-72 hours. Thereafter, movements of the embryo and the interlacing extra-embryonic circulation become increasingly apparent. Embryos which die early generally show coagulation of blood in the sinus terminalis (blood ring). From the seventh to the thirteenth days the chorioallantoic circulation can be seen, but after the thirteenth day the embryos appear more and more opaque, accentuating the air space at the blunt end. Embryos which die during the latter half of incubation show an indistinct air space demarcation.

There are two peaks in the mortality curve of incubated hen's eggs, one about the third or fourth day and the other just before hatching, when the extra-embryonic membranes are drying up. Under the most ideal conditions even the best eggs show 3% mortality on the fourth day, 15% on the 19th day, and 7% mortality during the balance of the incubation period of twenty-one days (Romanoff, 1931).

Egg mortality: While eggs may be layed the year around, under controlled conditions, the best season for high level of fertility and hatchability is between February and June. During the heat of the summer, and due to exposure to excessive cold in the winter, other periods may not prove as successful. An average hatching value of 80% should be considered as very good.

Staging of the chick embryo: For uniformity it is well to accept the designated chick stages in Hamilton's revision of Lillie's "Development of the Chick". A similar series is now available for the duck embryos in Koeckes 1958 paper. (See pages 410, 411, 413)

50. TECHNICAL AND OPERATING EQUIPMENT

Provided by the Institution:
    Temperature-controlled incubator(s) with turning and hatching trays.
    Autoclave
    Dry sterilizing oven
    Heating plates or electrically-controlled stage warmers for warming eggs or embryos during operations.
    Candling equipment
    100 cc. beakers with (soft) paraffin and small (paint-type) brushes
    Absorbent cotton
    Covered containers for discarded eggs
    Spencer microscope lamp, condensor and diaphragm.
    Dissecting microscope
    Round bottom (250 cc.) flask of water supported by double pinch-clamp, to absorb heat from light source.

Solutions:
    Glass distilled water
    Locke's (1907 Jour. Physiol. 36:208) solution

NaCl	- 0.9 gr.	$NaHCO_3$	- 0.02 gr.
KCl	- 0.04 gr.	Dist. water	- 100 cc.
$CaCl_2$	- 0.024 gr. (anhydrous)	(Use at 38° - 40° C.)	

    Romanoff's Isotonic Avian Ringer's Phosphate Buffer:
    1. Measure out 5 cc of concentrated (x20) avian Ringer's
        NaCl .... 8.6 gms.
        KCl .... 0.31 gms.
        $CaCl_2$ .... 0.20 gms.
        $MgCl \cdot 2H_2O$ .... 0.10 gms.
    2. Add 70 cc of distilled water.
    3. Add 0.2 gms. maltose (powdered, anhydrous)
    4. Add slowly 10 cc of primary and secondary phosphate buffer solutions:
        Na_2HPO_4; M/15 .... 800 cc.
        KH_2PO_4, M/15 .... 200 cc.   per 1000 cc.
        Make up to 100 cc. with distilled water.
    This medium has a pH of 7.3m., but by standing overnight this can change as much as to pH 6.9. It was first described in 1943 (Jour. Exp. Zool. 93:1-26) by Dr. Alexis Romanoff, but the above modification has never been published although it is in common use in Dr. Romanoff's laboratory.
    Physiological saline (0.9% NaCl)
    Phenol red (of known concentration)
    MS 222, made up 1/3,000 in Locke's of physiological saline (anesthetic).
    Fixatives: Bouin, Kleinberg's Picro-sulphuric, Aceto-formalin.

Provided by the Student:
    12 petri dishes (4" diameter)
    12 watch crystals (2" diameter)
    2 regulation finger bowls
    2 Erlenmeyer flasks (500 cc.)
    2 Erlenmeyer flasks (125 cc.)
    1 graduated cylinder (100 cc.)
    1 graduated cylinder (10 cc.)
    2 wide-mouthed pipettes, smooth edges (inside diameter 4 mm.)

2 fine pipettes (inside diameter 1 mm.)
12 regular medicine droppers
6 shell depression slides
1/2 oz. round cover glasses, #1 thickness (to cover depression)
1 small glass tumbler, cotton in bottom and partially filled with 70% alcohol for sterilization of operating instruments.
Absorbent cotton

Operating equipment:
    1 hack-saw with extra blades (ampoule saw may be satisfactory)
    2 watchmaker's forceps, #5
    1 pair regulation forceps
    2 steel needles, ground to fine points
    1 pair coarse scissors (large)
    1 pair fine scissors (small)

PREPARATION OF EQUIPMENT

All glassware and instruments should be thoroughly washed in non-caustic soapy water; rinsed in hot, running tap water; and put aside to dry on a clean cloth towel. The metal instruments and culture dishes may be further sterilized in the dry sterilizing oven while the solutions should be autoclaved at 15 pounds for at least 15 minutes. Thereafter the operating equipment may be kept in 70% alcohol to which a drop of iodine solution has been added. The greatest source of bacterial or mold infection is not from such pre-sterilized equipment but rather from the hands and breath of the operator. One should work in a draft-free room, away from windows, and the embryos should be exposed to the air only when absolutely necessary.

PRELIMINARY SUGGESTIONS

1. Become re-acquainted with the normal morphogenesis of the chick egg. (Hamilton's Lillie, 1952 and pages 410, 411, 413)
2. Select eggs that are uniform in size, shape, and color for any one experiment.
3. Check the incubator temperature and humidity at least once each day. Temperatures above 103° F. are more deleterious than below that level.
4. Remember that genetic factors may contribute to high mortality. It cannot be stressed too frequently that one must become thoroughly acquainted with the source of the eggs being used.
5. Do not wash or submerge the eggs for long in water because the embryo normally breathes air through its porous shell. Washing will remove a thin surface cuticle which protects the chick embryo against the invasion of microorganisms. Prior to operations within the egg, sterilization of the shell and exposed shell membrane may be accomplished with a cotton swab soaked in 70% alcohol, 1% iodine in alcohol, or chlorazene. The chlorazene is made up by adding 3 tablets to a quart of warm water.
6. The membranes should be observed just prior to the time for hatching. When the extra-embryonic circulation begins to regress, the incubation temperature can be lowered and the humidity raised. Should the chick's beak happen to lie beneath the artificial window, this window should be removed on the 19th or 20th day. Frequently operated chicks must be assisted in the hatching process on the 21st day. Do not attempt to remove the chick until the yolk sac is completely retracted into the chick mid-gut.

51. THE REMOVAL OF CHICK BLASTODERMS OR EMBRYOS

Early Blastoderms: The chick blastoderm always floats around to the upper surface of the heavier yolk mass. Hold the egg in the palm of the hand for a minute or two and then crack the underside of the shell on the edge of a finger bowl 2/3 full of Locke's or saline solution, and (in the manner of cracking an egg for frying) allow the egg contents to flow out into the solution. The blastoderm will shortly move around to the most dorsal position.

Grasp the chalaza or the yolk on one side with forceps held in the left hand (for right handed operators), then, with sharp-pointed scissors, quickly cut around the blastoderm 1/4" from its border. This movement of the scissors can be aided by a contrary movement of the forceps, turning the entire egg mass with the forceps as the blastoderm is being cut with the scissors. The cut is made through the very thin and transparent vitelline membrane, through the blastoderm proper, and into the underlying yolk.

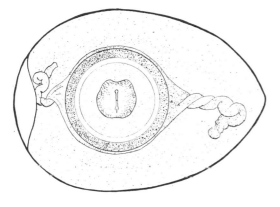

THE 24 HOUR CHICK EMBRYO

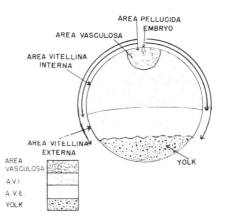

THE 50 HOUR CHICK EMBRYO
(ALBUMEN REMOVED)

Grasp the cut edge (vitelline membrane, blastoderm, and yolk) and roll it back from the bulk of the yolk mass. Draw it away from the yolk mass. Holding the edge of the vitelline membrane with forceps work a dissecting needle around its border, and use the needle to roll the blastoderm away from the membrane. Then, with a wide-mouthed pipette, remove the blastoderm to a Petri dish containing 20 cc. of Locke's or Saline solution. All of the yolky opaque area may now be trimmed off with scalpel or dissecting needles, beneath a dissecting microscope.

The young blastoderm is extremely yolk-adherent. Some investigators inject warm Locke's solution beneath the blastoderm before excising it. This raises the blastoderm off of the yolk by providing an elevating vesicle of fluid beneath, separating it from the yolk. Other investigators find it simpler to gently suck the blastoderm (after removal of the vitelline membrane) in and out of a wide-mouthed pipette, thereby removing most of the adherent yolk. Still others play a gentle stream of medium on the surface of the inverted blastoderm, blowing the yolk granules away.

The early stages are particularly fragile and the less handling the better. In most instances the peripheral yolk may be trimmed away with scalpel, scissors, or even with needles, and the yolk adherent to the underside of the area pellucida is negligible. It is particularly difficult to handle the blastoderms of less than 18 hours without damage.

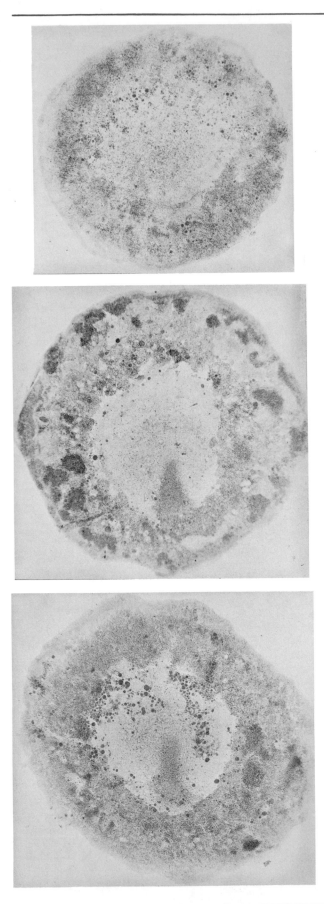

EXPLANATION OF CHICK PHOTOGRAPHS*

Fig. 1 - Embryonic shield, prior to appearance of prim.
      streak.
Fig. 2 - Initial streak at 6-7 hours.
Fig. 3 - Intermediate primitive streak at 12-13 hrs.

Fig. 4 - Definitive streak, max. length 1.88 mm. Pr.
      streak, pr. pit, and Hensen's node evident, area
      pellucida pear shaped, incubation age 18-19 hrs.
Fig. 5 - Head process stage with notochord, no head fold,
      age 19-22 hrs.
Fig. 6 - Head fold stage at 23-25 hrs.
Fig. 7 - First somite and neural folds at 23-26 hrs.
Fig. 8 - Blood islands forming posteriorly at 26-29 hrs. and
      4 somites.
Fig. 9 - Primary optic vesicles, heart primordia fuse, 29-
      33 hrs., 7 somites.
Fig. 10 - Cranial flexure indicated, 3 primary brain vesicles,
      heart bent at 33-38 hrs. and 10 somites.
Fig. 11 - Cranial flexure extensive, 5 neuromeres, optic
      vesicle well developed, heart bent, 40-45 hrs. &
      13 somites.
Fig. 12 - Neuropore indicated, telencephalon formed,
      auditory pits, head fold amnion, heart "S" shaped,
      45-59 hrs. and 16 somites.
Fig. 13 - Head turned to the left, cranial & cervical
      flexures clear out, head fold amnion present, 48-
      52 hrs., 19 somites.
Fig. 14 - Flexures extensive, body rotating, visceral arches
      forming, 50-53 hrs., & 21 somites.
Fig. 15 - Lateral body folds, limb primordia, amnion, eye
      cup, 50-55 hrs., 24-27 S.
Fig. 16 - Wing and leg primordia 51-56 hrs., & 26-28 S.
Fig. 17 - Tail bud, epiphysis, 52-68 hrs., 29-32 S.

*Some of these photographs were published by Dr. Nelson Spratt in Jour. Exp. Zool. 103:265 and 274; others by Hamburger and
Hamilton Jour. Morph. 88:49. All have since been published in Lillie's Development of the Chick, revised by H. L. Hamilton,
Copyright Holt, Rinehart and Winston, Inc. 1952, and used here with permission.

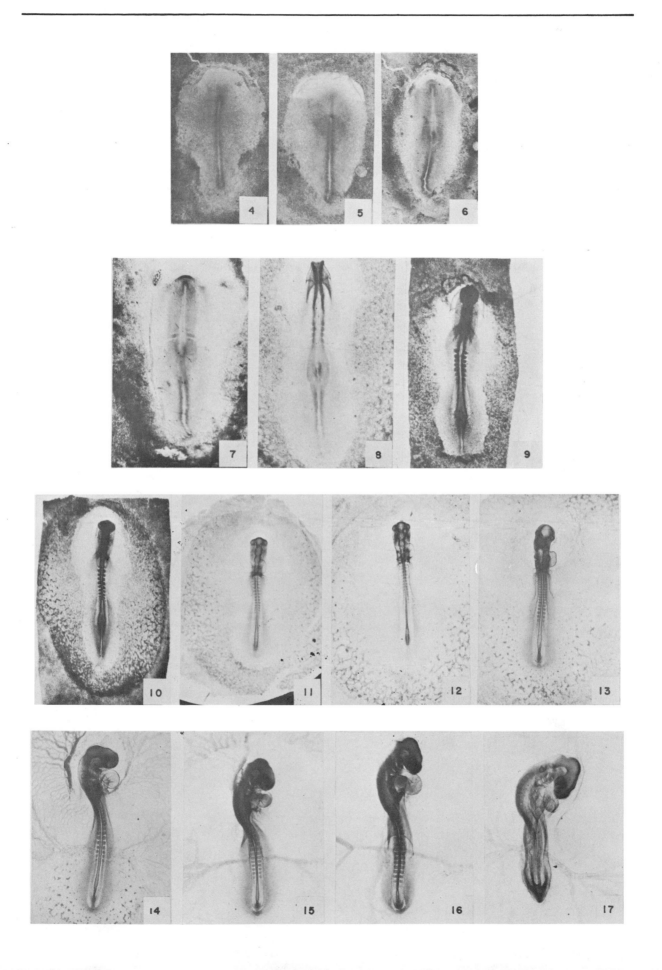

EXPLANATION OF CHICK PHOTOGRAPHS*

Fig. 18 - Visceral arches prominent, 65-69 hrs., & 30-36
          somites.
Fig. 19 - Allantois developing, 68-72 hrs., 37-40 S.
Fig. 20 - Eye pigment present, 70-72 hrs., 40-43 S.
Fig. 21 - Limbs enlarge, 3.5 days 43-44 somites.
Fig. 22 - Somites to tip of tail, 3.5 days +.
Fig. 25 - 4.5 days
Fig. 26 - 4.5 to 5.0 days
Fig. 32 - 7.5 days
Fig. 33 - 7.5 to 8 days
Fig. 34 - 8.0 days
Fig. 35 - 8 to 9 days
Fig. 42 - 16 days
Fig. 43 - 17 days
Fig. 44 - 18 days

*Some of these photographs were published by Dr. Nelson Spratt in Jour. Exp. Zool. 103:265 and 274; others by Hamburger and Hamilton Jour. Morph. 88:49. All have since been published in Lillie's Development of the Chick, revised by H. L. Hamilton, Copyright Holt, Rinehart and Winston, Inc. 1952, and used here with permission.

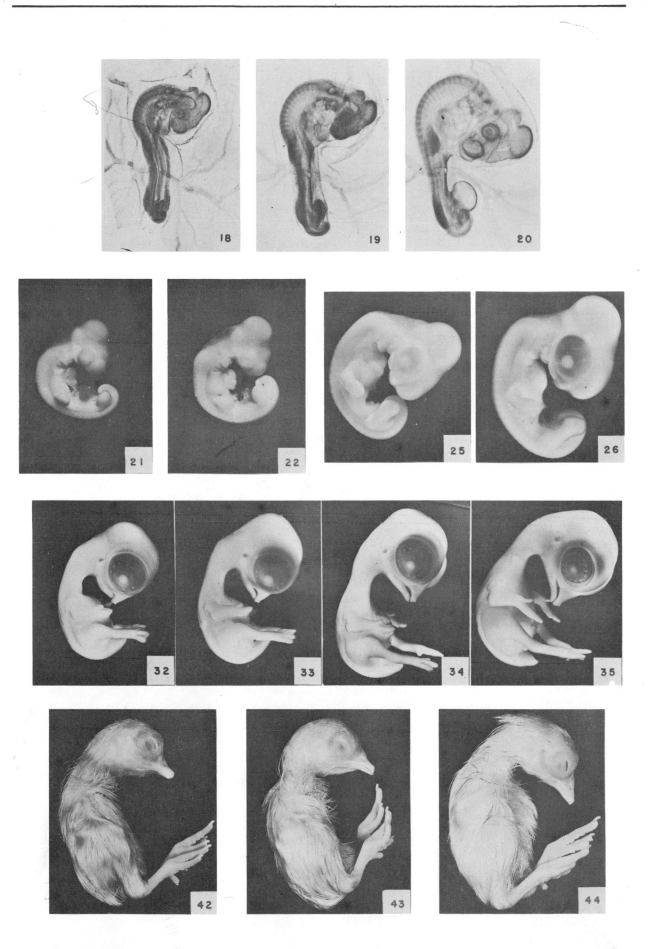

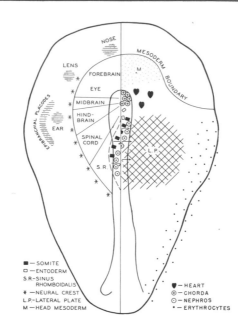

Prospective areas in the definitive primitive streak blastoderm of the chick. The superficial layer is shown at the left while the invaginated material is seen in the right half. The interrupted line on the left side of the anterior streak region marks the boundary between the ectoderm and the still uninvaginated mesoderm. This is on the assumptions that invagination is as yet incomplete and that future invagination will be limited to material destined to form the embryo proper. All mesodermal boundaries need accurate experimental verificiation.

This composite map is drawn by Rudnick (1944 Quart. Rev. Biol. 19:187) and is based largely on work of Pasteels. In addition, there have been contributions from the work of Hunt (endoderm cells), Wolff (morphogenesis of trunk and tail), and Yntema (ectodermal placodes).

Later Embryos: Chick embryos of 36 or more hours of incubation are rather simple to remove from their eggs. The entire egg mass is broken into a finger bowl of saline solution cracking the underside of the shell after allowing the egg to remain motionless for several minutes. The embryo, unless it is so far advanced that it is heavy, will float to the upper surface. Excise the embryo as in the manner described above or, if the embryo is well formed, grasp the yolk-sac umbilicus with forceps, cut it distally to the forceps, rupture other membranes, and draw the embryo away from its yolk. If the embryo is young it may be pulled into a submerged watchglass and transferred to a fresh finger bowl of solution. If it is advanced, it may be transferred in an ordinary teaspoon whose bowl has been perforated with many small holes.

*"Life is the continuous adjustment of internal relations
to external relations."*
                                            Herbert Spencer

"A living organism is both cause and effect in itself."
                                            E. Kant, 1892

52. HISTOLOGICAL PROCEDURES

EXAMINATION OF EXCISED CHICK BLASTODERMS

The early blastoderms may be transferred to a watchglass in several drops of Locke's or saline medium (warmed to 38° C.), oriented with needles into the proper position and then the medium sucked off by means of a fine bore pipette, while encircling the blastoderm. In this way the blastoderm will be flattened onto the dry bottom of the watchglass. Immediately add fresh medium (at 38° C.) so that it flows beneath the blastoderm, lifting it up on the surface tension of fluid. If 0.001% phenol red (pH indicator) is added to the medium, the slightly purple tinge of the alkaline medium will provide an excellent background for greater clarity of the chick embryo structures, without adding any toxic factor. Such a watchglass may be placed on a warming stage or on an electrically controlled heating stage and the living embryo examined for a considerable period of time.

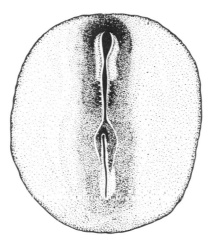

THE 24 HOUR CHICK EMBRYO

If one is interested in general morphology of these early stages it is advisable to mount embryos of the same age in the normal position, and also upside down, so that, in the latter instance, one has a view directly into the intestinal portals.

Such a mount may be made on a glass slide providing a cut-out in filter paper is made of just such size as to frame the area pellucida and mask out the area opaca. If such a blastoderm is first inverted, pulled up onto the slide (while the slide is submerged in solution), most of the medium drained off, and the filter paper frame added, the embryo will remain flat. The yolky margins of the blastoderm will adhere firmly to the filter paper. A cover glass may be added providing its corners are elevated slightly by bits of Permoplast, to prevent crushing. The embryo may now be hydrated with the appropriate medium. It must be remembered, however, that the chick embryo cannot acquire sufficient oxygen from any aqueous medium directly, and that it can be "drowned", particularly if it has already developed its own circulatory system. The ideal environment is a closed space, completely humidified, with the blastoderm floating on the surface of a nutrient medium.

The later stages may be examined in the manner of any vertebrate form. After about 5 days the embryo will take on a definite avian appearance, and it will shortly become possible to make a dissection to study the internal organs. This is so because the cartilage and bone will not have developed. There is very little cartilage, even at 8 days.

PERMANENT PREPARATIONS OF CHICK EMBRYOS

The primitive streak stages can be best fixed while still on the egg, by dropping the fixative onto the blastoderm gently from above. Since fixation renders the blastoderm rather brittle, it is best to cut it out within a few minutes after fixation, and then transfer it to a Syracuse dish with fresh fixative for the requisite time. (Use instruments other than those for operating purposes.)

Later blastoderm and embryos may be excised in the manner described on preceding page, and fixed either in Syracuse dishes or on slides (when they are held in place by the filter paper rings). Within a minute of fixation gently wash the entire flat blastoderm off of the slide and into adequate (similar) fixative by a gentle stream of fixative from a pipette. Some of the yolk will remain adherent to the slide, and if the blastoderm is allowed to remain long on the slide, it is apt to be torn during subsequent removal.

Still later stages (up to 8 or 9 days) may be fixed "in toto" in any of the standard fixatives. If it does not interfere with structures important in the examination, it is always well to slit the abdomen to allow fixative to penetrate to the viscera the more readily.

HISTOLOGICAL PROCEDURES:

Fixatives: Kleinberg's Picro-sulphuric, Bouin, Michealis' fluid, or 0.5% acetic acid in 10% formalin. (Given in order of preference.) Fixation should be for at least 4 hours for the earlier stages to 48 hours for the 9 day embryos.

Decoloration: The picric acid of the fixatives leaves the embryo stained a brilliant yellow. This may be removed with lithium carbonate but more quickly and satisfactorily by adding about 3% by volume of NH_4OH to the 70% alcohol during dehydration. The alkaline ammonia decolorizes the yellow picric acid. Bleaching of older stages may take 24 hours and several changes.

Dehydration: Dehydration must be slow in order to avoid damage to the delicate blastoderms and to insure complete dehydration of the larger, later embryos. One hour periods for the early stages and as much as 12 hour periods for the older embryos, in each of the graded alcohols, is generally indicated. The alcohols should include 35%, 70%, 80%, 90%, 95% and finally 100%. If the yellow picric is not entirely removed, a small amount of $LiCO_3$ may be added to each of the alcohols from 70% to 90%. Make two changes in absolute alcohol.

Clearing: This is best accomplished by transferring the embryo from absolute alcohol to pure cedar oil for 24 hours or more (i.e., until translucent). Then transfer to xylol for 30 minutes.

Embedding: Embed in 56°C. paraffin to which has been added 5% Bayberry Wax and 5% Beeswax (measurements by weight). A total of 1 hour for the earliest stages to as much as 5 hours for the 9 day chick embryo is indicated. For the large embryos with some cartilage a final embedding in a paraffin-rubber mixture is suggested (30-60 minutes).

Sectioning: For cytological studies the sections should be no more than 10 microns in thickness. For study of organs the sections may be as thick as 20 microns. Boil some distilled water, cool, and to every 10 cc. add 1 drop of egg albumen, mix thoroughly. Place a few drops of this albumen-water on the slide, and float the ribbon on it. When the ribbon is properly oriented, draw off the excess fluid with pipette and filter paper, and dry on a warming plate at 40° C.

Staining:
1. Sectioned material:
   a. Heidenhain's Iron Haematoxylin: Excellent for chromosome studies. Mordant the sections for 12 hours in 4% iron alum, rinse, stain for 6 or more hours in Heidenhain's Haematoxylin, then destain in 2% iron alum while observing it under the dissection microscope. Stop the destaining when the section has a uniform grayish appearance, by placing it in slowly running tap water.
   b. Conklin's Haematoxylin: Add 1 drop of Kleinberg's Picro Sulphuric to each 1 cc. of seasoned Delafield's Haematoxylin. Stain sections for 6 to 10 minutes, rinse in (alkaline) tap water. Counterstain with 1 dip in 0.5% eosin in 95% alcohol (counterstain not recommended for photographs).
   c. Harris' Haematoxylin: Stain for 6 minutes, blue in alkaline tap water, and counterstain if desired.
2. Whole mounts: These may be stained for from 6 hours to 2 days in either of the (above) Haematoxylins, depending upon the size and stage of the embryo. Large embryos (72 hours and older) may thus be stained in toto and later sectioned. If the stain does not penetrate adequately, the sections may be further stained after mounting.

LUNDVALL TECHNIQUE FOR STAINING OF CHICK EMBRYO CARTILAGE: (Anat. Anz. 25 and 27, 1905 and 1906)

This technique may be used either on a chorio-allantoic graft which has developed cartilage (and bone) or it may be used with the whole embryo of 9 to 10 days incubation age. The Spalteholz technique may be used even for later stages for complete transparencies.

1. Fix in Bouin's or Kleinberg's Picro-sulphuric for 24 hours.
2. Transfer to 70% alcohol containing 2% NH_4OH to decolorize. Several changes over a period of several hours may be necessary.
3. Using forceps, remove skin, feathers, and all fatty tissue.
4. Stain for 2 to 3 days in 0.25% methylene blue (or toluidine blue) made up in 70% alcohol to which is added 3% HCl by volume. This will overstain.
5. Destain in several changes of 70% alcohol for about 48 hours.
6. Dehydrate for 4 hours in 95% alcohol. The softer tissues will become destained and somewhat transparent.
7. Transfer the embryo to Methyl Salicylate (oil of wintergreen) to which has been added 25% (by volume) of benzyl benzoate. In this the embryo will clear completely and may be stored. (See Lundvall, 1904: Anat. Anzeiger 25 and 1906, Anat. Anzeiger 27.)

MODIFIED SPALTEHOLZ' METHOD FOR STAINING SKELETAL ELEMENTS:

The following procedure is excellent for post-metamorphic amphibia and for chick embryos beyond the 10th day of incubation.

1. Fix in 95% alcohol two weeks to harden.
2. Transfer to 1% KOH for 24 hours.
3. Transfer to tap water and, with forceps, pick off as much fleshy material as possible.
4. Transfer to 95% alcohol, change once in 6 hour period.
5. Transfer to ether for 1 to 2 hours to dissolve away any fat, or use acetone if there is little or no fat.
6. Transfer to 95% alcohol for 6 hours, change once.
7. Transfer to 1% KOH for 6 days.
8. Put in Alizarin red "S" for 12 hours.
9. Transfer to 1% KOH for 24 hours.
10. Put in Moll's solution for 24 hours.
11. Store in 100% glycerine.

53. METHODS FOR OBSERVING THE DEVELOPMENT OF THE CHICK EMBRYO

The hen's egg is fertilized at the upper end of the oviduct so that by the time it is layed the embryo has reached the stage of gastrulation, at least. The blastoderm of such an egg shows no visible structures at this time but after 18 hours of incubation the primitive streak may be discerned. Candling will not generally indicate any development before the 33 hour stage.

It is now possible to replace a portion of the shell with a cover-glass window through which development can be observed from day to day. A second method is to remove the shell over the air space (at the blunt end of the egg) and to provide a removable (shell) cover, so that the embryo can be watched at stated intervals for developmental changes.

These procedures have two uses: <u>First</u>, it is not possible to maintain an excised embryo on culture media and to have it develop perfectly normally for more than several days (and at early stages only). By these methods the embryo may be observed under perfectly normal conditions and morphogenesis can be studied, at least until the embryo as a whole becomes opaque from the development of its organs. Such embryos can be carried through to hatching. <u>Second</u>, when grafts are added to the chorio-allantois, they can be observed through the window, at least for a number of days.

THE WINDOW METHOD:

Secure an egg of less than 33 hours of incubation (7 or 8 day embryos may be similarly treated when making chorio-allantoic grafts) and place it in a bed of cotton in a finger bowl. Orient the smaller or pointed end of the egg to the right, and tilt it slightly below the horizontal so that the blastoderm will float slightly toward the blunt (air-space) end. Leave the egg in this position for a few minutes. Holding the egg in this exact position, remove it (without jarring) to the candler and locate the blastoderm. Mark its position with pencil on the shell above. Return the egg, in exactly the same position, to the cotton bed.

With forceps apply a cotton swab, soaked in 95% alcohol plus 1% iodine (or chlorazene solution), to the upper surface of the egg, including the area of the blastoderm. Wipe dry with sterile cotton. Arrange the microscope lamp so that its light shines at an angle onto the egg surface but have the light far enough away so that its heat is barely felt on the back of the hand. Check the temperature of the light at the egg surface by a thermometer. It should be less than 103° F.

Secure a previously sterilized mounting ring of non-toxic material such as glass, celluloid, pliofilm, pyralin, or thin rubber washers with a maximum diameter of not more than 3/4 of an inch. Place the ring on the shell over the region of the blastoderm and, with a sharp and sterile needle, scratch the shell along the inner margin of the ring. Replace the ring in 95% alcohol in a covered Stender, and brush away any shell particles with sterile cotton. A portion of the shell within the demarked area is now to be removed. Remember that all instruments used must be sterile, the hands must be clean, and the operator should avoid breathing into or allowing any dust to blow into the egg while opened.

There are various tricks to removing the egg shell, gained largely through experience. Aids to the removal, however, are a dental drill with circular disc; ordinary hack-saw blade; ampoule saws; or merely a sharp scalpel. The shell is to be sawed through, without damage to the underlying shell membrane. Rectangular, triangular, square or circular openings have been used. Probably the simplest procedure is to make a square opening by sawing through the shell by a slight rotary motion of the saw, following the outer curvature of the shell, on each of the four sides but working along parallel sides of the square for the first two cuts. Avoid cutting through the shell membrane. Some workers leave the fourth side as a sort of hinge, but it does not generally break straight so that cuts along all edges are advised. Saw gently, and only through the shell, brushing away the shell particles as they are dislodged. When the four sides are sawed through, make the corner breaks with a needle or scalpel, and gently grasp the square piece of shell and remove it, intact.

Before invading the shell membrane see that there are no shell fragments lying on it. Moisten the shell membrane with one drop of sterile Locke's solution. Re-sterilize instruments and the margins of the shell opening, if it seems desirable. (The host egg is left at this stage in chorio-allantoic grafting to await the preparation of the graft.) With a sharp (sterile) needle puncture the center of the shell membrane, directing the point of the needle under the membrane and away from you, and at right angles to the egg axis. If the needle is sharp, it can be brought upward and thus be used as a knife to cut a slit-like opening in the shell membrane. With sharp (sterile) scissors, cut away the shell membrane to the margins of the shell opening.

Remove the mounting ring from the 95% alcohol, let it air-dry briefly, dip it into 45° C. melted paraffin, and place it on the egg so that it encircles the shell opening. With a small water-color paint brush paint melted paraffin onto the outer margins of the mounting ring so that it is thoroughly sealed to the shell and no air can pass beneath. Do not allow any paraffin to get into the egg.

Secure a circular coverslip, previously cleaned, and holding it with forceps pass it through a gas flame, exposing both surfaces. The coverslip should just fit the mounting ring. While still warm, bring the coverslip into position on the mounting ring and gently press it into place. The paraffin adherent to the mounting ring should melt and fasten the coverslip tightly to it. Paint a ring of paraffin on the outer edge of the coverslip, further sealing it to the egg shell. The entire operation consists simply of providing a sealed window in the place of a limited amount of egg shell. Return the egg to the incubator, in the same position, for the first 24 hours. Thereafter the egg may be rotated somewhat, but the embryo and its membranes should be kept away from the window.

Two modifications of the above procedure have been practiced, but neither is necessary. One is to puncture the air space so that it will be deflated and the embryo will be further depressed away from the upper shell membrane. If this is done, simply cover the puncture with paraffin or scotch tape. The second modification consists of adding egg-albumen from a second egg, to fill up the space between the embryo and the glass window. While albumen is bacteriolytic, this practice is ill advised, because it tends to add to the infection hazard through handling, and it generally clouds up the window.

Of course, a glass window is not the only useful type. Pliofilm, cellophane, and even Scotch tape have been used. If there is apt to be considerable delay between the preparation of the host, and the graft tissues, it is advisable to protect the embryo with a temporary Scotch tape covering of the shell opening. Square and round coverslips may be used without a mounting ring, but paraffin sealing is the more difficult.

The embryo may be examined from time to time but it must be remembered that with each removal of the shell cap there is opportunity for bacterial infection and increased evaporation. Embryos may be carried through to hatching.

THE SHELL CAP METHOD:

This is the method of Price and Fowler (1940). It consists of using a shell from the
blunt end of one egg to cover the exposed (blunt) end of an egg from which the shell has
been removed. This cover may be removed at periodic intervals, and the embryo observed through a much larger aperture than in the case of the cover glass window. There
is, of course, added danger of infection. Instead of the shell cap, a fitted glass cap, the
edges of which are fastened to the shell, can be used and need not be removed to observe
the chick development within. This type of shell cap has the one disadvantage of not
allowing free transfer of respiratory gases.

Save the blunt half of egg shells from any unincubated eggs. The shell membrane should
be left in position, and the shells may be sterilized in alcohol, to which a little iodine is
added. The cut edges of the shell caps may be made smooth and less brittle by dipping
them in melted paraffin.

Candle a fertilized egg to mark the margin of the air space at the blunt end. Place the
fertilized egg in a Syracuse dish with Permoplast base so that the blunt end is uppermost.
Clean off the entire blunt end with iodized 95% alcohol, and wipe it dry with sterile cotton.
With needle, lancet, or forceps make a small hole in the center of the blunt end and then
gradually pick away the shell, making an ever-increasingly large circular hole. It will
help to limit the shell cracking if a small hack saw is used to cut a shallow ring around
the shell, just within the limit of the air space. The shell should be picked away to within
about 1/4 inch of the inner shell membrane and embryo. Pick away all of the outer shell
membrane, but remember that this membrane extends completely around the embryo.
Avoid ripping or tearing this tough membrane.

Place a sterile shell cap over the exposed embryo, see that the egg is securely held in
the Permoplast of the Syracuse dish, and return the egg to the incubator. The humidity
of the incubator must be increased to above 60% for these eggs, since there is a much
greater exposed surface for evaporation than in the other method. By the 17th day the
egg shell may be sprinkled twice daily with a small amount of sterile water at the incubator temperature, but do not immerse the egg in water. The embryo can be drowned
within the shell.

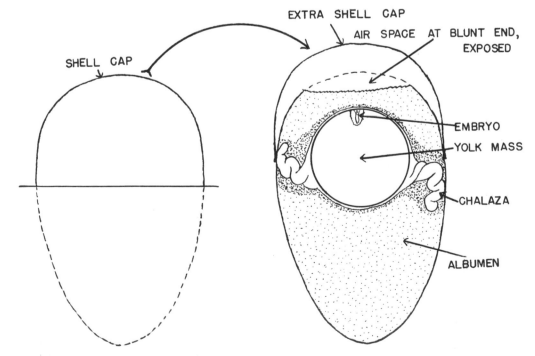

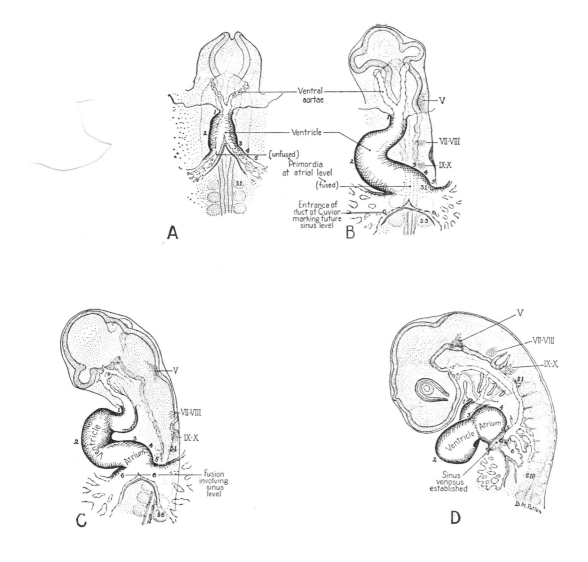

Formation of fundamental regions of chick heart by progressive fusion of its paired primordia. A. At 9-somite stage, when the first contractions appear. The ventricular part of the heart is the only region where the fusion of the paired primordia has occurred and the myocardial investment has been formed. B. At 16-somite stage, when the blood first begins to circulate. The atrium and ventricle have been established, but the sinus venosus exists only as undifferentiated primordial channels, still paired, and still lacking myocardial investment. C. At 19-somite stage. Fusion of the paired primordia is just beginning to involve the sinus region. D. At 26-somite stage. The sinus venosus is definitely established and its investment with myocardium well advanced. To facilitate understanding of the progress of fusion, arabic numerals have been placed against approximately corresponding locations. The 6 is located at the point of entrance of the duct of Cuvier as determined from injected specimens. (From Hoff, Kramer, DuBois, and Patten, Am. Heart J., 1939(2).) (Reproduced by courtesy Dr. B. M. Patten from Am. Naturalist 39:225, 1951)

54. MORPHOGENETIC MOVEMENTS DETERMINED BY VITAL STAINING AND CHARCOAL PARTICLES

Before beginning the following study of morphogenetic movements the student should re-acquaint himself with the various descriptions of the processes of normal development from the earliest primitive streak stage (about 16 hours of incubation) to at least 42 hours of incubation when the heart starts to beat. (See Lillie: "The Development of the Chick".) The pre-gastrulation stages are not available, since they occur within the oviduct and every fertilized egg is at least in the primitive streak stage when layed. A condensed survey is given below.

The primitive streak, considered by many as homologous to the blastoporal lips of the amphibia, consists of a longitudinal thickening of ectoderm extending through from almost the anterior limit through about 2/3 of the length of the area pellucida. The primitive groove is probably formed as a result of mesodermal outgrowth, and beneath it all is a thin layer of endoderm lying on the yolk and attached to the streak only at the level of Hensen's node. The bulk of the embryonic tissues arise from material of this streak as it becomes telescoped posteriorly in favor of an anteriorly elongating embryo. The margins of the area pellucida and the area opaca together form the extra-embryonic structures.

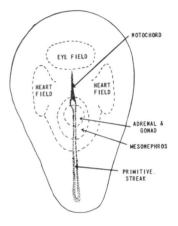

Presumptive areas of the chick primitive streak, modified from Willier & Rawles 1935: Proc. Soc. Exp. Biol. & Med. 32:1293.

At about 20 hours of incubation a head process appears anterior to the primitive streak, and this consists of the anterior limit of the notochord and overlying medullary plate ectoderm. There is definite cephalization (precocious development of the anterior structures) but as the embryo lengthens the primitive streak shortens (with the recession of its anterior end, or Hensen's node). As the neural folds of the future brain region become approximated, the medullary plate is lengthened posteriorly and the somites begin to appear, formed out of mesenchyme which was derived (by migration) from the sides of the primitive streak. The first pair of somites appear at about 21 hours of incubation and will be located at a position just posterior to the future otic vesicles. The first four somite pairs appear during the first day, all to be incorporated in the head (occipital) musculature. The primitive streak is therefore not to be considered as part of the embryo proper, but rather as a remnant of the blastoporal lips out of which are derived the tissues of the embryo.

Wetzel (1929) and Pasteels (1937) have mapped out the prospective organ-forming areas of the primitive streak stage of the chick embryo, in a manner similar to that used by Vogt (1926) and others on the amphibia, by the use of vital dyes. In fact, these investigators have found that there is surprising similarity in amphibian and avian morphogenetic movements, and that the three major movements of convergence, invagination, and elongation, are found in both. The notochord and the floor of the neural tube arise from the material of Hensen's node, as shown by deep vital dye staining. The anterior end of the primitive streak (exclusive of Hensen's node) gives rise to the lateral walls and roof of the neural tube, and to the somites. The anterior part of the head arises from pre-nodal materials. Vital staining and charcoal marking are useful procedures in determining the prospective significance of the various areas within the whole, normal, developing embryo. (Isolation of these same areas onto culture media indicates that their prospective potencies are even greater.)

THE METHOD OF VITAL STAINING:

Chick embryo areas are not as simple to stain with vital dyes as are the comparable areas of amphibian embryos except that the dye is more visible. The fat globules and yolk often absorb some of the stain and then disintegrate. Beyond a certain concentration, the living cells of the chick embryo seem unable to tolerate the vital dyes. However, the staining must be fairly deep to be significant for the primitive streak embryo is tridermic. In all instances the vitally stained embryo must be removed to a watchglass, cleaned of all excess and adherent yolk, and examined with transmitted light within 24 to 48 hours of the staining.

Procedure:
1. Prepare agar chips by soaking beaded agar in Nile Blue Sulphate (1/10,000) and also in Neutral Red (1/10,000) and drying on glass plates. The agar beads will take up the dye and, when dry, may be further cut down to any appropriate size under a dissection microscope. Another method is to prepare some 2% agar in distilled water, add the dye (above concentration), pour the hot agar onto glass plates and, when cool and dry, peel off the agar in thin and narrow strips by means of a scalpel. These strips may then be cut to any size or shape.

2. Wash instruments in warm soap and water, rinse, air dry and then place them in 80% alcohol for sterilization. The instruments include watchmaker's (#5) forceps, fine scissors, sharp scalpel, and hack saw blade.

3. Locate the blastoderm of an 18-20 hour incubated egg, outline it on the shell with pencil, and then place the egg (in the same position) in a finger bowl or #2 Stender on abundant cotton. Orient the egg with the blunt end to the left.

4. Following the procedure described above, make a window in the shell measuring from 12 to 15 mm. in diameter. Do not injure the shell membrane. The window should be within the circumscribed area, in the uppermost part of the shell.

5. Place a drop of sterile Locke's (or saline) solution on the shell membrane, and, when moist, rupture the membrane and remove it to the margins of the shell opening. Avoid touching the underlying blastoderm and, if necessary, remove any excess albumen with sterile pipette.

6. With watchmaker's forceps place a small piece of blue (Nile Blue Sulphate*) agar (or even a particle of Nile Blue Sulphate powder) on the central region of the blastoderm. The blastoderm, at this stage, is not readily visible but will become apparent with blue staining. Remove the blue agar after a few minutes, i.e., after some of the dye has diffused into the embryo through the vitelline membrane. (If powdered dye is used, this will be more difficult to remove.) Do not overstain.

7. Place a Neutral Red granule of red agar on the blastoderm in an anterior position, i.e., anterior to Hensen's node, for a few minutes. Remove with forceps. If this proves difficult, add a drop of sterile saline solution to float the granule upwards, and then remove with watchmaker's forceps.

---

* Gruebler's is best, but any dye used should be pre-tested because some samples have proven to be toxic to chick embryos. Neutral red can be used but is less satisfactory.

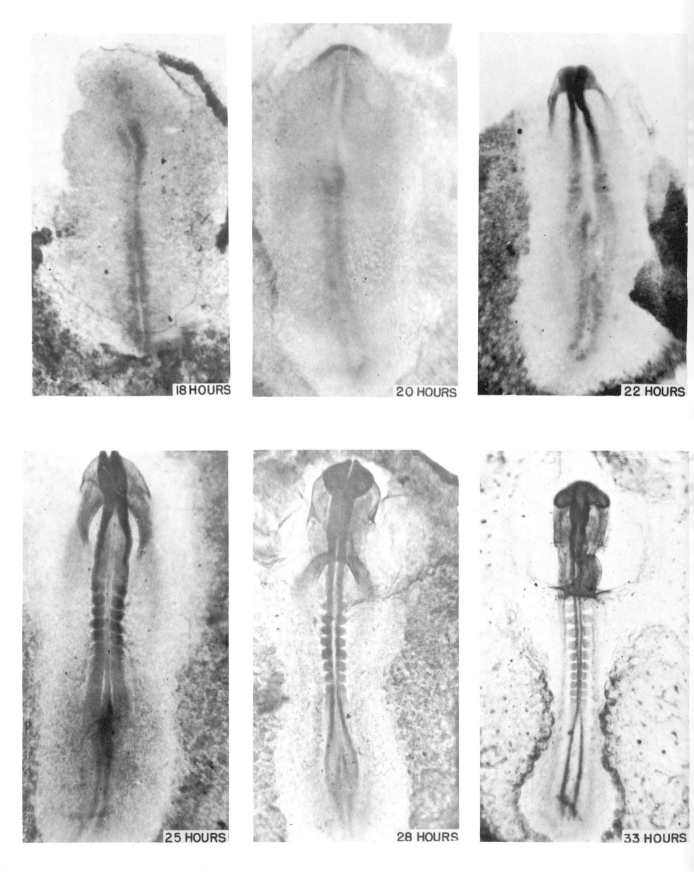

WHOLE CHICK EMBRYOS 18 — 33 HOUR STAGE

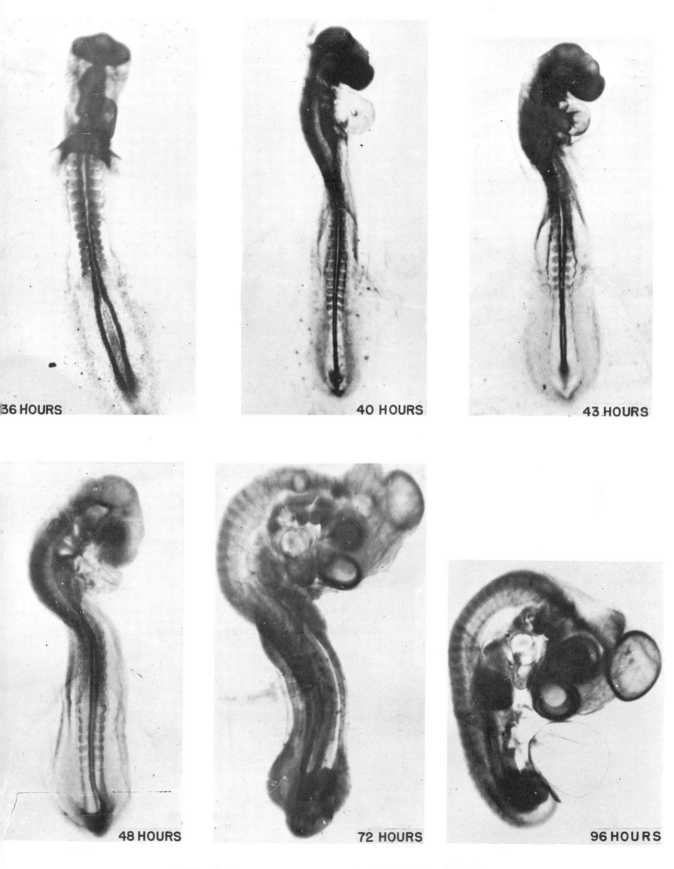

WHOLE CHICK EMBRYOS FROM 36 TO 96 HOURS

PHOTOGRAPHS

8.   Make a sketch of the blastoderm, any identifiable structures of the embryo, and the positions of the colored areas. If a temporary window is placed over the shell opening (coverslip) the sketch may be made during a brief candling.

9.   With melted, and soft paraffin seal a circular coverglass onto the egg surface, over the window. This need not be made with the care of transplantations for the duration of the experiment is short.

10. After 24, hours, crack the underside of the shell on the side of a finger bowl about 2/3 full of Locke's (or saline) solution, cut out the entire blastoderm, transfer it with a wide-mouthed pipette to a watchglass of saline solution, and examine by reflected and transmitted light on a warming stage, to determine the changes in the size and positions of the colored areas.

Variations in the procedure: 18-20 hour incubation stage.
1.   Attempt to stain Hensen's Node specifically, and 24 hours later excise the blastoderm, split the embryo lengthwise through the neural tube, invert the blastoderm, and locate the stain. If the Node was stained, the notochord and ventral neural tube should be stained.

2.   Stain the Primitive Streak posterior to Hensen's Node, and 24 hours later excise and examine the blastoderm for the position of the stain.

3.   Stain a spot directly anterior to Hensen's Node with Nile Blue Sulphate and a second spot to either side of the midline, at the same level as the Nile Blue, but use Neutral Red. In this way the movements of the Pre-Nodal areas may be determined 24 hours later.

4.   Stain the Primitive Streak stage with several spots in the two colors, excise quickly after 24 hours, and fix in an attempt to preserve the vital dye in position (see section on Morphogenetic Movements for specific directions, based on Detwiler's paper, for preserving vital dyes).

THE METHOD OF CARBON-MARKING IN VITRO: (Spratt, 1947, 1948)

By this method the entire blastoderm of an 18 to 20 hour incubated chick embryo is excised, placed on albumen medium and cultivated in vitro for 24 or more hours (at 103°F.) and the morphogenetic movements are determined by movement of adherent particles of blood charcoal.

1.   To prepare the albumen medium separate the yolk from the albumen of one unincubated egg and add the albumen to 50 cc. of chick Ringer's solution (0.9% NaCl, 0.042% KCl, and 0.024% $CaCl_2$ made up in glass distilled water) contained in a 500 cc. Erlenmeyer flask. Stopper and shake the flask vigorously for 1 minute.

2.   Excise the blastoderm from an 18 to 20 hour incubated egg and place it in chick Ringer's at 103°F. in a watchglass, and remove all excess yolk.

3.   With wide-mouthed pipette, remove the blastoderm in minimum of medium, and transfer it to the surface of the (above) albumen-Ringer's in a watchglass at 103°F. (on a warming stage). With micropipette, remove all excess medium from the surface of the blastoderm so that it floats freely on the surface film of the culture medium.

Carbon-marking in vitro: Chick blastoderm Primitive Streak Stage.

4. Place carbon (blood charcoal) particles on the Hensen's Node, directly in front of it, and at one or more levels of the Primitive Streak (see figures above). Indicate by parallel charcoal marks on the medium exactly where these particles are placed. These marks to be used as reference marks later. Watchmaker's forceps may be used for this marking. The forceps may be dipped into the charcoal, shaken of all excess particles, and then touched to the relatively dry upper surface of the blastoderm. There is sufficient moisture to provide a sticky surface so that the carbon particles will come off the forceps very readily, and will remain adherent to the blastoderm.

5. After 24 to 48 hours examine the blastoderm, cultured in vitro, for any change in the position of the carbon particles. It will, of course, be necessary (as always) to make sketches at the beginning and at the termination of the experiment.

SKETCH BELOW THE OBSERVED MORPHOGENETIC MOVEMENTS

55. EXPLANTING AND CULTIVATING EARLY CHICK EMBRYOS IN VITRO

Spratt (1947, 1948) has shown that the bacteriolytic property of egg albumen used in his various culture media makes it unnecessary to include the elaborate sterilization procedures used in the classical tissue culture methods. Tap water can be used in the place of distilled water when egg-albumen is included in the medium. When the egg-albumen is not included, the glassware and the instruments are dry sterilized and the solutions are autoclaved.

Preparation of the equipment:

1. Wash, rinse (in hot running water), and set aside the glassware and instruments to dry on a clean towel.

2. Prepare moist-chamber culture dishes as follows: Place a moist cotton ring in a Petri dish, set a watch crystal with concave side up in the center of the petri dish, and replace the cover of the dish. All parts must have been previously sterilized. (Method of Fell and Robison, 1929 and Waddington, 1932.)

Preparation of the culture media:

Physiologically balanced "Ringer's" for chick embryos:

  a. <u>Unbuffered isotonic salt</u> (Spratt, 1947)

NaCl	0.7	grams
KCl	0.042	grams
CaCl$_2$	0.024	grams
Doubly distilled water	100.0 cc	

  b. <u>Buffered isotonic salt</u> (Romanoff, 1943)

NaCl	0.86%
KCl	0.031%
CaCl	0.02%
MgCl$_2$·6H$_2$O	0.01%
KH$_2$PO$_4$	0.02%
Na$_2$KPO$_4$·12H$_2$O...	0.08%
Glucose	0.2%

Made up in glass distilled water.

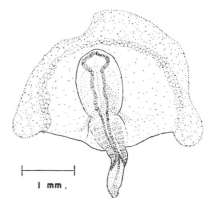

Camera lucida drawing of a typical 10-hour-old, living explant of the anterior portion of a short head-process blastoderm which was transected about 0.4 mm. posterior to the node. This result was obtained after carrying out verbatim the method outlined for saline-agar-albumen media. With a little practice, the student can accumulate many similar cases of beautifully symmetrical and essentially normal morphogenesis.

(From Spratt 1947
Science. 106:452)

(Note: Romanoff found that this medium could sustain a nearly constant rate of respiration of all embryonic tissues tested, without providing any pH change.)

1. <u>Ringer-albumen-Agar medium</u>: This medium is made up from 2 components, as follows.

  a. <u>Ringer-albumen component</u>:

    (1) Separate the yolk from the white (albumen) of a fresh, unincubated egg.

    (2) Add the albumen to 50 cc. of ordinary chick Ringer's in a 500 cc. Erlenmeyer flask, previously sterilized.

---

* The author is indebted to Dr. N. T. Spratt, Jr. for these procedures, and for helpful suggestions in the organization of this part of the exercise on the chick embryo.

(3) Stopper the flask and shake the contents vigorously for 1 minute.

(4) Add 0. 5 mg. of phenol red. This will cause the medium to become slightly purple, when the albumen is present, so that it will be the easier to see the white explants.

b. Ringer-Agar component:
(1) Place from 0. 13 to 0. 15 grams of powdered (USP X1) Agar in a small Erlenmeyer flask along with 30 cc. of chick Ringer's solution. The Agar may be increased to 0. 2 or 0. 4 grams, in which case a much firmer medium that is more easily handled, will result.

(2) Bring the Ringer-Agar mixture to a slow boil over a small flame of the Bunsen burner (or in a water bath). Agitate constantly to prevent the Agar from sticking or charring. After the Agar is completely dissolved, cool the mixture slowly down to 40° to 45°C.

(3) Add to this Ringer-Agar 20 cc. of the Ringer-Albumen mixture. Exclude the foamy portion. Gently shake to mix the two media.

c. The medium:
When the two components are mixed the medium is completed. Pour approximately 2 cc. of this mixture into each previously prepared, sterile, watch crystal which is supported in a cotton moat in a Petri dish. Cover the Petri dish and allow the medium to gel (about 30 minutes to 1 hour) before moving the dishes.

2. Saline-agar "A":
a. Make up 100 cc. of unbuffered chick "Ringer's" ("A" on preceding page).
b. Add 0. 25 grams of powdered Agar (USP X1).
c. Sterilize by boiling (gently) or autoclaving. Avoid charring the Agar.
d. Make up a stock solution of 1% $NaHCO_3$, sterilize by filtration (if possible) through a Berkefeld filter, and then saturate with CO_2.
e. Cool the saline solution down to 40°C. and add 1 to 2 cc. of the sterile bicarbonate solution.
f. With sterile pipette place 2 cc. of the medium in culture dishes, where it will slowly set to form a soft gel.

3. Saline-Agar "B": (See White, 1946)
a. Add the following salts to 100 cc. of double distilled water.

NaCl	0. 83 grams
KCl	0. 037 grams
$Ca(NO_3)_2 \cdot H_2O$	0. 021 grams
$MgSO_4$	0. 027 grams
$Fe(NO_3)_3 \cdot 9H_2O$	0. 00014

b. Add 0. 25 grams of Agar, gently boil to dissolve Agar (avoid charring).
c. Prepare the buffer separately, and sterilize it before adding to the medium.

$Na_2HOP_4 \cdot 12H_2O$	0. 0145 grams
KH_2PO_4	0. 0026 grams
$NaHCO_3$	0. 055

d. When the saline-agar is cooled to 40°C. add the buffer.
e. It is advisable to add 0. 001 gram percent of phenol red. The pH range is generally between 7. 5 and 8. 9.

4. Saline-agar plus yolk-albumen extract:
a. Place the entire contents of two fresh, unincubated eggs in a sterile 500 ml Erlenmeyer flask. Stopper and shake vigorously to homogenize.
b. Centrifuge portions of the above at 2-3000 rpm for about an hour. This much more concentrated extract makes it possible to cultivate unincubated blastoderms, heretofore almost completely refractory, with almost 100% development

up to a 10-20 somite stage <u>provided</u> one also explants the blastoderm <u>endo-</u>
<u>derm layer up</u>, upper surface against the medium. (See Biol. Bull 1960,
119:338). Explants should be removed to dish of saline for examination
against a black background.

5. <u>Saline-Agar plus yolk extract</u> (omitting all albumen):
    a. Separate the yolk from the albumen in about 50 to 100 cc. of chick Ringer's,
        without rupturing the vitelline membrane. Pull off the chalaza and such al-
        bumen as you can grasp with the forceps. With glass rod roll the yolk over
        to remove any adherent albumen. Pass the yolk through several changes of
        Ringer's, in each removing more of the albumen.
    b. When fully denuded of its albumen, pour off all the Ringer's, puncture the
        vitelline membrane with sharp forceps, grasp it, and allow the yolk to flow
        out into a sterile beaker.
    c. Add about 10 cc. of the albumen-free yolk to 20 to 40 cc. of saline-Agar "A",
        shake vigorously to mix.
    (Note: The unbuffered, pure yolk has a pH range of 4.5 to 6.0, hence this factor
            must be considered in relation to the results. It would be instructive to
            compare this with buffered saline "B".)

6. <u>Saline-Agar plus pure albumen</u> (omitting all yolk):
    a. Mix 10 cc. of pure egg albumen with from 15 to 40 cc. of chick Ringer's.
        Shake thoroughly, and centrifuge (as above).
    b. Mix 1 cc. of the above (supernatant) mixture with 1 cc. of saline-Agar "A"
        to make up the substrate.
        (This may be made up with the buffered "B" or the non-buffered "A" saline
         solutions.)

7. <u>Saline-Agar</u> (or blood plasma) <u>plus embryonic extract</u>:
    a. Place 3 embryos, ages from 5 to 8 days, in 20 cc. of Pannett-Compton saline
        and thoroughly crush.
    b. Centrifuge the embryonic mash and draw off the clear supernatant fluid.
    c. Mix the embryonic extract with
        (1) Buffered saline-Agar "B" at 40°C. <u>or</u>
        (2) Blood plasma.
<u>NOTE</u>: It is impractical for the average graduate student to test all of the above 7 media.
        It is therefore recommended that they be used in the sequence given (above) as
        far as time and facilities will allow.

<u>Preparation of the explant:</u>
    1. Incubate fertile eggs for 20 to 24 hours at 38°C.
    2. Open an incubated egg into a finger bowl containing 100 cc. of sterile chick
        Ringer's solution. Simply break the egg open as though it were to be fried, taking
        care not to break the yolk.
    3. With forceps, grab the chalaza or the yolk, and cut (with sharp scissors) through
        the vitelline membrane, making a circle around the blastoderm about 1/4 inch
        away from its border. By cutting in one direction and rotating the yolk mass
        (with forceps) in the opposite direction, the blastoderm can be quickly encircled.
    4. Grasp the margin of the blastoderm with the forceps, and roll it back and away
        from the yolk. When the blastoderm is entirely freed from the yolk mass, and
        can be clearly seen, work a blunt dissecting needle between the blastoderm and
        the thin, transparent vitelline membrane. Now transfer the blastoderm, by
        means of a wide-mouthed pipette, to a Petri dish containing about 20 cc. of
        sterile chick Ringer's solution.
    5. With fine dissecting (glass) needles trim away all of the yolky-opaque area. The
        early embryo is now ready to be cultured, in whole or in part.

Embryonic parts to be used as explants:

    Stages to be used:
        a. Definitive primitive streak
        b. Head-process stage
        c. Head-fold stage
        d. One to 6 somite stage

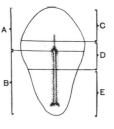

Primitive Streak
Stage showing levels
of transections.

    Cuts to be made: (See figure, at the right)
        a. Transversely (i. e. , at right angles to the embryonic axis) about 0. 2 to 0. 7 mm. posterior to the primitive pit, using both halves.
        b. Transversely through the primitive pit level, using both anterior and posterior halves.
        c. Transversely anterior to the primitive pit (i. e. , through the early notochord) and simultaneously through the middle of the primitive streak.   This gives three pieces of blastoderm, each potentially very different.
        d. Use also whole blastoderms.

THE DIFFERENTIATION OF CHICK EXPLANTS ON VARIOUS TYPES OF MEDIA

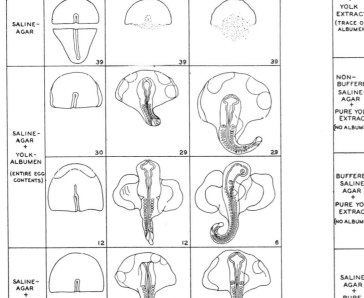

Development on various media. The sketches are based on camera lucida drawings of the living explants. All are drawn approximately to the same scale. The numbers in each block refer to the number of explants.

† i.e., 20 ± hours after explantation. Only the
* albumen which adheres to the yolk after the ordinary method of separating the 2. The yolk was not washed.

From Spratt 1947: Jour. Exp. Zool. 106:345.

Procedure for culturing:

1. Transfer the embryo, or parts, to be cultivated by means of a wide-mouthed pipette to the surface of a culture medium, orient as desired, and flatten it out by sucking away all excess superficial medium with a fine pipette. The embryo (or part) should float on a few drops (2 cc.) of culture medium.

2. Cover the Petri dish and return it carefully to the incubator.

Variations in the procedure:

1. Glucose medium: Some interesting effects can be seen if 100 to 800 mg. percent of glucose is added to the Ringer-Agar medium as a substitute for the albumen. Such a medium should be buffered to pH 7.8 to 8.3. (Sterilize the medium before adding the sterile buffer.) Spratt (1948, p. 64) gives the following formula for his "minimal medium":

    a. Add 0.10 to 0.15 grams powdered Agar (U.S.P. Xl) to 36 cc. of chick Ringer's, shake, add 0.34 grams of glucose, and 0.001 gram percent of phenol red. This mixture is autoclaved in a small Erlenmeyer flask for 8 to 10 minutes.

    b. Cool the mixture to 40°C.

    c. Add 2 cc. of 0.290 grams percent of $Na_2HPO_4 \cdot 12\,H_2O$, and 0.052 grams percent of KH_2PO_4 (previously mixed).

    d. Add 2 cc. of 1.10 grams percent of $NaHCO_3$.

    e. Saturate the mixture with CO_2.

    f. Immediately place 2 cc. of the prepared medium in each watch crystal.

2. Medium with other sugars:

    a. Sugars which serve as exogenous energy supply: mannose, fructose, maltose.

    b. Sugars which do not serve as an exogenous energy source: lactose, sucrose.

3. Medium with amino acids added: See Spratt (1948) for list of amino acids which can be tested for nutrient value.

4. Cultivation of chick structures on plasma-embryonic extract:
   The classic method of explant culturing has been on plasma clot or on a mixture of chick Ringer's and embryonic extracts. It is suggested that the student follow this procedure to compare its benefits with those described above.

    a. Place whole chick embryos (5 to 8 days) in a sterile beaker and cover with an equivalent volume of sterile Tyrode's solution, or sterile chick Ringer's. The embryos must be finely chopped.

    b. Centrifuge the embryonic mash at 2500 r.p.m. for 15 minutes.

    c. With sterile pipette, remove the supernatent fluid and, without dilution, place in culture dishes. About 1 to 2 cc. per dish.

    d. The culture dishes may be of several types, all dry sterilized.

    (1) Depression slides which are to be covered with coverslip, ringed with vaseline.

    (2) Coverslips ringed with paraffin (to limit the spread of the culture medium) inverted over a depression slide (hanging drop method) which acts as a moist chamber.

    e. With sterile pipette transfer the excised anlagé to the culture medium, seal, and incubate for from 1 to 8 days.

      In the case of the coverslip (hanging drop) method of culturing, add the culture medium (within the paraffin ring), transfer the anlagé to the medium, ring the margin of a depression slide with white vaseline, and invert the depression slide and bring it down over the coverslip so that it covers the explant. Gently press the depression slide into place, and transfer (without righting the depression slide) the whole to the incubator at 38°C. After the explant has been in the incubator for 6 to 8 hours, the depression slide and coverslip may be quickly inverted, whereupon the culture becomes a hanging drop.   During the preliminary interval the cells of the explant will have had an opportunity to become adherent to the coverslip, and the whole explant will be visible under the microscope through the thickness of the coverslip.

If the explant is transferred to fresh, sterile medium every 3 to 4 days, it may be carried for longer periods (e. g., 18 days).

For such in vitro studies it is suggested that the whole or parts of the eye of embryos ranging from 1 to 7 days be used (Dorris, 1938).   The eyes may be carefully dissected out in sterile chick Ringer's using fine glass needles. When whole eyes are transplanted, remove as much of the adherent mesen- chyme as possible, leaving only the ectoderm immediately covering the optic cup.   When parts of the optic cup are explanted, it is first necessary to punc- ture the border of the cup with a glass needle, impale the lens on the needle, and pull it out.   With the cup in position, the needle can be inserted between the two layers at the chorioid fissures, thus isolating the retina which can be removed as a firm cup-shaped structure.   In the older eyes the lens can be removed by dissecting away the overlying ectoderm, trimming the edge of the cup with fine scissors, and then separating the two layers with fine glass needles.   The cup, or parts of either layer, can then be cut into smaller pieces for explantation.

This type of study provides information relative to the self-differentiating capacities of whole eyes, and (in explantation of pieces) to the capacity for independent differentiation of the parts of the eye.

DISCUSSION:

The technique of tissue culture was first used by Dr. Ross Harrison in 1907.   Most of the work that has been done since with this technique has been with isolated cells of the relatively older (4 to 8 days) chick embryos.   Only recently has Spratt (1947, 1948) re- vitalized interest in this technique by finding that the entire blastoderm of the early (18 to 24 hour incubated embryo) stages could be cultured in vitro, either in toto or in transected parts.

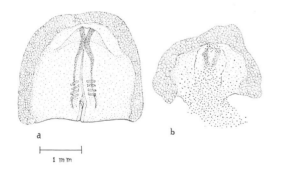

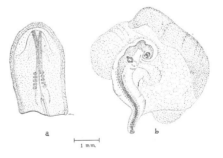

Camera lucida drawings of the anterior portion of a living 4-somite blastoderm explanted to a non- nutrient saline-agar medium: a, at the time of ex- plantation; b, after 20 ± hours' cultivation.   Note the failure of development and the loss of organiza- tion which had been attained at the time of embryo was removed from its normal food supply - the yolk and albumen.   Note also that presence of part of the opaque area has not prevented the characteristic "degenerative" changes.

From Spratt 1948: Jour. Exp. Zool. 107:39

Camera lucida drawings of a living ex- plant to a yolk-albumen extract saline- agar medium.   a, at the time of explan- tation.   b, after 55 hours' incubation. Note the remarkably normal morpho- genesis, differentiation, and increase in size of the explant.   The heart was beating rhythmically when the drawing was made.

From Spratt 1947: Jour. Exp. Zool. 106:345

Spratt (1947) sets up a group of criteria for the adequacy of the culture medium used in support of development, as follows:

1. Regression of the primitive streak, formation and elongation of the notochord.
2. Formation and closing of the neural folds.
3. Development of the brain and spinal cord.
4. Formation of somites.
5. Development of optic vesicles and otocysts.
6. Morphogenesis and pulsation of the heart.
7. Formation and extension of a "tail" from the cut edge of the anterior piece.

He states: "A medium which meets all of these requirements is considered adequate."

From the works of Spratt it seems evident that the early blastoderm does not have adequate endogenous food supply (as does the fish embryo) but depends upon some exogenous source for nutrition. The best medium proved to be the entire egg (yolk and albumen) extracted and added to a saline-agar base. The albumen seems not only to be bacteriolytic but also seems to help maintain the proper pH of the blastodermic environment. A "complete" synthetic medium was finally devised, containing saline-agar, glucose, amino acids, vitamins, etc. on which explants underwent essentially normal morphogenesis, differentiation, and some growth. However, Spratt subsequently found that the glucose component was the only absolutely essential exogenous source of energy for morphogenesis and differentiation of the explanted early blastoderm. These developmental processes occurred in the almost total absence of growth. Mannose, fructose, and maltose were apparently just as efficient as was glucose.

In a study by Rawles (1936) followed by Rudnick (1938) it has been possible, by explantation and chorio-allantoic grafting, to map the organ forming areas of the early chick blastoderm. Rawles found that the developmental potencies within each area diminish peripherally from the center, and that there is superior developmental capacity of the left side of the blastoderm over the right.

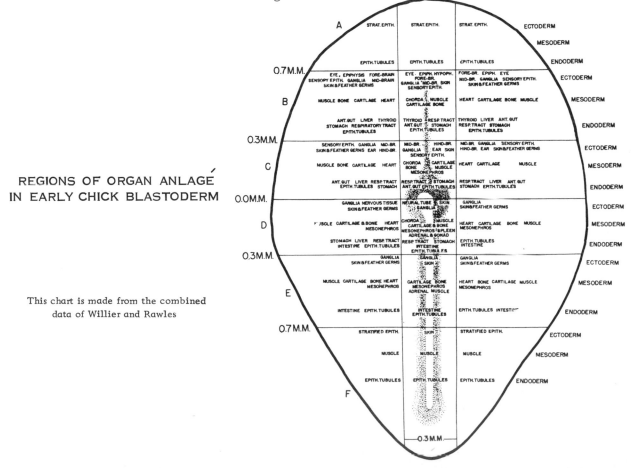

**REGIONS OF ORGAN ANLAGE
IN EARLY CHICK BLASTODERM**

This chart is made from the combined
data of Willier and Rawles

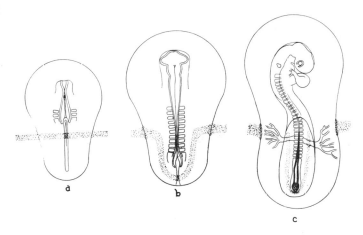

a b c

Summary diagrams based on a study of over 50 blasto-derms growing in ovo and stained as shown in (a) with a 1:1 mixture of 0.5% Nile blue sulfate and 0.5% Neutral red. In (b) is shown the position of the stained band of cells 6 hours later. In (c) (drawn to a some-what smaller scale than a and b) is shown the pattern of stained cells 14 hours later (20 hours after the original marking as in a). If (c) be compared with (b) it is to be noted that the end-bud and the neural tube have second-arily acquired the stain and keep it in the oxidized (blue) state. In the region just anterior and lateral to the bases of the omphalomesenteric arteries no stain can be seen (presumably it is in the reduced (colorless) state). The stained regions lateral and parallel to the neural tube are in the lateral plate mesoderm (cf. Pasteels, 1937, fig. 18). No exceptions to this result have been found.

Diagrams illustrating the pronounced anteroposterior "stretching" of the pre-nodal region (neural plate), the absence of invagination through the primitive pit, and the presence of invagination just behind the node during the early stages of regression of the streak. Time increases from left to right in the diagrams. Note the more rapid and extensive re-gression of the primitive streak relative to marked areas lying lateral to it.

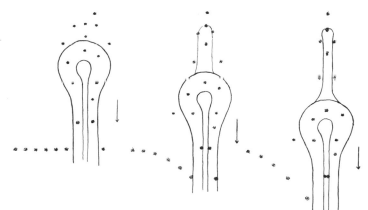

Two above diagrams from Spratt 1947:
Jour. Exp. Zool. 104:69

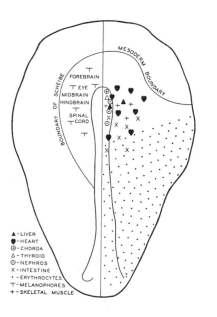

▲ - LIVER
● - HEART
⊕ - CHORDA
△ - THYROID
⊙ - NEPHROS
X - INTESTINE
• - ERYTHROCYTES
T - MELANOPHORES
+ - SKELETAL MUSCLE

DISTRIBUTION OF POTENCIES IN THE DEFINITIVE PRIMITIVE STREAK BLASTODERM, TESTED UNDER VARIOUS EXPERIMENTAL CONDITIONS

Ectodermal potencies shown on left, mesodermal and entodermal on right; these have not been tested sepa-rately. Posterior and lateral extent of mesodermal potencies has not been specified.

From Rudnick 1944: Quart. Rev. Biol. 19:187

Rudnick, on the other hand, by isolation culture methods on plasma clots, found that two primary germ layers the ectoderm and endoderm seem to function more-or-less independently, and that the notochord and axial mesodermal structures apparently depend on the deginitive organization of the streak and node, or the head process, for realization in vitro. Below is presented a figure from her paper showing the recognizable differentiations from various regions of the early blastoderm when explanted in vitro.

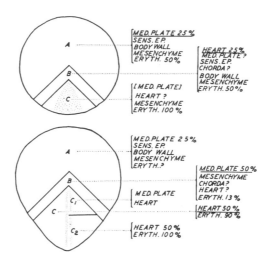

Operating diagrams, showing structures differentiating from each piece. Approximate percentages are given in cases where they are thought of significance.

From Rudnick 1938: Jour. Exp. Zool. 73:399.

"Classifications are subjective concepts, which have no absolute demarcation in Nature, corresponding to them . . . . Consequently, when we attempt to define anything complex . . . we can scarcely ever avoid including more than we intended, or leaving out something that should be taken in. Thus it happens that on seeking a definition of life, we have great difficulty in finding one that is neither more nor less than sufficient."

Herbert Spencer

"The whole development of science, especially in recent years, is a record of tearing down barriers between separate fields of knowledge and investigation. Little harm, and perhaps much gain, can come from a frank avowal that we are unable to state clearly the difference between living and non-living matter. This does not in any way commit us to the view that no such difference exists."

A. J. Lotka

56. THE METHOD OF CHORIO-ALLANTOIC GRAFTING

The grafting of early chick embryo parts to the chorio-allantois of an older (8 to 10 day incubated) embryo has long since been perfected (Hoadley, 1924, Willier, 1924). The highly vascularized chorio-allantois of the avian embryo is located close to the shell membrane of an 8-day embryo, so that the shell over it can be removed and the explant can be placed upon it as a substrate for nutrition and growth. If the shell is replaced and sealed into place with melted paraffin, the explant will generally become vascularized and will develop for 9 to 10 days and may be recovered before the natural breakdown of the extra-embryonic membranes on the 19th day of incubation.

Chick egg with window above the developing embryo. Black washer is sealed to the egg shell and to the covering coverglass with paraffin. Irregular margin of torn shell membrane visible through the window. Embryo can develop and hatch.

Hen's egg showing attached window through which the development of the embryo can be observed.

(Courtesy General Biological Supply House, Chicago.)

Since there is complete isolation of the explant, there are no persistent inductive influences. However, the explant does come under the hormonal and other influences emanating from the blood of the host, and these must be considered. Further, there is a space limitation (within the host environment) and the further possibility that the graft may develop a parasitic relationship to the host, thereby utilizing some of the nutritional requisites of the host and indirectly alter the normality of the host environment.

Nevertheless, the chorio-allantois is proving of value in the study of mammalian isolates (Nicholas and Rudnick, 1933) and in the culturing of bacteria and viruses (Goodpasture, 1938). Experience has indicated that the 48 hour eye and the 72 hour limb are the most satisfactory anlagé to transplant.

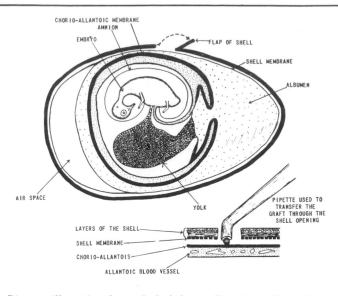

Diagram illustrating the method of chorio-allantoic grafting. Host embryo is generally incubated for 8 to 9 days, the graft may be any anlagé (e.g., the limb bud of 72 hour stage). The graft is generally recovered at about the 19th day, just before the time of hatching of the host when the membranes begin to dry up.

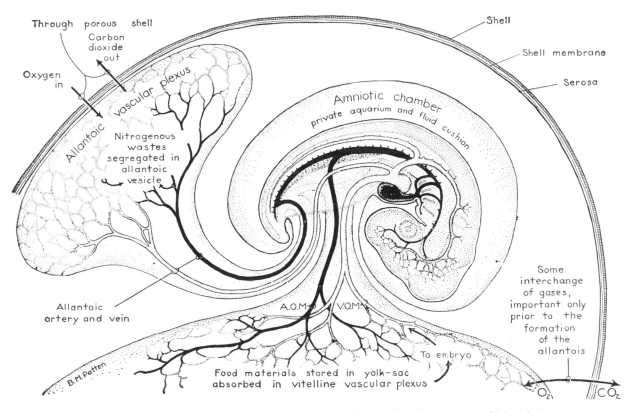

Schematic diagram showing the arrangement of main circulatory channels in a young chick embryo. The sites of some of the extraembryonic interchanges important in its bioeconomics are indicated by the labelling. The vessels within the embryo carry food and oxygen to all its growing tissues, and relieve them of the waste products incident to their metabolism. Abbreviations: A.O.M., omphalomesenteric artery; V.O.M., omphalomesenteric vein.

From Patten, B.M. - 1951 - Am. Nat. 39:225 (with permission)

THE PROCEDURE:

1. <u>Preparation of the hosts</u>: Begin incubation of fertile host eggs, properly marked, about 8 days before the operation. Turn the eggs twice daily.

2. <u>Preparation of the donors</u>: Begin incubation of donors on the 5th or 6th day of host incubation, so that the donors will be either 48 or 72 hours along at the time the hosts are 8 days incubated. Mark the eggs, and rotate twice daily.

3. <u>Preparation of the host for the graft</u>: (Work fast under the most sterile conditions)

    a. Candle the host eggs, select and mark the regions most suitable for a graft. The forked junction of large blood vessels at some distance from the embryo should be indicated by a pencil drawing on the shell.

    b. Prepare a window in the shell, under aseptic conditions (see directions for this above). Remove the shell in one piece. Moisten the shell membrane with several drops of sterile Locke's or chick Ringer's solution. This is necessary in order to avoid injury to the underlying and sometimes adherent chorio-allantoic membrane, and consequent rupturing of the blood vessels. Cover the aperture with a sterile cover glass, or replace the shell, and return the (host) egg to the incubator while preparing the graft.

4. <u>Preparation of the transplant</u>: (Eye - 48 hours, limb - 72 or more hours)

    a. Candle the donor to determine the approximate age. Crack the underside of the shell on the side of a finger bowl containing about 100 cc. of sterile chick Ringer's solution. When the blastoderm has moved around the dorsal position, quickly excise it, separate it from the vitelline membrane, and transfer it in a wide-mouthed pipette to a sterile watchglass under a dissection microscope. Confirm the age and stage of development.

    b. Quickly, and with sterile needles and watchmaker's forceps, excise the anlagé to be studied and transfer it in a drop of the sterile medium to the chorio-allantois of the prepared host. Replace the shell, and seal it with a ring of melted paraffin. Replace the host egg in the incubator without shifting its gravitational axis, and leave it unmoved for 6 to 8 hours. After this interval, treat the egg as any regularly incubated egg.

        <u>The eye</u>: The eye graft may be taken from any stage after about the 33 hour stage. The retina, pigmented layer, and lens may be easily distinguished in the graft, upon recovery. It is, of course, possible to study the independent differentiation of parts of the early optic vesicle, cup, etc. Final study may be made after clearing with oil of wintergreen, when the pigment and retina show up well, and then after sectioning and staining.

        <u>The limb bud</u>: Under the dissecting microscope, locate the wing and leg buds (72 hours or older). Make transverse cuts with a sharp needle through the embryo, one through the neck level and the other between the wing and the leg buds. Then dissect out each appendage bud in the following manner: Cut parallel to the body at the base of the bud, but include some of the body somites. Then cut (at right angles to the first cut) at the anterior and the posterior limits of the bud. Finally make the cut parallel to the first, beyond the outer limit of the bud, thus excising the bud in a rectangular piece of tissue. Remove all yolk and loose tissue adherent to the bud. A single donor may provide several appendage buds, and occasionally a single host may survive the implantation of several buds.

    c. Make a complete record, including sketches, of the condition of the chorio-allantois and the donor (explant) at the time of the operation.

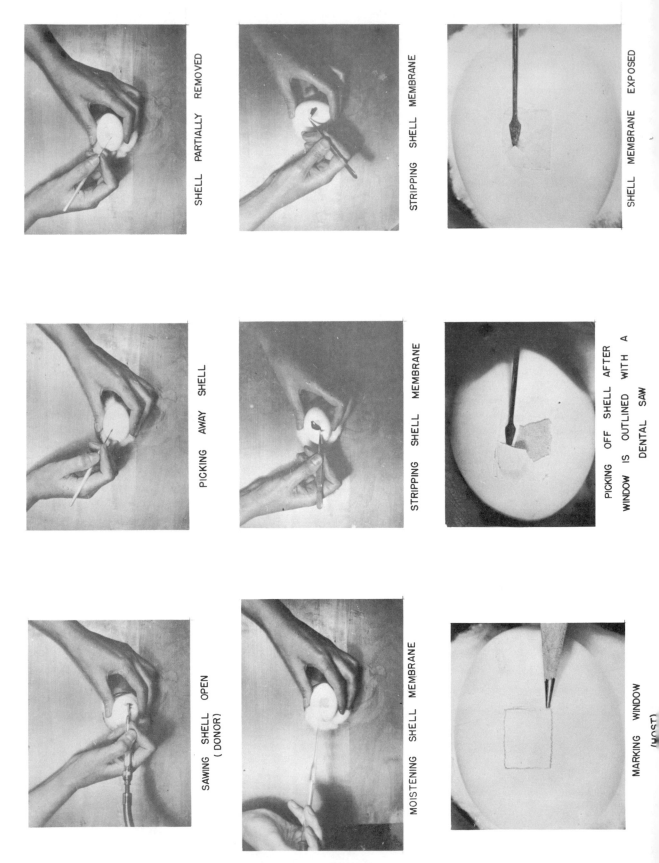

(Demonstrated by Dr. Frances Dorris Humm)

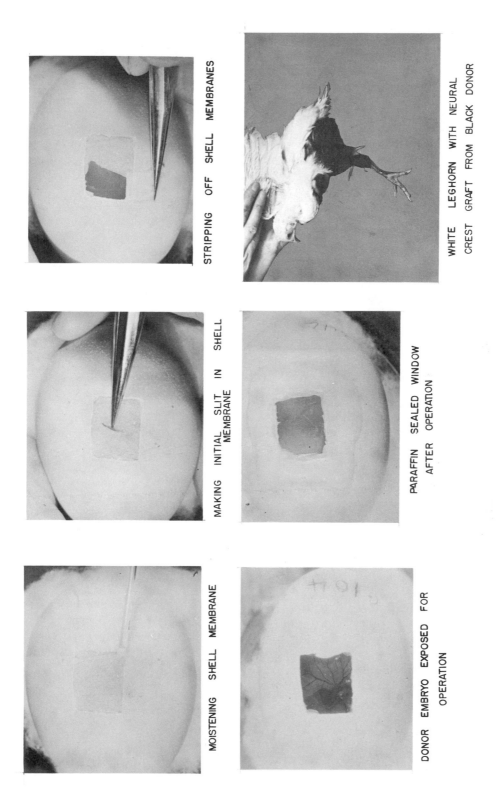

STRIPPING OFF SHELL MEMBRANES

WHITE LEGHORN WITH NEURAL CREST GRAFT FROM BLACK DONOR

MAKING INITIAL SLIT IN SHELL MEMBRANE

PARAFFIN SEALED WINDOW AFTER OPERATION

MOISTENING SHELL MEMBRANE

DONOR EMBRYO EXPOSED FOR OPERATION

(Courtesy of Dr. Frances Dorris Humm)

5. Recovery of the graft:
    a. The graft must be removed before the host extra-embryonic membranes
        begin to dry up. This is generally by the 18th day of incubation, or about 9
        to 10 days after the transplantation of the graft is made.
    b. Candle the host to attempt to locate the graft. This is generally difficult be-
        cause of the opacity of the host. However, if the graft has "taken" it will be
        found close to the original window. Make a cut through the shell about 1 cen-
        timeter outside of the original window, and remove the shell carefully, with-
        out rupturing the underlying chorio-allantois. Examine the underside of the
        shell to see if the explant may be adherent to it. The graft will generally
        appear as a fluid-filled vesicle, opaque, and without discernible structure.
        Particularly in the case of the appendage anlagé, the detailed structure will
        not be seen until the tissues are histologically cleared.
    c. Use the Lundvall technique (see above) for quick staining of cartilage, etc. of
        differentiated limbs. The eyes should be sectioned after normal fixation
        (Bouin or Kleinberg's) and stained with Conklin's Haematoxylin.
6. Other embryonic areas to be tested by chorio-allantoic grafting: It is suggested
    that the following additional structures be given the opportunity to develop on the
    chorio-allantois.
    a. Anterior half of the primitive streak, including Hensen's node.
    b. Neural crests and nerve cord, from embryos with 3 to 10 somites.
    c. Somite blocks.
    d. Heart anlagé of 42 hour stage.
    e. The entire blastoderm of primitive streak stage.

(Note: For further instructions the student is advised to consult Hamburger's:
        "A Manual of Experimental Embryology")

    *"The hen does not produce the egg, but the egg produces
the hen and also other hens . . . We know that the child comes
from the germ cells and not from the highly differentiated body
of the parents, and furthermore, that these cells are not made
by the parents' bodies but these cells have arisen by the division
of antecedent germ cells . . . . Parents do not transmit their
characters to their offspring, but these germ cells in the course
of long development give rise to adult characters similar to
those of the parent."*

                                                        E. G. Conklin

57. INTRA-EMBRYONIC TRANSPLANTATIONS

The most productive and successful investigators in this field are Willier and Hamburger, and the student is directed to their papers. In some instances the graft (whether limb, eye, or neural crest) is merely inserted into the coelom through a slit in the somatopleure and in other instances the transplant is placed in a more solid (flank) region where it may be incorporated in an otherwise normal organ. These latter transplantations are the more difficult, but possibly the more significant.

The coelom of the 3-day embryo allows freer expansive growth than does the chorioallantois, and it is an ideal nutritive environment. However, the graft may attach itself to any of a number of surfaces within the coelom, such as mesenteries, coelomic epithelium, or the surface of the gonad and mesonephric primordia. Such grafts cannot be properly innervated, and limbs may develop morphologically but without movement. Hamburger and Waugh (1940) found excellent histological differentiation which rapidly regressed without such innervation.

The method of candling, excising the blastoderm, trimming away the yolk and non-essential parts, and the final dissecting out of the organ anlagé are all described (above) and are so well known that they will not be repeated here. The student must be reminded, however, of the increased necessity of absolute aseptic conditions, since transplants are to be introduced directly into the tissues of the (3 day) host.

Limb primordia grafted into the coelom:
1. Under aseptic conditions, expose a 3-day embryo through a shell aperture, and apply a small strip of sterile Neutral Red stained Agar to the flank region, cover the opening of the shell, and return the egg to the incubator for 10 minutes. It is best to rupture the vitelline membrane with #5 watchmaker's forceps so that the dye can penetrate the faster.
2. Under aseptic conditions excise the wing or leg bud (72 hours or older) of another embryo, clean it of all excess yolk and membranes, and place the watchglass containing the donor tissue on a warming plate at 38°C.
3. Prepare the host by opening the shell, adding a drop of sterile chick Ringer's solution, and removing the dyed agar with forceps. Should the blastoderm adhere to the shell or window, shake it gently to separate it from the attachment.
4. If the amnio and chorion have grown over the flank region, insert a (sterile) glass needle into the amnion, parallel with the body, and with an upward (cutting) movement, make a slit in the extra-embryonic membrane directly above the flank region where the graft is to be inserted. The membranes will heal, particularly if there has been no hemorrhage.
5. Make a longitudinal slit posterior to the forelimb bud, just above the entrance of the vitelline veins into the body. Avoid injury to any blood vessels. The posterior cardinal veins lie ventral to the lateral edges of the somites, and the lower splanchnopleure is highly vascular. Make the slit long enough for the insertion of the transplant.
6. Suck the transplant into the end of a micro-pipette and, under good lighting and a dissecting (binocular) microscope with high power objectives, drop the transplant onto the embryo as near the slit as possible. With (sterile) glass needles orient the transplant and insert it into the coelom. It may be further oriented after the insertion, by using a blunter needle. Add a few drops of sterile chick Ringer's.
7. Replace the shell and seal the window with melted paraffin. Return the egg to the incubator in the same position for 24 hours.

8. Allow the host to continue development for about 9 days, and recover the trans-
    plant at about 12 days of incubation of the host. The recovery may be difficult
    since the transplant may be hidden by some of the host tissues, and it may re-
    quire an exploratory dissection of the host.
9. Make drawings, gross and histological analysis of the development of the trans-
    plant.

Limb primorida grafted into the flank: (See Hamburger, 1938, 1939)
1. Follow the preliminary directions of the preceding exercise.
2. Preparation of the transplant: When excising the limb buds leave extensions of
    tissue from both the anterior and the posterior limits of the bud. These will be
    used to tuck the bud into the slit.
3. Preparation of the host: Make a longitudinal slit between the wing and leg bud of
    the 3-day host embryo. The slit should be no longer than the actual bud, and
    should be close to the somites so that during growth it may pick up some of the
    developing muscles. Avoid hemorrhages.
4. Implantation: Drop the bud onto the host embryo in the vicinity of the slit, and
    work the anterior end into the slit by means of a (sterile) glass needle. Then
    work the posterior end into the slit and, finally, using a blunter needle, force
    the bud itself into the slit leaving the bulge of the bud exposed. It may be neces-
    sary to lengthen the slit slightly during this process. The slit will close suffi-
    ciently to hold the bud in place. It must not be allowed to slip into the coelom.
5. Gently transfer the host egg (after sealing, etc.), without jarring, to the incuba-
    tor and leave undisturbed for 48 hours.

Eye primordia grafted into the flank region: (See Gayer, 1942)
1. Prepare hosts of about 60 to 72 hours incubation and donors of about 30 to 36
    hours of incubation. Donor should have from 10 to 12 somites.
2. With Neutral Red or Nile Blue Sulphate agar stain the right wing bud of the host.
3. Quickly dissect out the right optic vesicle of the donor (in sterile, chick Ringer's)
    by making a transverse cut at the level of the infundibulum (just behind the optic
    vesicle) and then a median cut anteriorly. The piece will include the entire right
    side of the prosencephalon. (The left side may be used for a second host.)
4. Make a longitudinal slit at the base of the wing bud of the 72 hour host, at about
    the level of the 20th somite.
5. Drop the excised optic cup onto the host embryo, in a minimum of sterile me-
    dium, and with the tip of a glass needle (not too sharp) tuck the cut surface of
    the brain into the slit. This will leave the optic vesicle exposed at the surface.
6. Since the eye is essentially complete by about 10 days of incubation, the host
    may be sacrificed at that time and the transplant recovered. It should be com-
    pared with the eye at the donor age, the eye of any 10-day incubated embryo,
    and the eye of the hatching chick. The graft may be fixed in Kleinberg's (or
    Bouin's), dehydrated, and cleared in oil of wintergreen for gross study after
    which it may be sectioned.
    (There is no particular point in carrying the host to hatching although this may
    be attempted. If successful it would indicate the achievement of a very delicate
    operation, but generally the eye would be resorbed.)

Interspecific transplantation of neural crests:

The neural crest of vertebrates gives rise, not only to the dorsal root ganglia, and to
the sympathetic system, but also the the pigmented cells known as melanophores, wherever they are found, (see exercise on "Origin of Amphibian Pigment"). Since their ultimate location is often far removed from the neural crest, these cells exhibit extensive
powers of migration and of proliferative capacity. They are found in the skin of amphibia,
the feathers of birds, and in the mesenteries of the body cavity.

Willier and Rawles have successfully transplanted neural crests between bird species which exhibit radically different color patterns, and some which are white. They found that the color pattern, in all cases, was due to the intrinsic genetic factors of the specific melanophores concerned, rather than to the feather structure. There was found to be some slight modification of pigment expression of the melanophores by the host feather germs. (See Willier 1941: Amer. Nat. 75:136 for review.)

If the student has had success with transplantation of limb primordia, he might carry out the following procedure which has as its aim the study of neural crests transplanted from dark to light breeds of fowl.

1. Donors consist of any dark breed (e.g., Brown Leghorn, Barred Rock, New Hampshire Red). They should be from 30 to 48 hours incubated (less than 15 somites) at the time of the excision of the neural crest.
2. Hosts should be about 60 hours incubated. They should be White Leghorns.
3. Under the usual aseptic conditions, make a longitudinal slit in the chorion, the amnion, and finally at the base of the wing bud. Return the covered host to the incubator.
4. With a piece of Nile Blue Stained agar, stain for 10 minutes the head, anterior to the otocyst.
5. Quickly excise the donor embryo from its yolk, remove all yolk, and strip a piece of skin from the dorsal and dorso-lateral surface of the head (where it is stained). The neural crest cells will be adherent to the undersurface of this piece of skin.
6. With pipette and sterile chick Ringer's transfer this neural crest material, to the previously prepared slit at the base of the wing bud of the host. Gently push it deeply into the opening and make certain that it sticks.
7. Seal the window, and incubate the egg (without rotation for 48 hours) for at least two weeks. If development seems normal, allow some hosts to go to hatching.

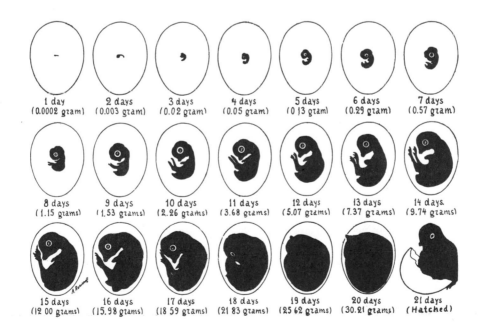

DAILY CHANGES IN THE WEIGHT AND FORM OF THE DEVELOPING CHICK EMBRYO (WHITE LEGHORN)

Reprinted by permission of N. Y. State College of Agriculture
from Bulletin #205, Romanoff, 1931.

REFERENCES

ADAMS, A. E. & V. HIRCHINSON, 1959 - "Growth-retarding effect of reserpine on the chick embryo." Anat. Rec. 134:699-724.

ALEXANDER, L. E., 1937 - "An experimental study of the role of optic cup and overlying ectoderm in lens formation in the chick embryo". Jour. Exp. Zool. 75:41.

BEAUDOIN, A. R. & J. G. WILSON, 1958 - "Teratogenic effect of trypan blue on the developing chick." Proc. Soc. Exp. Biol. & Med. 97:85-90.

BLATTNER, R. J., A. P. WILLIAMSON & L. SIMONSEN, 1958 - "Teratogenic changes in early chick embryos following administration of antitumor agent." Proc. Soc. Exp. Biol. & Med. 97:560-564.

BEVERIDGE, W. I. B., 1947 - "Simplified techniques for inoculating chick embryos and a means of avoiding egg white in vaccines." Science. 106:324.

BOLAND, J., 1954 - "The lethal effects of x-rays on the chick embryo: the mode and time of death and their bearing on the determination of the LD50." Brit. Jour. Radiol. 27:680-687.

BRAYER, F. T., S. R. GLASSER, G. W. CASARETT & J. W. HOWLAND, 1958 - "Indirect effects of x-irradiation on the thyroid of the chick embryo." Univ. Rochester AEC Proj. UR-526, p. 1-17.

CARD, L. E., 1952 - "Poultry Production". 8th ed., Lea & Febriger.

CARPENTER, E., 1942 - "Differentiation of chick embryo thyroids in tissue culture." Jour. Exp. Zool. 89:407.

CARREL, A & L. E. BAKER, 1926 - "The chemical nature of substances required for cell multiplication." Jour. Exp. Med. 44:503.

CATOZONE, O. & P. GRAY, 1941 - "Experiments on chemical interference with the early morphology of the chick." Jour. Exp. Zool. 87L71.

CHAPMAN, A. O. & J. S. LATTA, 1956 - "Abnormalities produced in the chick embryo by radioactive phosphorus." Anat. Rec. 124:452.

COHN, A. E. & A. E. MIRSKI, 1929 - "Physiological ontogeny. A chicken embryo. XIX The hydrogen ion concentration of the blood of chicken embryos as a function of time." Jour. Gen. Physiol. 12:463.

DOSSEL, W. E., 1954 - "New method of intracoelomic grafting." Science. 120:262.

DORRIS, F., 1941 - "The behaviour of chick neural crest in grafts to the chorio-allantoic membrane." Jour. Exp. Zool. 86:205. (see also vols. 78:385 and 80:315).

DuSHANE, G. P., 1944 - "The embryology of vertebrate pigment cells. II. Birds." Quart. Rev. Biol. 19:98.

EASTLICK, H. L., 1943 - "Studies on transplanted limbs of the chick." Jour. Exp. Zool. 93:27.

FELL, H. B. & R. ROBISON, 1929 - "The growth, development and phosphate activity of embryonic avian femora and limb buds cultivated in vitro." Bioch. Jour. 23:767. (see also 24:1905).

FOWLER, I., 1953 - "Responses of the chick neural tube in mechanically produced spina bifida." Jour. Exp. Zool. 123:115.

FRAPES, R. M., M. W. OLSEN & B. H. NEHER, 1942 - "Forced ovulation in normal ovarian follicles in the domestic fowl." Proc. Soc. Exp. Biol. & Med. 50:308.

FUGO, N. W., 1940 - "Effects of hypophysectomy in the chick embryo." Jour. Exp. Zool. 85:271.

GAYER, H. K., 1942 - "A study of coloboma and other abnormalities in transplants of eye primordia from normal and Creeper chick embryos." Jour. Exp. Zool. 89:103.

GLASSER, R. & F. T. BRAYER, 1958 - "Influence of x-irradiation on the thyroid response of 12- and 15- day chick embryos." Rad. Res. 9:119.

GLUECKSOHN-SCHOENHEIMER, S., 1941 - "The development of early mouse embryos in the extra-embryonic coelom of the chick." Science. 93:502.

GOFF, R. A., 1959 - "The acute lethal response of the chick embryo to x-radiation." Jour. Exp. Zool. 141:477-497.

GOODPASTURE, E. W., 1938 - "Some uses of the chick embryo for the study of infection and immunity." Am. Jour. Hyg. 28:111.

GRABOWSKI, C. T., 1960 - "Teratogenic significance of vascular difficulties induced by hypoxia in the chick embryo." Anat. Rec. 136:200.

GREEN, T. W. & J. M. BIRKELAND, 1942 - "Use of the chick embryo in evaluating disinfectants". Proc. Soc. Exp. Biol. & Med. 51:55.

GROBSTEIN, C. & E. ZWILLING, 1953 - "Modification of growth and differentiation of chorio-allantoic grafts of chick blastoderm pieces after cultivation at a glass-clot interface." Jour. Exp. Zool. 122:259.

HAMBURGER, V. C., 1941 - "Transplantation of limb primordia of homozygous and heterozygous chondrodystrophic (Creeper) chick embryos." Physiol. Zool. 14:355.

HAMBURGER, V. & H. HAMILTON, 1951 - "A series of normal stages in the development of the chick embryo." Jour. Morph. 88:49-92.

HAMBURGER, V. & M. WAUGH, 1940 - "The primary development of the skeleton of nerveless and poorly innervated limb transplants of chick embryos." Physiol. Zool. 13:367.

HAMBURGER, V. & E. KEEFE, 1944 - "The effects of peripheral factors on the proliferation and differentiation in the spinal cord of chick embryos." Jour. Exp. Zool. 96:223.

HANKS, J. H., 1948 - "The longevity of chick tissue cultures without renewal of medium." Jour. Cell. Comp. Physiol. 31:

HARRISON, R. G., 1907 - "Observations on the living developing nerve fiber." Proc. Soc. Exp. Biol. & Med. 4:140.

HARRISON, R. G., W. T. ASTBURY & K. M. RUDALL, 1940 - "An attempt at an x-ray analysis of embryonic processes." Jour. Exp. Zool. 85:339.

HETHERINGTON, D. C., 1944 - "Frozen-dried serum as a medium constituent for tissue cultures." Proc. Soc. Exp. Biol. & Med. 57:196.

HILLEMAN, H. H., 1942 - "The design and use of micro-electrodes for the production of lesions in the pituitary rudiment of the chick embryo." Anat. Rec. 84:343.

HOADLEY, L., 1929 - "Differentiation versus cleavage in chorio-allantoic grafts." Arch. f. Ent. Mech. 116:278.

HUMM, Francis D., 1942 - "The growth and migration of cultured melanophores from the neural crest when grafted into the embryo." Jour. Exp. Zool. 90:101.

HUNT, E. A., 1932 - "The differentiation of chick limb buds in chorio-allantoic grafts with special reference to the muscles." Jour. Exp. Zool. 62:57.

HUNT, E. R., 1953 - "Radioiodine uptake during the development of the chick embryo." Anat. Rec. 115:325.

HYMAN, L. H., 1927 - "The metabolic gradients of vertebrate embryos. III. The chick." Biol. Bull. 52:1.

JACOBSON, W., 1938 - "The early development of the avian embryo." Jour. Morph. 62:445.

JACOBSON, P. M. & C. L. COMAR, 1957 - "Autoradiographic studies of the utilization of S-35 sulfate by the chick embryo." Jour. Bioph. & Biochem. Cytology. 3:231-238.

JOY, E. A., 1939 - "Intra-coelomic grafts of eye promordia of the chick." Anat. Rec. 74:461.

JULL, M. A., 1951 - "Poultry Husbandry". 3rd ed. McGraw-Hill Pub. Co.

KARNOFSKY, D. A., 1955 - "The use of the developing chick embryo in pharmacological research." Stanford Med. Bull. 13:247-259.

KEIBEL, F. & K. ABRAHAM, 1900 - "Normentafel zur Entwicklungsgeschichte des Huhnes." G. Fischer, Jena.

KIRBY, D. B., 1927 - "The cultivation of lens epithelium in vitro." Jour. Exp. Med. 45:1009.

KOECKE, H., 1958 - "Normalstadien der Embryonal-Entwicklung bei der Hausente." Embryologie. 4:55.

KOSIN, I. L., 1944 - "Macro- and microscopic methods of detecting fertility in unincubated hen's eggs." Poultry Sci. 23:266. (see also Anat. Rec. 91:245)

KUME, Matozo, 1935 - "The differentiating capacity of various regions of the heart rudiment of the chick as studied in chorio-allantoic grafts." Physiol. Zool. 8:73.

LANDAUER, W., 1951 - "The hatchability of chicken eggs as influenced by environment and heredity." Rev. ed. Storrs Agric. Exp. Sta.

LANDAUER, W. & L. BAUMANN, 1943 - "Rumplessness of chick embryos produced by mechanical of eggs prior to incubation." Jour. Exp. Zool. 93:51.

LILLIE, F. R., 1942 - "On the development of feathers". Biol. Rev. 17:247 (see also Lillie & Wang, 1944, Physiol. Zool. 17:1)

LILLIE, F. R., 1952 - "Development of the chick." Revised ed. by H. Hamilton, Henry Holt, N. Y.

LOKEN, M. K., A. A. BEISANG, D. G. MOSSER & J. F. MARVIN, 1959 - "Some effects of roentgen rays (220 KVP) and gamma rays (Cobalt-60) on chicken eggs." Atompraxis. 12:469-472.

MEYER, H., 1936 - "Zuchtung du Retina des Huhnes in vitro." Zeitschr. f. Mikroskop. Anat. Forsch. 39:151.

MOOG, F., 1944 - "Localization of alkaline and acid phosphatases in the early embryogenesis of the chick." Biol. Bull. 86:51.

MORGAN, V. F. & D. R. CHICHESTER, 1935 - "Properties of the blood of the domestic fowl." Jour. Biol. Chem. 110:285.

NEHER, B. H. & R. M. FRAPS, 1946 - "Fertility and hatchability of the prematurely ovulated hen's egg." Jour. Exp. Zool. 101:83.

NICHOLAS, J. S. & D. RUDNICK, 1933 - "The development of embryonic rat tissues upon the chick chorio-allantois." Jour. Exp. Zool. 66:193.

OLSEN, M. W., 1942 - "Maturation, fertilization, and early cleavage in the hen's egg." Jour. Morph. 70:513.

OLSEN, M. W. & S. J. MARSDEN, 1954 - "Natural parthenogenesis in turkey eggs." Science. 120:545-546.

PASTEELS, J., 1937 - "Etudes sur la gastrulation des Vertebres Mesoblastiques." Arch. de Biol. 48:382.

PATTEN, B. M., 1951 - "The first heart beats and the beginning of embryonic circulation." Am. Naturalist. 39:225-243.

PHILIPS, F. S., 1942 - "Comparison of the respiratory rates of different regions of the chick blastoderm during early stages of development." Jour. Exp. Zool. 90:83.

PICKELS, E. G., 1942 - "Apparatus for rapid, sterile removal of chick embryos from eggs." Proc. Soc. Exp. Biol. & Med. 50:224.

PRICE, J. W. & E. V. FOWLER, 1940 - "Egg shell cap method of incubating chick embryos." Science. 91:271

RAWLES, M. E., 1936 - "A study of the localization of the organ-forming areas in the chick blastoderm of the head-process stage." Jour. Exp. Zool. 72:217.

RAWLES, M. E., 1943 - "The heart forming areas of the early chick blastoderm." Physiol. Zool. 16:22 (see also 18:1, 1946).

RAWLES, M. E., 1952 - "Transplantation of normal embryonic tissues." in "The Chick Embryo in Biological Research". Abb. N. Y. Acad. Sci. 55:302.

REYES-BRION, M., 1956 - "La sensibilite differentielle de certaines ebauches de l'embryon de poulet aux rayons x, a differents stades du developpement. Arch. Anat. Mik. et Morph. Exp. 45:342.

ROMANOFF, A. L., 1943 - "Cultivation of the early chick embryo in vitro." Anat. Rec. 87:365.

ROMANOFF, A. L., 1945 - "Hydrogen-ion concentration of albumen and yolk of the developing avian egg." Biol. Bull. 87:223.

ROMANOFF, A. L., G. BUMP & E. HOLM, 1938 - "Artificial incubation of some upland game bird eggs." Bull. #2, N. Y. State Conserv. Dep't.

RUDNICK, D., 1938 - "Differentiation in culture of pieces of early chick blastoderm." Jour. Exp. Zool. 79:399.

RUDNICK, D., 1944 - "Early history and mechanics of the chick blastoderm - a review." Quart. Rev. Biol. 19:187.

RUDNICK, D., 1948 - "Prospective areas and differentiation potencies in the chick blastoderm." Ann. N. Y. Acad. Sci. 49:761.

RUDNICK, D., 1955 - "Teleosts and Birds." in Willier, Weiss, and Hamburger (eds.) "Analysis of Development." Saunders.

SALZBERGER, B., 1955 - "Modification observees dans les organs genitaux de l'embryon de Poulet in vitro, apres traitement par diverantes substances teratogenes." C. r. Soc. Biol. 149:190-192.

SALZBERGER, B., 1957 - "Influence de facteurs teratogenes sur l'evolution des organes sexuelles de l'embryon de Poulet". Bull. Biol. de France et de Belgique. 91:354-438.

SANDSTROM, C. J., 1940 - "Heteroplastic transplantation and species specificity." Biol. Bull. 79:329.

SANDVIK, O., 1958 - "The effect of chronic gamma radiation on the hatchability of chicken eggs." Hereditas Gen. Ark. 44:348-406.

SAUER, M. E., 1960 - "Radiation injury resulting from nuclear labelling with thymidine-H^3 in the chick embryo." Anat. Rec. 136:272.

SCHECHTMANN, A. M., 1947 - "Antigens of early developmental stages of the chick." Jour. Exp. Zool. 105:329.

SCHMIDT, G., 1937 - "On the growth stimulating effect of egg white and its importance for embryonic development." Enzymologia. 4:40.

SCHNELLER, M. B., 1951 - "The mode of action of hard x-rays on the 33- and 60-hour chick embryo." Jour. Morph. 89:367-396.

SMITH, A. H., T. J. HAGE, L. M. JULIAN & D. M. REDMOND, 1955 - "The effect of x-irradiation of the oviduct on egg production and egg quality in the fowl." Poultry Science. 35:539.

SPRATT, N. T., 1947 - "A simple method for explanting and cultivating early chick embryos in vitro." Science. 106:452.

SPRATT, N. T., 1948 - "Development of the early chick blastoderm on synthetic media." Jour. Exp. Zool. 107:39. (see ibid. 114:375)

SPRATT, N. T., 1957 - "Analysis of the organizer center in the early chick embryo." Jour. Exp. Zool. 134:577.

SPRATT, N. T. & H. HAAS, 1960 - "Morphogenetic movements in the unincubated chick blastoderm." Anat. Rec. 137:394 (abs.)

STEARNER, S. P. et al 1960 - "Modes of radiation death in the chick embryo." Rad. Res. 12:286-300.

STILES, K. A. & R. W. WATTERSON, 1938 - "The effects of jarring upon the embryogeny of chick embryos." Anat. Rec. 70:7.

STILWELL, E. F., 1947 - "The influence of temperature variation upon the occurrence of multipolar mitoses in embryonic cells grown in vitro." Anat. Rec. 99:

STRANGEWAYS, T. S. P. & H. B. FELL, 1926 - "Experimental studies on differentiation of embryonic tissues growing in vivo or in vitro." Proc. Roy. Soc. 100:273 (see also 102:9, 1927)

SWEZY, O., 1915 - "Egg albumen as a culture medium for chick tissues." Biol. Bull. 28:47.

TAYLOR, R. M. & R. J. CHIALVO, 1942 - "Simplified technique for inoculating into amniotic sac of chick embryos." Proc. Soc. Exp. Biol. & Med. 51:328.

TERASKI, P. I. & J. A. CANNON, 1957 - "A technic for cross-transfusion of blood in embryonic chicks and its effect on hatchability." Proc. Soc. Exp. Biol. & Med. 94:103-107.

TOMPKINS, E. R., B. B. CUNNINGHAM & P. L. KIRK, 1947 - "Mitosis, cell size and growth in culture of embryonic chick heart." Jour. Cell. & Comp. Physiol. 30:

VOGEL, H. H. & D. L. JORDAN, 1959 - "The relative biological effectiveness of Co^{60} gamma rays and fission neutrons: Lethal effects on the 4-day chick embryo." Rad. Res. 11:667-683.

VOLLMER, H., 1935 - "Eine Methode zur beobachtung der Entwicklung des Huhn-embryo in vitro." Ztschr. Zellforsch. mikr. Anat. 23:566.

WADDINGTON, C. H., 1932 - "Experiments on the development of chick and duck embryos, cultivated in vitro." Phil. Trans. Roy. Soc. London B. 221-:179.

WADDINGTON, C. H., 1952 - "The epigenetics of birds." Cambridge Un. Press.

WATERMAN, A. J., 1944 - "Viability of embryonic chick tissues following storage at low temperatures." Growth. 8:205.

WEISS, P., 1944 - "In vitro transformation of spindle cells of neural origin into macrophages." Anat. Rec. 88:205.

WEISS, P. & R. AMPRINO, 1940 - "The effect of mechanical stress on the differentiation of scleral cartilage in vitro and in the embryo." Growth. 4:245.

WETZEL, P., 1925 - "Untersuchungen zum Huhnerkeim. Arch. f. Ent. Mech. 106:463 (sell also 119:118, 1929 and Ergebn. d. Anat. u. Entwick. 29:1)

WHITE, P. R., 1946 - "Cultivation of animal tissues in vitro in nutrients of precisely known constitution." Growth. 10:231.

WILLIER, B. H., 1942 - "The control of hair and feather pigmentation as revealed by grafting melanophores in the embryo." Annals of Surgery. 116:598.

WILLIER, B. H. & M. E. RAWLES, 1931 - "The relation of Hensen's node to differentiating capacity of whole chick blastoderms as studied in chorio-allantoic grafts." Jour. Exp. Zool. 59:429 (see also Genetics. 1944, 29:309).

WOLFF, E., M. KIENY & M. SCHUE, 1958 - "Sur la variabilite du perone de l'embryon de poulet demonstree par les irradiations aux rayons x". Compt. rendu. Soc. Biol. 152:1459.

WRIGHT, G. P., 1926 - "Presence of a growth-stimulating substance in the yolk of incubated hen's eggs." Proc. Soc. Exp. Biol. & Med. 23:603.

ZWILLING, E., 1945 - "Production of tail abnormalities in chick embryos by transecting the body during the latter part of the second day of incubation." Jour. Exp. Zool. 98:237.

ZWILLING, E., 1959 - "A modified chorio-allantoic grafting procedure." Transplantation Bull. 6:115.

V. EXPERIMENTAL MAMMALIAN EMBRYOLOGY

Suggested Procedures for Obtaining and Experimenting with the Mouse Embryo

PURPOSE: To introduce the student to a mammalian embryo which can be used easily in laboratory xperimentation.

MATERIALS: The mouse. Any strain or species of mouse which is adjusted to laboratory conditions may be used. Some are more viable than others, some more fertile (larger and more frequent litters), and some have low levels of intra-uterine death, resorption and anomaly development. A white Swiss strain is, in general, very satisfactory. *

   Cage: There are various types from wood, to plastic, to stainless steel. Satisfactory size is 7 x 10 x 6.5 inches, with removable cover and built-in food hopper and holder for water bottle. There should be a holder for the record card, with 1/2 inch lip. The capacity of such a box is 5 to 7 adult mice, or two litters for the first two weeks. (See illustration)

   Food: Various rat, dog, and mouse chows can be used, supplemented when there are litters with coarse oatmeal. These foods are generally well balanced, with vitamins, etc. added.

   Water: This must be continuously available from an inverted bottle having a glass or stainless steel tube from which the water will not run by itself. The outlet should be checked because the lack of water can cause anorexia and death.

   Temperature: Should be near 72° F., but tolerance is wide.

   Antiseptics and diseases: Rodents are susceptible to certain diseases which may ruin a research project. However, caution as to source of animals, brief quarantine, and prophyllaxis should be adequate to keep epidemics under control. For ringworm use iodine or mercurochrome painted on, or specific powder; for mites, bedbugs, lice, etc., any powder insecticide that is nontoxic to mammals, or brief dipping in 1% carbolic acid; for mouse typhoid (showing diarrhea, anorexia, death) there is no known cure, but it can probably be prevented by adding 1% tetracyclene or terramycin to the drinking water for a two-week period, and occasionally thereafter. Food treated by soaking in an antibiotic, and drying in forced draft, is good for newborn and weanling rodents. There are vaccines which may prevent the disease. Ringworm is almost universally prevalent but rather innocuous.

METHOD: The mammal (except primates) will mate only when mature eggs are available and could be fertilized. That is, the female will not accept the male except at estrous. The mouse has a 5 to 5.5 day estrous cycle and estrous seems to occur most frequently at night (see papers by Austin and by Braden). A laborious but fruitful procedure is to examine mice by the vaginal smear method, segregating those in estrus or pro-estrus for immediate mating. Matings may be observed to get exact timing of conception but it is possible to estimate this time within a few hours, as follows:

   1. Place sexually mature male with 5 or 6 mature females at 5 P.M. (Mice should be 3 or more months of age).
   2. Remove male at 9 A.M. the next morning.
   3. Examine each female for the presence of a vaginal plug. This consists of secretions from the vesicular and coagulating glands of the male and appears as a white coagulum blocking the vaginal orifice. (See illustration) A double

---

* Mice can be obtained from Carworth Farms, New City, N.Y., Roscoe B. Jackson Memorial Laboratory, Bar Harbor, Maine. (Normal and tumor-bearing strains) and Texas Inbred Mice Company, R.F.D. #7, Box 1232-C, Houston 21, Texas.

check may be made (until one has had experience in identifying the plug) by means of a vaginal smear. This is done by inserting a few drops of physiological saline into the vagina with tapered pipette tip, sucking it out and examining it for spermatozoa. The females with plugs (or sperm) should be segregated and labelled for time of mating.

4. To calculate the time of conception: Since this can occur at any time that the sexes are together, but under the above conditions is limited to from 5 P.M. until 9 A.M., and is most likely to occur around midnight, the range of error is, at most, a matter of a few hours. Thus, with some variability most evident only during the earliest development, females with vaginal plugs at 9 A.M. may be labelled as 0.5 day pregnant. The mating period for any female is short, and occurs every 5 days, so that one could hardly expect more than 10% successful copulations under the above conditions. Thus, to obtain 10 simultaneous matings one would have to expose over 100 females simultaneously to an adequate number of males. On five successive night matings with the same males and females, one often finds certain nights most productive.

At stated times after conception, embryonic material may be observed in the following manner: Kill the female by cervical dislocation. This is done by grasping the neck just behind the head with thumb and forefinger of one hand, and quickly pulling (jerk) on the tail with the other hand. This is the most quick and considerate method of killing a mouse. The bicornuate uterus and attached ovaries may be quickly dissected out, with minimum handling, and placed upon a piece of white filing card to which it will stick. Immerse in Bouin's (or other fixative) after labelling the card in pencil as to exactly what stage of development (and experimental condition) is involved. After several hours gently remove the fixed uteri from the card, but leave in Bouin's for 24-48 hours. Later stages of development will require longer fixation. Embryos older than 9.5 days should be exposed by opening the uterus and piercing the membranes to allow penetration of the fixative. (See Rugh's revised edition 1961: "Laboratory Manual of Vertebrate Embryology" for the normal embryonic stages of the mouse. See also Austin & Smiles 1948: Jour. Roy. Micr. Soc. 68:13). It is also possible to flush eggs and/or early embryos from the oviducts or uteri, prior to implantation at 4.5 days, and observe them in physiological saline in toto.

GENERAL OUTLINE OF DEVELOPMENTAL STAGES OF THE MOUSE:*

1. Fertilization in upper oviduct, generally monospermic.
2. First cleavage at 24 hours, in upper oviduct.
3. Second cleavage at 36 hours, in upper oviduct. Holoblastic.
4. Sixteen cell morula at 2.5 days, free in uterus.
5. Blastula stage (32+ cells) at 3.5 days, free in uterus.
6. Implantation stage at 4.5 days, spaced in uteri.
7. Germ cell layers differentiated at 4.5 to 5.0 days.
8. Egg cylinder stage at 6 to 6.5 days.
9. Embryonic and extra-embryonic regions distinguished at 7.0 to 8.0 days. Head process, primitive streak, mesodermal cavities, active neurogenesis, extra-embryonic membranes including amnion which extends over the entire dorsal surface, and the first definitive somites appear. Embryo early "C" shape.
10. Heart formed and circulation starts at 9.0 days. Tissue differentiation active, as in all mammalian embryos.

Artificial insemination as well as the transplantation of fertile and non-fertile ova is possible in the mouse (see McLaren & Biggers '58) for specific research purposes.

---

* Rat data are so close to the mouse that substitution is possible, except that more space, food and water per animal are required.

Under natural conditions the mammalian embryo is not readily accessible and cannot be observed during development, and allow it to survive more than a few hours as can be done with the frog and chick. Experiments with the mammalian embryo must therefore be conducted somewhat differently. A few suggestions follow:

1. <u>Cell Dissociation and Tissue Culture</u>: The mouse embryo is excellent material for such studies (see Ex. 28, 29). The 9-day embryo has a diameter of about 1 millimeter, can be easily dissected out, and is as sterile as possible until contaminated by the operator, the air or instruments. Later stages would have further development of certain organ systems.

2. <u>Dietary Effects</u>: It is a simple matter to regulate the food intake of the pregnant mouse, either with respect to quantity or quality. Vitamin imbalance will cause drastic effects at certain stages of development, and deprivation of essential minerals can affect both mother and litter members.

3. <u>Chemical Effects</u>: Certain drugs are highly toxic, such as trypan blue, insulin, etc., and will alter development in the embryo and/or fetus without killing (in low doses). Any endocrine imbalance has dramatic effects. Try CO_2 and O_2 shifting.

4. <u>Traumatic Effects</u>: While the mammalian embryo is cushioned, and efficiently protected, there is evidence that moderate handling of the pregnant mouse at certain stages of gestation will result in drastic effects on the embryos. Electric shock, ultra-sonic vibration, etc. have not been fully investigated, and may well cause congenital anomalies.

5. <u>X-Irradiation</u>: Most Colleges and Universities have available adequate x-ray equipment for such studies. X-rays have the advantage of being highly penetrating, and highly damaging to the early embryo without concomitant damage to the mother. It is suggested that mice at 8.5 to 9.0 days gestation be exposed to 150 r whole body x-rays (dose at level of gravid uterus) and examined by Caeserian section at 18.5 days for congenital anomalies which are invariably present.

6. <u>Genetic Effects</u>: The literature on mouse genetics is accumulating rapidly, and fertility between divergent strains is generally so good that the study of lethal genes that kill before birth comes within the scope of this book.

EXPERIMENTAL DATA:

The variety of effects of experimental procedures on the mammalian embryo ranges from unrecognized but nevertheless demonstrable anomalies (heart or kidneys), through gross anomalies (brain hernias, anencephalies, malformations of either end) to fetal deaths, early embryonic deaths and resorptions, to failure even to divide or implant. Thus, it is generally necessary to examine the fetuses prior to the time of expected delivery. This is because in the mouse, contrary to other (and possibly less wise) mammals, the female usually kills and devours its abnormal offspring at birth. The pregnant mouse at 18.5 days may have its cervical vertebrae dislocated (see above) and the uteri opened quickly. If the fetuses are placed in warm saline they will be active for some time.

In every instance it is necessary to simultaneously dissect control mice and compare litter members with those experimentally treated. This is because size variations (stunting) will not otherwise be recognized. Further, some strains of mice are genetically predisposed to develop certain anomalies such as eye defects, overlapping teeth, etc. more than do other strains. In quantitative experiments, no less than 100 offspring for each set of categories should be examined, in addition to controls.

RESULTS:

The results of any mammalian embryo experiment may be statistical (weight, sex, size differences) and can well be illustrated by compilation of data and by photographs. It may

be <u>qualitative</u>, requiring histological and even cytological techniques. It should be remembered than even with highly penetrating and uniform x-irradiation, there are variations in response within a litter (which contains genetically different individuals) so that
spot testing of litter members may not be scientifically adequate. Congenital anomalies
of gross dimensions may be seen at 18.5 days gestation by sacrificing the pregnant
mouse and dissecting out the fetuses. Anomalous mice are usually destroyed at birth
by the mother.

The mammalian embryo is almost an unexplored field for experimentation. This exercise is added to stimulate interest and investigation in a field which the author is certain
will become very active in the immediate future.

REFERENCES

ALDEN, R. H., 1954 - "A laboratory atlas of the mouse embryo." Div. Anatomy, Univ. Tennessee Med. Unit.
ALFERT, M., 1950 - "A cytochemical study of oögenesis and cleavage in the mouse." Jour. Cell. Comp. Physiol. 36:381.
ALLEN, E., 1922 - "The oestrous cycle in the mouse." Am. J. Anat. 30:297-371.
ALLEN, E. & E. C. CAMPBELL, 1940 - "Variation in mouse embryos of 8 days gestation." Anat. Rec. 77:165-173.
AUERBACH, R., 1955 - "The development of x-ray induced spina bifida in the mouse." Anat. Rec. 121:258.
AUSTIN, C. R., 1955 - "Polyspermy after induced hyperthemia in rats." Nature. 175:1038.
AUSTIN, C. R., 1956 - "Ovulation fertilization, and early cleavage in the hamster." F. R. Micr. Soc. 75:141-154.
AUSTIN, C. R., 1956 - "Effect of hypothermia and hyperthermia on fertilization in rat eggs." Jour. Exp. Biol. 33:348-358.
AUSTIN, C. R. & A. W. N. BRADEN, 1956 - "Early reactions of the rodent egg to spermatozoon penetration." Jour. Exp. Biol.
    33:358-365.
BAXTER, H. & F. C. FRASER, 1950 - "The production of congenital defects in the offspring of female mice treated with cor-
    tisone." McGill Med. Jour. 19:245-249.
BEAUDOIN, A. R., 1959 - "Chemical interference with the teratogenicity of trypan blue." Anat. Rec. 133:249.
BECK, F. & J. S. BASTER, 1960 - "The effect of trypan blue on rat embryos." Anat. Rec. 136:161.
BLANDAU, R. J. & W. C. YOUNG, 1939 - "The effects of delayed fertilization on the development of the guinea pig ovum."
    Am. J. Anat. 64:303-320.
BLANDAU, R. J., 1952 - "The female factor in fertility and infertility. 1. Effects of delayed fertilization on the development
    of the pronuclei in the rat ova." Fertility and Sterility. 3:349.
BOYER, C. C., 1953 - "Chronology of development for the golden hamster." Jour. Morph. 92:1.
BRADEN, A. W. H. & C. R. AUSTIN, 1954 - "The fertile life of the mouse and rat eggs." Science. 120:610.
BRADEN, A. W. H., 1957 - "The relationship between the diurnal light cycle and the time of ovulation in mice." Jour. Exp.
    Biol. 34:177-186.
BRADEN, A. W. H. & C. R. AUSTIN, 1954 - "Fertilization of the mouse egg and the effect of delayed coitus and of hot-shock
    treatment." Australian Jour. Biol. Sci. 7:552-565.
BRAMBELL, F. W. Rogers, 1948 - "Prenatal mortality in mammals." Biol. Rev. 23:370-407.
CARPENTER, E., 1958 - "Uptake of I^{131} by fetal rat thyroids." Anat. Rec. 132:420.
CARTER T. C., 1959 - "Embryology of the Little & Bragg x-rayed mouse stock". Jour. Genetics. 56:401-435.
CHASE, H. & E. CHASE, 1941 - "Studies on an anophthalmic strain of mice. I. Embryology of the eye region." Jour. Morph.
    68:279-301.
COHLAN, S. Q., 1959 - "The effect of endocrines on the teratogenicity of excess vitamin A." Third. Teratology Conf., Port-
    land, Oregon.
DEGENHARDT, K. H. & H. J. GRUTER, 1959 - "Radioinduced development disturbances in rabbit embryos." Z. Naturforsch.
    14b:753-761.
FEKETE, E., 1940 - "Observations on three functional tests in a high-tumor and low-tumor strain of mice." J. Cancer. 38:234-238.
FEKETE, E., O. BARTHOLOMEW & G. D. SNELL, 1940 - "A technique for the preparation of sections of early mouse embryos."
    Anat. Rec. 76:441-447.
FERM, V. H., 1959 - "Relative effect of teratogenic and non-teratogenic dyes on adrenal weight." Anat. Rec. 133:379.
FISH, M. I., 1960 - "The erythropoietic function of 10 to 15-day mouse embryonic liver." Anat. Rec. 136:193.
FISCHBERG, M. & R. A. BEATTY, 1952 - "Heteroploidy in mammals. II. Induction of triploidy in pre-implantation mouse
    eggs." Jour. Genetics. 50:455-470.
FRASER, A. S. & R. J. HALL, 1958 - "Effects of x-irradiation on foetal development." Austral. J. Biol. Sci. 2:425-433.
FRASER, F. C. & T. D. FAINSTAT, 1951 - "The causes of congenital defects: A review." Am. J. Dis. Childhood. 82:593-613.
FRIEBERG, U. & N. R. RINGERTZ, 1956 - "An autoradiographic study of the uptake of radiosulphate in the rat embryo." J. Emb.
    Exp. Morph. 4:313-325.
GATES, A., 1956 - "Viability and developmental capacity of eggs from immature mice treated with gonadotrophins." Nature.
    177:754-755.
GIROUD, A., H. GOWNELLE & M. MARTINET, 1956 - "Concentration de la vitamin A chez la mere et le foetus au cours de la
    teratogenese par hyper-vitaminose A." Compt. rendu. Soc. Biol. 150:2064.

GLUECKSOHN-WAELSCH, S., 1953 - "Lethal factors in development." Quart. Rev. Biol. 28:115-135.

GREENMAN, M. & F. L. DUHRING, 1933 - "Breeding and care of the albino rat for research purposes." Wistar Institute for Anatomy, Philadelphia.

GRUNBERG, H., 1939 - "Fertility in cross-bred mice." Jour. Hered. 30:83-84.

HALL, E. K., 1960 - "Potassium effects on the embryonic rat hearts: rate determinations and EGG studies." Anat. Rec. 136:205.

HAMBURGH, M., 1952 - "Malformations in mouse embryos induced by trypan blue." Nature. 169:27.

HESS, A., 1957 - "The experimental embryology of the foetal nervous system." Biol. Rev. 32:231-260.

HICKS, S. P., 1958 - "Radiation as an experimental tool in mammalian developmental neurology." Phys. Rev. 38:337-356.

INGALLS, T. H., F. J. CURLEY & R. A. PRINDLE, 1950 - "Anoxia as a cause of fetal death and congenital defect in the mouse." Am. J. Dis. Children. 80:34.

JACOBSON, A. G. & R. L. BRENT, 1959 - "Radioiodine concentration by the fetal mouse thyroid." Endocrin. 65:408-416.

JOHNSON, E. M. & M. M. NELSON, 1959 - "Comparative effects of 9-methyl-PGA- and X-methyl-PGA on embryonic development in the rat." Third Teratology Conf., Portland, Oregon.

KALTER, H., 1960 - "Teratogenic action of a hypocaloric diet and small doses of cortisone." Proc. Soc. Exp. Biol. & Med. 104:518-520.

KILE, J. C., 1951 - "An improved method for the artificial insemination of mice." Anat. Rec. 109:109-117.

LEVINSON, B., 1952 - "Effects of fetal irradiation on learning." J. Comp. Physiol. & Psychol. 45:140-145.

LEWIS, W. H. & E. S. WRIGHT, 1935 - "On the early development of the mouse egg." Carnegie Inst. Washington Pub. #459:113-144.

LOFSTRAM, J. E., 1957 - "Studies on the effects of maternally administered phosphorus-32 on fetal and post-natal development of the rat." AECU-3891.

LOGAN, W. P. D., 1951 - "Incidence of congenital malformations and their relation to virus infections during pregnancy." Brit. Med. Jour. Sept. 15, p. 641-645.

MAGNUSSON, G., 1955 - "Studies on the uptake of Fe^{59} in rat embryo, placenta, uterus, and mammary gland." Acta. Radiol. 43:227-232.

McLAREN, A. & J. D. BIGGERS, 1958 - "Successful development and birth of mice cultivated in vitro as early embryos." Nature. 182:877-878.

MERTON, H., 1938 - "Studies on reproduction in the albino mouse." Proc. Roy. Soc. Edin. 58:80-96.

MARKERT, C. L., 1959 - "Biochemical embryology and genetics." Nat. Cancer Inst. Monogr. #2.

MARTIN, D. L., 1959 - "Self-regulation in living systems." Nature. 183:370.

MURAKAMI, U. & Y. KAMEYAMA, 1958 - "Effects of low-dose x-radiation on the mouse embryo." Am. J. Dis. Child. 96:272-277.

NELSON, M. M., R. M. CHRISTY, H. V. WRIGHT & J. W. MONIE, 1959 - "Abnormalities in ocular development resulting from maternal pteroylglutamic acid deficiency beginning on the 11th day of gestation." Third Teratology Conf., Portland, Oregon.

NICHOLAS, J. S., 1935 - "The normal stages in the development of the rat." Photostatic volume at Osborn Zool. Lab., Yale Univ.

NICHOLAS, J. S. & D. RUDNICK, 1938 - "Development of rat embryos of egg-cylinder to head-fold stages in plasma cultures." Jour. Exp. Zool. 78:205-232.

OTIS. E. M. & R. BRENT, 1952 - "Equivalent stages in mouse and human embryos." UR-194.

PATTEN, B. M., 1957 - "Varying developmental mechanisms in teratology." Pediatrics. 19:734-748.

BINCUS, G., 1936 - "The egg of mammals." Macmillan Co., N.Y.

PINSKY, L. & F. C. FRASER, 1959 - "Production of skeletal malformations in the offspring of pregnant mice treated with 6-amonoicotinamide." Biol. Neonatorum. 1:106-112.

POTTER, R. G., 1958 - "Artificial insemination by donors." Fert. & Sterility. 9:37-53.

PURDY, D. M. & H. HILLEMANN, 1950 - "Prenatal growth in the golden hamster." Anat. Rec. 106:591-598.

ROTHSCHILD, Lord, 1956 - "Fertilization". London, Metheyn & Co.

RUGH, R., 1959 - "Vertebrate embryology-radiobiology". Ann. Rev. Nuclear Sci. 9:493-522. (See ibid. 1953, Vol. 3:271-302)

RUGH, R. & E. GRUPP, 1959 - "Response of the early mouse embryo to low levels of ionizing radiations." Jour. Exp. Zool. 141:571-587.

RUGH, R., 1959 - "Ionizing radiations: Their possible relation to the etiology of some congenital anomalies and human disorders." Military Med. 124:401-416.

RUGH, R., 1961 - "Radiobiological Techniques". Chap. in "Encyclopedia of Medical Radiology". Eds. Lund, Strand, Vieten, and Zuppinger (Bern). Pub. Springer-Verlag.

RUNNER, M. N., 1959 - "Embryocidal effect of handling pregnant mice and its prevention with progesterone." Anat. Rec. 133:330.

RUNNER, M. N., 1959 - "Metabolic mechanisms of teratogenic agents during morphogenesis." Nat. Cancer Inst. Mon. #2.

RUSSELL, L. B., 1956 - "X-ray induced developmental abnormalities in the mouse and their use in analysis of embryological patterns." Jour. Exp. Zool. 131:329-395.

SALEM, A. J. & R. M. HOAR, 1960 - "The teratogenic effects of trypan blue in guinea pigs." Anat. Rec. 136:270.

SCOTT, J. P., 1937 - "The embryology of the guinea pig." Am. J. Anat. 60:397-432.

SIKOV, M. & T. NOONAN, 1959 - "Anomalous development induced in the embryonic rat by the maternal administration of radiophosphorus." Am. J. Anat. 103:137-161.

SMITHBERG, M., 1960 - "Teratogenic effects of some hypoglycemic agents in mice." Anat. Rec. 136:280.

SNELL, G. D. & F. B. AMES, 1939 - "Hereditary changes in the descendants of female mice exposed to Roentgen rays." Am. J. Roent. Rad. Ther. 61:248-255.

SNELL, G. D., 1941 - "Biology of the laboratory mouse." Dover Pub., N.Y.   (Rep. McGraw Hill Book Co., N.Y.)

SNELL, G. D., E. FEKETE, K. P. HUMMEL & L. W. LAW, 1940 - "Relation of mating, ovulation, and the oestrous smear in the house mouse to the time of day." Anat. Rec. 76:39-54.

SNELL, G. D., K. P. HUMMEL & W. H. ABELMANN, 1944 - "A technique for the artificial insemination of the mouse." Anat. Rec. 90:243-253.

TUCHMANN-DUPLESSIS, PAROT & MERCIER, 1956 - "Role des facteurs externes dans la production des anomalies." Gazette des Hopitaux. 12:511.

VENABLE, J. H., 1946 - "Pre-implantation stages in the golden hamster." Anat. Rec. 94:105-120.

WEI, Cheng, D., 1959 - "Factors affecting teratogeny due to maternal vita, in E. deficiency." Third Teratology Conf., Portland, Oregon.

WESLEY, J. P., 1960 - "Background radiation as the cause of fatal congenital malformations." Int. J. Radiation Biol. 2:97-118.

WILSON, J. G., 1958 - "Time of teratogenic action of trypan blue in the rat." Anat. Rec. 130:388.

"Standard Nomenclature for Inbred Strains of Mice." 1952, Cancer Research - by Committee on Standardized Nomenclature for Inbred Strains of Mice.

THE MOUSE EMBRYO: 0.5 TO 2.5 DAYS POST—CONCEPTION

Fig. 1 - Female mouse at 9 A.M. after previous night of mating opportunity showing presence of vaginal plug, certain indication of mating.

Fig. 2 - Contents of bicornuate uterus after copulation showing abudant viscous coagulum containing abundant spermatozoa.

Fig. 3 - Sperm entrance into the egg cortex, showing dissolution of the cortex at point of invasion. Note protruding sperm tail.

Fig. 4 - Contents of sperm head, without tail, being reorganized within the egg cytoplasm.

Fig. 5 - Early stage in polar body formation. Note chromosomes.

Fig. 6 - Polar body now separate from egg cytoplasm, with distinct nucleus and small amount of cytoplasm.

Fig. 7 - Extruded polar body quite distinct from the egg.

Fig. 8 - Large post-maturational female germinal vesicle (nucleus).

Fig. 9 - Same as fig. 8 but stained heavily to show cell membrane and rather granular cytoplasm.

Fig. 10 - Two pronuclei as they are approaching each other, female (larger) on the left and male (smaller) on the right.

Fig. 11 - Approximation of the two pronuclei, female the larger.

Fig. 12 - Upper oviduct 0.5 day after conception showing four eggs close together.

Fig. 13 - Fertilization complete in that polar body is extruded and the two pronuclei are approaching each other. Male pronucleus appears to swell slightly.

Fig. 14 - Both polar bodies show, but pronuclei are unstained.

Fig. 15 - Two cell stage at 1.5 days after conception, also showing polar body.

Fig. 16 - Upper oviduct containing three embryos as seen also in

Fig. 17 - Enlarged view showing two two-cell stages, and a single cell with prominent polar body.

Fig. 18 - Four cell stage.

Fig. 19 - Four plus cells, showing persistent polar body, at 2.5 days.

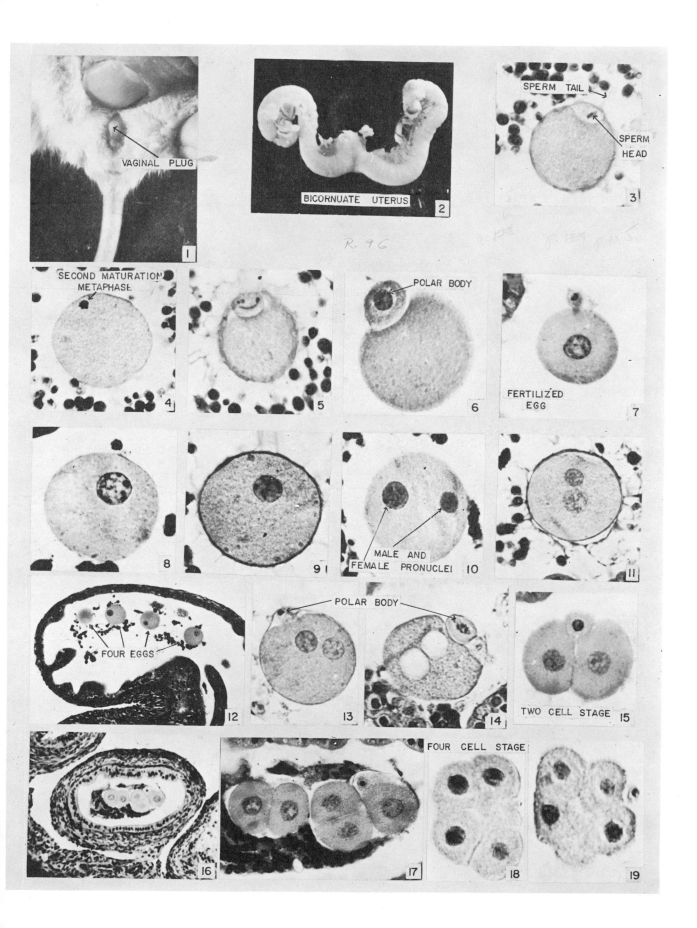

THE MOUSE EMBRYO: 3.5 TO 5.5 DAYS POST—CONCEPTION

Fig. 20 - Longitudinal section of gravid uterus at 3.5 days after conception, showing three blastulae in suspension within the uterine cavity.

Fig. 21 - Enlarged view of portion of figure 20.

Fig. 22 - Slightly later stage when the blastula is "trapped" within a uterine crypt, prior to implantation.

Fig. 23 - Embryo at 3.5 days showing cell structure. Pre-implanted blastula.

Fig. 24 - Inner cell mass, trophectoderm, and blastocoel easily identified.

Fig. 25 - Blastula at about 4 days showing embryonic and extra-embryonic ectoderm, proximal and distal endoderm, and blastocoel (yolk cavity).

Fig. 26 - Blastula at the moment of adhesion to the uterine epithelium, low power.

Fig. 27 - Same as fig. but at high magnification.

Fig. 28 - Active implantation processes have begun, at 4.5 days.

Fig. 29 - Embryo at 5.5 days showing little change in the surrounding uterus.

Fig. 30 - Enlargement of the embryo to distinguish between the inner solid embryonic ectoderm and the outer thin layer of proximal endoderm.

Fig. 31 - Separation of the first two primary germ layer.

Fig. 32 - Separation of distal and proximal endodermal layers, with a central core of solid ectoderm. Note early dissolution of contiguous uterine epithelium.

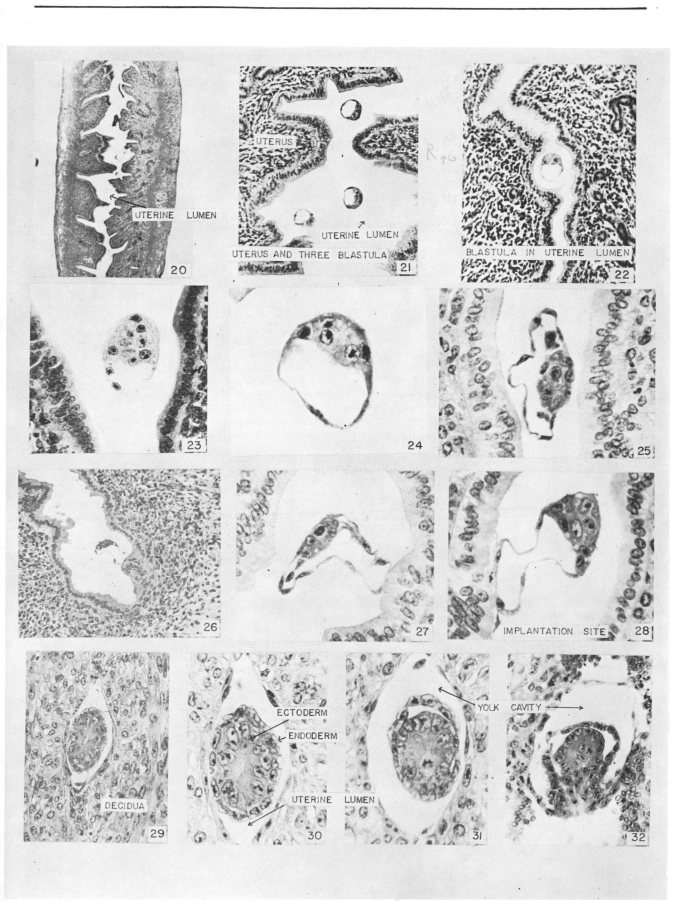

UTERINE LUMEN

20

UTERUS

UTERINE LUMEN

UTERUS AND THREE BLASTULA

21

BLASTULA IN UTERINE LUMEN

22

23

24

25

26

27

IMPLANTATION SITE

28

DECIDUA

29

ECTODERM

ENDODERM

UTERINE LUMEN

30

31

YOLK CAVITY

32

THE MOUSE EMBRYO: 6.5 TO 14.5 DAYS POST—CONCEPTION

Fig. 33 - Mouse embryo at 6. 5 days showing relation to surrounding uterine epithelium. Note breakdown of
adjacent uterine tissue.

Fig. 34 - Section distinguishing between inner solid ectoderm
and outer flocculent-type endoderm.

Fig. 35 - Thickening of inner ectoderm of the head process,
at 6. 5 days.

Fig. 36 - Section through uterus at level of 7. 5 day embryo
showing extent of uterine involvement. Ectoplacental cone is solid mass toward center of section.

Fig. 37 - Transverse section through more posterior level of
embryo showing exocoelom and two portions of pro-
amniotic cavity.

Fig. 38 - Longitudinal section at about 7. 0 days showing first
appearance of all three germ layers.

Fig. 39 - Longitudinal (sagittal) section at 7. 5 days showing
all structures from ectoplacental cone (above) to
head process (below).

Fig. 40 - Mouse embryo at 8. 5 days. Note earliest neural
invagination to form the central nervous system in
inner thick ectoderm. Section through entire
uterus at this level.

Fig. 41 - Enlarged view of 8. 5 day embryo showing earliest
neural differentiation.

Fig. 42 - Embryo at 8. 5 days showing amniotic membrane
across center of embryo, saccular allantois above
and to the left, ectoplacental cavity slit-like and
above, large amniotic cavity (below) with early
differentiation of the primary neural axis (thickening below).

Fig. 43 - Transverse section through early head structures at
9. 5 days showing two dorsal and two ventral aortae
and enclosed lateral coelomic spaces. Archenteron
is the central cavity above which is the notochord
and the closed neural tube. Easily compared with
frog, chick or any other mammal.

Fig. 44 - Section at 10. 5 days of the head process level with
brain ectoderm still unclosed, but with notochord
and archenteron distinct.

Fig. 45 - Section of eye at 12. 5 days development, at level
of origin of the optic nerve. Note state of development of the lens, cornea and retina.

Fig. 46 - Eye of the mouse embryo at 14. 5 days showing considerable further development beyond that of fig. 45.

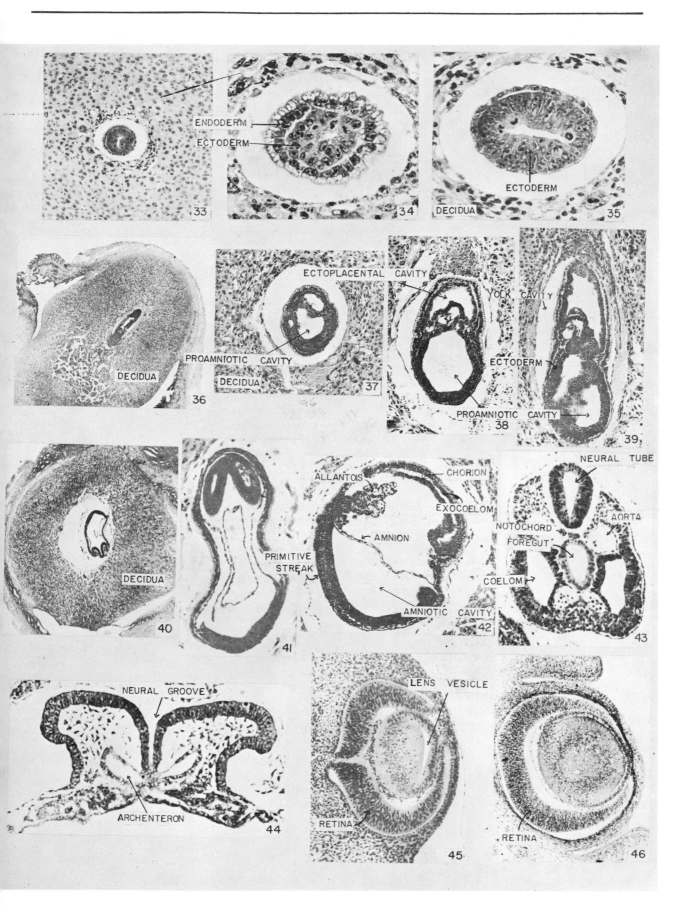

THE MOUSE EMBRYO: 6.5 TO 18.5 DAYS POST—CONCEPTION

Fig. 47 - Paired uteri of mouse at 6.5 days showing 11 implantation sites. Note ovaries at upper end, and
coiled oviducts.

Fig. 48 - Genital system of pregnant mouse at 7.5 days
with 11 implantations.

Fig. 49 - Same at 8.5 days. Note enlarging embryonic
masses.

Fig. 50 - Same at 9.5 days. Note only two implantations
on left.

Fig. 51 - Same at 10.5 days with embryos on left exposed;
14 implantations.

Fig. 52 - Enlarged view of embryos in situ at 10.5 days.
Note very vascular amnion covering lowermost
embryo.

Fig. 53 - Exposed mouse embryos at 11.5 days. Note
appendage development.

Fig. 54 - Implantation sites of left uterus at 12.5 days.
Right side not shown.

Fig. 55 - Uteri at 13.5 days with four embryos partially
exposed. Next to lowest implantation on right
is probably a resorption site.

Fig. 56 - Entire litter of six (only) at 16.5 days liberated
from their uterine sites but still attached by
umbilical cords to placentae. Development such
that they should be regarded as fetuses.

Fig. 57 - Sagittal section or mouse fetus at 15.5 days gesta-
tation. Note particularly the hepatic vein to the
sinus venosus; the vertebrae; and the development
of the cerebral vesicles.

Fig. 58 - Sagittal section of entire fetus at 16.5 days gestation, showing brain and cord; aortic arch from
ventricle; and prominent tongue muscles.

Fig. 59 - Sagittal section of mouse fetus at 17.5 days.
Note well differentiation of the brain and spinal
cord; heart; and viscera.

Fig. 60 - Sagittal section of mouse embryo at 18.5 days.

Fig. 61 - Same as Fig. 60 but at different level.

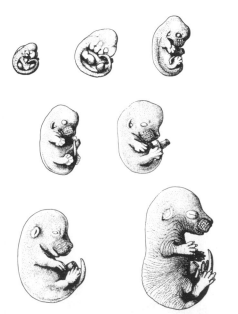

MOUSE EMBRYOS: 11.5 to 17.5 DAYS GESTATION

(Drawings by R. van Dyke, from Rugh's "Embryology",
Harcourt, Brace & Co., 1963)

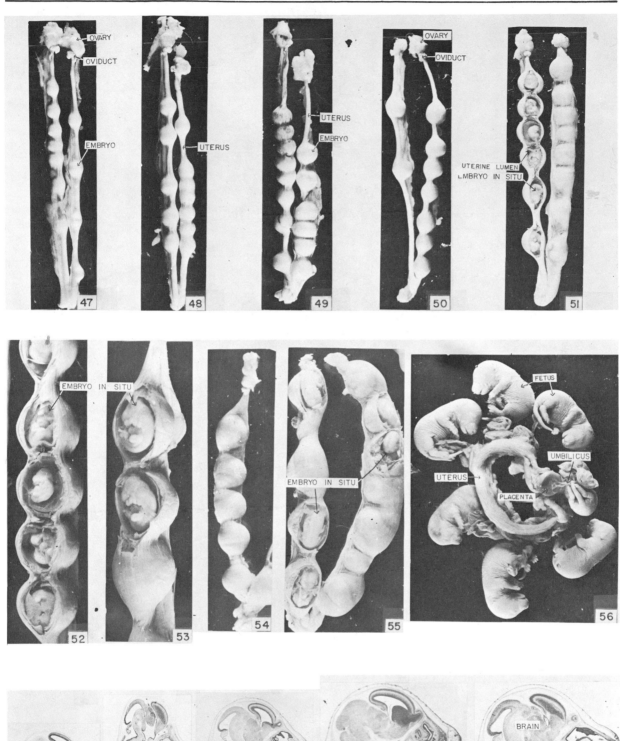

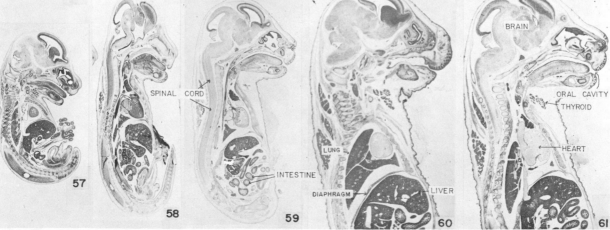

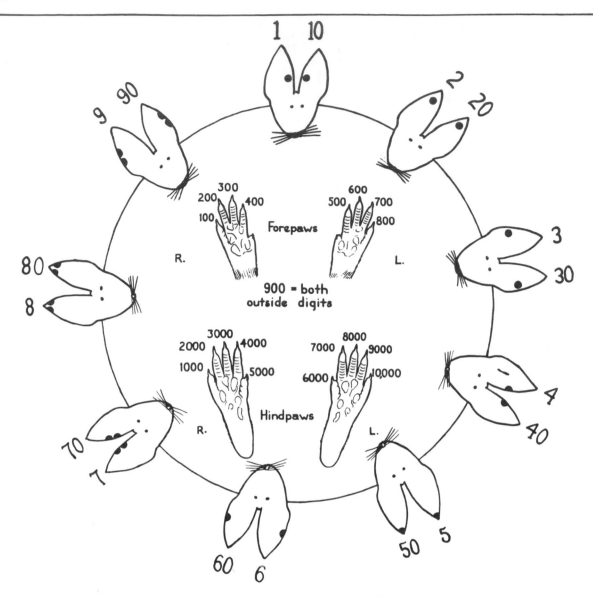

Method for marking mice or rats for identification.
By clipping ears and/or toes one can number the
animals up to 10,000, if necessary.

Mouse cage, made of stainless steel and measuring
7 x 10 x 6.5 inches, having cover with built-in food
hopper and holder for inverted water bottle, provided
with stainless steel tubing for water outlet. Card
holder for record at one end.

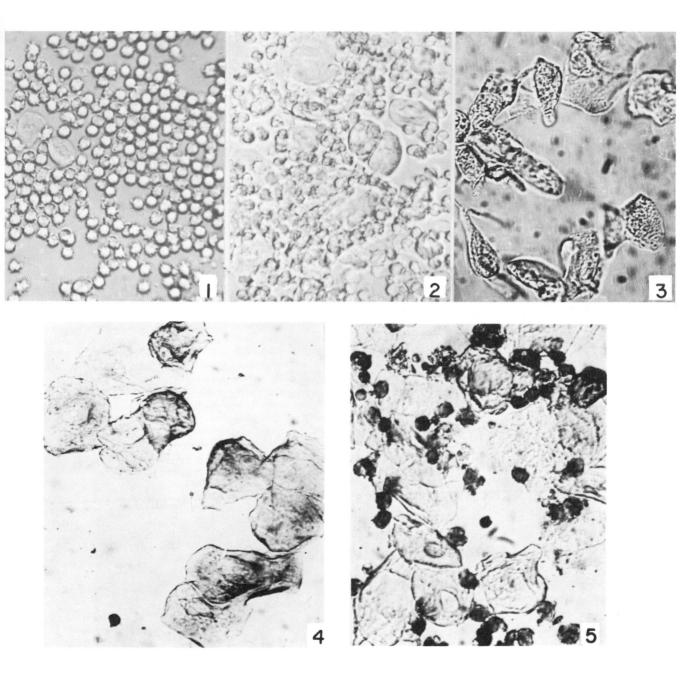

PHASES OF ESTRUS IN THE MOUSE

1. Diestrus - almost exclusively leukocytes.
2. Pre-estrus showing both leukocytes and nucleated epithelial cells in approximately equal numbers.
3. Early estrus - showing clearly defined epithelia cells, some with distinct nuclei.
4. Estrus - large, squamous type epithelial cells without clearly defined nuclei. Many folds, thin and transparent.
5. Post-estrus showing again approximately equal numbers of leukocytes and epithelial cells, but the latter are large, folded, and with translucent nuclei.

(Mating occurs at stages 2 to 4 above, but these occur rather rapidly. The major part of the 5 day cycle is spent in diestrus)

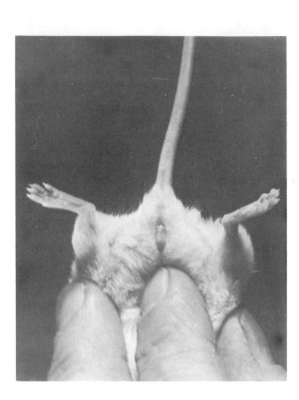

Vaginal plug of female mouse the morning after successful mating. This plug arises from secretions from the male, and is certain sign of copulation. Usually it means successful fertilization as well, but there are species differences so that in some strains this is not a guarantee of fertilization. This plug generally disappears within a few hours after mating.

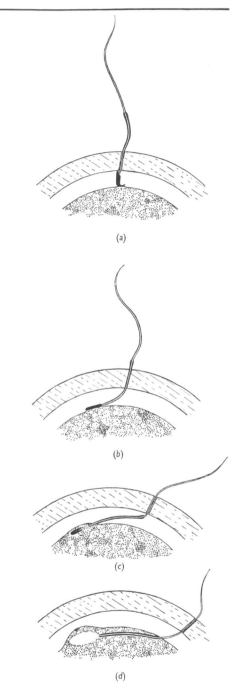

(a)

(b)

(c)

(d)

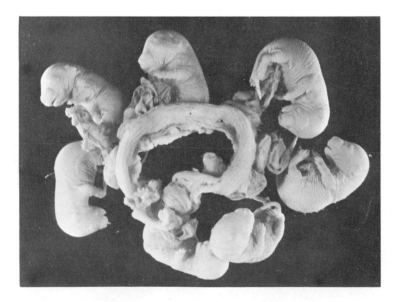

Entire litter of mice liberated from but still attached to the uterus by umbilical cords, at 17.5 days gestation.

The figures illustrate four stages in the penetration of a rodent egg by a spermatozoon. (a) The spermatozoon head has just passed through the zona pellucida and made contact with the vitellus. (b) The spermatozoon head is lying flat upon the vitelline surface to which it is now attached. (c) The whole of the spermatozoon mid-piece has entered the egg and the head has passed through the surface of the vitellus. The spermatozoon head shows an early phase in its transformation to a male pronucleus--the posterior end of the head is becoming indistinguishable from the egg cytoplasm. (d) The head and mid-piece of the spermatozoon have now entered the vitellus. Transformation of the head has proceeded to the stage immediately before the appearance of nucleoli. The cytoplasmic elevation over the spermatozoon head, just evident in (c) has now become much larger. From Austin C.R., A. W. H. Braden, 1956, Jour. Exp. Biol. 33:360.

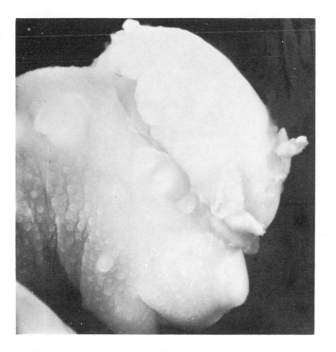

Head of mouse embryo at 18.5 days showing pronounced
exencephalia (brain hernia) following exposure to x-rays
at 8.5 days gestation.

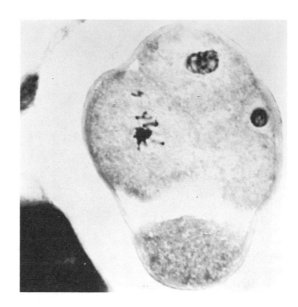

Delayed cleavage at 2.5 days after conception of the
mouse egg, showing the effect of x-irradiation at 0.5 days
(before the first cleavage) in the form of lagging and sticky
chromosomes, pyknotic nuclei, separation of cytoplasm of
adjoining cells.

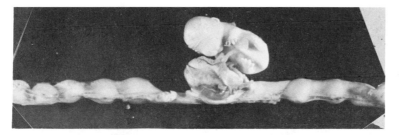

Implantation sites of nine mouse embryos, and one surviving
fetus following x-irradiation at 2.5 days after conception. The
one survivor appears to be normal but was grossly stunted when
compared with the controls.

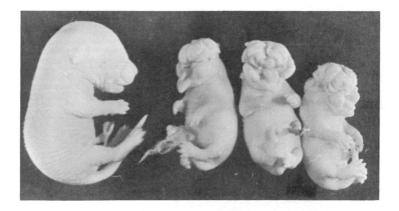

One control (left) and three mouse embryos at 18.5 days, following exposure of the three at 2.5 days post-conception to 50 x-rays.
Note complete disorganization of all cephalic structures, and pronounced stunting when compared with the control.

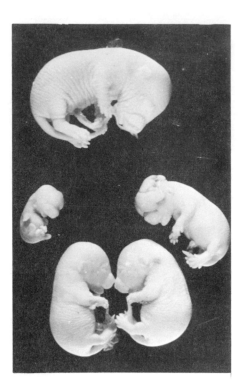

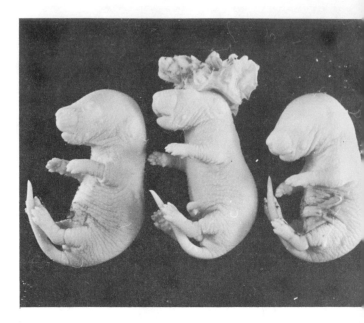

Massive brain hernia following two exposures of 25 r each of
x-rays, one before and the other after implantation but both
before the onset of neurogenesis. Note litter mates which
"appear" to be normal, but which are stunted and would
exhibit other anomalies less obvious.

Four members of a single litter (below) to be compared with
a single comparable control (above), the irradiated mice
showing stunting, exencephalia (brain hernia) and "apparent
normality" but obvious stunting. Exposed at 3.5 days to 50 r.

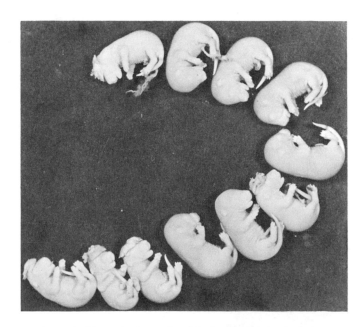

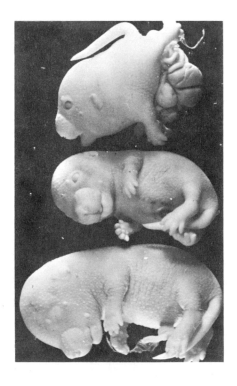

An entire litter of mice as found in the bicornuate uteri at
18.5 days after conception. The embryos were x-irradiated
at 8.5 days, or during early neurogenesis. Note that five (5)
of the litter of 11 show the CNS anomaly of exencephalia or
herniated mid-brain. In the mouse, the abnormal offspring
are killed and devoured at birth, but those that "appear to
be normal" are, as among humans, allowed to survive.

One control (left) along with two members of a litter from
a cross between CF1 and C57 mice, showing a greater
variety of anomalies following x-irradiation at 7.5 days
gestation.

VI. GLOSSARY OF TERMS IN EXPERIMENTAL EMBRYOLOGY

Many of the following terms were used for the first time within the last decade. The definitions are derived from numerous current writings of Experimental Embryologists and the author has attempted to incorporate the various shades of meaning into succinct statements.

ABORTION - termination of pregnancy at a non-viable stage of the foetus.

ACHONDROPLASTIC - refers to miniature adult skeletal condition of some midgets.

ACIDOPHIL - oxiphil; cell constituents stained with acid dyes, often used to designate an entire cell type. (See basophil)

ACTION, DYNAMIC - Weiss' variation of the field theory or concept.

ACTIVATION - stimulation of spermatozoon to accelerated activity, generally by chemical means (e.g., fertilizin); process of initiating development in the egg; the liberation of naturally occurring evocators from an inactive combination.

ACTIVATION CENTER - one of the two organization centers in the insect egg.

ACTIVITY, FUNCTIONAL - stimulation or inhibition of a developing organ by environmental variables (e.g., hypertrophy of the urodele gills in an oxygen deficient medium).

ADAPTATION - functional and correlative change, however brought about.

ADAPTATION, FUNCTIONAL - an organ will adapt itself structurally to an alteration, qualitative or quantitative, of function (Roux).

ADNEXA - extra embryonic structures discarded before the adult condition is attained.

AESTIVATION - reduced activity during the summer period by some animals, term opposed to hibernation.

AFFINITÄT - tendency to contact; may be positive, resulting in maximal contact or may be negative, resulting in minimal contact (Holtfreter, 1939). Not thigmotaxis.

AFFINITÄT, INTERFAZIALE - tendency to contact between marginal surfaces or interfaces of different blastomeres (Lehmann).

AFFINITÄT, INTRABLASTEMATISCHE - tendency to contact between cells of the same blastema (Lehmann).

AFFINITY - tendency of cells and tissues of the early embryo to cling together when removed from their normal environment. Equivalent to the cytarme of Roux.

AGENESIS - developmental failure of a primordium (e.g., absence of arm or kidney).

AGGLUTINATION - cluster formation; a spontaneously reversible reaction of spermatozoa to the fertilizin of egg-water.

AGGREGATION - coming together of cells (e.g., spermatozoa) without sticking, a non-reversible response comparable to chemotropism.

AGNATHUS - absence of lower jaw.

AKINETIC - without a kinetochores (e.g., in a chromosome).

ALIMENTARY CASTRATION - prolonged starvation (Adams, 1930).

ALLANTOIN - nitrogenous portion of allantoic fluid.

ALLANTOIS - an extra embryonic sac-like extension of the hindgut of amniotes, having the dual function of excretion and respiration.

ALLO-HAPLOID - androgenetic haploid.

ALLOMETRY - study of the relative sizes of parts of animals at different absolute sizes, ages, weights, or chemical compositions. Term now used in place of heterogony by Huxley and Teissier (1936).

ALLOMORPHOSIS - the physical or chemical relation of parts of an organism at some early stage to either the whole or part of a later stage, (e.g., the egg size compared with the adult size or weight).

ALLOPHORES - red pigment in solution.

ALLO-POLYPLOID - polyploid species hybrid.

AMBOCEPTOR - a synonym used for fertilizin in suggesting its double combination with the sperm and egg receptors in the process of fertilization. This double receptor may also receive blood inhibitors, or anti-fertilizin.

AMELUS - failure of the extremities to develop, remaining as mere stubs.

AMNION - thin, double membrane enclosing the embryos of some invertebrates and of reptiles, birds, and mammals. It is derived from the somatopleure in vertebrates.

AMNIOTIC BANDS - fibrous bands from the amnion to the embryo due to local necrosis of foetal tissues.

AMNIOTIC RAPHÉ - point of junction of the amniotic folds as they encircle the embryo, synonymous with sero-amniotic or chorio-amniotic junction.

AMPHIBLASTIC - complete but unequal segmentation in telolecithal eggs.

AMPHITOKY - parthenogenetic reproduction of both males and females.

---

* Glossaries of terms in normal embryology may be found in Rugh's "The Frog: Its Reproduction and Development" (McGraw-Hill, N.Y.) and in his "Laboratory Manual of Vertebrate Embryology" (Burgess 1961)

AMPLEXUS - the sexual embrace of female by the male amphibian. This may or may not occur at the time of oviposition.

AMPHOTEROKY - production of both sexes in a single parthenogenetic brood.

ANALOGOUS - structures said to have the same function but different embryological and/or evolutionary origin. Opposed to homologous.

ANDROGAMONES - the anti-fertilizins of Lillie, so named by Hartmann. An acidic protein of low molecular weight.

ANDROGENESIS - development of the egg with paternal (sperm) chromosomes only, accomplished by removing the egg nucleus after activation by the spermatozoön but before syngamy (Wilson, 1925). May also be accomplished by irradiation damage of egg nucleus.

ANDRO-MEROGONES - egg fragments developing with the sperm nucleus only, achieved either through surgical removal of the egg nucleus and some cytoplasm; by constricting the pro-nuclei apart prior to syngamy; or by centrifuging the pro-nuclei apart.

ANEUPLOIDY - deviation from normal diploidy but involving partial sets of chromosomes (Tächkohn, 1922).

ANEUPLOIDY, MULTIFORM - complex chromosomal mosaics, possibly the result of multipolar mitoses (Böok, 1944).

ANEUROGENIC - used in relation to organs developed without proper components of the central nervous system (e.g., limb buds in embryos without spinal cords).

ANENTERION - formation and constriction of archenteron by evagination instead of invagination, following the application of heat (Driesch, 1895).

ANGENESIS - regeneration of tissues.

ANLAGE - a rudiment; a group of cells which indicate a prospective development into a part or organ. Syn., ebauché or primordium.

ANIMALIZATION - changing by physical or chemical means the presumptive fate of embryonic areas which normally would have become endodermal. Syn., ectodermization, or animalisierung of Lindahl.

ANORMOGENESE - a course of development which deviates in a typical manner from the normal (Lehmann).

ANTERIOR - toward the head; head end. Syn., cephalic, cranial, rostral.

APROSOMUS - featureless face due to the arrest of development, the skin covering normal but lacking in eyes, nose, and mouth.

ARCHENCEPHALON - anterior portion of the brain which gives rise to the telencephalon and the diencephalon; pre-chordal brain.

ARCHIPLASM - specific material which gives rise to the asters and spindle (Boveri).

AREA - a morphogenetic cell group representing one of the constituent regions of a fate-map, generally of a blastula stage or later.

AREAL - first an invisible, then a sharply differentiated region of the blastema, out of which develops a primitive organ; the organ arising from the blastema through segregation, (organogenetisches of Lehmann).

AREA OPACA - the marginal ring or extra-embryonic blastoderm of the chick embryo around the area pellucida, opaque because of direct contact with the underlying yolk.

AREA PELLUCIDA - the central portion of the chick blastoderm from which the embryo is developed, pellucid because it is lifted off of the underlying yolk, providing a space beneath the blastoderm through which light can be transmitted.

AREA VASCULOSA - the portion of the area opaca of the chick blastoderm in which the extra-embryonic blood vessels will develop.

AREA VITELLINA - the portion of the area opaca of the chick blastoderm peripheral to the area vasculosa.

ARRHENOKARYOTIC - refers to a blastomere of the normally fertilized egg where there has been a separation of the nuclear components; or in cases of dispermy, where the haploid chromosomes from the single sperm are isolated in the blastomere.

ARRHENOTOKY - parthenogenetic production of males, exclusively.

ASSIMILATION - process of determinative incorporation of a foreign blastema into the functional status of the host blastema.

ASTER - the "star-shaped structure" surrounding the centrosome (Fol, 1877); lines radiating in all directions from the centrosome during mitosis.

ASTOMUS - complete lack or atresia of the mouth.

ASYNTAXIA DORSALIS - failure of the neural tube to close.

ATELIOTIC - arrested development of the skeleton due to non-union of the epiphyses, characteristic of some dwarfs.

ATOKUS - without offspring.

ATTRACTION, NON-SPECIFIC - attraction of nerve fibers toward any structure in the vicinity, (e.g., graft rudiments of chick embryos such as brain tissue, if placed on the chorio-allantois, will often send out nerve fibers toward the nearby muscle segments, a situation that would not occur under normal conditions).

AUFLAGERUNG - the placing of competent or responsive ectoderm on a dead inductor in order to test the inductive power of the latter.

AUTOGAMY - self-fertilization.

AUTOPARTHENOGENESIS - parthenogenetic stimulation of eggs to develop by materials from other eggs.

AUXESIS - growth by cell expansion but without cell division.

AXIS - central or median line. The egg axis takes into account the concentration of deutoplasm, cytoplasm, and the position of the nucleus, so that the egg axis and egg polarity are essentially the same.

AXIS OF THE CELL - a line passing through the centrosome and nucleus of the cell.

AXIS OF THE EMBRYO - a line representing the antero-posterior axis of the future embryo.

BÄHNUNG - competence or labile determination (Vogt, 1928).

BALANCER - cylindrical and paired projections of ectoderm with mesenchymatous cores, used as tactile and balancing organs by some urodeles in the place of (anuran) suckers. (Rudimentary or absent in A. tigrinum.)

BALFOUR'S LAW - the intervals between cleavages are longer the more yolk a cell contains in proportion to its protoplasm. "The velocity of segmentation in any part of the ovum is, roughly speaking, proportional to the concentration of the protoplasm there; and the size of the segments is inversely proportional to the concentration of the protoplasm." (Balfour - "Comparative Embryology).

BARFUTH'S RULE - when oblique cuts are made on amphibian tails, the axis of the regenerated tail will be at first perpendicular to the cut surface (Barfuth, 1891).

BATESON'S RULE - (a) The long axes of reduplicated structures lie in the same plane. (b) Two reduplicated limbs are mirror images of each other about a plane which bisects the angle between the long axes of the members, and which is at right angles to the plane of these axes.

BASOPHIL - cell constituents having an affinity for basic dyes, often used as an adjective for an entire cell. (See acidophil).

BAUCHSTÜCK - that portion of the amphibian gastrula (i.e., the ventral half) from which all the organizer area has been removed, thus preventing the formation of any neural axis.

BEDEUTUNGSFREMDE SELBSTDIFFERENZIERUNG - self-differentiation independent of the original presumptive fate or the presumed fate, implied by the new environment. Neither selfwise nor neighborwise.

BIDDER'S ORGAN - anterior portion of the gonad which is ovarian in character, developing from part of the rudiment consisting wholly of cortex. A structure indicating failure of medullary substance to diffuse to the anterior extremity of the gonad rudiment, found most frequently in male toads.

BIO-ELECTRIC CURRENT - an electrical potential characteristic of life, disappearing upon death, associated with activities of muscle, nerve, secretion, and early embryos.

BIOGENETIC LAW - ontogeny is a recapitulation of the early development of ancestral phylogeny. Embryos of higher forms resemble the embryos of lower forms in certain respects but they are never like the adults of the lower (or ancestral) forms. Not to be confused with the recapitulation theory.

BIOLOGICAL MEMORY - ontogenetic unfolding of anlagen phyletically accumulated.

BIOLOGICAL INTEGRATION - correlation of parts through neural or humoral (or both) influences, acquired during development.

BIOLOGICAL ORDER - fundamental basis of experimental studies, the conformity of biological processes to causal postulates.

BIORGAN - an organ in the physiological rather than the morphological sense.

BIOTONUS - the ratio between assimilation and dissimilation, A/D ratio (Verworn).

BLASTEMA - an indifferent group of cells about to be organized into definite tissues, kept together by the ectoplasmic matrix of the constituent cells. Considered to be primitive, embryonic, relatively undifferentiated regenerating cell masses. Thought by some to be produced by reserve cells which were arrested during earlier embryonic development.

BLASTEMFELD - unitary field-like structure (or functional state) without an anlagé. Primordial fields present in the egg stage, and other fields activated only by the processes of induction during development (Lehmann).

BLASTOCOEL - cavity of the blastula. Syn., segmentation or subgerminal cavity.

BLASTODERM - "Because the embryo chooses this as its seat and its domicile, contributing much to its configuration out of its own substance, therefore, in the future, we shall call it blastoderm." (Plander, 1817).

BLASTOKINESIS - a reversal of the cephalocaudal axis in an egg, often accomplished by movement during early development (e.g., insects). Syn., revolution.

BLASTOMERE - one of the cells of the early cleavage of an egg. When there is a discrepancy in size the smaller blastomere is a micromere; the intermediate one is a mesomere; and the larger one is a macromere, but all are blastomeres.

BLASTOPORE - the opening of the archenteron (gastrocoel) to the exterior, occluded by the yolk plug in amphibian embryos; consisting of a slit-like space between the elevated margin of the blastoderm and the underlying yolk of the chick blastoderm; and represented in the amniota as the primitive streak. Approximate region of the future anus.

BLASTOPORE, DORSAL LIP OF - the region of initial involution of cells in the amphibian or chick gastrula; general area of the "organizer"; original grey crescent area of many amphibia; the cells which turn in beneath the potential central nervous system (Amphioxus) and form the roof of the archenteron (urodela). Syn., germ ring or marginal zone.

BLASTOPORE, VENTRAL LIP OF - region of the germ ring opposite the dorsal lip after involution has reached this point; region which gives rise to the peristomial mesoderm of the frog. Syn., germ ring. (Note: The lips of the blastopore are continuous and represent the involuted germ ring.)

BLASTOTOMY - separation of cells or groups of cells of the blastula, by any means.

BLASTULA - a stage in embryonic development between the appearance of distinct blastomeres and the end of cleavage (i.e., the beginning of gastrulation); a stage generally possessing a primary embryonic cavity or vesicle known as the blastocoel; invariably monodermic, although the roof may be multi-layered.

BLOOD ISLANDS - pre-vascular groups of mesodermal cells found in the splanchnopleure, from which arise the blood vessels and corpuscles. Generally extra-embryonic (chick).

BOTTLE CELLS - long-necked, cylindrical cells of the blastoporal lips (amphibia) whose function may be purely morphogenetic and related to the involutionary processes of gastrulation, (Holtfreter, 1943). Ruffini (1925) showed that flask-shaped cells appear wherever infoldings occur, as in the formation of the neural tube, eye vesicle, nasal placode, stomodeum, proctodeum, etc. These cells are held together by strands of surface coating.

BRADYAUXESIS - negative heterogony (Needham & Lerner, 1940), the part grows more slowly than the whole.

BRADYGENESIS - lengthening of certain stages in development.

BRANCHIAL - having to do with respiration (e.g., branchial vessel in gill).

BRANCHIOMERY - type of metamerism exemplified in the visceral arches.

BRYSHTHALMIA - eyes that are too large, may be due to oversized lenses.

BUD - an undeveloped branch, generally an anlage of an appendage (e.g., limb or wing bud).

BUPHTHALMIA - eyes that are too large (Harrison, 1929).

CACOGENESIS - inability to hybridize; means "bad descent" (kakogenesis).

CAENOGENETIC - term for new stages in ontogeny which have been intercalated as an adaptation to some inevitable condition which the mode of life of the young animal imposed (Haeckel).

CALCIUM-RELEASE THEORY - theory of Heilbrunn that the activating agent in parthenogenetic stimulation releases calcium from calcium proteinate in the cell cortex, and the free calcium then brings about a protoplasmic clotting necessary to the initiation of development.

CARCINOGEN - a chemical substance which is capable of causing living cells to become cancer-like in growth and behavior.

CARYOLYSIS - solution or dissolution of the nucleus.

CARYORHEXIS - breaking up of the nucleus, or its rupture.

CELL - protoplasmic territory under the control of a single nucleus, whether or not the territory is bounded by a discrete membrane. By this definition a syncitium is made up of many cells with physiological rather than morphological boundaries.

CELL CHAIN THEORY - theory of neurogenesis wherein the peripheral nerve is of pluricellular origin; opposed to the outgrowth theory.

CELL-CONE - a sub-system of an ordered class of cells; a single cell (other than a zygote) and all cells derived from it in a division heirarchy.

CELL LINEAGE - the study of the origin and fate of specific cells (blastomeres) in early embryonic development. Syn., cytogeny.

CELLULATION - development of cytoplasmic areas around normal (syncitial) nuclei or by nuclei migrating from living blastomeres as in the chick blastoderm.

CELL THEORY - the body of any living organism is either a structural and functional unit or is composed of a nucleus and its sphere of influence, whether or not that sphere is bounded by a morphological entity. "Omnis cellula e cellula." Virchow

CENTRIOLE - the granular core of the centrosome, the radiating area comprising the centrosphere. Appears within the centrosome during mitosis. (Conklin).

CENTROSOME - the dynamic center involved in mitosis, including the central granule (centriole) and the surrounding sphere of rays (centrosphere). It is the center of the aster which outlasts the astral rays. Double centrosome called diplosome.

CENTROSOME, HETERODYNAMIC - Ziegler's hypothesis that centrosomes may have different powers, thereby causing unequal division of the blastomeres such as occurs in many molluscs (e.g., Crepidula). No evidence of this although there are occasionally size differences in asters of the same spindle complex.

CEPHALO-THORACOPAGUS - fusion of the head and chest regions in conjoined twins.

CERVICAL CYST - imperfect occlusion of a branchial (2nd) cleft. Syn., branchial cyst.

CERVICAL FISTULA - incomplete closure of the branchial cleft.

CHALONES - internal secretions with depressing effects, opposed to hormones.

CHEMO-NEUROTROPISM - chemical attraction of degenerating nerve upon regenerating nerve fibers. The chemical nature of nerve orientation (growth and connections) depending upon diffusing substances which seem to attract nerve fibers.

CHIMERA - compound embryo derived by grafting together major portions of two embryos, generally of different species; exchange of parts too great to be called a transplant. From Greek mythology: forepart a lion, middle a goat, and hindpart a dragon.

CHORDA-MESODERM - region of the dorsal lip of the blastopore, arising from the grey crescent area, destined to give rise to notochord and mesoderm in the amphibia.

CHORIO-ALLANTOIS - a common membrane formed by the fusion of the inner wall of the chorion and the outer wall of the allantois (chick), consisting of outer ectoderm, intermediate fused mesoderm, and inner endoderm.

CHORIO-ALLANTOIC GRAFT - graft from various sources which, by virtue of its weight and other factors, provides local irritation of the chorio-allantoic membrane of the chick so that the graft becomes vascularized and surrounded by indifferent tissue, offering the graft excellent conditions for survival, growth, and differentiation. Graft not incorporated by the host from which it receives nutrition for growth.

CHORION - an embryonic membrane developed in the chick as a corollary to the amnion; encloses both the amnion and the allantois. Never maternal in mammals.

CHROMATID - longitudinal half of an anaphase, interphase, or prophase chromosome at mitosis. One of four strands (in meiosis) involved in crossing over and visible after pachytene. Becomes a chromosome at metaphase of the second (reduction) division.

CHROMATIN - deeply staining substance of the nuclear network and the chromosomes, consisting of nuclein; gives Feulgen reaction and stains with basic dyes.

CHROMATOBLASTS - potential pigment cells which, upon proper extrinsic stimulation, will exhibit pigmentation.

CHROMATOPHORE - pigment bearing cell frequently capable of changing size, shape, and color; responsible for superficial color changes in many animals (e.g., squid and chameleon), under the influence of the sympathetic nervous system and/or the neurohumors.

CHROMIDIA - extra-nuclear granules of chromatin.

CHROMONEMA - optically single thread within the chromosome, a purely descriptive term without functional implications.

CHROMONUCLEIC ACID - one of the two types of nucleic acid detected in chromatin only (Pollister & Mirsky, 1944). Syn., desoxyribose nucleoprotein, thymonucleic acid. (See plasmonucleic acid.)

CHROMOPHOBE - cells whose constituents are non-stainable; no affinity for dyes.

CHROMOSOME - the chromatic or deeply staining bodies derived from nuclear network, which are conspicuous during mitotic cell division and which are represented in all of the somatic cells of an organism in a number characteristic for the species; bearers of the genes.

CHROMOSOME ABERRATION - an irregularity in the constitution or the number of chromosomes which may produce modifications in the normal course of development.

CHROMOSOMIN - acidic protein, present in nuclei, considered an essential part of the chromosomes (Stedman, 1945).

CLEAVAGE - the mitotic division of an egg resulting in blastomeres. Syn., segmentation.

CLEAVAGE, ACCESSORY - cleavages in peripheral or deeper portions of the (chick) germinal disc caused by supernumerary sperm nuclei following (normal) polyspermy.

CLEAVAGE, ASYMMETRICAL - extremely unequal divisions of the egg as in Ctenophores.

CLEAVAGE, BILATERAL - cleavage in which the egg substances are distributed symmetrically with respect to the median plane of the future embryo.

CLEAVAGE, DETERMINATE - cleavage in which certain parts of the future embryo may be circumscribed in certain specific (early) blastomeres; cleavage which produces blastomeres that are not qualitatively equipotential, (i.e., when such blastomeres are isolated they will not give rise to entire embryos). The early embryo is a mosaic of qualitatively different blastomeres with respect to further ontogeny.

CLEAVAGE, DEXIOTROPIC - cleavage resulting in a right-handed production of daughter blastomere(s), as in some cases of spiral cleavage.

CLEAVAGE, DISCOIDAL - cell division restricted to a more-or-less circular disc of protoplasm to one side of a relatively enormous mass of yolk (e.g., chick egg). Syn., meroblastic cleavage.

CLEAVAGE, EQUATORIAL - cleavage at right angles to the egg axis, opposed to vertical or meridional. Often the third cleavage plane. Syn., latitudinal or horizontal cleavage.

CLEAVAGE, HOLOBLASTIC - complete division of the egg into blastomeres, generally equal in size (Asterias, Arbacia) although not necessarily so (Amphioxus, Frog). Syn., total cleavage.

CLEAVAGE, HORIZONTAL - (See cleavage, equatorial.)

CLEAVAGE, INDETERMINATE - cleavage resulting in qualitatively equi-potential blastomeres in the early stages of development. When such blastomeres are isolated from each other they tend to give rise to complete embryos. Opposed to mosaic development. Syn., regulatory cleavage, or development.

CLEAVAGE, LATITUDINAL - (See cleavage, equatorial.)

CLEAVAGE LAWS - (See specific laws under names of Balfour, Hertwig, and Sachs.)

CLEAVAGE, LEVOTROPIC - cleavage resulting in left-handed or counter-clockwise production of daughter blastomere(s) as in some cases of spiral cleavage.

CLEAVAGE, MERIDIONAL - cleavage along the egg axis, opposed to equatorial. Generally the first two cleavages of any egg. Syn., vertical cleavage.

CLEAVAGE, MEROBLASTIC - (See discoidal cleavage.)

CLEAVAGE NUCLEUS - the nucleus which controls cleavage. This may be the syngamic nucleus of normal fertilization; the egg nucleus of parthenogenetic or gynogenetic eggs; or the sperm nucleus of androgenetic development.

CLEAVAGE PATH - path taken by the syngamic nucleus to the position awaiting the first division.

CLEAVAGE, RADIAL - holoblastic cleavage which results in (two) super-imposed tiers of cells as early as the 8-cell stage. Opposed to spiral cleavage.

CLEAVAGE, SPIRAL - cleavage at an oblique angle with respect to the egg axis so that the resulting blastomeres (generally upper micromeres at the 8-cell stage) lie in an interlocking fashion within the furrows of the original blastomeres. The shift in expected position is due to intrinsic genetic factors rather than external pressure. (e.g., Mollsuca.) Opposed to radial cleavage.

CLEAVAGE, SUPERFICIAL - cleavage around the periphery of centrolecithal eggs. Syn., peripheral cleavage.

CLEIODOIC - refers to eggs that are more-or-less closed off from their environment (e.g., Chick).

CLINOSTAT - apparatus for keeping objects in constant rotation.

COADAPTATION - correlated variation in two mutually dependent organs.

COELOBLASTULA - spherical ball of cells (blastomeres) developing in early cleavage as a result of segmentation, provided with a large central cavity (blastocoel). (e.g., Echinodermata.)

COELOM - mesodermal body cavity of chordates, from the walls of which develop the gonads. It is subdivided in higher forms into pericardial, pleural, and peritoneal cavities. Extended as the exocoel or extra embryonic body cavity of chick embryo.

COENOBLAST - the layer which will give rise to the endoderm and mesoderm (obsolete).

COLLOID - dispersed substance whose particles are not smaller than 1μ nor larger than 100μ, approximately. Physical state of protoplasm.

COLORLESS PIGMENT CELL - same as dependent or potential pigment cell of DuShane and Hamilton. Syn., farblose pigmentzellen.

COMPETENCE - state of reactivity, of disequilibrium in a complex system of reactants. Possessing labile determination (Reakionsfahig) or having reaction possibility (Raven). Competencies may appear simultaneously or in sequence within a given area, some to disappear later even without function. Embryonic competence seems to be lost in all adult tissues but may be reclaimed in a blastema. It is a name for the state of the cell area at or before the time when irritability is resolved and a developmental path is chosen. The word supercedes the older words of "potence", "potency", or "potentiality".

COMPRESSION - either the acceleration of development or the extension of a certain (e.g., pre-hatching) period, resulting in the completion (or omission) of certain (larval) stages, in an unbalanced time schedule.

CONCRESCENCE - the coming together of previously separate parts (cell areas) of the embryo, generally resulting in a piling up of parts. One of the corollaries of gastrulation where a bottle-neck of cell movements occurs at the lips of the blastopore. Original meaning (His, 1874) referred to presumed pre-formed parts of the fish germ ring. (See confluence.)

CONE, EXUDATION - (See cone fertilization.) Term used by Fol, 1879.

CONE, FERTILIZATION - a conical projection of the cytoplasm from the surface of the egg to meet the spermatozoön which is to invade the egg cortex. The cone makes contact and then draws the sperm into the egg. Not universally demonstrated but seen in the starfish (Chambers). Syn., exudation cone.

CONES OF GROWTH - the enlarged outgrowth of the neuroblast forms the axis cylinder or axone of the nerve fiber and is termed the cone of growth because the growth processes by which the axone increases in length are supposed to be located there.

CONFLUENCE - similar to concrescence except that this term refers specifically to the "flow" of cells (or cell areas) together, without presumption of any organ preformation. Said areas have certain potentialities in unaltered normal development. (See concrescence.)

CONSTRICTION - gradual closure of the blastopore (germ ring) over the yolk toward the vegetal pole. May be due to stretching of the marginal zone, to a pull or tension of the dorsal lip, or even to the narrowing of the marginal zone. Syn., convergence of Jordan or Konzentrisches Urmundschluss of Vogt.

CONVERGENCE, DORSAL - material of the marginal zone moves toward the dorsal mid-line as it involutes and invaginates during gastrulation, resulting in a compensatory ventral divergence. Syn., confluence of Smith or dorsal Raffung of Vogt.

CORDS, MEDULLARY - structures which give rise to the urogenital connections and take part in the formation of the seminiferous tubules, and are derived from the blastema of the mesonephric cords (amphibia).

CORDS, SEX - strands of somatic cells and primordial germ cells growing from the cortex toward the medulla of the gonad primordium. Best seen in early phases of testes development.

CORRELATION COEFFICIENT - correlation of growth rates of different parts (of embryo).

CORTICIN - sex differentiating substances spread in some amphibia by the blood stream and in other forms by diffusion, acting as a hormone. (See medullarin.)

CRANIAL - relative to the head; "craniad" means toward the head. Syn., rostral, cephalad.

CRANIOPAGUS - cranial union in conjoined twins.

CRANIOSCHISIS - open-roofed skull associated with undeveloped brain. Syn., acrania.

CRESCENT, GREY - crescentic area between the original animal and vegetal hemispheres on the surface of the (frog) egg, grey in color because of the migration of black pigment away from the area and toward the sperm entrance point (Roux, 1888) which is therefore opposite; region of the presumptive chorda-mesoderm, the future blastopore and anus.

CRESCENT, YELLOW - crescentic area on the surface of the (Ascidian) egg, yellow in color. Gives rise to the mesoderm of such embryos.

CREST, NEURAL - paired cell masses derived from ectoderm cells along the edge of the former neural plate, and wedged into the space between the dorso-lateral wall of the closed neural tube and the integument. Gives rise to spinal ganglia after segmentation.

CREST SEGMENT - the original neural crests which become divided into segments, with the aid of the somites, from which develop the spinal and possibly also some cranial ganglia.

CROSS-FERTILIZATION - union of gametes produced by different individuals which, if they are of different species, may produce hybrids with variable viability.

CYCLOPIA - failure of the eyes to separate; median fusion of the eyes which may be due to suppression of the rostral block of tissue which ordinarily separates the eyes; exaggeration of the vegetativization tendencies.

CYTARME - flattening of previously rounded blastomeres against each other following the completion of cleavage.

CYTASTERS - asters arising independently of the nucleus in the cytoplasm. May contain centrosomes, and achromatic figure with attraction sphere and astral rays and may divide and even cause the cytoplasm around them to divide. Activity and structure unrelated to chromosomal material.

CYTE - a suffix meaning "cell" as oö-cyte (egg forming cell), spermato-cyte (sperm forming cell), or osteo-cyte (bone forming cell). (See specific definitions.)

CYTOCHORISMUS - apparent partial separation of the blastomeres at the flat, previously continuous surface (Roux).

CYTOCHROME - an oxidizable pigment found in nearly all cells exhibiting definite spectral bands in reduced form, discovered by Keilin (1925). Insoluble in water, poisoned by HCN, CO_2, and H_2S.

CYTOLISTHESIS - tendency of embryonic cells to aggregate and to fill up disruptions of their union even in the absence of a common surface membrane, due to surface tension and selective adhesiveness (Roux, 1894). Moving of cells over one another by sliding, rotation, or both processes.

CYTOLYSIS - breakdown of the cell, indicated by dispersal of formed components.

CYTOSOME - cytoplasmic mass exclusive of the nucleus.

CYTOTAXIS - coming together of (amphibian) blastula cells after being teased apart in salt solution (positive cytotaxis). Crawling, amoeboid movement similar to chemotaxis (Roux). May also include repulsive movements of cell groups (negative cytotaxis).

CYTOLEOSIS - process by which a cell, already irreversibly differentiated, proceeds to its final specialization (Hoadley).

CYTOTROPISM - inevitable movement of a cell in response to external forces (Rhumbler, 1899).

DARK-FIELD RING - an orange-yellow colored illuminated ring as opposed to the silvery white surface of the sea urchin egg as described by Ruünstrom (1928) under dark field illumination. Not related to echinochrome. May be the area which is invaginated during gastrulation.

DEDIFFERENTIATION - process of giving up specialized characters and returning to the more primitive (embryonic) conditions, supposedly regaining the original and wider range of potencies. Manifestation of powers of cell adaptation to an abnormal environment such as in tissue culture, not normally found in the living organism except possibly in the blastema of regenerating tissue. The existence of this change in cell structure and function now questioned. Syn., catachony and einschmelzung.

DEFLECTION - when dedifferentiated cells remain unable to redifferentiate, lying outside the area determined by the term modulation. Cells turned away from the line of normal ontogenesis (Kasahara, 1935).

DEGROWTH - actual reduction in mass subsequent to prolonged period of growth, probably indicating greater catabolic than anabolic processes. Follows inanition.

DELAMINATION - separation of cell layers by splitting, a process of mesoderm formation.

DETERMINANT - a Weismanian concept of a corpuscular unit which determines the qualities and actions of cells in which it is contained. Determinants possess powers of growth and propagation and together constitute the germ plasm. This concept suggests that histological differentiation is brought about by differential division until a single determinant is left within the cell.

DETERMINATION - a process of development indicated when a tissue, whether treated as an isolate or a transplant, still develops in the originally predicted manner; the fixing of fates or final assignments of parts of the embryo at definite ontogenetic time; the firm capacity of a tissue for self-differentiation from which it cannot be deterred, no matter what its environment, within viable limits. An embryological rather than a genetic concept. (Harrison, 1933. Am. Nat. 67:306)

DETERMINATION, DYNAMIC - opposed to induction and refers, for example, to the tendency of the marginal zone to invaginate even when transplanted. (Vogt, 1925.) Formative movements.

DETERMINATION, FIELD - state of organization within an embryonic area probably independent of the substrate; field of action (Wirkungsfeld) or province of action (Wirkungskreis) of Weiss (1925). (See Field.)

DETERMINATION, LABILE - definite but not irrevocably fixed ability of tissue exposed to inductive influences to continue development in the induced direction even though isolated as fragments. Syn., competence, or Bähnung.

DETERMINATION, MATERIAL - formative movements which result in histological differentiation.

DETERMINATION, NEGATIVE - lack of certain essential ingredients within the blastomere necessary to the formation of a complex embryo (e.g., blastomere "D" in Dentalium and Tubifex).

DETERMINATION, PROGRESSIVE - determination in time rather than in space, advancing from the more general to the more specific.

DETERMINATIONSGESCHEHEN - all of the invisible processes in a blastema (and its vicinity) which determine the morphogenesis of the region. These processes may involve two phases, those of self-organization and those of segregation. (Lehmann, 1942.) Syn., determinatorsystem or realisatorsystem (Lehmann, 1942).

DEUTENCEPHALON - caudal region of the brain which later forms the mesencephalon, metencephalon and myelencephalon.

DEUTEROKY - reproduction of both sexes from parthenogenetic eggs (see arrhenotoky and thelytoky).

DEUTOPLASM - yolk or secondary food substance of the egg cytoplasm, non-living.

DEVELOPMENT - gradual transformation of dependent differentiation into self-differentiation; transformation of invisible multiplicity into a visible mosaic; elaboration of components in successive spatial hierarchies.

DEVELOPMENT, MOSAIC - "all the single primordia stand side by side, separate from each other like the stones of a mosaic work, and develop independently, although in perfect harmony with each other, into the finished organism." (Spemann, 1938). Some believe there is pre-localization of embryonic potencies within the egg, the test for which would be self-differentiation.

DEVELOPMENT, REGULATIVE - type of development requiring organizer or inductor influences since each of the early blastomeres could develop into whole embryos. Structures are progressively determined through the action of evocators.

DIAPAUSE - a normal state of dormancy in the development of some animals (e.g., insects) not to be confused with hibernation because this condition is independent of any environmental factors.

DICEPHALUS TETRABRACHINUS - condition attained when the first furrow of the amphibian egg coincides with the sagittal plane and the constriction is exaggerated, resulting in duplications of the chorda, auditory vesicles, and fore-limbs.

DICHIRUS - partial duplication of digits in hand or foot, possibly inherited. A type of poly-dactyly.

DICHOTOMY, DIFFERENTIAL - embryonic segregation; capacity of embryonic cells for self-differentiation becomes itself differentiated (Lillie, 1929).

DIFFERENTIATING CENTER - area responsible for the localization and determination of various regions of the embryo, resulting in harmonious proportioning of parts.

DIFFERENTIATION - acquisition of specialized features which distinguish areas from each other; progressive increase in complexity and organization, visible and invisible; elaboration of diversity through determination leading to histogenesis; production of morphogenetic heterogeneity. Syn., differenzierung.

DIFFERENTIATION, AXIAL - variations in density of chemical and often indefinable inclusions in the direction of one diameter of the egg, called the egg axis (see gradient).

DIFFERENTIATION, CELLULAR - the process which results in specialization of a cell as measured by its distinctive, actual, and potential functions (Bloom, 1937).

DIFFERENTIATION CENTER - one of the true organization centers in the developing insect egg. Syn., differenzierungszentrum (of Lehmann, 1942).

DIFFERENTIATION, CORPORATIVE - differentiation resulting from the physiological functioning of parts.

DIFFERENTIATION, DEPENDENT - all differentiation that is not self-differentiation; the development of parts of the organism under mutual influences, such influences being activating, limiting, or inhibiting. Inability of parts of the organism to develop independently of other parts. Such a period in ontogeny always precedes that of irreversible determination. "Experimental embryology is a study of the differentiations which are dependent, causally effected." (Roux, 1912). Syn., correlative differentiation, Abhängige Differenzierung, Différentiation provoquée.

DIFFERENTIATION, FUNCTIONAL - differentiation of tissues resulting from forces associated with functions (stresses and strains) which they are performing.

DIFFERENTIATION, INDIVIDUATIVE - differentiation due to the action of morphogenetic fields rather than to physiological functioning of parts; opposed to corporative differentiation.

DIFFERENTIATION POTENCY - the total repertoire of differentiations, cytological and histological, available to a given cell. Wider significance than prospective fate.

DIFFERENTIATION, REGIONAL - refers to fact that different parts of the organizer will induce different end organ formation; also refers to organ districts in a (limb) field.

DIFFERENTIATION, SELF - the perseverance in a definite course of development of a part of an embryo, regardless of its altered surroundings (Roux, 1912). Syn., differentiation spontanée.

DIKENETIC - dicentric, having two kinetochores.

DIMEGALY - possessing spermatozoa of two sizes.

DIPHYGENIC - having two types of development.

DIPLICHROMOSOME - two identical chromosomes, held together at the kinetochore and originated by doubling of chromosomes without separation of daughter chromosomes.

DIPLOID - normal number of chromosomes, double the gametic or haploid; complete set of paired chromosomes as in the fertilized egg or somatic cell.

DIPYGUS - (See duplicatus inferior.)

DISSOGENY - having two sexually mature periods, one as a larva and one as an adult.

DISTRICT - a portion of a morphogenetic field with certain specific determinations. Syn., territoire.

DIVERGENCE, VENTRAL - divergence of material from the mid-ventral line, compensatory to the process of dorsal convergence in gastrulation (Vogt).

DIVISION HIERARCHY - "four dimensional array of cells of which one and only one member (the zygote) is before all other members in time, and is the only one to which every other term stands in a relation which is some power of D (i. e., the relation is Dpo)." (Bertelanffy & Woodger, 1933.)

DOMINANCE - in embryology this term refers to parts of a system which have greater growth momentum and also which gather strength from the rest, such as the dorsal blastoporal lip.

DONNAN EQUILIBRIUM - distribution of ions on two sides of a semi-permeable membrane with diffusion until concentration of diffusible ions on the two sides of the membrane is the same, involving ionic rather than molecular balance.

DOPA - 3:4:dioxyphenylalanin, an intermediate oxidation product of tyrosine and one that appears as a precursor of melanin pigment in mammals (Black, 1917).

DORSO-VENTRAL - orientation of a graft or transplant so that the original dorsal-ventral axis is inverted in relation to the host field.

D-QUADRANT - one of the four early blastomeres of the annelid embryo which has the prospective function of giving rise chiefly to mesoderm.

DOUBLE ASSURANCE - cases where inductions usually occur but are not absolutely necessary; two processes working together, either one of which would be sufficient to accomplish the end result. Ability to bring about a morphogenetic process by means other than the usual one, (e. g., removal of the eye cup in R. esculenta and the overlying ectoderm will form a lens anyway, without the normal inducing influences of the eye cup). Term used by Rhumbler (1897) in connection with cell division and by H. Braus (1906) in development. Syn., doppelte sicherung.

DUPLICITAS CRUCIATA - double monsters, obtained by grafting or by inversion of the 2-cell amphibian embryo.

DUPLICITAS INFERIOR - conjoined twins fused anteriorly, having two rumps. Syn., dipygus.

DYSMEROGENESIS - cleavage resulting in unlike parts.

DYSPLASTIC TREATMENT - introduction of a transplant from organism of a different phylum. (E. g., frog to mammal or vice versa.)

DYSTELEOLOGY - apparent lack of purpose in organic processes or structures although they may ultimately be shown to be teleological.

ECDYSIS - process of moulting a cuticular layer, shedding of epithelium by amphibia.

ECHINOCHROME - red pigment of Echinoderm eggs which probably has respiratory function.

ECTODERM - the outermost layer of a didermic embryo (gastrula). Syn., epiblast.

ECTOPIC - out of its normal position, used in connection with transplants.

ECTOPLASM - external layer of protoplasm of the (egg) cell, the layer immediately beneath the cell membrane. Seat of Lillie's fertilizin and of all developmental processes, according to Just. Syn., egg cortex plasmalemma.

EGG, ALECITHAL - eggs with little or no yolk.

EGG, CLEIDOIC - egg which is covered by a protective shell (e. g., eggs of reptiles, birds, and oviparous mammals).

EGG, ECTOLECITHAL - egg having the formative protoplasm surrounded by yolk.

EGG ENVELOPE - material enveloping the egg but not necessarily a part of the egg, generally derived from the ovary (vitelline membrane or chorion of fish) or from the oviducts (jelly or albumen).

EGG, GIANT - abnormal polyploid condition where chromosome complexes are multiplied, resulting in giant cells and embryos.

EGG, HOMOLECITHAL - egg which has little yolk scattered evenly throughout the cytoplasm (e.g., sea urchin, mammal). Syn., isolecithal egg and absolete term, alecithal egg.

EGG JELLY - the mucin covering deposited on the amphibian egg as it passes through the oviduct.

EGG, MACROLECITHAL - egg with large amount of yolk, generally telolecithal.

EGG MEMBRANES - includes all egg coverings such as vitelline membrane, chorion, and the tertiary coverings from the oviduct.

EGG, MICROLECITHAL - egg with small amount of yolk. Syn., meiolecithal, oligolecithal.

EGG RECEPTOR - part of Lillie's scheme picturing parts that go into the fertilization reaction involving fertilizin. Egg receptor plus amboceptor plus sperm receptor gives fertilization.

EGG, TELOLECITHAL - egg with large amount of yolk concentrated at one pole.

EGG WATER - watery extract of materials diffusing from living (Echinoderm) eggs, presumably the "fertilizin" of Lillie. Syn., egg water extract.

EIDOGEN - a chemical substance possessing the power to modify an embryonic organ otherwise induced; force in regional differentiation, possibly including inductors of the second-grade level.

EINSTECKUNG - method of testing the power of induction by implanting a tissue, living or dead, or a chemical substance, into the blastocoel of a living gastrula.

ELECTRODYNAMIC THEORY OF DEVELOPMENT - theory that cell mitoses establish a definite differential potential capable of orienting growing nerve roots (axis cylinders) and thereby directing them (e. g., toward the brain).

EMANCIPATION - dynamic segregation from "autonomisation" (Weiss, 1935); establishment of local autonomy within embryonic areas.

EMBRYO - a stage in the ontogeny of the fertilized egg limited to the period before the intake of food.

EMBRYOMA - (See teratoma)

EMBRYONIC FIELD - region of formative processes within the embryo, larger than the area of ultimate realization of structures concerned (Gurwitsch, 1922).

EMBRYONIC SHIELD - thickened, shield-like region of the blastoderm which will give rise to the body of the (fish) embryo.

EMBRYOTROPHY - the means or the actual nourishment of the embryo.

ENCAPSIS - superordinate system within the embryo. Processes may be purposeful for a subordinate system and yet destroy another system to which it itself is subordinate. These relations are called encapsis (Heidenhain).

ENCHYLEMA - the liquid phase of the endoplasm in which are suspended yolk granules and mitochondria (Monné).

ENDODERM - the innermost layer of the didermic gastrula. Arises from the vegetal hemisphere of amphibia. Syn., entoderm.

ENDODERMISATION - shifting of an animal-vegetal gradient of an egg toward the vegetal gradient, causing hyper-development of the endodermal structures. Can be brought about by physical, chemical, or surgical means.

ENDOPLASM - inner medullary substance of the egg cell which is generally granular, soft, watery, and less refractory than the ectoplasm. Surrounded by ectoplasm.

ENDYSIS - the development of a new cuticular covering, opposed to ecdysis.

ENTELECHY - Driesch's theory of harmonious, equipotential system suggested an agent controlling development which he termed "elan vital". An intensive manifoldness; the intangible controlling order of development ("intensive Mannigfaltigkeit" of Driesch).

ENTOMESOBLAST - cell which will give rise to the trunk mesoderm in the determinate type of cleavage characteristic of annelids.

ENTO-MESODERM - refers to that portion of the invaginating blastoporal lips which will induce the formation of medullary fields in the amphibia.

ENTOPIC - in the normal position, opposed to ectopic (referring to transplants).

ENTRANCE CONE - the temporary depression on the surface of the egg following the entrance of the spermatozoön.

ENTRANCE PATH - (See path, entrance or penetration)

ENTWICKLUNGSMECHANIK - causal embryology (Roux); the seat and effective duration of the morphogenetic forces which are explored, by microsurgical means, and which seem to be responsible for the development of embryonic segregation (Lehmann, 1942).

ENTWICKLUNGSPOTENZEN - the total accomplishment of a blastema, experimentally determined (Raven).

EPIBOLY - growing, spreading, or flowing over; surrounding of inner masses (yolk and/or cells) by overgrowing ectoderm; process by which the rapidly dividing animal pole cells (often micromeres) grow over and enclose the vegetal hemisphere material. Increase in areal extent of the ectoderm. (Simile: rubber cap being pulled down over grapefruit.)

EPIGAMIC - tending to attract the opposite sex.

EPIGENESIS - developing of systems starting with primitive, homogeneous, lowly organized condition and achieving great diversification. Term coined by Harvey, the antithesis of preformation.

EPIGNATHUS - union upon the jaw of parasitic growth.

EPIMORPHOSIS - proliferation of material precedes the development of new parts.

ERGASTOPLASM - basophilic parts of the cytoplasm, mitochondria of cytologists.

ERRERA'S LAW - "a cellular membrane at the moment of its formation tends to assume the form which would be assumed under the same conditions by an elastic membrane destitute of weight" (Gray, 1931).

ESTROGEN - secretion product of the ovary which controls oestrus and endometrial growth.

ESTROUS CYCLE - the periodic series of changes which occur in the mammalian uterus, related to the preparation of the uterus for implantation of the ovum, and to repair.

ESTRUS - period of the reproductive cycle of the mammal when the uterus is prepared for implantation of the ovum.

ETHEOGENESIS - development of the spermatozoön without fertilization; male parthenogenesis.

EUCHROMATIN - the part of the regular chromatic structure of the nucleus which is rich in thymonucleic acid, and presumably the genes, alternating (in the chromosomes) with achromatic regions. It is in the form of discs, and takes methyl green stain.

EUPLOIDY - deviation from the normal diploid condition but involving complete sets of chromosomes (Tackholm, 1922).

EUTELY - constancy of cell numbers in the various organs of plants and animals, more dependable in animals than in plants (Wettstein, 1927, Heilborn, 1934).

EVAGINATION - the growth from any surface outward.

EVOCATION - mere calling forth of potentialities through contact; non-assimilative induction, no organization except that which is present within the host material; that portion of the inductive response which can be achieved by killed, crushed, or narcotized organizers of any level.

EVOCATOR - a chemical substance which has the power of calling forth the latent potentialities of an embryonic area; a morphogenetic stimulus.

EXCLUSIVITY - discreteness of the differentiation process (Weiss).

EXGENITO-VIVIPARITY - the embryo in a stage of development which corresponds to the egg stage of ovoviviparous forms, obtains its nourishment by means of a trophamnion, trophoserosa or trophochorion. Development occurs in the haemocoele, not in the uterus (e.g., Strepsystera).

EXOGASTRULA - gastrulation modified experimentally by abnormal conditions so that invagination is partially hindered and there remains some mesendoderm not enclosed by ectoderm; evagination of the primary intestinal cavity, or archenteron. (See vegetativisation.)

EXOGENOUS - originating from without the organism.

"EX OVO OMNIA" - all life comes from the egg (Harvey, 1657).

EXPERIMENTAL METHOD - concerted, organized, and scientific analysis of the causes, forces, and factors operating in any (embryological) system.

EXPERIMENTUM CRUCIS - the final, concluding experiment when a control is no longer needed; presumably a method of final and triumphal demonstration when all pioneer work has come to a successful ending.

EXPLANTATION - culturing of isolated blastema or tissues in vitro.

EXPRESSIVITY - the degree to which a group of organisms is affected by the presence of a particular gene (see penetrance).

EXTENSION - process of gastrulation; elongation of central cells of the marginal zone, and then the more peripheral cells, toward the groove of the blastopore. Syn., elongation, self-stretching (Schechtman), Strekung, Staffelung (Vogt).

EXTRA-OVATE - extrusion of a portion of the egg substance beyond the cell boundary, achieved in hypotonic solutions. Syn., exovate.

EYE, ANTERIOR CHAMBER OF - one of the best sites for observation of transplanted tissues, which tissues can be seen through the transparent cornea. The aqueous humor often is not as species specific as a nutrient environment as may be other tissues of the same organism.

FARBLOSE PIGMENTZELLEN - colorless pigment cell in dermal and subcutaneous tissues (e.g., in axolotl). (Schuberg, 1903.)

FATE MAP - a map of a blastula or early gastrula stage which indicates the prospective significance of the various surface areas, based upon previously established studies of normal development aided by means of vital dye markings.

FATE, PROSPECTIVE - destination towards which we know, from previous experience, that a given part would develop under normal conditions; lineage of each part of the egg through its cell descendants into a definite region or portion of the adult organism.

FEEDING, MAXIMAL - procedure whereby the organism is provided with all the food that it can possibly consume.

FETUS PAPYRACEUS - compressed fetus, abnormal: "paper-doll fetus".

FERTILIZATION - activation of the egg by a spermatozoön and syngamy of the two pronuclei; union of male and female gamete nuclei; amphimixis.

FERTILIZATION CONE - conical projection of the egg cortex to meet the spermatozoön destined to invade the egg, generally en-

gulfing the spermatozoön. Seen in annelids, molluscus, echinoderms, and ascidians.

FERTILIZATION, DRY - placing milt (concentrated sperm) of aquatic forms directly over practically dry eggs, the procedure allowing greater concentration of sperm before flooding the eggs with water.

FERTILIZATION, FRACTIONAL - fertilization following partial removal of sperm by centrifugation after partial penetration (Lillie, 1912). Elongated heads of some sperm (e.g., Nereis) are easily fragmented during penetration by centrifugation.

FERTILIZATION MEMBRANE - a non-living membrane seen to be distinct from the egg shortly after fertilization, very probably the vitelline membrane elevated off of the egg (or from which the egg has shrunken away by exosmosis). (See Costello, 1939: Phys. Zool. 12.)

FERTILIZATION, PARTIAL - cases where sperm head, after entering the egg cortex, does not move fast enough toward the egg nucleus to arrive before cleavage sets in, although the sperm aster may have reached the egg nucleus and given rise to the segmentation spindle.

FERTILIZATION, SELECTIVE - physiological block to some combinations of sperm and egg, such as in cases of self-sterility (e.g., Ciona). May indicate differential fertilizing powers of spermatozoa even from a common source.

FERTILIZIN - chemical substance in the egg cortex of mature (Echinoderm) eggs, called "sperm isoagglutinin" (Lillie, 1916) since its presence is necessary for fertilization of certain forms. Supposedly possesses two side chains, one spermophile and the other ovophile. Soluble colloidal substance (agglutinin) produced by eggs to attract sperm.

FERTILIZIN, ANTI - "Eggs contain in their interior a substance capable of combining with the agglutinating group of the fertilizin, but which is separate from it as long as the egg is inactive" (Lillie).

FEULGEN REACTION - Schiff's aldehyde test accomplished by hydrolysis of thymonucleic acid to yield the aldehyde which reacts with fuchsin giving a brilliant violet or pink color, a specific test for the thymonucleic acid of chromosomes.

FIBRILLATION - process of formation of (collagenous) fibers by the aggregation of ultramicrons whose axes are nearly parallel. May be the method of axis formation in limb rudiments (Harrison).

FIELD - mosaic of spatio-temporal activities within the developing organism constitute fields; areas of instability with positional relations to the whole organism, within which specific differentiations are about to

take place (e. g. , heart or limb fields).
Dynamic system of interrelated parts in
perfect equilibrium in the undifferentiated
organism. Not a definite circumscribed
area (like a stone in a mosaic) but a center
of differentiation with intensity diminishing
with the distance from the center, and with
different fields overlapping (Harrison, 1918).
A system of patterned conditions in a self-
sustaining configuration (Weiss, 1926).
Has a material substratum which may be
reduced without fundamentally altering the
original field pattern. Field is both heteroaxial and heteropolar. "Morphe concept"
of Gurwitsch (1914).

FIELD, DISTRICT - a district whose activities
show field character although none of its
elements can be identified with any particular component of the field.

FIELD, GRADIENT - the direction along which
the field intensity changes most rapidly.

FIELD, HETEROAXIAL - field in which developing structures vary along three coordinates
in space.

FIELD, HETEROPOLAR - the effects within a
field differ in two opposing senses along
the same axis.

FIELD, INDIVIDUATION - fields are under the
control of the organizing forces of the host
whose differentiation leads toward the realization of a complete individual.

FIELD LAWS - (1) When material is split off
from a field bearing system,
that portion remaining contains the field in its typical
distribution and structure.
(2) When unorganized but labile
material enters the field it
is included within the field.
Any field spreads over the
whole of the material at its
disposal, preserving its
initial structure even though
somewhat enlarged.
(3) Fields have the tendency of
taking up and including within
themselves any equivalent
fields from contiguous environment (e. g. , whole embryos formed from two fused
eggs). (See Schotte, 1940:
Growth suppl. p. 64.)

FIELD, MORPHOGENETIC - embryonic area out
of which specific structures will develop;
fields which determine the development of
form in a unitary structure (Gurwitsch,
1930).

FIELD, ORGAN - area in which a specific organ
of the embryo will develop (e. g. , eye field).

FIELD, TACTIC - field governing the displacement of cells (e. g. , grouping of cells in the
cartilaginous primordium of the amphibian
skeleton - Anikin, 1929).

FIELD, VEGETATIVE - early differentiated
part of the Echinoderm embryo; presumptive endoderm.

FOLLICLE - a cellular sac within which the egg
generally goes through the maturation stages
from oögonium to ovum; made up of follicle
cells, theca interna and externa.

FOVEA GERMINATIVA - pigment-free spot of
the animal hemisphere where the amphibian
germinal vesicle gives off its polar bodies.

FRAMBOISIA - protrusion of cells following
treatment of the embryo with anisotonic
solutions (Roux).

FREEMARTIN - mammalian intersex due to
masculinization of a female by its male part-
ner when the foetal circulations are continuous and the sex hormones are intermingled,
as in parabiosis.

FUNCTION, HOMOLOGOUS - synchronous behaviour (e. g. , when supernumerary limbs
are grafted near the control limb, they may
acquire innervation from the plexus of the
control and will thereafter contract synchronously and with the same degree of intensity as the control) (Weiss, 1936: Biol.
Rev. 2 - Resonance Theory of Reflex Activity.)

FURCHUNG - division of the egg cell into blastomeres by mitosis.

GALVANO-NEUROTROPISM - differences in
electrical potential responsible for growth
and connections of developing nerves. Gal-
vanic forces in neurogenesis.

GAMETE - a differentiated (mature) germ cell,
capable of functioning in fertilization. (e. g. ,
spermatozoön, ovum.) Syn. , germ cell.

GAMETOGENESIS - the process of developing
and maturing germ cells.

GASTROSCHISIS - improper closure of the body
wall along the mid-ventral line.

GASTRULA - the didermic or double-layered
embryo, possessing a newly formed cavity
known as the gastrocoel or archenteron.
The two layers are ectoderm (external) and
endoderm (internal) with only positional
significance when first formed.

GASTRULATION - dynamic processes involving
cell movements which change the embryo
from a monodermic to a di- or tri-dermic
form, generally involving inward movement
of cells to form the enteric endoderm.
Process varies in detail in different forms,
but may include epiboly, concrescence, confluence, involution, invagination, extension,
convergence - all of which are descriptive
terms for morphogenetic movements.

GEFÄLLE - a continuous, quantitative grada-
tion of a definite condition within a cell
colony. (See gradient)

GEL - a system in which there is a reduction in
the amount of solvent relative to the amount
of solid substance, thereby causing the
whole to become viscous (e. g. , asters).

GENE - self-producing molecule transmitted by the chromosome which determines the development of the characters of the individual, some of which may be solely embryonic.

GENETIC LIMITATION - each cell must react exclusively in accordance with the standards of the species which it represents.

GENOME - haploid gene complex; minimum (haploid) number of chromosomes with their genes derived from a gamete.

GENOTYPE - the actual genetic make-up of an individual, regardless of its appearance (opposed to phenotype).

GEOTONUS - position correct in respect to gravity.

GERM - the egg throughout its development, or at any stage.

GERM BAND - distinguishable bands of material in the (Molluscan) egg which will give rise respectively to ectoderm, endoderm, and mesoderm of the embryo.

GERM CELL - a cell capable of sharing in the reproductive process, in contrast with the somatic cell. (E. g., spermatozoön or ovum.) Syn. gamete.

GERM LAYER - a more-or-less artificial spatial and histogenic distinction of cell groups beginning in the gastrula stage, consisting of ectoderm, endoderm and mesodermal layers. No permanent or clear cut distinctions, as shown by transplantation experiments.

GERM RING - ring of cells which show accelerated mitotic activity, generally a synonym for the marginal zone which becomes the lips of the blastopore. The rapidly advancing cells in epiboly. (Syn., marginal zone)

GERM WALL - advancing boundary of the (chick) blastoderm including syncitia and the zone of junction.

GERMINAL LOCALIZATION - every area of the blastoderm (or of the unfertilized egg) corresponds to some future organ. Unequal growth produces the differentiation of parts (His, 1874). This concept led to the Mosaic Theory of Roux. (See fate map.)

GERMINAL VESICLE - the pre-maturation nucleus of the egg.

GERONTOMORPHOSIS - phylogenetic effects produced by modifying characters which are present in the line of adults.

GESTALTEN - a system of configurations consisting of a ladder of levels; electron, atom, molecule, cell, tissue, organ, and organism, each one of which exhibits specifically new modes of action that cannot be understood as mere additive phenomena of the previous levels. With each higher level new concepts become necessary. The parts of a cell cannot exist independently, hence the cell is more than a mere aggregation of its parts, it is a patterned whole. Coherent unit reaching a final configuration in space (W. Köhler). Gestaltung means formation.

GESTATION - period of carrying the young (mammal) within the uterus.

GIBBS-THOMPSON LAW - solidification from the accumulation of surface-acting substances by the lower surface tension at the surface of a drop (or cells), causing the potential energy of the combined system (liquid drop immersed within another liquid drop with which it is not miscible) to drop to a minimum.

GONOCHORISM - development or history of sex differentiation (Haeckel). Opposed to hermaphroditism.

GONOMERY - continued separation during cleavage of the chromosome sets from sperm and from egg in hybrid crosses. Theory that the maternal and paternal chromosomes remain apart throughout development.

GRADIENT - gradual variation along an axis, scaled regions of preference, two-dimensional pattern. (gefalle of Boveri.) (See writings of Child.)

GRADIENT, ACTIVITY - gradient established with appearance of the grey crescent in the amphibian egg, extending dorso-ventrally across the equator.

GRADIENT, AXIAL - metabolic gradient determined by differences in electrical potential or by experiments demonstrating differential susceptibility (e. g., to KCN).

GRADIENT CONCEPT - idea of physiological polarity indicated when an individual (e. g., Planaria) is transsected and each fragment reproduces the missing portions while retaining the original polarity; any two-dimensional concentration gradient as shown, for instance, by animalizing or vegetalizing factors in early morphogenesis (Ruünstrom).

GRADIENT, INHIBITION - refers to the balance of animal and vegetal hemisphere gradients in the (sea urchin) egg (Ruünstrom) which gradients are actually antagonistic to each other and yet both are necessary for normal (balanced) development.

GRADIENT, PIGMENT - when pigment is present it is generally concentrated at the centers of greatest metabolic activity.

GRAFT - a portion of one embryo removed and placed either among the tissues (a transplant) or the membranes (e. g., chorio-allantoic graft) of another embryo.

GRAFT, CHORIO-ALLANTOIC - method of growing a graft on the extra-embryonic membranes of the chick, the membranes reacting to the local irritation of a (foreign) graft in such a manner as to surround it with a richly vascular tunic of indifferent tissue, rich in the requisites for survival, growth, and differentiation of the graft. The graft is never incorporated as a transplant by the host itself. Graft on the chick chorio-allantois.

GRAFT HYBRID - organism formed from host and graft, showing characteristics of both stocks.

GROWTH - cell proliferation; a developmental (synthetic) increase in total mass of protoplasm at the expense of raw materials; an embryonic process generally following differentiation (see heterogony).

GROWTH, ACCRETIONARY - growth involving increase in non-living structural matter.

GROWTH, AUXETIC - growth involving increase in cell size alone.

GROWTH CIRCUMSTANTIALS - factors not responsible for the characteristics but for the realization of growth.

GROWTH COEFFICIENT - growth rate of a part relative to the growth rate of the whole (organism) depending on factors inherent in the tissues concerned (see heterogonic growth).

GROWTH, DYSHARMONIC - heterogonic growth to an extreme, relative growth rates become extremely unbalanced (Champy, 1924).

GROWTH EQUILIBRIUM - regulation of growth of part in respect to the organism as a whole.

GROWTH GRADIENT - quantitative grading of growth variables in such a way that the body appears to be a field system of interconnected metabolic areas.

GROWTH, HETEROGONIC - different rates of growth in different regions of the embryo, or in transplant as compared with host control organ. (See heterauxesis.)

GROWTH, ISOGONIC - similar rates of growth in different regions of the embryo.

GROWTH, MULTIPLICATIVE - growth involving increase in the number of nuclei and of cells. Syn., meristic growth.

GROWTH, PARTITION COEFFICIENTS OF inherent growth rates (e.g., in limb rudiments) involving changes in proportions.

GROWTH POTENTIALS - capabilities or predispositions for growth.

GROWTH REGULATION - a substance (R) postulated by Harrison, distinct from nutritional factors, present in the circulating medium of the organism, which controls growth.

GUANOPHORES - pigmented cells found in lateral line organs and in pericardium, having yellow guanin crystals which give a highly refractive metallic luster to the cells.

GYNANDROMORPH - condition where part of an animal may be male and another part female, not to be confused with hermaphroditism which is concerned primarily with the gonads.

GYNOGAMONES - highly acidic, polysaccharide, containing protein of low nitrogen content, and elongate, gel-forming molecular structure. Possibly the fertilizins of Lillie, but so named by Hartmann.

GYNOGENESIS - development of an egg with the egg nucleus alone. This may be brought about by rendering the sperm nucleus func-

tionless for syngamy by irradiation or other means, or by surgical removal. Opposed to androgenesis.

HAEMOTROPHE - the nutritive substances supplied to the embryo from the maternal blood stream of viviparous animals.

HAPLOID - having a single complete set of chromosomes, none of which appear in pairs, the condition in the gametic nucleus. Opposed to diploid, or twice the haploid, where the chromosomes appear as pairs (e.g., as in somatic cells).

HARMONIOUS-EQUIPOTENTIAL SYSTEM - an embryonic system in which all parts are equally ready to respond to the (organism as a) whole. The segmenting egg is a system of equivalent parts subdividing harmoniously, according to inherent tendencies, into smaller systems until the proper role in development has been assigned to each part of the embryo (Driesch). Isolated blastomeres tend to give complete but smaller embryos.

HARRISON'S RULE OF MINOR SYMMETRY -
(1) If the antero-posterior axis of a limbbud is reversed in a graft, the resulting limb will have the asymmetry proper to the opposite side of the body from that on which it is placed (i.e., it becomes disharmonic, whether originally taken from the same or the opposite side).
(2) If the antero-posterior axis is not reversed in grafting, the resulting limb will have the asymmetry proper to the side on which it is placed (i.e., it becomes disharmonic, whether originally taken from the same or the opposite side).
(3) If double limbs arise, the original member (i.e., the first to begin development) will have its asymmetry fixed with rule (1) or (2) depending upon the orientation of the graft, while the secondary member will be the mirror image of the first.

HATCHING - the beginning of the larval life of the amphibian, accomplished by temporarily secreted hatching enzymes which aid the embryo to escape its gelatinous capsule; the process of emergence of the chick embryo from its shell, involving critical changes in structure and functions.

HEDONIC - reptilian skin glands which secrete musk and are active during the breeding season.

HEMIBLASTULA - half-blastula derived by cauterizing one blastomere of the 2-cell stage (Roux).

HEMIGONY - one-half egg fragment (Delage, 1899).

HEMIKARYOTIC - haploid. In merogony, hemikaryotic arrhenokaryotic androgenetic or in artificial parathenogenesis, hemikaryotic thelykaryotic gynogenetic.

HEMIMELUS - failure of distal portion of appendages to develop.

HENSEN'S NODE - anterior end of the primitive streak of the chick embryo, corresponding to the region of the dorsal lip of the amphibian egg; region of future midbrain (position).

HENSEN'S THEORY - nerve fibers are formed out of protoplasmic bridges which exist throughout the embryonic body, protoplasmic bridge theory.

HERMAPHRODITE - an individual capable of producing both spermatozoa and ova.

HERTWIG'S LAW - the nucleus tends to place itself in the center of its sphere of activity; the longitudinal axis of the mitotic spindle tends to lie in the longitudinal axis of the yolk-free cytoplasm of the cell.

HETEROAGGLUTININ - agglutinin (fertilizin) of eggs which acts on sperm of different species, substance extractable from egg water which causes irreversible agglutination of foreign sperm.

HETERAUXESIS - the relation of the growth rate of a part either to another part of or to the whole organism. May include comparison of organisms of different sizes and ages, but of the same group. (See growth, heterogonic; isauxesis, bradvauxesis, tachyauxesis.)

HETEROCHROMATIN - part of the chromatic structure which seems to be related to the formation of the nucleolus. Takes a violet stain after methyl green but is digested away by ribonuclease. Probably represents both thymo- and ribo-nucleic acids.

HETEROCHRONY - alteration and reversal of the sequence of stages in ontogeny.

HETEROGONY - constant differential growth ratios (Pezard, 1918).

HETEROGONY, NEGATIVE - when the growth coefficient is below unity.

HETEROGONY, POSITIVE - when the growth coefficient is above unity, the parts increasing in relative size.

HETEROMORPHOSIS - differential morphological differentiation under varying environmental conditions wherein the major animal gradient is flattened; appearance of an embryonic organ inappropriate to its site; regenerated part different from that which was lost. Bateson's homoeosis or Goethe's metamorphy.

HETEROPLASIA - development of a tissue from one of a different kind.

HETEROPLEURAL - transplant to the other of bilateral sides.

HETEROPLOIDY - any deviation from the normal diploid number of chromosomes (Winkler, 1916).

HETEROPYCNOSIS - condensation of some (sex) chromosomes in gametogenesis.

HETEROTOPIC - transplant to same side but different region from the original.

HETEROTROPHIC - acquiring nourishment from without the organism.

HIBERNATE - to spend the cold (winter) period in a state of reduced activity (n., hibernation). Opposed to aestivate.

HISTOGENESIS - the appearance, during embryonic development, of histological differentiation; the development of tissue differentiation.

HISTOLYSIS - the destruction of tissues.

HISTOTELEOSIS - process by which a cell-line, already irreversibly differentiated, proceeds to its final histological specialization (Hoadley).

HISTOMERE THEORY - ontogenetic division of histological systems resulting in the synthesis of an (higher) organ (Heidenhain).

HISTOTROPHE - the nutritive substances supplied to the embryos of viviparous forms from sources other than the maternal blood stream (e. g., from uterine glands).

HOLOENTOBLASTIA - blastula almost entirely composed of endoderm used by Herbst for sea urchin larvae with nearly complete suppression of ectoderm by lithium salts.

HOLOMORPHOSIS - entire lost part replaced at once or later.

HOLTFRETER'S SOLUTION - now designated (by Holtfreter's request) Standard Solution. NaCl - 3.5 gr., KCl - 0.05 gr., $CaCl_2$ - 0.1 gr., $NaHCO_3$ - 0.2 gr., H_2O - 1 liter.

HOMOIOTHERMAL - refers to condition where the temperature of the body of the organism is under the control of an internal mechanism; the body temperature is regulated under any environmental conditions. Opposed to poikilothermal. Syn., warm blooded (animals).

HOMOIOTRANSPLANTATION - transplantation between different but related individuals.

HOMOLOGOUS - organs having the same embryonic development and/or evolutionary origin, but not necessarily the same function.

HOMOMORPHOSIS - new part like the part removed (Driesch).

HOMOPLEURAL - transplant to some same as that from which it was removed.

HORIZONTAL - an unsatisfactory term sometimes used synonymously with frontal, longitudinal, and even sagittal plane or section. Actually means across the lines of gravitational force.

HORMONE - a secretion of a ductless gland which can stimulate or inhibit the activity of a distant part of the biological system already formed.

HORMONE, MORPHOGENETIC - term used by Needham to refer to inductors which manifest distant effects.

HUMORAL SYSTEM - body fluids carrying specific chemical substances which may circulate in formed channels (blood vessels or lymphatics) or diffuse freely in the body cavities or tissue spaces, (c. g., neurohumors of Parker which act on the pigmentary system).

HYBRID - a successful cross between different species, although organism may be sterile (e. g., mule).

HYBRIDIZATION - fertilization of an egg by sperm of a different species.

HYDRODYNAMICS - process by which the detailed architecture of the blood vessels is derived, such details as size, angles or branching, courses to be followed, etc. The internal water pressure may be the cause of specific developmental procedure.

HYALOPLASM - ground substance of the cell apart from the contained bodies.

HYPERINNERVATION - supplying an organ with more than a single (normal) nerve fiber.

HYPERMETAMORPHOSIS - protracted and complete metamorphosis.

HYPERMORPHOSIS - overstepping previous ontogenies, though harmonious.

HYPERPLASIA - overgrowth; abnormal or unusual increase in elements composing a part.

HYPERTROPHY - increase in size due to increase in demands upon the part concerned.

HYPERTROPHY, COMPENSATORY - increase in size of part or a whole organ due to the loss or removal of part or the whole of an organ (generally hypertrophy in one member of the pair of organs).

HYPOMORPHIC - cells or tissues which are subordinate to formative processes (Heidenhain).

HYPOMORPHOSIS - harmonious underdevelopment.

HYPOPHYSIS - an ectodermally derived solid (amphibia) or tubuler (chick) structure arising anterior to the stomodeum and growing inwardly toward the infundibulum to give rise to the anterior and intermediate parts of the pituitary gland. Syn., Rathke's pocket (chick).

HYPOPLASIA - undergrowth or deficiency in the elements composing a part.

HYPOTHESIS - a complemental supposition; a presumption based on fragmentary but suggestive data offered to bridge a gap in incomplete knowledge of the facts. May even be offered as an explanation of facts unproven, to be used as a basis of expectations to be subject to verification or disproof.

HYPOTHESIS, WORKING - an attempt to find an answer to some feature of a complete biological situation by utilizing accepted physical and chemical principles.

HYSTEROTELY - formation of a structure is relatively delayed.

IDIOPLASM - equivalent to germ plasm of Weismann. Dissimilar determinant units of self-differentiating capacity (genes) each representing some part or character of the organism arranged in some plan comparable to the future arrangement of organic parts (Weismann).

IMPLANT - tissue or organ removed to an abnormal position; graft.

IMPLANTATION - process of adding, superimposing, or placing a graft (or a chemical fraction thereof) within a host without removal of anything from the host. Implants may be into the body cavity or into the orbital or anterior eye chamber cavities.

INCOMPATIBILITY - opposed to affinity; tendency of cells or cell groups to repel each other when removed from their normal environment. May be expressed in terms of cytolysis or histolysis of one of the cells or groups of cells.

INDIVIDUATION - assimilative induction concerned with regional character of the structure derived in response to (living) organizer activity; opposed to evocational responses. Refers to process in different regions as affected by the organizer, not by a single chemical substance such as an evocator. Regional nature affected by host environment.

INDUCTION - causing cells to form an embryonic structure which neither the inductor nor the reacting cells would form if not combined; the calling forth of a morphogenetic functional state in a competent blastema as a result of contact. In contrast with evocation, induction is successive, and purposeful in the sense that one structure leads to another. Sometimes loosely used to include evocator influences from non-living materials. Originally meant diversion of development from epidermis toward medullary plate (Marx, 1925).

INDUCTION, ASSIMILATIVE - transformation of one presumptive area into a different direction under the influence of inductive forces (Spemann).

INDUCTION, AUTONOMOUS - if the inducing implant and the host do not cooperate to form an harmonious whole, the material of the implant may not be used although the inductive forces are unimpaired. The inductor takes no part in the inducted structure (e. g., all chemical inductions). Opposed to complementary induction.

INDUCTION CAPACITY - organizational capacity; acquired with age and subsequently lost.

INDUCTION, COMPLEMENTARY - when the inductor, using some of its own material, completes itself out of the reacting system (host material); (e. g., when presumptive epidermis is transplanted to presumptive brain region and the embryo completes itself out of the transplanted material). Opposed to autonomous induction.

INDUCTION, DIRECT - case where a chemical compound acts in a manner similar to the naturally occurring inductor to produce a new neural axis in competent ventral ectoderm.

INDUCTION, HETEROGENETIC - when an organizer induces something other than itself, such as secondary organizer optic vesicle inducing lens formation.

INDUCTION, HOMOIOGENETIC - where embryonic part induces its like (e. g. , medullary plate induces medullary plate).

INDUCTION, INDIRECT - induction by a chemical compound in ventral ectoderm of a new neural axis by the liberation of a masked evocator in the reacting tissue.

INDUCTION, PALISADE - induction of neural-like tissue but without tube formation; cells arranged in palisade manner around an inductor.

INDUCTOR - a loose word which includes both organizer and evocator (Needham). Generally means a piece of living tissue which brings about differentiations within otherwise indifferent tissue.

INDUCTOR, NUCLEAR - a morphogenetic stimulating substance which is derived from the nucleus and therefore bears hereditary influences, but generally operating within the cell in question. The influence may be diffusible.

INFECTION - the acquisition of inductive power by a group of cells not normally possessing such power, but acquiring it by diffusion from temporarily contiguous organizer material. Syn. , Weckung.

INFUNDIBULUM - funnel-like evagination of the floor of the diencephalon which, along with the hypophysis, will give rise to the pituitary gland of the adult.

INGRESSION - inward movement of the yolk endoderm of the amphibian blastula. (Nicholas, 1945.)

INHIBITION - restraint or nullification of a tendency to differentiate.

INHIBITION, DIFFERENTIAL - restraint in a gradient field where toxic agents inhibit regeneration in the most active regions.

INHIBITION, TROPHIC - functional inhibition, contrasted with morphogenetic.

INSTINCT - "the overt behavior of the organism as a whole"..... "which is in physiological condition to act according to its genetically determined neuromuscular structure when adequate internal and external stimuli act upon it. " (Hartmann, 1942, Psychosomatic Med. 4:206.)

INSTITUTION - labile determination or competence of early germ (Graeper).

INTERSEX - an individual without typical sexual differentiation. Not hermaphrodite.

INVAGINATION - movement by in-sinking (Einstulpung of Vogt) of the egg surface and forward migration (Vordringen) involving displacement of inner materials. The folding or inpushing of a layer of (vegetal hemisphere) cells into a preformed cavity (blastocoel) as one of the methods of gastrulation. Not to be confused with involution.

INVOLUTION - rotation of a sheet of cells upon itself; movement directed toward the interior of an egg; the rolling inward or turning in of cells over a rim. One of the movements of gastrulation (e. g. , chick). Syn. embolic invagination (Jordan); einrollung, or umschlag (Vogt).

IRIDIOCYTES - inorganic salt crystals.

ISAUXESIS - relative growth comparisons in which the rate of the part is the same as that of the whole. (Syn. , isogony.) (Needham, 1940.)

ISO-AGGLUTININ - (Syn. , for fertilizin.)

ISO-ELECTRIC POINT - set of conditions under which the protein tends to give off hydrogen ions just sufficient to balance the tendency to give off hydroxyl ions; a state where the ionization of the protein is balanced.

ISOGONY - proportionate growth of parts so that growth coefficient is unity and there are constant relative size differences. Equivalent relative growth rate.

ISOLATION - removal of a part of a developing organism and its maintenance in the living condition as in tissue cultures. Physiological isolation may be achieved by interposing a mass of inert material (e. g. , yolk) between two regions. The bifurcations of regenerating limbs or the production of double hearts by interposing an inert barrier or one which is not subject to assimilative induction.

ISOMETRY - study of relative sizes of parts of animals of the same age.

ISOTROPIC - synonym for pluripotent (Lillie, 1929).

ISOTROPY - originally used (Pfluger, 1883) to mean absence of predetermined axes within the egg; now means condition of egg where any part can give rise to any part of the embryo (i. e. , equivalence of all parts of the egg protoplasm).

JANICEPS - Janus monster, face to face union of conjoined twins.

JANUS EMBRYO - double monster with faces turned in opposite directions. Syn. , duplicitas cruciata typica.

JELLY - mucin covering of (amphibian) egg, derived from the oviduct and applied to the outside of the vitelline membrane. In Frog, apparently necessary for successful fertilization.

KERN-PLASMA RELATION - ratio of the amount of nuclear and of cytoplasmic materials present in the cell. It seems to be a function of cleavage to restore the kern-plasma relation from the unbalanced condition of the ovum (with its excessive yolk and cytoplasm) to the gastrular or the somatic cell.

KINETOCHORE - spindle fiber attachment region. Syn., centromere.

LAEOTROPIC - turned, coiled, inclined to the left or counter-clockwise. Syn., leiotropic.

LAMP-BRUSH EFFECT - the side branches and loops from the chromosomes of young oöcytes give such an appearance. Syn., "Bürsten" effect of Ruckert and Carnoy.

LARVA - stage in development when the organism has emerged from its membranes and is able to lead an independent existence, but may not have completed its development. Except for neotony and paedogenesis, larvae cannot reproduce themselves.

LARVAL CHARACTERS - characters seen in the larva which may be dominant or recessive (as indicated when hybrid crosses are reversed) but which are not dependent upon an F_2 to determine the status. Egg cytoplasm is dominant over sperm influences in early development of hybrids. Larval skeletal differences seen in Echinoderm larvae of different combinations.

LATERAL LINE SYSTEM - a line of sensory structures along the side of the body of fishes and larval amphibia, generally embedded in the skin and innervated by a branch from the vagus ganglion. Presumably concerned with the recognition of low vibrations in the water.

LEAST SURFACE PRINCIPLE OF FLATEAU - homogenous system of fluid lamellae so arrange themselves that the individual lamellae adopt a curvature such that the sum of the (external) forces of all is, under the specific conditions, at a minimum.

LECITHIN - organismic fat which is phosphorized in the form of phosphatides.

LETHAL DEFECT - the suppression of a vital organ or of some vital function by a local defect.

LIESEGANG'S FIGURES - process of stratification as of formative substances in the egg.

LIMICOLA CELL TYPE - the movement of isolated embryonic cells resembles that of Amoeba limicola (Rhumbler, 1898) having balloon-like pseudopodia.

LIPIN - fats and fatty substances such as oil and yolk (e.g., lecithin) in eggs, important as water holding device in cells as well as insuring cell immiscibility with surrounding media. (E.g., cholesterol, ergosterol.)

LIPOGENESIS - omission of certain stages in ontogeny.

LIPOPHORES - pigmented cells in the dermis and epidermis, derived from neural crests and characterized by having diffuse yellow (lipochrome) pigment in solution.

LIPOSOMES - droplets of yellow oil which may be formed by the coalescence of droplets of broken down lipochondria (Holtfreter, 1946).

LITHOPEDION - mummified or calcified fetuses; "stone-child".

LOBSTER CLAW - missing digits in hands or feet, or split hand or foot; probably inherited.

LOCALIZATION - cytological separation of parts of the mosaic egg, each of which has a known specific subsequent differentiation. There is often a substratum associated with these areas, made up of pigmented granules, but it is the cytoplasm rather than the pigmented elements in which localization occurs.

LUNAR PERIODICITY - maturation and oviposition during certain phases of the lunar cycle (e.g., Nereis limbata sheds its gametes in the period from the full moon to the new moon in June to September).

MACERATION - to swell by soaking. In water the connective tissue between cells is loosened and the cells tend to separate.

MACROCEPHALUS - abnormally large head due to abnormal development of the cranium. Often the brain is swollen with cerebrospinal fluid. Syn., hydrocephalus.

MACROMERE - larger of the blastomeres where there is a conspicuous size difference, generally the yolk-laden endoderm forming cells. Opposed to micromere.

MACROSOMIA - gigantism, enlarged skeleton due to disturbed function of the pituitary and possibly also the thyroid glands.

MACROSTOMUS - failure of the primitive mouth slit to reduce normally.

MARGINAL BELT - ring of presumptive mesoderm of the amphibian blastula, essentially similar to the grey crescent of the undivided egg.

MATRIX - ground substance surrounding the chromonemata, usually less chromatic and making up the body of the chromosome. Syn., kalymma or hyalonema.

MATRIX, INTERCELLULAR - the cytoplasmic wall substance of cells in a whole blastema which forms an integrated foam structure and, because of its continuity, shows a very definite syncitial character. (Moore)

MATURATION - the process of transforming a primordial germ cell (spermatogonium or öogonium) into a functionally mature germ cell, the process involving two special divisions, one of which is always meiotic or reductional.

MAUTHER'S FIBERS - two highly differentiated, giant neurones found in the medulla of teleost fishes and amphibia and possessing extensive dendritic connections; axones extend from VIII cranial ganglion through the spinal cord. The fibers are functional particularly in maintaining the sense of equilibrium and are indispensible for sustained rhythmic motor reflexes.

MECHANICS, DEVELOPMENTAL - "analysis of the first found results of the experimental study of development of the egg." (Morgan)

MECHANISM - assumption that biological processes do not violate physical and chemical laws but that they are more than the mere functioning of a machine because material taken into the organism becomes an integral part of the organism, through chemical changes. Syn., the scientific attitude.

MEDIAN PLANE - "middle" plane (of the embryo). May be median sagittal or median frontal.

MEDULLARIN - a sex differentiating substance spread in some amphibia by the blood stream as a hormone, and in other forms by diffusion (see corticin).

MELANOBLAST - prospective pigment cell which will bear melanin (Ehrmann, 1896) but confused by some authors to include any pigment synthesizing cell. May be present and yet unable to develop pigment (e. g., white axolotl).

MELANOKINS - stimuli which act upon melanophores, such as temperature, humidity, light, hormones, and certain pharmacological agents (Bytinski-Salz, 1938).

MELANOPHORES - cell with brown or black (melanin) pigment granules or rods, found in every class of vertebrates. Derived from the neural crests and migrating throughout the body.

MELANOPHORE, ADEPIDERMAL - dermal melanophore.

MELANOPHORES, DEPENDENT - dermal melanophores (e. g., in white axolotl) which will develop pigment only under the influence of overlying transplanted pigmented epidermis. (Du Shane, 1943.)

MEMBRANOUS CELL TYPE - fan-like protuberances of isolated embryonic cells, having serrated pseudopodia (Holtfreter, 1943).

MEMBRANE, DESEMET'S - thinned out ectoderm of the cornea which occurs in response to the contact of the developing optic cup.

MEMBRANE, FERTILIZATION - a membrane representing either the elevated vitelline membrane or a newly formed membrane found at the surface of an egg immediately upon fertilization or following artificial parthenogenetic stimulation (activation); generally considered an adequate criterion of successful activation of the egg. First seen by Fol (1876) on the starfish egg.

MERISIS - growth by cell multiplication (in plants).

MEROGON - an egg fragment, generally with incomplete nuclear components.

MEROGONY - development of fertilized but enucleated egg fragments (Delage, 1899).

MEROGONY, ANDRO - development of an egg fragment which contains the sperm nucleus only (Bataillon & Tchou-Su, 1934). This may be accomplished by surgical removal of the egg nucleus (as it is giving off its polar body) or by irradiation damage of the egg nucleus (e. g., androgenesis).

MEROGONY, DIPLOID - fragment of an egg developing under the influence of the normal diploid nucleus.

MEROGONY, DOUBLE - cases where both halves of an egg develop following fertilization, one with a diploid fusion nucleus and the other with an haploid sperm nucleus (Dalcq, 1932).

MEROGONY, GYNO - the development of a fragment of a fertilized egg which fragment contains the egg nucleus only.

MEROGONY, PARTHENOGENETIC - development of a fragment of an unfertilized egg containing the egg nucleus and activated by artificial means (E. B. Harvey, 1935).

MEROGONY, PARTHENOGENETIC GYNO - fragment of an egg containing the egg nucleus only, stimulated to develop by artificial means.

MEROMORPHOSIS - the new part regenerated is less than the part removed.

MESENDODERM - newly formed layer of (Urodele) gastrula before there has been separation of endoderm and mesoderm, group of cells lying posteriorly to the lip of the blastopore, invaginated during gastrulation. Syn., mesentoblast, ento-mesoblast.

MESENCHYME - the form of embryonic mesoderm or mesoblast in which migrating cells unite secondarily to form a syncitium or network having nuclei in thickened nodes between intercellular spaces filled with fluid. Often derived from mesothelium.

MESIAL - Syn., median, medial, middle.

MESODERM - primary germ layer which arises from the marginal zone to take up its assigned position between the outer ectoderm and the inner endoderm.

MESOMERE - cells of intermediate size when there are cells of various sizes (macromeres and micromeres being the largest and the smallest, respectively). Also used as synonym for intermediate cell mass which gives rise to the nephric system.

METABOLISM - the sum total of chemical changes occurring in the life of an organism.

METABOLISM, ANIMAL - metabolism which brings about or is associated with the differentiation in the animal (ectodermal) direction (e. g. , sea urchin eggs in sulphate ions) characterized by increased oxygen consumption. Can be checked by lithium. (See animalization.)

METABOLISM, VEGETAL - metabolism which brings about or is associated with the differentiation in the vegetal (endodermal) direction (e. g. , sea urchin eggs in lithium chloride) characterized by a breakdown of proteins and checked by an absence of sulfate ions. (See vegetativisation.)

METAMORPHOSIS - the end of the larval period of amphibia when growth is temporarily suspended. The change is from the larval (aquatic) to the adult (terrestrial) form. There is autolysis and resorption of old tissues and organs such as gills, and the development of new structures such as eyelids and limbs; changes in structure correlated with changes in habitat from one that is aquatic to one that is terrestrial; change in structure without retention of original form, as in the change from spermatid to spermatozoon.

METAMORPHOSIS, ANURAN - loss of tail, larval mouth, and gills; reduction in the gut; development of limbs. Period ends with the appearance of the tympanum.

METAMORPHOSIS, URODELE - period of gill reduction, shedding of skin and the development of eyelids.

METAPLASIA - permanent and irreversible change in both type and character of cells; transformation of potencies of an embryonic tissue into several directions, generally an indication of a pathological condition (e. g. , bone formation in the lung). It is thought that some differentiated tissue may become undifferentiated and then undergo a new differentiation in a different direction.

METATHETELY - the appearance of early embryonic structures at a stage later than normal (e. g. , the retention of larval organs by insect pupae). Opposed to prothetely.

MICROCEPHALUS - small or pin-headed; a condition due to the arrested development of the cranium and the brain, accompanied by reduced mentality.

MICROGNATHUS - retarding of lower jaw in the new born.

MICROMERE - smaller of the cells when there is variation in the size of blastomeres.

MICROMETRY - measurement of a microscopic object, using an ocular micrometer.

MICROPHTHALMIA - eyes that are too small, often due to undersized lenses (Harrison, 1929).

MICROPYLE - an aperture in the egg covering (e.g., fish eggs) through which spermatozoa may enter. Generally the only possible point of fertilization in eggs bearing micropyles.

MICROSOMIA - dwarfism, reduced skeleton, due possibly to disturbed function of the pituitary and thyroid glands.

MICROSTOMUS - small mouth; excessive closure of the mouth.

MICROSURGERY - procedures described by Spemann, Chambers, Harrison and others where steel and glass instruments of microscopic dimensions are used to operate on small embryos.

MILIEU - term used to include all of the physico-chemical and biological factors surrounding a living system (e. g. , external or internal melieu).

MITOCHONDRIA - small, permanent cytoplasmic granules which stain with Janus Green B, Janus Red, Janus Blue, Janus Black 1, Rhodamin B, Dietheylsafranin, dilute methylene blue, and which have powers of growth and division and are probably lipoid in nature, and may contain proteins, nucleic acids, and even enzymes. Syn. , plastens.

MITOGENETIC RAYS - rays of short wave-length emanating from a growing point (e. g. , onion root tip - Gurwitsch, 1926) which rays excite cell division when they encounter tissues capable of proliferation. Such rays come from disintegrating, dead tissues of regenerating tails (e. g. , axolotls - Blacher, 1930).

MITOTIC INDEX - the number of cells, in each thousand, which are in active mitosis at any one time and place in an organism (Minot, 1908); the percentage of actively dividing cells. Often considered as a measure of growth activity.

MODULATION - physiological fluctuation of a cell in response to environmental conditions, indicating latitude of cell adaptation; cellular changes reversible without residue (Weiss, 1939); temporary reactions of cells to new environmental conditions without loss of original potential functions (e. g. , reversible histological differentiation at the end of ontogeny).

MODULATOR - specific inducing substance which goes beyond basic evocation and will induce a specific kind of tissue characteristic of a definite region (e. g. , neural tube of mid-body level - Waddington).

MOLTING - periodic shedding of the upper, cornified epidermis, common among amphibia and reptiles, and possibly associated with breeding activity.

MONOSPERMY - fertilization accomplished by only one sperm. Opposed to polyspermy.

MONSTER, AUTOSITE-PARASITE - double embryos with great size discrepancy so that the smaller one bears a parasitic relationship to the larger; variously produced.

MONSTER, DICEPHALUS - double-headed abnormality, produced by any means.

MONSTER, ISCHIOPAGUS - double embryos, widely separated except at the tail; produced by any means.

MORPHOGENESIS - all of the topogenetic processes which result in structure formation; the origin of characteristic structure (form) in an organ or in an organism compounded of organs.

MORPHOGENETIC MOVEMENTS - cell or cell area movements concerned with the formation of germ layer (e.g., during gastrulation) or of organ primordia. Syn., Gestaltungsbewegungen.

MORPHOGENETIC POTENTIAL - product of a reaction between the cortex and the yolk just sufficient to bring about response in a competent area; threshold value (Dalcq and Pasteels).

MORPHALLAXIS - an old part transformed directly into a new part or whole organism, a type of regeneration, resulting in a whole from a part (e.g., each piece of a dissected Planaria or Tubifex becomes a complete organism).

MOSAIC - a type of egg or development in which the fate of all parts are fixed at an early stage, possibly even at the time of fertilization. Local injury or excisions generally result in the loss of specific organs in the developing embryo. Such eggs or embryos react by recovery to such experimental procedures as blastomere separation, parabiosis or merogony. Opposed to regulative development.

MOVEMENT, FORMATIVE - localized changes in cell areas resulting in the formation of specifically recognizable embryonic regions (Vogt).

MOVEMENT, HOMOLOGOUS - movement of homologous muscles in transplanted limbs, the synchronous contraction of muscles.

NACHBARSCHAFT - morphogenetic effects produced by contact with other tissues or structures of a developing organ; contiguity effects.

NECROHORMONES - the chemical substances produced by degenerating nuclei which cause the premature and incomplete divisions of öocytes in sexually mature mammals and in the formation of oligopyrene spermatozoa in Mollusca.

NECROSIS - local death of a cell or group of cells, not the whole body.

NEIGHBORWISE - the reaction of a transplant appropriate to its new environment, indicating its plasticity, pluripotency, or lack of determination. Syn., Artsgemäss.

NEMAMERE - one of the physical units composing a gene-string or genonema, which carries the genes. May be composed of several genes, or a single gene may extend over several nemameres. Governs biophysical reactions of the gene-string.

NEOMORPHOSIS - new part not only different from part removed but also like an organ belonging to another part of the body; or unlike any organ of the body.

NEOPLASM - a new growth, generally a tumor. Histologically and structurally an atypical new formation.

NEOTONY - sexual maturity in the larval stage; a condition of many urodeles (e.g., Necturus, Azolotl) and of experimentally produced thyroidless anuran embryos where the larval period is extended or retained, i.e., the larvae fail to go through metamorphosis. Appearance of larval conditions in the adult.

NEURAL CREST - a continuous cord of ectodermally derived cells lying on each side in the angle between the neural tube and the body ectoderm, separated from the ectoderm at the time of closure of the neural tube and extending from the extreme anterior to the posterior end of the embryo; material out of which the spinal and possibly some of the cranial ganglia develop, and related to the development of the sympathetic ganglia and parts of the adrenal gland by cell migration.

NEUROBIOTAXIS - concentration of nervous tissue takes place in the region of greatest stimulation.

NEUROGEN - an evocator which causes neural induction in vertebrates. May include the organizer, chemical substances, carcinogens, oestrogens, etc.

NEUROGENESIS, MECHANICAL HYPOTHESIS OF - mechanical tension of plasma medium in any definite direction is said to orient and aggregate the fibrin micellae in a corresponding direction.

NEUROHUMORS - hormone-like chemical substance produced by nerous tissue, particularly the ends of developing nerves which consequently act as stimulating agents.

NEURULA - stage in embryonic development which follows gastrulation and during which the neural axis is formed and histogenesis proceeds rapidly. The notochord and neural plate are already differentiated, and the basic vertebrate pattern is indicated.

NEUTRAL MEDIUM - an environmental medium for the embryo which is free from any chemical or physical inductors, and is physiologically isotonic.

NORMALIZING - formative action anchored in the organization associated with the determination of development, not super-material entelechy but an integral part of the organism itself. Integrating and balancing tendencies.

NUCLEAL REACTION - sections of tissue hydrolyzed with HCl before treating with Schiff's reagent may give a characteristic red or purple color known as the nucleal reaction. (See Feulgen reaction.)

NUCLEAR MEDIUM - calcium free but otherwise balanced and isotonic salt medium in which the isolated germinal vesicle can survive for some time.

NUCLEOFUGAL - refers to outgrowth in two or more directions from the nuclear region as a center, such as in the formation of myelin around a nerve fiber, starting at the sheath cell nucleus as a center and growing in two directions.

NUSSBAUM'S LAW - the course of the nerve within the muscle may be taken as the index of the direction in which that particular muscle has grown.

OEDEMA - excessive accumulation of water (lymph) in the tissues and cavities of the body; may be subcutaneous and/or intracellular. Due to a block in drainage channels and generally associated with cardiac inefficiency.

OMNIPOTENT - used in connection with a cell which could, under various conditions, assume every histological character known to the species, or which, by division, could give rise to such varied differentiations.

ONTOGENY - developmental history of an organism; the sequence of stages in the early development of an organism.

"OMNE VIVUM E VIVO" - all life is derived from pre-existing life (Pasteur).

"OMNIS CELLULA E CELLULA" - all cells come from pre-existing cells (Virchow).

ÖOPLASM - cytoplasmic substances connected with building rather than reserve materials utilized in the developmental process.

OPTICO-OCULAR APPARATUS - includes all the structures related to the eye: optic vesicles, optic stalks, and primary optic chiasma, which develop from the simple median anlagé precociously found in the medullary plate (LePlat, 1919).

ORGAN-FORMING SUBSTANCE - substances which, by chemo-differentiation and segregation are localized in different blastomeres bringing about a mosaic of development.

ORGAN, RUDIMENTARY - organ which is present but without any detectable physiological manifestation.

ORGANIC POINTS THEORY - discarded theory of Bonnet and yet much like chemo-differentiation. The preformed determinants are unequally distributed between blastomeres during early cleavage.

ORGANICISM - laws of biological systems to which the ingredient parts are processes are subordinate; idea of organism as whole (Loeb).

ORGANIZATION - indicated by the inter-dependence of parts and the whole. "When elements of a certain degree of complexity become organized into an entity belonging to a higher level of organization" says Waddington, "we must suppose that the coherence of the higher level depends on properties which the isolated elements indeed possessed but which could not be exhibited until the elements entered into certain relations with one another." Relations beyond mere chemical equations; bordering on the philosophical idea. Process of differentiation or specialization which takes place according to a definite pattern in space and time, not chaotically in the direction of haphazard distribution (see Gestalten).

ORGANIZER - the chorda-mesodermal field of the amphibian embryo; a living tissue area which has the power of organizing indifferent tissue into a neural axis. Organizer is more than an evocator or inductor because definite axial structures are caused to develop. Term first used by Spemann to describe a "dorsal quality" qualitatively different from vegetal hemisphere material. Term organizer now used for graded inductions such as primary or first grade organizer (dorsal lip; induces neural axis) secondary or second grade organizer (optic cup induces lens); and tertiary or third grade (annulus tympanicus induced tympanic membrane formation).

ORGANIZER, NUCLEOLAR - localized region of a particular set of chromosomes where the nucleolus is found, each nucleolus being associated with a set of chromosomes.

ORGANOGENESIS - emancipation of parts from the whole; appearance or origin of morphological differentiation.

ORTHOTOPIC - transplant to homologous region.

OSMOTIC PRESSURE - P equals kCT; P is the force under which water tends to pass through a membrane into a substance that cannot diffuse through this same membrane (e.g., sugar and collodion membrane) and this force is directly proportional (k) to the molecular concentration (C) of the substance (sugar) and to the absolute temperature (T). The terms isotonic, hypertonic, and hypotonic are used to express osmotic pressure relations such as exist between the cell contents and its environment.

OTOCEPHALY - tendency to fusion or approximation of ears, accompanying cyclopia.

OUTGROWTH NEURONE THEORY - the cells found along the course of a nerve fiber, the fiber developing as a protoplasmic outgrowth (extension) from a single ganglion cell.

OVOPHILE - presumed receptor portion of amboceptor suitable to receive the egg receptor, anti-fertilizin, or blood inhibitors, in the fertilizin reaction (Lillie).

OVIPOSITION - the process of egg laying.

OVOVIVIPARITY - condition in which egg contains enough yolk to carry the embryo to hatching. After this stage the larva is liberated from the maternal organism without receiving further nourishment.

OVULATION - the release of eggs from the ovary, not necessarily from the body.

PAEDOGENESIS - relative retardation of the development of body structures as compared with the reproductive organs; reproduction during larval stage; precocious sex development.

PAEDOMORPHOSIS - introduction of youthful characters into the line of adults.

PALINGENETIC - term used for repeated or recapitulated stages which reflect the history of the race (Haeckel).

PARABIOSIS - lateral fusion of embryos by injuring their mirror surfaces and approximating them so that they grow together (see telobiosis).

PARTHENOGENESIS - development of the egg without benefit of spermatozoa; development stimulated by artificial means.

PARTHENOGENESIS, ARTIFICIAL - activation of an egg by chemical or physical means (e.g., butyric acid, hypertonic solutions, irradiation, needle prick. etc.)

PARTHENOGENESIS, FACULTATIVE - eggs normally fertilized before development, may, on occasion, develop when fertilization is delayed before sperm penetration.

PARTHENOGENESIS, NATURAL - maturation of the egg leads to development without the aid of spermatozoa (e.g., some insects).

PARTITION-COEFFICIENT - the factor which determines the size of any part at any time by parcelling out materials; relative capacity for various parts of the embryo to absorb food from a common supply at different times. Such coefficients are expressions of intrinsic growth potentials, so balanced in normal development that no single structure can monopolize the nutriment to the detriment of other structures.

PARTHENOGENETIC CLEAVAGE - fragmentation of protoplasm of old and unfertilized chick eggs, originally thought to be true cleavage.

PATH, COPULATION - path along which the pronuclei approach each other, the sperm of the amphibia generally leaving a trail of pigment taken in from the surface coat.

PATH, PENETRATION - the path of the sperm as it enters the egg before it veers into the copulation path.

PATHFINDERS - pioneering nerve fibers which assume the task of growing into the uninvaded peripheral tissues (Weiss).

PENETRANCE - the degree to which a group of organisms expresses the presence of a gene. (See Expressivity.)

PERIBLAST, CENTRAL - cells of syncitial nature beneath and separate from the blastoderm of fish.

PERIBLAST, MARGINAL - cells of syncitial nature bounding the central blastoderm of the fish or chick.

PERMEABILITY - property of a membrane indicated by the rate at which substances pass through, the phenomenon involving four attributes of mass, area, time, and concentration as well as the nature of the environment.

PFLUGER'S LAW - the dividing nucleus elongates in the direction of the least resistance.

pH - method of stating the measure of the hydrogen ion concentration, expressed as the log of the reciprocal of the hydrogen ion concentration in gram-mols per liter. The negative value of the power of 10 equivalent to the concentration of hydrogen ions in gram-molecules per liter. The neutral solution (neither acidic nor basic) has a pH value of 7: pH values less than 7 are acid and those more than 7 are alkaline.

PHENOCOPY - the imitation of a particular genotype by response to physiological factors in the environment, but carrying no hereditary implication.

PHENOCRITICAL PERIOD - the period in the development of an organism when a particular gene effect can be most easily influenced by environmental factors.

PHENOTYPE - the expressed genetic influences.

PHOCOMELUS - failure of proximal portion of appendages to develop, distal parts may be normal.

PHYLOGENY - series of stages in the history of the race; the origin of phyla.

PLACODE - plate or button-like thickening of ectoderm from which will arise sensory or nervous structures (e.g., olfactory placode).

PLANE - (See "section".)

PLASM - a distinguishable region of mosaic eggs which gives rise to later and specific organ development.

PLASMALEMMA - the outermost, thin, viscous layer of the ectoplasm in the fertilized egg which does not change by centrifugation.

PLASMAL REACTION - related to the presence of fat and aldehydes in the cytoplasm (Feulgen and Voit, 1924). It is not specific, however, as positive reactions are given by certain alkalis, aliphatic ketones, some unsaturated compounds (e.g., oleic acid), weak salts of strong bases (e.g., acetates and phosphates), some amino oxides and certain catalytic oxidizing systems.

PLASMODEMS - fine protoplasmic threads (presumably) connecting cells mitotically derived from a parent cell; used in connection with marginal cells in the blastodisc of fishes and birds.

PLASMODESMATA - protoplasmic bridges claimed (Paton, 1907) to be the means of

nerve fiber growth; plasmodesmata supposedly incorporated into the substance of
the axone during its origin.

PLASMONUCLEIC ACID - one of the two types
of nucleic acid, this one occurring in the
cytoplasm, in the plasmosome (nucleolus),
and possibly in minute quantities in the
chromatin (Pollister & Mirsky, 1944: Nature 153:711). (See chromonucleic acid.)

PLASTENS - (See mitochondria.)

PLASTICITY - the ability of early cell areas
(tissues) to conform to environmental influences, such plasticity disappearing at
the end of gastrulation. Syn., pluripotency.

PLASTIN - thread-like structural elements of
the cytoplasm which form a gel framework
by net formation. (Frey-Wyssling)

PLATEAU'S LAWS - not more than three (3)
planes can meet at any one edge and not
more than four edges can meet at any one
point. Reference is made to cleavage
planes.

PLEIOTROPISM - multiple effects of a single
gene due to effects upon metabolism.

PLURIPOTENT - condition where cell or embryonic area is amenable to several courses
of differentiation. An undetermined state.

POIKILOPLOID - variable chromosome number.

POIKILOTHERMOUS - cold-blooded; animals
which depend upon the environment to regulate their body temperature. Animals
lack temperature regulating mechanisms.
(E.g., amphibia, fish). Opposed to homo-
iothermous.

POLAR FURROW - space between blastomeres
of 40 cell stage due to shifting of the mitotic
axes in each of the blastomeres, generally
associated with spiral cleavage.

POLARITY - stratefication; axial distribution;
assumption that behind any visible differences in the egg (cell or embryo) there is
an invisible arrangement of some (imag-
ined?) basic material. The type of polarity may be inherent, predetermined, while
the direction of polarity may be conditioned
by the environment. Related to the animal-
vegetal and anterior-posterios axes. (See
gradient.) Syn., Schicktungspolarität.

POLAR LOBE - lobe which remains attached to
one blastomere into which it is periodically
withdrawn during the intervals between
mitoses, and which gives rise to the ento-
mesoblast and hence to mesoderm. Also
"yolk lobe," although this lobe may actually
to devoid of yolk.

POLAR PLASM - in determinate cleavage (e.g.,
annelid and mollusc eggs) some of the vegetative pole protoplasm may be identified
in early blastomeres by its particular consistency. This may be the material of the
polar pole.

POLE, ANIMAL - the protoplasmic portion of
a telolecithal egg from which the polar

bodies are given off, in which the germinal
vesicle is found, and which has the highest
metabolism and gives rise to the principal
parts of the nervous system and sense organs. Region of least yolk concentration.
Syn., apical pole or hemisphere (See animalization).

POLE, VEGETAL - region of the egg opposite
the animal pole; region of lowest metabolic
rate; pole with greatest density of yolk in
telolecithal eggs, generally the endoderm
forming portion of the early egg. (See
vegetativisation.)

POLYDACTYLY - extra digits in hands or feet;
in man probably inherited.

POLYEMBRYONY - natural isolation of blastomeres leading to the production of multiple
embryos; development of several embryos
from a single zygote.

POLYHYDRAMNIOS - condition where the amniotic fluid exceeds two liters.

POLYPLOID - possessing a multiple number of
chromosomes, such as triploid (3 times
the haploid number) tetraploid (4 times the
haploid), etc. Always more than the normal
diploid number of the typical zygote. (Winkler, 1916.)

POLYPLOIDOGEN - a chemical substance which
brings about the polyploid condition, usually
by inhibiting certain phases of nuclear division.

POLYSPERMY - entrance into the egg of more
than a single sperm, normally (e.g., chick
and urodele) or under pathological conditions (e.g., Anura, Echinodermata, Mollusca, etc.) (Hertwig, 1887; Boveri, 1907;
Herlant, 1911). Normal polyspermy is
sometimes called "physiological polyspermy"
while the abnormal is pathological, brought
about by chemical or physical conditions
(see Clark, 1936. Bio. Bull.).

POST-GENERATION - regeneration out of newly
formed rather than already differentiated
tissues; restoration of parts of the embryo
by utilization of materials (unused) from an
injured (cauterized) blastomere (Roux).

POTENCY - ability to develop embryologically;
capacity for completing destiny; ability to
perform an action; "future development
verbally transformed to an earlier stage
(Waddington). The test of potency is actual
realization in development. It is not the
same as competence. It is an explanatory
rather than a descriptive term (Roux, 1892)
for developmental possibility." "A piece of
an embryo has the possibility of a certain
fate before determination, and the power to
pursue it afterwards." (Needham, 1942.)

POTENCY, ACTIVE - cases of self-differentiation where potencies are realized in isolation even without inductive forces (Bautzmann, 1929).

POTENCY, PASSIVE - potencies formed in the presence of inductive forces only (Bautzmann, 1929).

POTENCY, PROSPECTIVE - the sum total of developmental possibilities, the full range of developmental performance of which a given area (or germ) is capable. Somehow more than, and inclusive of, prospective fate and prospective value. (See these terms.) Connotes possibility, not power. Not to be confused with competence.

POTENTIAL, MORPHOGENETIC - the strong or weak ability to develop into specific structures (Dalcq and Pasteels, 1938).

PREFORMATIONISM - arrangement of parts of the future embryo are spatially identical in the egg (ovist) or in the homunculus of sperm (spermist); anlagen of all parts of the organism are already present in the egg (or sperm).

PREFUNCTIONAL PERIOD - period during which the morphological and histological differentiations proceed to prepare the organs for functioning (Roux).

PRESUMPTIVE - the expected (e.g., the fate of a part in question) based on previous fate-map studies.

PRIMORDIA, PRESUMPTIVE - place and extent of prospective values of early gastrular surface as regards its realization into specific organ areas in the normal process of development. Not necessarily checked by self-differentiating technique.

PRIMORDIUM - the beginning or earliest discernible indication of an organ. Syn., rudiment, anlagé.

PRONUCLEUS - either of the gametic nuclei in the egg after fertilization and before syngamy; female pronucleus is the mature egg nucleus after the elimination of the polar bodies, distinct from the germinal vesicle which is the pre-maturation nucleus.

PROSPECTIVE SIGNIFICANCE - the normal fate of any part of an embryo at the beginning of development. Syn., prospective Bedeutung, Potentialité reelle.

PROTANDROUS - hermaphroditism in which the male elements mature prior to the female.

PROTHETELY - the appearance of structures at an early stage of development which normally appear later (e.g., pupal organs in larval insects). Opposed to metathely. (Schultze)

PROTOGYNOUS - hermaphroditism in which the female elements mature prior to the male.

PROTOPLASMIC BRIDGE THEORY - (See Hensen's theory and plasmadesmata.)

PYCNOSIS - increase in density of the nucleus (or the cytoplasm) which may be hyperchromatic. Pycnotic cells in the central nervous system are called chromophile cells. Such cells have an increased affinity for haematoxylin and methylene blue.

PYGOPAGUS - rump union in conjoined twins.

RACHISCHISIS - cleft spine, due to failure to close completely.

RANDZONE - term (German) for marginal zone, the line between the animal and the vegetal hemispheres of amphibian eggs or the region of initial involution for gastrulation.

RATE-GENES - one and the same gene may lead to different rates of formation of specific materials such as melanin.

REALISATORSYSTEM - pertaining to the nonspecific complexity of the metabolism-apparatus which guarantees the normal course of determination and topogenetic transformations in a blastema. (Lehmann.) (See determination.)

REALIZATION FACTOR - factor involved in the achievement of a certain end organ production, often associated with the establishment of a gradient.

RECONSTITUTION - an aspect of regeneration where a new organ is formed within old tissues rather than by regeneration from a cut surface. A re-arrangement of parts to give new form, particularly in hydroid experiments (see blastema).

RECOVERY, DIFFERENTIAL - differential acclimatization in a gradient system where a low concentration of depressants indicates that regions of highest activity show greatest powers of adjustment.

RECUPERATION - the reappearance of competence at a late stage in development (e.g., limb or tail blastema cells).

REDIFFERENTIATION - secondary differentiation within the area delimited by the term modulation. (Kasahara, 1935: Arch. f. Exp. Zell. 18). A return to a position of greater specialization in actual and potential functions (Bloom, 1937: Physiol. Rev. 17).

REDUPLICATION - double or even treble growths (e.g., limbs) connected with one another at some point along their length, reduplicated member being (usually) a mirror image of the original (see Bateson's Rule).

REGENERATION - repair or replacement of lost part or parts by growth and differentiation past the phase of primordial development. The vast organizing potencies of the different regions of the early embryo are lost after the completion of development and there remain only certain regions of the body which are said to be capable of regeneration. Regenerative powers are more extensive among embryos and adults of phyletically low forms.

REGENERATION, BIAXIAL - regeneration which leads to two apical or two basal regions, accomplished in a form like Planaria by cutting off the head and splitting the body from the anterior cut surface, or from the posterior. The latter procedure will often give rise to a crotch head.

REGENERATION, PHYSIOLOGICAL - changes which occur as a part of the life cycle of the organism.

REGENERATION, RESTORATIVE - changes occurring in regular fashion after an accident, bringing about a replacement of lost or damaged parts.

REGENERATION, WOLFFIAN - appearance of a new lens in the eye after removal of the former lens, due to possible regeneration from the upper margin of the iris.

REGENERATIVE CAPACITY - the ability to replace lost parts, the ability which varies (generally) inversely with the scale of degree of development.

REGION, PRESUMPTIVE - regions of the blastula which, by previous experimentation, have been demonstrated to develop in certain specific directions under normal ontogenetic conditions (e. g., presumptive notochord or lens). Not as definite as anlagé.

REGULATION - a reorganization toward the whole; the power of pre-gastrula embryos to utilize materials remaining, after partial excision, to bring about normal conditions in respect to the relation of parts; somewhat comparable to regeneration of later stages, but more flexible and more extensive in early development. Ability to adjust to a strange environment and yet to develop along lines of normal development.

REINTEGRATION - the restoration to the organism, after the period of self differentiation and through the action of hormonal and neural factors, of control by its individuation field.

RESONANCE THEORY OF REFLEX ACTIVITY - the central nervous system can emit different forms of excitation and a specific muscle will respond only to the excitation appropriate to it. Rather than different conducting pathways for the central nervous system and peripheral end organs (e. g., limbs), all components of an excitation are transmitted to all muscles, but only that muscle, for which a specific component is contained, will respond. Each muscle has motor neurones which act as selective transmitters. This is the explanation (Weiss, 1936: Biol. Rev. 2:464) for the simultaneous movement of homologous muscles even though transplanted limbs may be supplied by non-homologous nerves. (See function, homologous.)

RESPONSE, HOMOLOGOUS - an extra (transplanted) muscle is made to act by the central nervous system together with the normal muscle of the same name.

REUNITION - reassembling of parts of an organism into a functional whole (e. g., sponges as Microciona) after separation of component parts.

RICHTUNGSPOLARITAT - (German) polarity of direction, orientation of particles toward the animal or the vegetal pole, but found throughout the ovum.

ROHON-BEARD CELLS - giant ganglion cells in the spinal cord, derived from the trunk neural folds, and which form the sensory pathway including that of the peripheral sensory nerves. They have large rounded nuclei and a considerable amount of cytoplasm which stains differentially with Heidenhain's modification of Mallory. They are never found in the ventral part of the cord. They are associated with that sensory area which is functional during the flexure of the tail following tactile stimulation.

RHYTHM, METACHRONAL - sequential contraction (cilia or muscle).

RHYTHM, SYNCHRONAL - simultaneous contraction (cilia or muscle).

SECTION CROSS - cut made at right angles to the long axis of the embryo. Syn., transverse section.

SECTION, FRONTAL - cut made parallel to the longitudinal axis of the embryo and separating the more dorsal from the more ventral. Syn., horizontal section.

SECTION, SAGITTAL - cut made parallel to the longitudinal axis of the embryo but separating the right from the left portions. Term often confused with "median" or "longitudinal" which really mean no more than "axial," hence could also be "frontal".

SECTIONS, SERIAL - thin (microscopic) slices of an embryo laid on the slide in sequence (generally from left to right, as one reads) so that the beginning of the embryo is at one side (left) and the end of the embryo at the opposite side (right) of the slide.

SEGMENTATION - term used synonymously with cleavage. Also means serial repetition of embryonic rudiments (structural patterns) in successive levels of regular spacing, as in the case of somites, and spinal nerves. Syn., cleavage.

SEGREGATION - the separation of self-differentiating embryonic rudiments; the organizational process of embryogeny; autonomizing (Weiss); the aggregation of various spatial systems independent of each other and leading to self-differentiating potentialities. Originally used (Ray Lankaster) in discussing the gastrea theory to mean a separation of the physiological molecules that are going to form ecto- and endoderm.

SEGREGATION, EMBRYONIC - progressive restriction of original potencies in the embryo; the process of step by step repartitioning of the originally homogeneous zygote into the separate parts of the presumptive embryo.

SEGREGATION, PRECOCIOUS - segregation found in mosaic eggs where local differences arise even before cleavage and a minimum of modification in response to any internal environmental factors occurs in subsequent development (Lankester, 1877).

SELBSTORGANIZATION - invisible process of construction and reconstruction of a normal blastema, with its quantitative organization gradient which is itself the basis for the segregation from qualitatively differing organ-forming regions.

SELF-DIFFERENTIATING CAPACITY - the capacity of a part of a developing system to pursue a specific course. The characters of that course are determined by intrinsic properties of the part (Roux, 1881). There can be no self-differentiation without prior induction. (See differentiation, self.)

SELF-ORGANIZATION - obsolete term which meant the alleged appearance of a lens without the stimulus normally coming from the optic cup (see double assurance).

SELFWISE - behavior of a transplant in a manner expected in its original environment, in accordance with its normal prospective significance.

SENESCENCE - the progressive loss of growth power; old age.

SENSITIZATION THEORY - calcium is the true activating agent in artificial parthenogenesis and other substances increase the permeability of the egg cortex to calcium (Pasteels).

SENSORY LOAD - determined by the number of receptor organs associated with a specific nerve.

SEX, HETERODYNAMIC - the sex in which the gametes are of two kinds with respect to the possession of specific sex influencing chromosomes, such as the X-chromosome in Drosophila. The frog and human male are presumably heterogametic.

SIGNIFICANCE, PROSPECTIVE - actual fate of any part of the original egg. Syn., Driesch's "prospektive Bedeutung".

SITUS INVERSUS - an inversion of the bilateral symmetry; reversal of right and left symmetry.

SITUS INVERSUS VISCERUM - twisting of the digestive tract and sometimes the heart, occurring naturally (rarely) or as a result of shifting of embryonic parts (Spemann, 1906) as in reversing a square piece of presumptive neural plate and archenteron of the early gastrula.

SOL - a colloidal system in which the particles of a solid or of a second liquid are suspended in a continuous phase of a liquid, the particles or their aggregates being too large to go through animal membranes rapidly or at all.

SOMATIC DOUBLING - doubling of the initial number of chromosomes with which the egg begins development, occurring (probably in most cases) at the first or early mitotic divisions (cleavages) of the egg, after fertilization.

SOMATOBLAST - blastomere with specific germ layer predisposition such as actodermal somatoblasts.

SPALTUNG - (German) fusion of posterior neural axes in a twin embryo, simulating an induction.

SPECIFICITY - the summation of the cytochemical characteristics of different protoplasms (Humphrey and Burns, 1939).

SPERMOPHILE GROUP - portion of the amboceptor in Lillie's fertilizin hypothesis into which sperm receptors fit in the fertilization reaction.

SPERM RECEPTOR - chemical group associated with the spermatozoa, reacting with fertilizin (amboceptor) in Lillie's side chain hypothesis of the fertilizin reaction.

SPINA BIFIDA - split tail caused by a variety of abnormal environmental conditions such as heat, cold, lack of oxygen, centrifugation, any of which may prevent the proper closure of the blastopore which leads to this split-tailed condition.

STEPWISE INHIBITION - successive inhibitions of organic processes by successively stronger applications of external agents.

STEREOBLASTULA - solid blastula experimentally produced by subjecting (Echinoderm) eggs to alkaloids; normal blastocoel filled with solid mass of cells (e.g., Crepidula).

STERILITY, SELF - inability of eggs and sperm of the same (hermaphroditic) individual to fuse and give rise to an embryo (e.g., Ciona intestinalis, an Ascidian).

STERNOPAGUS - sternal union of conjoined twins.

STICOTROPISM - faculty of acquiring and losing claviform shape of the bottle cells of the blastoporal lip during gastrulation (Ruffini, 1925).

STIMULATION, DIFFERENTIAL - varying responses of a gradient system to favorable conditions, as when an optimally high temperature is applied to a regenerating Planarian and a bigger and better head results than under normal (temperature) conditions. (See inhibition, differential.)

STIMULUS, FORMATIVE - concentration of (chemical) substance in the dorsal lip of the blastopore leading to the formation and demarcation of embryonic fields.

STIMULUS, OXYGENOTACTIC - differential stimulation of a developing organism by exposure to oxygen. Presumably a factor in the spreading of the blastoderm (chick) over the yolk. Syn., oxygenotaxis.

STOKE'S LAW - formula for determining viscosity $V = \dfrac{2cg\,(\sigma - p)a^2}{9\,qn}$ (formula generally omits c and q) where V is the speed at which granules travel through cytoplasm under a centrifugal force of cq absolute units; g is the gravity constant;

d is the specific gravity of the granules; p is the specific gravity of the cytoplasm; a is the radius of the granules; n is the coefficient of viscosity of the cytoplasm; q is a factor which allows for the fact that there are many granules plus the displacement of cytoplasm in granule movement.

SUBSTRATE - the substance which is acted upon by an enzyme.

SUCKER - adhesive, cementing organ of the oral region of anuran larvae.

SUSCEPTIBILITY, DIFFERENTIAL - evidence of non-homogeneity when diffusely applied injurious agent brings about varying local reactions on the embryo.

SYMPODIA - fusion, to varying degrees, of the legs (e. g., mermaid or siren condition!).

SYNCYTIUM - propagation of nuclei with cytoplasmic growth but without cytoplasmic division so that there results a mass of protoplasm with many and scattered nuclei but with inadequate cell boundaries (e. g., chick marginal periblast and adult Nematodes).

SYNDACTYLY - either bony fusion or fleshy webbing of the digits, generally the second and third digits being involved. Probably inherited in man.

SYNERESIS - a segregation of the colloidal phases, a corollary of ageing.

SYNGAMY - fusion of gametes, applied specifically to the merging of sperm and egg nuclei.

SYNOPHTHALMIA - fusion of the eyes as in cyclopia.

SYNTONIC FACTOR - some regulating force which enables a particular cell to live harmoniously with other cells of the same type so that an organ will develop, not found in tissue cultures of cells isolated prior to differentiation, present during organogene

SYNTONY - indwelling integration of parts (Heidenhain); a natural force within and between cells developing from the specific organization of living matter.

TACHYAUXESIS - positive heterogony (Needham, 1940).

TACHYGENESIS - speeding up and compression of ancestral stages in development.

TACTILE DISPLACEMENTS - movements of parts of the embryo relative to each other, resulting in definite formations and distributions of the germinal material; evidence of organizational influences.

TELOBIOSIS - terminal fusion of embryos through operative procedures (see parabiosis).

TENDENZEN - (German) autonomous abilities of a germ layer to reach developmental capacities as such without the influence of inductive effects (Lehmann, Raven). (See neighborwise and selfwise.)

TERATOGENETIC - abnormality producing.

TERATOLOGY - study of the causes of monster and abnormality formation.

TERATOMA - structure which results from random differentiations; malignant assembly of tissues, often well differentiated histologically, generally embedded in an otherwise healthy organ. Some use term embryoma to refer to histological differentiation and teratoma to mean both histological and morphological differentiation of the abnormal growth.

TETRAD - precocious splitting of the chromosomes in anticipation of both maturation divisions.

THIXOTROPY - isothermal reversible sol-gel transformations (Fremdlich's monograph). A thixotropic gel will liquefy if shaken or stirred, later to return to its previous consistency.

THORACO-GASTROSCHISIS - failure of the body wall to close along the mid-ventral line, including the thoracic region.

THORACOPAGUS - thoracic union of conjoined twins.

TISSUE CULTURE - condition where an explant is able to survive and manifest vital activity; in vitro as opposed to in vivo culturing of excised tissues or organs (see isolation culture).

TOGOGENESIS - all of the processes of movement which result in structure formation.

TOTIPOTENCY - related to theory that the isolated blastomere is capable of producing a complete organism. Roux (1912) included several faculties such as (1) for self-differentiation; (2) for influencing differentiation or induction of other parts; (3) for specific reaction to differentiating influences as in dependent differentiation.

TRANSPLANT - an embryonic area (cell or tissue) removed to a different environment. Syn., graft.

TRANSPLANTATION - transfer of an embryonic blastema from one region to another of from one germinal layer to another. Incorporation of an isolated fragment by a living organism, not merely the sticking on of a graft.

TRANSPLANT, AUTOPLASTIC - exchange of different parts within the same organism.

TRANSPLANT, HETEROPLASTIC - exchange of parts between individuals of different species but within the same genus (e. g., from Amblystoma punctatum to A. tigrinum).

TRANSPLANT, HETEROTOPIC - graft location different from graft source; exchange made to a non-homologous region of the host; transplantation to a new site.

TRANSPLANT, HOMOPLASTIC - grafts exchanged between members of the same species. Syn., homoioplastic transplant.

TRANSPLANT, HOMOTOPIC - graft location the same as the graft source; transplant to the identical site or homologous region. Syn., orthotopic.

TRANSPLANT, XENOPLASTIC - graft between organisms of different genera or those still further resolved phylogenetically. Graded series would be autoplastic-heteroplastic - xenoplastic.

TRIASTER - abnormal mitotic figure possessing three asters generally causing irregular distribution of chromosomes and abnormal cleavages. Other multiple aster conditions moted, (e.g., tetraster, etc.)

TRIGGER REACTION - condition where the character, pattern, vigor, progress and speed of a response are in no way related to the releasing event.

TRITOGENY - one-third of a fragment (see merogony).

TROPHIC - the action of the nervous system in the absence of which the muscle tonus fails and in consequence, regeneration is impossible.

TROPHOCHROMATIN - nutritive chromatin of the nucleus.

TRUE KNOT - slipping of the fetus through a looped umbilical cord to produce a true knot, distinguished from looped blood vessels which cause external bulgings called false knots.

TWINS, IDENTICAL - true twins, from a single egg and having common membranes and umbilicus.

TWINS, ORDINARY - pleural pregnancy resulting from the fertilization of separate ova simultaneously liberated from individual follicles. Separate development, implantation, decidua capsularism, and fetal membranes.

UMHULLUNG - (German) the process of wrapping an inductor in sheets of competent ectoderm to test its inductive power.

UNIPOTENT - attribute of certain cells which can give rise to only one simple type of differentiation; presumptive fate and presumptive potency are identical.

VALUE, PROSPECTIVE - the realization value of a part of the sum total represented by the prospective potencies.

VEGETATIVISATION - shifting of the presumptive fate of normal ectoderm to become endoderm. Syn., vegetalization, endodermization. Opposed to animalization.

VERMIFORM CELL TYPE - elongated form of isolated embryonic cells with finger-like protuberances at the antipole of the coated side (Holtfreter).

VESICLE, GERMINAL - nucleus of the egg while it is a distinct entity and before the elimination of either of the polar bodies.

VISCOSITY - measure of inner molecular friction (see Stoke's Law).

VITAL STAINING - localized staining of embryonic areas with vital, non-toxic dyes, for purposes of studying morphogenetic movements (method of Roux).

VITALISM - a philosophical approach to biological phenomena which bases its proof on the present inability of scientists to explain all the phenomena of development. Idea that biological activities are directed by forces neither physical nor chemical, but which must be supra-scientific or super-natural. Effective guidance in development by some non-material agency (see mechanism).

VITELLIN - egg-yolk phospho-protein.

VITELLINE - adj., pertains to yolk, vein, or membrane.

VITELLINE MEMBRANE - delicate, outer, non-living and non-cellular egg membrane derived (while in the ovary) probably by the joint action of the egg and its follicle cells. It is probably the same membrane that is lifted off of the egg at fertilization and is subsequently known as the fertilization membrane. Syn., zona radiata (mammals).

WEBER'S-LAW - the degree of sensitivity to a stimulus in any reacting system is not constant but depends, not alone on the nature of the stimulus, but upon the period of life and the strength of an already existing stimulus. A stimulus therefore represents a change, but a reacting system takes into account any pre-existing stimulus upon which this change is built. Theory that equal relative differences between stimuli of the same kind are equally perceptible.

WOLF SNOUT - projecting of the premaxilla beyond the surface of the face, accompanying double (hare) lip and sometimes a cleft palate.

XANTHOLEUCOPHORES - crystals and soluble yellow pigment; cells bearing such.

XANTHOPHORES - yellow pigment in solution; cells bearing this yellow pigment.

XIPHOPAGUS - xiphoid fusion of conjoined twins; sometimes the skin alone.

YOLK LOBE - lobe of early developing mollusce embryo in which there is actually almost no yolk, but it appears hernia-like from one of the early blastomeres, disappearing between cleavages and capable, when isolated, of giving rise to a dwarfed larva. Syn., antipolar or basal lobe. Opposed to polar lobe.

YOLK NUCLEI - bodies responsible for precocious digestion of yolk, derived from nucleoli which break up and pass out through the nuclear membrane. Centers of yolk organization during the growth period of öogenesis.

YOLK PLUG - large yolk cells which are too large and sluggish to be immediately incorporated in the floor of the archenteron, hence are found protruding slightly from the mouth of the blastopore to form a plug which is distinct by color from the surrounding pigmented marginal zone (amphibia).

Term used as identification of a late stage in gastrulation.

ZONE, MARGINAL - presumptive chorda-mesodermal-endodermal complex at the junction of the roof and the floor of the early gastrula. Syn., germ ring.

NOTE: A glossary of some 350 terms in morphological embryology may be found in the author's revised edition of "Laboratory Manual of Vertebrate Embryology". (1961)

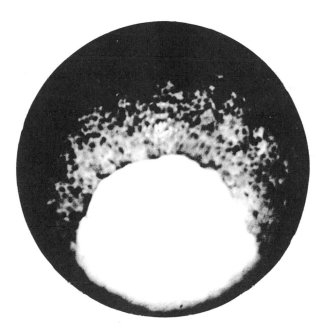

"OMNE VIVUM EX OVO"

HARVEY

"OMNIS CELLULA E CELLULA"

VIRCHOW

INDEX